Good desi...

for ease of revision

C000272542

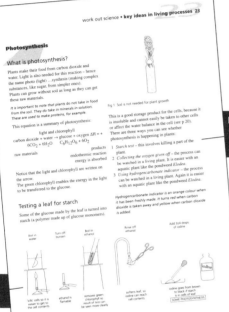

Key facts for the exam

Helpful cross-referencing

Real GCSE questions Cover up the answer and try the question yourself. It's best to write the answer out, imagining you are in the exam! Notice how many marks are available.

Useful diagrams

The questions are where you need them, just after the key facts you've been checking

Answer: use this to check your answer. Read carefully any comments – they will help you to get all the marks

Revision sheets (and answers) for each topic in the section

ightforward stions show what you w about a c

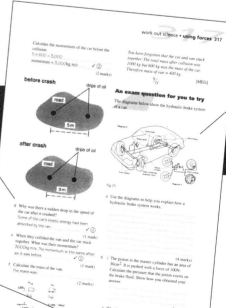

Student answers, with comments, completed under examination conditions

Check your answers against those given. If you get an answer wrong, try really hard to see just why you made the mistake

Marks and comments show you why the student lost marks

Longer questions for you to try. Answers are given for you to compare an ideal response with your own

Revision
Points for passing

Point 1

Well in advance of the examination check that you do not have big gaps in your notes - for example, have you missed any topics? If you find a gap, try and understand the topic using this book. If you are still unsure ask someone to help, preferably your teacher. It might be a good idea to talk to a classmate about this - talking about the topic will help both of you.

Point 2

Be honest with yourself. As you use this book and study the many questions it contains, try to really understand and learn as you go along. Telling yourself that you understand when you don't is not clever.

Point 3

Pace yourself when revising. Don't try and do too much at once. It is a good idea to choose a topic and revise it thoroughly so you feel you have completed it. If you sit down for an hour and try to revise without an aim in mind you are less likely to spend your time wisely.

Point 4

Be active in your revision. Ask yourself questions all the time - for example, 'What do I know about photosynthesis?' You can do this in any spare moment. Or try to persuade someone at home to help you. Many of the sections in this book have questions as headings. See if you can give a sensible answer to the question before reading what it says below. Attempt the exam questions before looking at the answers. But don't be tempted to copy out the book - asking yourself questions is far more useful.

Point 5

Apart from being confident that you understand the basic ideas of the subject, there are certain general things that you should be able to do if you are aiming for higher grades. For example:

- link ideas about animals and plants, such as describing the passage of a nitrogen atom from a fallen leaf through to urine, explaining what is happening at each stage.
- balance symbolic equations.
- re-arrange formulae, which is particularly important in physical processes.

Don't lose your head in the exam room

Point 1

In the actual examination read each question carefully. It is a common mistake to re-write the question as the answer.

Point 2

Look for key words in the question, such as **describe** and **explain**. If the question asks you to explain, it wants a reason - not just a simple statement. It may help to highlight words like this during the examination.

Point 3

It is likely that the question will indicate how many marks are available. Make sure that you have included sufficient scientific detail to achieve these marks. Remember that if the question is set in context, for example it asks about the properties of a babies' nappy, the examiner is still looking for a scientific answer - not something in 'everyday speak' that someone could guess.

Point 4

Write clearly and precisely; you are likely to be awarded some marks for spelling, punctuation and grammar.

Point 5

Try to produce a well presented examination paper. The examiner will have lots of papers to mark and it will give him or her pleasure to read clear, scientifically accurate and thoughtful answers.

Exam Boards Addresses

For syllabuses and past papers contact the Publications office at the following addresses:

Midland Examining Group (MEG)
c/o University of Cambridge Local Examinations Syndicate
1 Hills Road
CAMBRIDGE
CB1 2EU
Tel. 01223 553311

Southern Examining Group (SEG)
Publications Department
Stag Hill House
GUILDFORD
Surrey
GU2 5XJ
Tel. 01483 302302 (Direct line)

Northern Examinations and Assessment Board (NEAB)
12 Harter Street
MANCHESTER
M1 6HL
Tel. 0161 953 1170
(Also shop at the above address)

University of London Examinations and Assessment Council (ULEAC)
Stewart House
32 Russell Square
LONDON
WC1B 5DN
Tel. 0171 331 4000

Northern Ireland Council for the Curriculum, Examinations and Assessment (NICCEA)
Beechill House
42 Beechill Road
BELFAST
BT8 4RS
Tel. 01232 704666

Welsh Joint Education Committee (WJEC)
245 Western Avenue
Llandaff
CARDIFF
CF5 2YX

Scottish Examination Board (SEB)
for full syllabuses
Ironmills Road
Dalkeith
Midlothian EH22 1LE
Tel. 0131 663 6601

or recent papers from the SEB's agent
Robert Gibson & Sons Ltd
17 Fitzroy Place
Glasgow G3 7SF
Tel. 0141 248 5674

Remember to check your syllabus number with your teacher!

Contents

Acknowledgements

We would like to thank all the science staff at Bungay High School and Stowmarket High School who helped us while we were writing this book and especially Angela Scott and John D'Mello from Bungay and Rachel Southgate and Andy Catterall from Stowmarket. We would like to thank the GCSE students that gave particular help but most thanks must go to our son Robert. He was in his final GCSE year while this book was being produced. He worked through all the text advising on what was really needed in such a book as well as encouraging us to keep going!

The authors and publishers wish to thank the following for permission to use copyright material: The Southern Examining Group, Midland Examining Group, The Northern Examinations and Assessment Board (incorporating Northern Examining Association and the Joint Matriculation Board), University of London Examinations And Assessment Council, and the Welsh Joint Education Committee for questions from past examination papers.

Every effort has been made to trace all the copyright holders but if any have been inadvertently overlooked the publishers will be pleased to make the necessary arrangement at the first opportunity.

The Southern Examining Group state that any answers or hints on answers are the sole responsibility of the author and have not been provided or approved by the Group.

First published 1996 by
MACMILLAN PRESS LTD
Houndmills, Basingstoke, Hampshire RG21 2XS
and London
Companies and representatives
throughout the world

ISBN 0-333-63465-9

A catalogue record for this book is available from the British Library.

10   9   8   7   6   5   4   3   2   1
04   03   02   01   00   99   98   97   96

Printed in Great Britain by Biddles Ltd,
Guildford and King's Lynn

Janet and Michael Major

Work Out
Science
GCSE

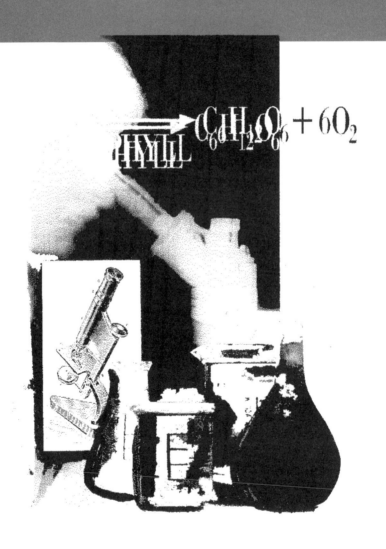

MACMILLAN

Coursework

Key to these pages in the rest of the book

✓ = questions on this topic could se set in any tier of the exam

H = most questions on this topic will be set in the highest tier of the exam

Blank space = questions on this topic are unlikely to be set in this syllabus

Coursework	Midland (MEG)				Northern (NEAB)			London (ULEAC)			Southern (SEG)		Welsh (WJEC)
	Own	Nuffield	Salters	Suffolk	Co-ordinated	Modular	Modular GASP	Combined	Co-ordinated	Modular	Double	Modular	Co-ordinated

All science syllabuses include 25% of the final marks from coursework. For a double award syllabus this is 25% for *each* of your two GCSEs.

During the course your teacher will assess how you carry out experimental and investigative science. This is your coursework and it will count for up to 25% of your final grade.

To do well in your coursework you will need to:

- link your practical work with your theory work, particularly when predicting what might happen, planning what to do and considering your results.
- carry out the practical work as accurately as possible so that you have sufficient evidence to make some conclusions.

The following discussion covers some important points in the three main areas of an investigation:

- Before you start the practical work
- Carrying out the practical work
- Thinking about the data you have collected

You will see some examples of students' work indicated in boxes like this!

Before you start the practical work

Understanding the task

What have you been asked to do? Are you clear? If not, ask the teacher to explain.

Planning the time

Have you got a time limit? If so, you will need to plan your work to allow time to obtain results. Don't be rushed into starting to use the apparatus too quickly. Planning what you are going to do will save time later.

Background knowledge

What do you know about the topic already? Look at the relevant theory work – use your notebook, your text books, a CD-ROM and anything else that you think might help. Note which books you use and the relevant page numbers, you may need to look at them later or give a reference in your final report of the investigation. While you are carrying out this research you may find some data about a similar experiment. Note this carefully; you may need to discuss it in your conclusions.

Making a prediction

Can you make a prediction about what you think will happen in your investigation? If you can, you should be able to explain why. It should not just be a guess. Try to be as precise as you can when you make a prediction.

Here are parts of three predictions from students carrying out the same investigation. The title was:
  Investigate the reaction between magnesium and hydrochloric acid.

Claire
I think that the reaction will be faster as I use hotter acid. Reactions always work better when we heat them up.

Jason
I think that the rate of reaction will increase with temperature. As the acid is heated the particles have more energy. They bump into each other more and so are more likely to have a reaction.

Yasmin
The rate of reaction will increase with temperature. The ions in the acid will have more energy, due to the heat. So they are likely to have more collisions and many more of these collisions are likely to be successful. There is a general rule which says that for every 10°C rise in temperature the rate of reaction doubles. This is a sketch of the general shape of the graph that I expect to get from my experiment.

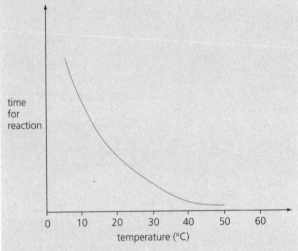

Fig 1 Sketch of how the time for reaction will decrease with temperature (prediction)

As you read these you will see that the predictions improve. Yasmin has used some background knowledge and been able to predict the shape of the graph. She therefore has a much better prediction.

Trials

Once you have made your prediction you need to carry out some trials for your experiment so you know what quantities to use.

> Matthew was investigating how the size of canopy affects the way a parachute falls. He experimented until he made a parachute that fell slowly enough for him to time it. In this case he made a tiny canopy and as large a canopy as he could, then used these results to decide which in-between size of canopy would allow him to get some sensible results.

Controlling factors

It is a good idea to list all the possible factors that might affect your results. Once you have drawn up a list, you will need to decide which factors:

- you are going to investigate.
- you are going to keep the same to make the experiment 'fair'.
- you cannot do anything about, but which might affect your results. These are particularly important in investigations which involve living organisms.

> Vicky was investigating feeding relationships in a habitat. It was winter. She realised that she was likely to get different results from a similar investigation carried out in the summer. She discussed this in her conclusion. She didn't just say it would be different in the summer, but discussed the increased plant life and the effect this had on herbivores and other trophic levels in feeding relationships.

How much evidence?

If you are investigating the effect of temperature on a reaction, you may decide to do one 'cold' and one 'hot'. This would give you some results. However, you would have much more evidence if you:

- repeated each reading more than once – to give you more confidence in the results.
- arranged to collect a range of results so that you could draw a graph. This would show you any trends and might allow you to make predictions beyond the range of data collected.

Justifying the method

Once you have decided how to do the investigation, the range you will find out about and the number of readings you will take, stop and think carefully.

- Is there another way that you could collect the data?
- Is this the best way of carrying out the investigation? Why are you doing it this way? If you can answer these questions satisfactorily then you are ready to begin. Do check with your teacher before you start.

> Robert was measuring the rate of a reaction by noting the loss in mass of the reactants during a reaction. He also decided to collect the gas given off and if see if the general pattern of the results was the same. This helped to make the results more valid.

Carrying out the practical work

The aim here is to collect some results that you can understand. You should have carried out some trials so that you know how to go about your task.

Be systematic

Once you start your experiment you'll probably get carried away! It's easy to start changing things but you must remember to keep a note of:

- any results.
- any change you made and why you made it.
- the date of this piece of practical work.

It's a good idea either to write in a book *or* number your pages of file paper. Otherwise when you come to look at your results you may not know which ones relate to which part of your experiment.

How accurate do I need to be?

Be as accurate as you need to be. There are times, for example, when you can roughly measure out a volume of liquid using a beaker. At other times you'll need a measuring cylinder, and sometimes you may need a burette to measure an accurate volume.

What apparatus should I use?

You will probably have found the best apparatus to use during the trials. For example, if you are measuring the volume of gas given off by pond weed, you will need to consider whether to count the bubbles, use a measuring cylinder, or use a gas syringe. Note the advantages and disadvantages of each method and explain your chosen method. It might be that you would like to use a gas syringe but you cannot use one. Don't worry if this happens, but do show why you considered using one in your discussion.

What about safety?

The rule here is ask if you are not sure! It is not clever to guess how to use equipment or carry out a technique. You can try out your own ideas but you must ALWAYS CHECK WITH THE TEACHER BEFORE STARTING. For example, you may decide to use a cork borer to put cylinders from a potato in an enzyme experiment. You will then need to push the cylinder out of the cork borer. Don't use a glass stirring rod. It could easily break and cut your hand.

Which observations should I make?

All relevant observations should be noted, even if they are unexpected.

> In a reaction between magnesium and hydrochloric acid, Jake noticed that tiny pieces of magnesium ribbon float on the surface of the acid but larger pieces sink. This is relevant and should be noted. Similarly, he noticed that some of the magnesium looked corroded – this could also be important.

How many readings should I take?

There is no definite answer; you should take 'sufficient to test your prediction'. For example:

- if you are investigating how different materials insulate a cup, you need to allow the liquid in the cups to cool sufficiently so that you get a clear

difference between the materials that you are testing.
- if you are carrying out an enzyme experiment and suspect that the enzyme is denatured at 40°C but the rate of reaction is still high at 50°C, you ought to repeat it at higher temperatures until the rate of reaction decreases.

Remember that the more readings you take the more accurate a graph will be (if your investigation allows you to draw a graph!).

How can I be sure my measurements are O.K.?

There are two things you can do here:

- repeat them a few times and try to calculate a mean value.
- try and collect your data by a different method. For example, in a reaction between calcium carbonate and hydrochloric acid you could collect the carbon dioxide produced and also measure the mass lost, as Robert did in the example mentioned earlier.

Some other ways of checking your data would be:

- seeing if anyone else is doing the same experiment. Are they getting the same pattern of results?
- checking any published results. For example, in a data book.
- monitoring the experiment using a computer.
- simulating the experiment using a computer.

What should I do if I get an unexpected reading?

If you are collecting a set of results to calculate a mean and one result appears very different (called anomalous) then:

- think carefully about what you did differently to try and explain this.
- repeat this one case and see if you get the expected result the second time. It is probably best to leave an anomalous result out of any calculation but you must include a discussion of it when analysing your data (see later).

There are many reasons why you might get anomalous results! You need to analyse each situation clearly. For example:

- are you using the same thermometer each time? Any one thermometer may only be accurate to 5°C.

- are you using a range of solutions, e.g. 0.1 mol dm⁻³, 0.5 mol dm⁻³, 1 mol dm⁻³ and 2 mol dm⁻³ of hydrochloric acid. Is just one of these giving unexpected results?

How should I present my data?

The answer is *clearly* and *appropriately*. A table is usually a clear way of summarising your results. If you include the mean of a set of results, do indicate that it is not the only result that you took.

Think carefully about:

- headings of columns and rows in your table.
- including units where they are needed.

A computer spreadsheet may also be a good way of presenting your data.

Thinking about the data you have collected

What sort of graph should I draw?

It is usually a good idea to present your data as a graph or bar chart. In this way it is easier to pick out any patterns – and also spot any anomalous results!

- **A bar chart:** you need to draw one of these when the data is discrete.

For example:

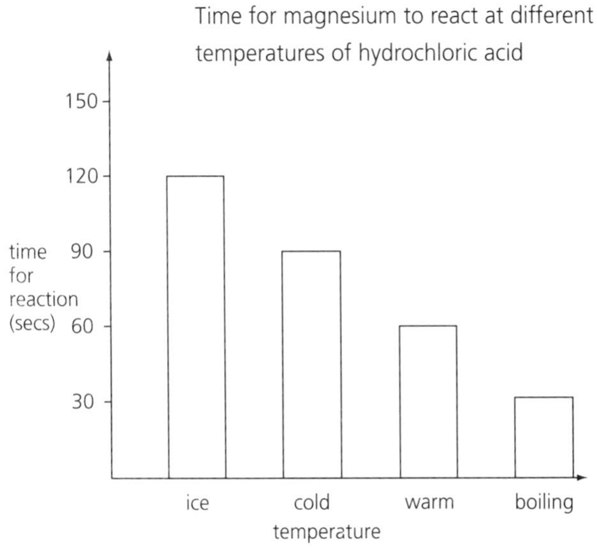

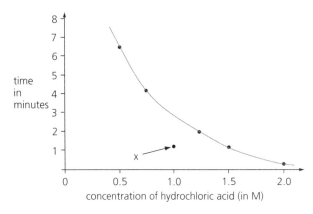

Fig 2

'I stood my test tube of magnesium and hydrochloric acid in a beaker of water to give me these different results. This is the temperature of the water.'

In this case a bar chart is appropriate, but if the student had used a thermometer to take the temperature then a line graph could have been drawn.

- **A line graph:** you need to draw one of these if the data is continuous.

For example:

Fig 3 Time for magnesium to react at different concentrations of hydrochloric acid

In this case it is appropriate to draw a curve of *best fit*. Your data should be accurate enough to know when to draw a curve or when to draw a straight line. If it's not – then you probably need to collect more data. (In this case it would be a good idea to repeat the measurement 'X'. If you obtain the same result a second time – try and explain why.)

- **Using all the paper**

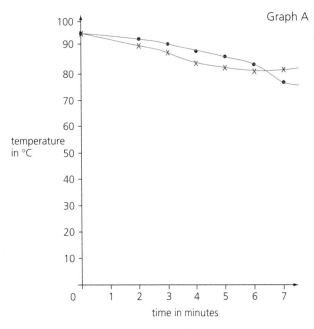

Fig 4a Cooling a cup – trying out different materials

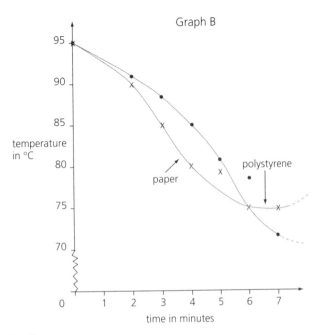

Graph B

Fig 4b

Graph B makes better use of the paper and also shows more clearly how the temperature appears to increase after 7 minutes. But why has the student stopped after 7 minutes? It does not look long enough to see what is really happening!

Does the evidence fit the conclusion?

This is very important. Your conclusions *must* be based on your data and evidence – not on what you thought would happen!

- Do look carefully at the actual figures that you collected.

Paul was investigating the change of mass on heating a substance and these were his results:
    Mass at beginning 26.03g
    Mass at end 26.01g
The substance has lost mass but only $\frac{2}{100}$th of a gram! If the substance was a powder $\frac{2}{100}$th of a gram could easily be lost, so Paul would not be sensible to make a statement such as "The substance lost mass on heating".

- Don't think that just because you used a digital clock to time to three decimal places (i.e. 0.001) your results must be very accurate.

If you timed the dropping of a parachute, how you arranged the dropping to coincide with starting the clock would have a big effect on the accuracy of the results.

- The following results were collected in an experiment in which cups of water were allowed to cool and the effect of different insulating materials was studied.

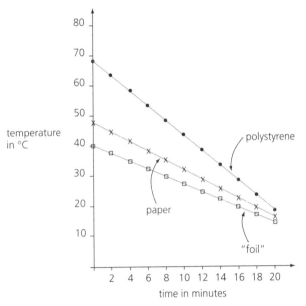

Fig 5 Finding out how effective different materials are as insulators

Conclusion: Polystyrene is the best insulator. The final temperature of 22°C was the highest of my three test materials. Polystyrene is a good insulator because it traps air

Look carefully at the graphs. The final temperature is highest with polystyrene, but if you look carefully the temperature using the "foil" and paper dropped by much less. It seems that in this case polystyrene is the worst insulator! The explanation about polystyrene trapping air is suitable, but the conclusions must be gained from the evidence of the experiment.

Do you have sufficient evidence for firm conclusions?

Jane was investigating the effect of caffeine on pulse rate. She had chosen to use a boy and girl in the class who both had a resting pulse of 80. Both volunteers drank 200ml of coffee and then took their pulse rate 10 minutes afterwards. At first they did the test with caffeine-free coffee and then after one hour with coffee containing caffeine. These are the results.

Results

	Girl	Boy
Pulse rate at first	80	80
Pulse rate having drunk caffeine-free coffee	80	86
Pulse rate having drunk coffee containing caffeine	82	81

From this it can be seen that the pulse rate of the boy went up more after drinking coffee without caffeine than after drinking coffee with caffeine, while the pulse rate of the girl went up by two after drinking coffee containing caffeine. Jane concluded that the pulse rate of females is affected more by caffeine in coffee than the pulse rate of males. There is obviously not enough evidence from this investigation to draw such firm conclusions.

Whilst it is easy to agree with this statement in such an extreme case, beware that you don't make similarly wild claims from results in your own investigations!

Could the results be repeated?

Think about this carefully. If somebody else carried out your experiment and was able to get the same results, this would be good evidence for your conclusions. How you carried out the experiment is very important.

In fieldwork investigating the distribution of plants over two areas of field, you need to place the quadrats randomly. If you chose to place your quadrats over the only ten plants of one species, then your conclusions about the populations of the different species would not be correct. If the investigation were repeated it would be unlikely to give the same result.

Explaining the conclusions

You must do three things:

• look back at your predictions.
• consider your results.
• use your knowledge and understanding of the topic.

You need to think carefully about your predictions and your reasons for making them. Here Kate thinks carefully about her prediction once she has collected her results.

Kate was investigating the effect of *seed size* and *amount of water* on the germination rate of seeds. She predicted that larger seeds would germinate faster than smaller ones, and that as long as the seeds were damp they would germinate. She discussed the importance of the size of the seed in terms of the amount of stored food in it. She also described how important the water was in the enzyme-controlled reactions that turned this stored food into a soluble form. She carried out her investigation and collected a range of results. On analysing these results, it seemed that the amount of water had more effect on how fast the seeds germinated than the size of the seed. This was not what she had predicted! She thought carefully about her hypothesis and decided to do some calculations on the surface area of the seeds. Even though her results did not entirely support her hypothesis, she was able to build on this, using her results to undertake a further investigation.

Here William uses his knowledge and understanding of the topic to explain the results that he obtained during an investigation.

In an enzyme experiment, William predicted that the rate of reaction would increase with temperature. However, unlike an experiment involving a catalyst, the rate would reach a peak (an optimum) and then rapidly decline as the enzyme was denatured. As his results confirmed this, in his discussion he explained how enzymes are thought to work by lowering the activation energy for the reaction and how temperature affects the rate of reaction in terms of collisions. He also explained how denaturing enzymes affects the shape of the enzyme, and hence their ability to operate as visualised by the lock and key model.

Improvements to the method

Be particularly careful with this one. 'I could have done it more accurately' is probably true but is not very helpful unless you are able to explain how! For example, did you measure the volume of a gas collected over water with a measuring cylinder? If so, a gas syringe is likely to have been more accurate. Did you cut your length of magnesium ribbon to 1cm, or did you weigh it? Did you do the experiment once or several times to give you a mean? If your investigation involved the conductivity of a substance, did you use wire or did you investigate solutions as well?

Can you suggest some further investigations?

Just saying you would do the same investigation again, but with a bigger range and better equipment, probably wouldn't enable you to find out much more about your topic.

Vincent carried out an investigation into the action of the enzyme catalase, obtained from a potato. This enzyme is a catalyst for the breakdown of hydrogen peroxide into water and oxygen. He predicted that the optimum temperature for this reaction would be 40°C, and above that the enzyme would be denatured. In the investigation, the potato and hydrogen peroxide were put in a water bath at different temperatures. Even when the hydrogen peroxide was at 60°C, the reaction rate was still increasing. Vincent suggested a number of further investigations to try and find out whether this enzyme was denatured at 40°C or at a higher temperature. These investigations involved:
- heating the potato to different temperatures before adding it to the hydrogen peroxide.
- using a temperature sensor to find out the actual temperature of the potato.
- trying to obtain catalase to find out the optimum temperature without using living tissue.

Key ideas in living processes

Key ideas in living processes	Midland (MEG)				Northern (NEAB)			London (ULEAC)			Southern (SEG)		Welsh (WJEC)
	Own	Nuffield	Salters	Suffolk	Co-ordinated	Modular	Modular GASP	Combined	Co-ordinated	Modular	Double	Modular	Co-ordinated
SOME IMPORTANT BIOLOGICAL IDEAS													
Living processes	✓	✓	✓	✓	✓	✓	✓	✓	✓	✓	✓	✓	✓
Metabolism and enzymes	✓	✓	✓	✓	✓	✓	✓	✓	✓	✓	✓	✓	✓
Features of cells	✓	✓	✓	✓	✓	✓	✓	✓	✓	✓	✓	✓	✓
Movement of substances between cells	✓	✓	✓	✓	✓	✓	✓	✓	✓	✓	✓	✓	✓
PHOTOSYNTHESIS													
The importance of photosynthesis	✓	✓	✓	✓	✓	✓	✓	✓	✓	✓	✓	✓	✓
Testing a leaf for starch	✓	✓	✓	✓	✓	✓	✓	✓	✓	✓	✓	✓	✓
Limiting factors	✓	H	✓	H	H	H	✓	✓	H	✓	✓	✓	H
The leaf	✓	✓	✓	✓	✓	✓	✓	✓	✓	✓	✓	✓	✓
How the plant uses sugars	✓	✓	✓	✓	✓	✓	✓	✓	✓	✓	✓	✓	✓
Mineral salts and healthy plant growth	✓	✓	✓	✓	✓	✓	✓	✓	✓	✓	✓	✓	✓
NUTRITION													
The importance of food	✓	✓	✓	✓	✓	✓	✓	✓	✓	✓	✓	✓	✓
A balanced diet	✓	✓	✓	✓	✓	✓	✓	✓	✓	✓	✓	✓	✓
Digestion and absorption	✓	✓	✓	✓	✓	✓	✓	✓	✓	✓	✓	✓	✓
What happens to absorbed food?	✓	✓	✓	✓	✓	✓	✓	✓	✓	✓	✓	✓	✓

Some important biological ideas

What are living processes?

It is very difficult to give a definition of life, other than to say it is to be alive. It is possible to list the characteristic processes (often called living processes) that living organisms carry out, whether they are animals, plants or belong to another kingdom (see p 108).

These processes are:

- Movement
- Respiration
- Sensitivity
- Growth
- Reproduction
- Excretion
- Nutrition

Some people find that it helps to remember these by learning: Mrs Gren.

Movement

This is an obvious characteristic of animals. Either parts of the animal move, for example your arm if you are making notes, or the whole body moves to change the position of the organism. Plants also move, but this involves growth, for example towards light.

Respiration

This is the process in which glucose is broken down, usually by reacting with oxygen to produce carbon dioxide, water and the energy needed for reactions in cells. Respiration occurs in all cells.

Don't confuse this with breathing, see p 47.

Sensitivity

This is the ability of the organism (animal or plant) to respond to a stimulus. The stimulus might come from:

- the environment of the organism; for example a loud noise, the smell of food or a change in light intensity.
- inside the organism itself; for example a foreign protein in the blood which could cause antibodies to be formed.

Growth

Cells grow when they undergo a permanent increase in size. For example, we would not say that a cell had grown because it had taken in more water. In growth there is an increase in the cytoplasm of the cell. When a cell reaches a certain size it is likely to divide (see cell division).

Reproduction

This is the ability to produce other individuals. If more than one parent is involved this is called sexual reproduction and the offspring, although similar to the parents, will not be identical to them. Some organisms reproduce by asexual reproduction, where only one parent is involved and the offspring are identical to each other and to the parent.

Excretion

This is the elimination of waste products produced by chemical reactions occurring in cells. For example, we excrete urine (containing urea made in the liver), carbon dioxide from the lungs and salt from the skin in sweat. (*Do not get confused here. Solid waste that passes out of the gut has not been excreted because it has not been formed as a waste product from reactions inside cells. It has been eaten but could not be digested.*)

Nutrition

Nutrition provides the energy that an organism needs to carry out the other life processes and the materials it needs to build the structures necessary for those processes. Animals and plants both carry out the process of nutrition but the way they do so differs. Plants make use of energy from the sun to turn simple raw materials (water and carbon dioxide) into nutrients. This is called photosynthesis. They are thus the producers in a food chain. Animals rely on existing nutrients that have to be broken down in the gut. The products can then be combined in many different ways to suit the requirements of the organisms. Animals are thus the consumers in a food chain.

QUESTION

a Each of the three sentences below has an important word missing. Choose the correct word for each sentence from the words in the box. Write it in the gap.

breathe   feed   grow   move   reproduce
sense

i   Humans .... by giving birth
to babies. (1 mark)
ii All babies take in air when they ....
.... (1 mark)
iii Babies .... into adults.
(1 mark)
Part question [SEG 1994]

ANSWER

i   reproduce
ii breathe
iii grow

What is metabolism?

All cells carry out a number of chemical reactions.
These reactions either break down big molecules into
smaller ones or build up big molecules from smaller
ones. Both kinds of reaction make up what is known
as metabolism. This term is used to describe all the
reactions going on in an organism while it is carrying
out the life processes listed above. We talk about the
'metabolism of a cell' and the 'metabolism of an
organism' when we mean how the cell and the
organism are 'working'.

Enzymes controlling metabolism

The chemical reactions that occur in cells all the time
do not happen at random. They are under the control
of the nucleus. The nucleus controls which enzymes
are produced and it is the enzymes which directly
control the reactions.

Characteristics of enzymes

* They are large proteins. Each enzyme has an
active site which is responsible for controlling one
reaction. An enzyme is said to be specific to a
reaction.
* They act as catalysts and change the rate of
reactions.
* Only a small amount of enzyme is needed for a
reaction.
* Generally, as the temperature increases the rate of
the reaction increases (usually the rate doubles for

every 10°C increase in temperature). However, as
enzymes are proteins they lose their shape above
about 40°C. We say they are denatured. They
therefore can not control the reaction above this
temperature.
* They are affected by changes in pH. Some
enzymes, such as proteinase in the stomach, work
best in an acidic environment and others work best
in an alkaline environment. We say they are pH
specific. Most work best at pH 7.

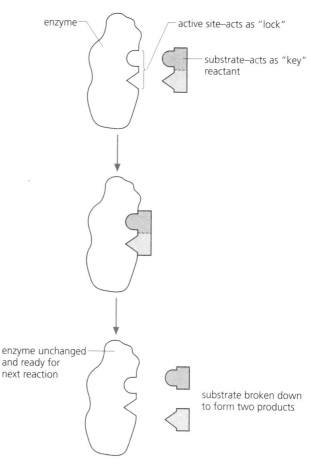

Fig 1 The 'lock and key' model of how an enzyme works

When enzymes control reactions in which big
molecules are built up, the diagrams would be drawn
in the reverse order – and of course the reactant
would be labelled the product and the product
labelled the reactant.

How do enzymes speed up reactions?

Molecules are moving all the time but to react they
need a certain amount of energy. This energy is
called the activation energy. You can think of it as an
initial energy barrier that has to be overcome. The
higher the activation energy, the higher the barrier,

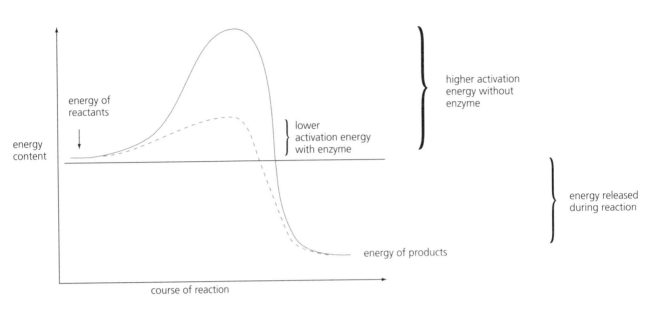

Fig 2 How an enzyme lowers the activation energy of a reaction

and the less likely the reaction is to take place. Enzymes increase the rate of reaction by lowering the activation energy needed for the reaction to take place.

Life processes in humans

A human is a very complex organism. To carry out each of the life processes involves the co-ordination of many structures and different activities. Two examples of how this occurs follow:

- movement
- excretion

(details of all the other processes can be found later in this book).

Movement

One of the reasons why locomotion (the ability to move from place to place) is necessary in animals is that they need to obtain food, unlike plants which are able to manufacture carbohydrates by photosynthesis. For an animal to move three features are necessary:

- a rigid skeleton
- tissue which contracts (muscle)
- a supporting surface (in the case of humans, the ground)

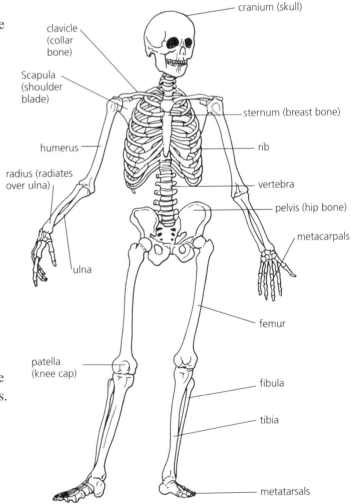

Fig 3 The skeleton

The bones of the skeleton are made up of bone tissue. The bones end in cartilage (another tissue) which acts partly as a shock absorber and also reduces friction during movement. The long bones (for example those of the leg) are not solid – if they were, moving about would require a lot of effort. Instead, they contain bone marrow which manufactures red blood cells and certain white blood cells.

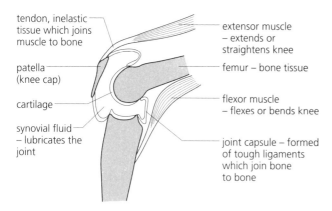

tendon, inelastic tissue which joins muscle to bone

patella (knee cap)

cartilage

synovial fluid – lubricates the joint

extensor muscle – extends or straightens knee

femur – bone tissue

flexor muscle – flexes or bends knee

joint capsule – formed of tough ligaments which join bone to bone

. . . and movements caused by the contraction of the antagonistic pair of muscles

extensor muscle contracts (flexor muscle relaxes)

flexor muscle contracts (extensor muscle relaxes)

Fig 4 The structure of the knee joint – an example of a hinge joint

Muscles can only move bones when they contract. Therefore, at every point there are two muscles which work together as an antagonistic pair; when one contracts to move a bone the other relaxes. For example, a message for the extensor muscle to contract is received from the central nervous system. It arrives via the motor nerve which ends in the muscle. A chemical substance is released which causes the muscle to contract, and the lower leg moves forward. After this a message is received for the flexor muscle to contract and when this muscle contracts the leg is bent again. These two movements are important in walking. However, walking itself is a complicated process and involves the contraction and relaxation of several other sets of muscles, such as those controlling the movement of the ankle.

In walking, when the extensor contracts the flexor relaxes, and when the flexor contracts the extensor relaxes.

Excretion

The cells of the body carry out many chemical reactions all the time. If these reactions produce toxic waste products they must be removed from the cells immediately and eliminated from the body. Carbon dioxide, a waste product of respiration in cells, is removed from the blood at the alveoli of the lungs. If the diet contains a lot of protein, the body of an adult is unlikely to need it all – unless recovering from a severe illness. Neither proteins nor amino acids can be stored in the body, and need to be eliminated if present in excess. Proteins are digested into amino acids in the gut and are absorbed through the villi of the small intestine into the blood. From here they are taken to the liver where they are deaminated – that is converted to urea. This is less poisonous and can be removed from the blood by filtration at the kidneys.

Note the kidneys do not make urea, they filter it from the blood.

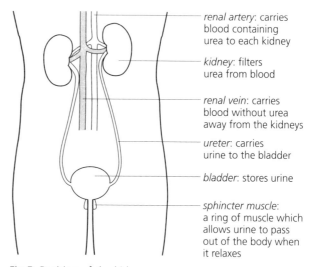

renal artery: carries blood containing urea to each kidney

kidney: filters urea from blood

renal vein: carries blood without urea away from the kidneys

ureter: carries urine to the bladder

bladder: stores urine

sphincter muscle: a ring of muscle which allows urine to pass out of the body when it relaxes

Fig 5 Position of the kidneys

How the kidney removes urea from the blood

Blood containing urea is taken to the kidneys by the renal artery. This branches into a network of capillaries in a cup shaped structure, called the Bowman's capsule, which is the filtration end of a long tubule. Here the urea passes into the inside of the capsule and the blood leaving the capillary network contains no urea. However, this blood is much reduced in volume as water and glucose also pass through the filter. The body cannot afford to lose either the glucose or the water. All the glucose and much of the water returns to the blood before it

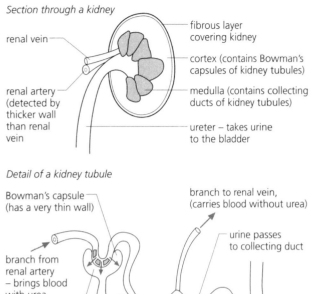

Section through a kidney

renal vein

renal artery (detected by thicker wall than renal vein)

fibrous layer covering kidney

cortex (contains Bowman's capsules of kidney tubules)

medulla (contains collecting ducts of kidney tubules)

ureter – takes urine to the bladder

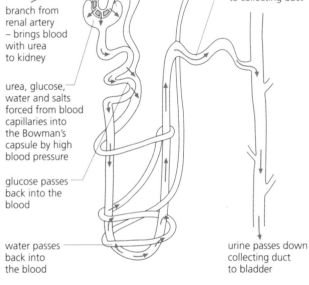

Detail of a kidney tubule

Bowman's capsule (has a very thin wall)

branch to renal vein, (carries blood without urea)

branch from renal artery – brings blood with urea to kidney

urine passes to collecting duct

urea, glucose, water and salts forced from blood capillaries into the Bowman's capsule by high blood pressure

glucose passes back into the blood

water passes back into the blood

urine passes down collecting duct to bladder

Fig 6 Section thorough a kidney and detail of a kidney tubule

finally leaves the kidney in the renal vein. Urea, now in an aqueous solution called urine, passes down collecting ducts from each tubule which connect up to form the ureter. One ureter from each kidney empties into the bladder. The urine is stored in the bladder until it is expelled from the body when the sphincter muscle opens.

The kidneys are important in controlling the water content of body fluids. This is covered in the section on osmoregulation on p 76.

QUESTION

a The diagram shows some organs in the human body.
  i Clearly label a kidney on the diagram. (1 mark)

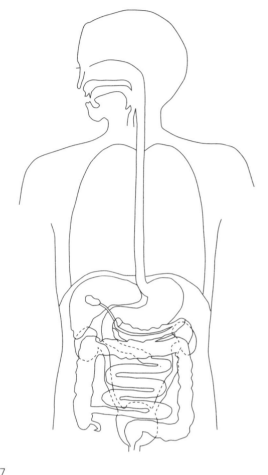

Fig 7

  ii Tick two statements from the list which explain the job of the kidney. (2 marks)
  The kidney:
  digests food
  filters the blood
  produces sex cells
  removes excess water from the blood
  removes oxygen from the blood

[MEG]

ANSWER

a i The kidneys are the two bean shaped organs shown behind the large intestine.
  ii The kidney: filters the blood and removes excess water from the blood

QUESTION

The diagram below shows part of the excretory system.
a i Name organ X.
    .... (1 mark)
  ii Name the organ to which blood in Y is transported. .... (1 mark)

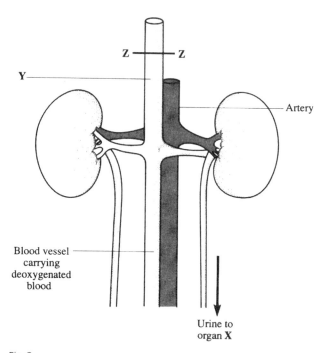

Fig 8

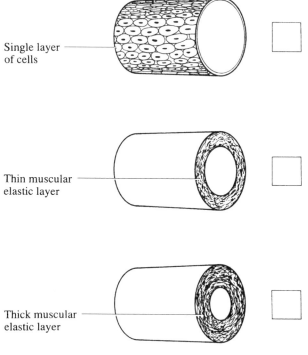

Fig 9

b A section of the blood vessel is taken at Z. What will the section look like? Tick the box beside the correct answer. (1 mark)

See p 51 if you need some help with circulation.

c About 1000cm³ of blood flows through the kidney every minute. About 120cm³ of liquid is filtered from this blood by the kidney. Eventually, 99 per cent of this filtered liquid is returned to the blood.

i State one substance other than water that is filtered from the blood by the kidney.

.... (1 mark)

ii What volume of liquid is permanently removed every minute from the blood by the kidney? Show how you obtained your answer.

....

....

.... (2 marks)

iii What name is given to the liquid that is permanently removed from the blood by the kidney?

.... (1 mark)

d If a person's kidney fails to work, he or she can be treated on a kidney machine, or by having a kidney transplant.
Suggest one reason why receiving a kidney from a living relative is a more successful treatment than receiving a kidney from a dead person.

....

....

.... (1 mark)

Part question [SEG 1994]

ANSWER

a i bladder
   ii heart
b middle box – this is the vein
c i urea (*This is the obvious answer but the following are also correct: glucose, uric acid, vitamins. 'Poisons' is also correct but try and avoid giving a vague answer like this.*)
   ii 1.2cm³ (*This is 1 per cent of 120cm³. Make sure that you include the units here.*)
   iii urine
d There are two main reasons that you could chose from here:
   – the generic make-up of the donor is matched (as closely as possible) to the person that needs the kidney, so there will be less chance of rejection.
   – the organ is likely to be in a better condition.

What are the important features of cells?

Living organisms are made up of cells. A cell is the basic unit of life; it is the smallest part that can be alive. You are made up of more than 50,000 million cells. A cell is very small. Most are between 10 and 150 thousandths of a millimetre across.

Both animal and plant cells have three features in common:

- a nucleus which controls and co-ordinates the processes taking place in the cell. It is important in the reproduction of the cell.
- cytoplasm where the chemical reactions in the cell take place.
- a cell membrane (also called a plasma membrane) which keeps the contents of the cell in place. It is the barrier which substances entering and leaving the cell must cross.

Cell (or plasma) membranes also form small compartments in cells allowing different processes to occur in different parts of the cell.

What are the differences between animal and plant cells?

Plant cells have three additional features which animal cells do not have:

- a cell wall containing cellulose. This helps to support plants, it is permeable and does not act as a barrier to substances moving into and out of the cell. Note it is not instead of a cell membrane – it is on the outside of the cell membrane.
- a vacuole which is actually a bag containing fluid, surrounded by a membrane. It contains cell sap, which is more than just water; it is an aqueous solution of food substances, waste materials etc. The size of the vacuole is important in supporting the plant and the movement of water into the vacuole is due to osmosis (see later).
- chloroplasts which absorb light during photosynthesis (p 23). Many more of these are found in some cells, for example palisade mesophyll cells of the leaf, than other plant cells.

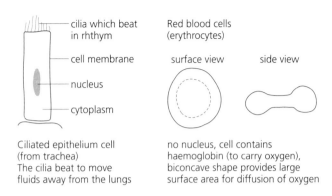

Ciliated epithelium cell (from trachea) The cilia beat to move fluids away from the lungs

no nucleus, cell contains haemoglobin (to carry oxygen), biconcave shape provides large surface area for diffusion of oxygen

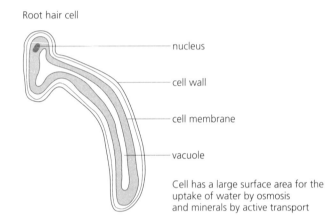

Cell has a large surface area for the uptake of water by osmosis and minerals by active transport

Fig 11 Some cells and how they are adapted for their functions

Fig 10 shows the general structure of an animal and plant cell. Cells in plants and animals rarely have exactly this structure. Cells have different structures depending on how specialised they are for a particular function in the whole organism.

QUESTION

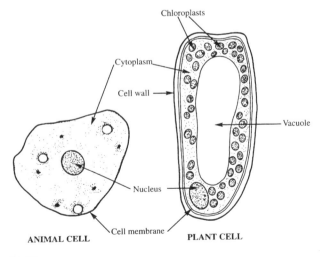

Fig 12

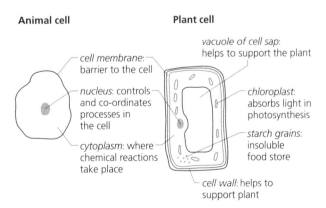

Fig 10 The structure of an animal and plant cell

a Use only the drawings above to fill in the table below to show three differences between plant and animal cells. (3 marks)

Plant Cells	Animal Cells
1	
2	
3	

Fig 13

b What is the job of each of the following parts of a cell:
   i nucleus; ....
   ii cellulose cell wall; ....
   iii cytoplasm; ....
   iv cell membrane? ....
   (2 marks)
c i What substance is contained in the chloroplasts? ....
   (1 mark)
   ii Why is this substance important to all living things? ....
   (1 mark)
   [WJEC]

ANSWER

a *Try to give those differences that distinguish plant and animal cells rather than such things as: 'there is more cytoplasm in the animal cell', which may just be true of these diagrams but not of other plant and animal cells!*
   Suitable answers are:
   chloroplasts are present in plant cells but not in animal cells
   a vacuole is present in plant cells but not in animal cells
   a cellulose cell wall is present in plant cells but not in animal cells
   Remember that plant cells still have a cytoplasmic membrane – the cell wall is outside this. Do not say 'plant cells have a cell wall not a cell membrane'.
b i nucleus – controls the cell's activities, passes on genetic information at cell division. *'Tells the cell what to do' is too vague!*

ii cellulose cell wall – helps to keep the shape of the cell, helps to support the cell.
iii cytoplasm – carries out the activities of the cell, involved in metabolism.
iv cell membrane – acts as a barrier to the cytoplasm and is selectively permeable.
c i chlorophyll
   ii it allows the cell to carry out photosynthesis. Plants are the producers in food chains.
   (see p 117 if you need more information on this)

QUESTION

Fig 14 shows three human cells

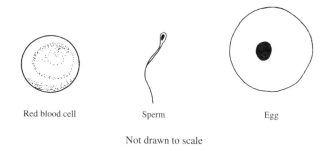

Red blood cell   Sperm   Egg

Not drawn to scale

Fig 14

a i State ONE visible difference between the red blood cell and the other two cells that you can see in the diagram.
   .... (1 mark)
   ii Explain how this difference is related to the functions of these three cells.
   ....
   ....
   ....
   .... (4 marks)
   [ULEAC]

ANSWER

a i The red blood cell does not have a nucleus but the egg and the sperm both have a nucleus.
   ii The red blood cell takes oxygen to the cells of the body. As there is no nucleus, there is more space available for haemoglobin, which carries oxygen in the form of oxyhaemoglobin.
   The sperm and egg are gametes. When they fuse they form a zygote which develops into an adult. The nucleus contains the chromosomes

which carry the genetic information for this developing organism.

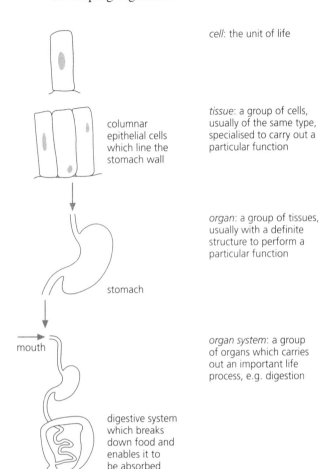

cell: the unit of life

tissue: a group of cells, usually of the same type, specialised to carry out a particular function

columnar epithelial cells which line the stomach wall

organ: a group of tissues, usually with a definite structure to perform a particular function

stomach

organ system: a group of organs which carries out an important life process, e.g. digestion

mouth

digestive system which breaks down food and enables it to be absorbed into the blood

Fig 15 Cells to systems

How are cells organised in a complex organism, such as a human?

In our bodies the cells are grouped together to carry out particular functions. Fig 15 shows how cells are grouped into tissues, which are themselves grouped into organs and then into systems.

QUESTION

Different organs and organ systems in humans and plants have different jobs. Use the words from the following list to complete the table to show which part carries out each job.

You may use each word once, more than once or not at all. (4 marks)

flower   heart   kidneys   large intestine   leaves
liver   lungs   roots   skeleton   stem

job	part which does the job	
	in humans	*in plants*
takes in and gives out gases	lungs	
takes in water		
gives support		stem

Fig 16

[MEG]

ANSWER

takes in and gives out gases   humans – lungs (given)
                                plants – leaves
takes in water   humans – large intestine
                                plants – roots
gives support   humans – skeleton
                                plants – stem (given)

Do be careful here that you use words from the list given.

QUESTION

The drawing below shows an outline of a person's body. The arrows point to the positions of three organs inside the body. The three organs are heart, lung and kidney.

a   Write down the name of the organ to which each arrow is pointing. (3 marks)

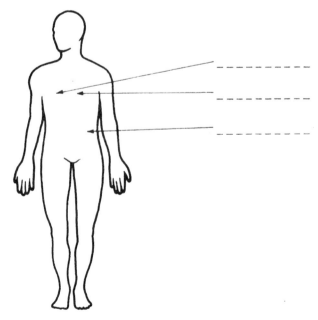

Fig 17

b Each organ of the body does its own important job in keeping you alive and healthy.
   i What is the job of your heart?

   ....
   .... (2 marks)
   ii What is the job of your lungs?

   ....
   .... (2 marks)
   iii What is the job of your kidneys?

   ....
   .... (3 marks)
c Your stomach and small intestine are two organs of your digestive system.
   i What happens to food in your stomach?
   .... (1 mark)
   ii What happens to food in your small intestine?

   ....
   ....
   .... (2 marks)
   [SEG 1994]

ANSWER

a From top to bottom: lung, heart, kidney
b i The heart pumps blood around the body to the cells.

ii At the lungs, oxygen diffuses into the blood and carbon dioxide diffuses from the blood into the air in the process of gaseous exchange. *If you wanted to put 'respiration' as the answer you need to see p 47!*
iii The kidneys filter urea out of the blood. They are also involved in regulating the water content of the fluids – particularly the blood. (osmoregulation see p 76)
c i In the stomach the food is mixed with gastric juices, in physical digestion. Pepsin digests the proteins into amino acids. *(Hydrochloric acid also destroys any 'germs' present.)*
   ii In the small intestine the soluble products of digestion are absorbed into the blood. *See p 37–38 for more details about what happens in the gut.*

How do substances move between the different cells?

Lots of substances move between cells. The following table gives a summary of some of these.

type of cell	what moves	why it is needed
animal and plant	oxygen taken in	respiration
	carbon dioxide leaves	respiration
	ions such as sodium	metabolism
	water taken in	chemical reactions in the cell occur in aqueous solution
	waste products of metabolism leave	harmful if they build up in the cell
	enzymes	control reactions
	hormones	co-ordination
	energy – in molecules and as light and heat	metabolism
animal	food substances in	metabolism
	receive substances due to nerve impulses	co-ordination
plant	carbon dioxide taken in	photosynthesis
	oxygen leaves	photosynthesis
	cellulose	construction of cell wall

Water also leaves plant and animal cells, due to evaporation.

Water surrounds all cells in all organisms. Therefore the substances that move into and out of the cells do so in water.

There are three important ways that substances move in organisms:

- diffusion
- osmosis
- active transport

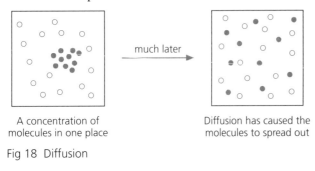

A concentration of molecules in one place

Diffusion has caused the molecules to spread out

Fig 18 Diffusion

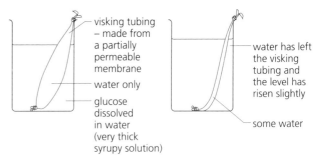

visking tubing – made from a partially permeable membrane

water only

glucose dissolved in water (very thick syrupy solution)

water has left the visking tubing and the level has risen slightly

some water

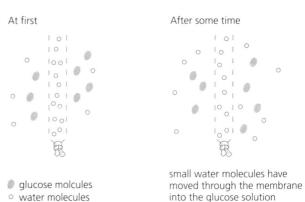

At first

After some time

- glucose molcules
- water molecules

small water molecules have moved through the membrane into the glucose solution

Fig 19 An explanation of osmosis

What is diffusion?

Diffusion is the movement of particles from a high concentration to a low concentration. Particles, whether they are atoms, ions or molecules (p 159) move randomly all the time. If the particles are not evenly distributed at first, the movement is such that they end up being evenly distributed. Substances move around in the cytoplasm of cells by diffusion. For substances to move between cells by diffusion it is helpful if:

- the thickness of the surface that the substance has to cross is small.
- the surface area is large.
- there is a big difference in concentration between two places.
- the molecules that need to move are small.

Some examples of diffusion in organisms

- Diffusion at the small intestine
  The products of digestion move into the blood at the villi mainly by diffusion.
- Diffusion at the alveoli
  Oxygen moves into the blood and carbon dioxide leaves the blood. This is called gaseous exchange.
- Diffusion at the capillaries
  Oxygen leaves the capillaries for the cells where it is needed for respiration. Carbon dioxide, the waste product of this process, returns to the blood.

How is osmosis different from diffusion?

Osmosis is a special type of diffusion. It is the movement of water molecules from a region where there are many water molecules to a region where there are few water molecules, through a partially (or selectively) permeable membrane.

Try to avoid saying things like 'an area of high concentration of water', as this leads to all sorts of confusion.

Some things to remember:

- small molecules such as water pass through a partially permeable membrane, but bigger molecules such as glucose do not.
- a solution which contains many *water molecules* (and few of the solute, for example glucose) is a *weak* solution.
- a solution which contains *few water molecules* (and many of the solute, for example glucose) is a *concentrated* ('strong') solution. We usually talk about a *high concentration of the solute* that is dissolved in the water, rather than a 'strong' solution.

Some examples of osmosis in organisms

*   Helping to support a plant
    The vacuole of a plant cell contains cell sap, which is a solution of different solutes in water. Water therefore enters the cell sap by osmosis, and the vacuole has the appearance of a blown up balloon. This forces the cytoplasm against the cell wall. The cell is said to be *turgid*. This is an important way in which plants, which do not have a skeleton like us, are able to stand upright. If a plant is short of water, for example a pot plant which has not been watered recently, the cell vacuole is *flaccid* and the plant wilts.
*   A plant root cell taking in water
    The vacuole of the root hair cell is more concentrated than the soil water. Water therefore enters the root by osmosis (p 56 contains more details).
*   Controlling the stomata in leaves
    The size of the stomata is controlled by the guard cells which surround them. As the guard cells become turgid they cause the stomata to open, thus allowing more gases to enter and leave the leaf.
*   Red blood cells and osmosis
    Animal cells do not have a cell wall. If the concentration of the blood plasma became very weak, ie it contained a lot of water, then water would enter the red blood cells by osmosis and eventually they would burst. Alternatively, if the concentration of the blood plasma increased then water would leave the red blood cells and they would shrink. Either state would be dangerous as the red blood cells could no longer carry oxygen to the cells. It is therefore important that the concentration of the blood and other body fluids is carefully controlled. The kidney is important in this osmoregulation of the body (p 76).

QUESTION

A pupil investigated osmosis using uncooked potato chips and Visking tubing bags.
Two different varieties of potato, *Cara* and *Rocket*, were each tested separately, and the chips were all the same size and shape.
The Visking tubing bags were of equal size and contained a ten per cent (10%) sugar solution. They were carefully sealed to avoid leaks.
The chips and the Visking tubing were then tied to the ends of a balance and immersed into concentrated sugar solution and water.

Three sets of apparatus were used, one for potato *Cara*, one for potato *Rocket* and one for Visking tubing bags.
The diagrams below show each set of apparatus before and after the experiment.

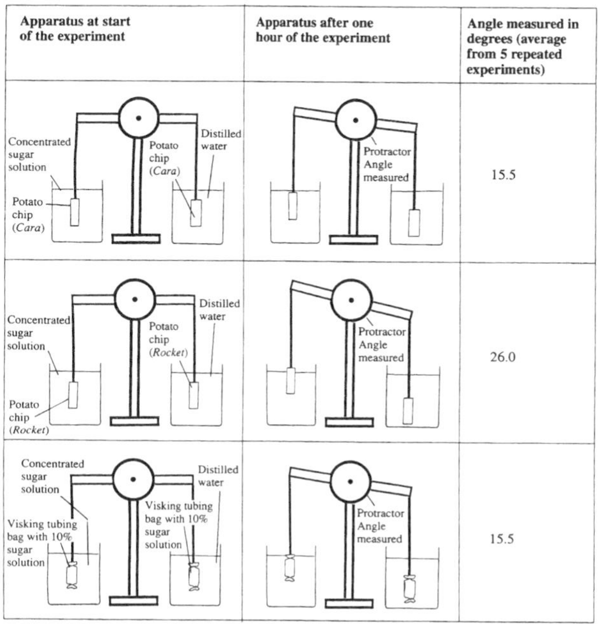

Fig 20

a   The balance beam became higher on the left hand side but lower on the right hand side at the end of each experiment. Explain why this happened.

....
....
....
....
....
.... (4 marks)

b   What is the approximate concentration of the sap inside the potato cells of the variety *Cara*?
Concentration of sap ....
Reason ....
....
.... (2 marks)
[ULEAC]

ANSWER

a   In each of the three cases in the diagram:
    On the left, water left the potato (or the Visking tubing) by osmosis, as the concentrated sugar solution was more concentrated than the solution in the vacuoles of the potato cells or the Visking

tubing. Therefore the potato chips and Visking tubing became lighter.

On the right, water entered the cells of the potato (or the Visking tubing) as the solution in the cells of the potato (or the Visking tubing) was more concentrated than the distilled water. Therefore the potato chips and Visking tubing became heavier. This caused the beam to tilt as it did.

Do use the space to give a clear logical answer.

b Concentration of the sap: 10% (sugar solution)
  Reason: The movement in the apparatus with *Cara* was the same as the movement in the apparatus with the Visking tubing containing a 10% sugar solution.

How is active transport different from diffusion?

The name gives a hint to the main difference – it is an active process and energy is required when substances are moved in this way. This process is needed to move a substance from where there is a little to where there is a lot (that is, in the opposite direction from diffusion and osmosis.)

Some examples of active transport

- Movement of glucose into the phloem cells of plants
  Glucose is moved through the plant in the phloem. There is a high concentration of glucose in these cells. To collect more glucose (which has been made in the leaf) the cells requires energy to be used.
- Movement of ions into the root hair cell
  The root needs to take up mineral ions from the soil. The cell sap is likely to contain a higher concentration of a particular ion than there is in the solution of soil 'water'. Energy from respiration is needed for the ion to enter the root hair cell.
- Movement of glucose, amino acids and salts into blood in the intestine
  Soon after digestion there is a higher concentration of these substances in the small intestine than in the blood. The substances move into the blood by diffusion, but this is a slow process and over a period of time it is increasingly helped by active transport.

- Movement of glucose, amino acids and ions in the kidney
  Active transport is very important in the re-absorption of glucose, amino acids and ions into the blood from the kidney tubule.

QUESTION

Barley is a type of cereal. The roots of barley are able to absorb potassium ions more effectively if they have a good supply of oxygen.

Which of the following statements explains this observation.

A The ions are used up in respiration.

B To absorb the ions, the cells need to expend energy.

C Oxygen activates the ions.

D The root needs a supply of energy to grow.

(1 mark)

ANSWER

B Absorbing potassium ions involves active transport, therefore energy is required for this process.

QUESTION

Farmers that drain their waterlogged soil find that the crops grow better. Explain why this is.   (5 marks)

....
....
....
....
....
....
....
....
....
....

ANSWER

In well drained soil, there is air between the soil particles. Oxygen in the air is used by the root cells in cell respiration. This provides the energy to take in important ions (needed for growth by the plant) from the soil. The ions are taken into the plant by active transport. If the soil is waterlogged, the air spaces are filled with water and the root cannot get the oxygen it requires for this process.

Photosynthesis

What is photosynthesis?

Plants make their food from carbon dioxide and water. Light is also needed for this reaction – hence the name photo (light) …synthesis (making complex substances, like sugar, from simpler ones).
Plants can grow without soil as long as they can get these raw materials.

It is important to note that plants do not take in food *from the soil. They do take in* minerals *in solution. These are used to make proteins, for example.*

This equation is a summary of photosynthesis:

$$\text{carbon dioxide} + \text{water} \xrightarrow{\text{light and chlorophyll}} \text{glucose} + \text{oxygen} \quad \Delta H = +$$
$$6CO_2 + 6H_2O \qquad C_6H_{12}O_6 + 6O_2$$

raw materials   products
endothermic reaction
energy is absorbed

Notice that the light and chlorophyll are written on the arrow.
The green chlorophyll enables the energy in the light to be transferred to the glucose.

Testing a leaf for starch

Some of the glucose made by the leaf is turned into starch (a polymer made up of glucose monomers).

Fig 1 Soil is not needed for plant growth

This is a good storage product for the cells, because it is insoluble and cannot easily be taken to other cells or affect the water balance in the cell (see p 20). There are three ways you can see whether photosynthesis is happening in plants:

1 *Starch test* – this involves killing a part of the plant.
2 *Collecting the oxygen given off* – the process can be watched in a living plant. It is easier with an aquatic plant like the pondweed *Elodea*.
3 *Using hydrogencarbonate indicator* – the process can be watched in a living plant. Again it is easier with an aquatic plant like the pondweed *Elodea*.

Hydrogencarbonate indicator is an orange colour when it has been freshly made. It turns red when carbon dioxide is taken away and yellow when carbon dioxide is added.

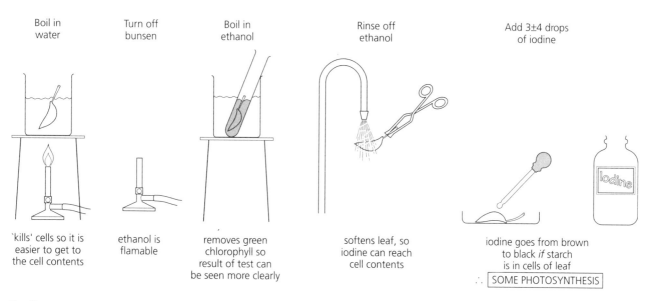

Boil in water
Turn off bunsen
Boil in ethanol
Rinse off ethanol
Add 3±4 drops of iodine

'kills' cells so it is easier to get to the cell contents
ethanol is flamable
removes green chlorophyll so result of test can be seen more clearly
softens leaf, so iodine can reach cell contents
iodine goes from brown to black *if* starch is in cells of leaf
∴ SOME PHOTOSYNTHESIS

Fig 2

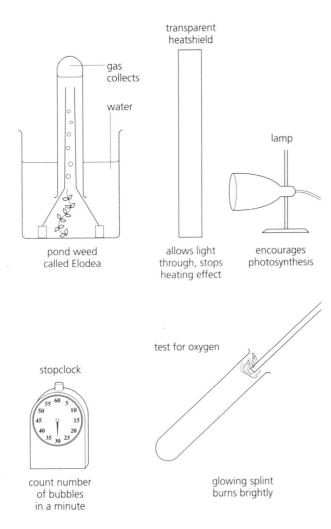

Fig 3 Collecting the oxygen given off

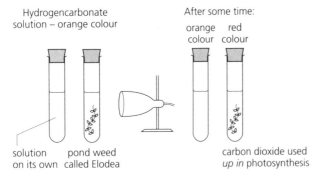

Fig 4 Using hydrogencarbonate indicator

QUESTION

a Complete the word equation for photosynthesis.

energy

carbon dioxide + _____ → glucose + _____

chlorophyll

(2 marks)

b What is the function of chlorophyll in photosynthesis?

.... (1 mark)

[ULEAC]

ANSWER

a water, oxygen

b to absorb the light or to convert light into chemical energy

Evidence that carbon dioxide, light and chlorophyll are needed for photosynthesis

The starch test is often used as evidence that photosynthesis has taken place. Before any of the experiments are set up the plant must be placed in a dark place for 48 hours. This is called *de-starching*. During this time starch that is already in the leaves is used up by the plant and no more can be made.

QUESTION

Before using a geranium plant in a photosynthesis experiment, it is usual to put the plant in the dark for 48 hours before setting up the experiment. Explain why this is done.

ANSWER

To remove any starch that is already in the plant, so any starch found will have been produced during the experiment.

Evidence for Light

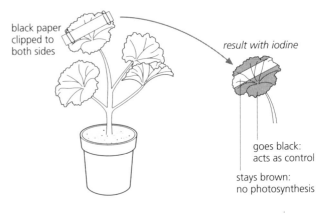

Fig 5

Evidence for chlorophyll

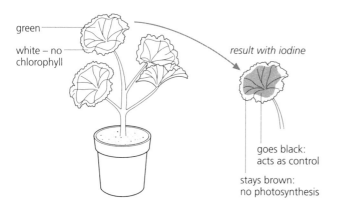

green

white – no chlorophyll

result with iodine

goes black: acts as control

stays brown: no photosynthesis

Fig 6

Evidence for carbon dioxide

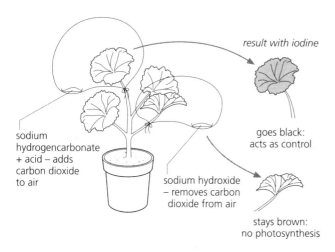

result with iodine

sodium hydrogencarbonate + acid – adds carbon dioxide to air

goes black: acts as control

sodium hydroxide – removes carbon dioxide from air

stays brown: no photosynthesis

Fig 7

You need to know that sodium hydroxide *absorbs carbon dioxide from the air, but* sodium hydrogencarbonate *is used to add carbon dioxide to the surroundings.*

Evidence for water

You cannot perform a similar experiment for water. Not watering the plant has an effect on the whole plant – not just on photosynthesis.

If plants are watered with water containing the radioactive isotope O^{18}, then this is found in the oxygen given off by the plant as a product of photosynthesis.

QUESTION

In which of these jars will most starch be made?

In which of these jars will most starch be made?

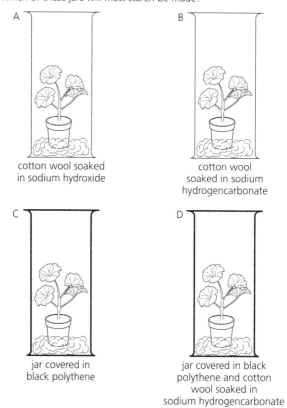

A

B

cotton wool soaked in sodium hydroxide

cotton wool soaked in sodium hydrogencarbonate

C

D

jar covered in black polythene

jar covered in black polythene and cotton wool soaked in sodium hydrogencarbonate

Fig 8

ANSWER

B – *the sodium hydrogencarbonate increases the amount of carbon dioxide in the air.*

QUESTION

The diagram below represents the flow of chemicals and reactions taking place in the leaf.

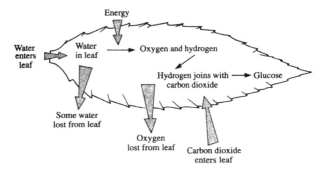

Energy

Water enters leaf

Water in leaf

Oxygen and hydrogen

Hydrogen joins with carbon dioxide

Glucose

Some water lost from leaf

Oxygen lost from leaf

Carbon dioxide enters leaf

Fig 9

a   i   Where does the energy come from?

.... (1 mark)

   ii   What name is given to the process of water loss from leaves?

.... (1 mark) iii Carbon atoms with a mass number of 14 are radioactive. Describe how carbon-14 could be used to prove that glucose in a leaf has been made from carbon dioxide.

....

....

....

.... (3 marks)

iv In which part of the leaf do the reactions shown in the diagram take place?

....

.... (2 marks)

Part question [SEG 1994]

ANSWER

a i The sun or light

ii Transpiration or evapotranspiration
   (see p 58 if you need reminding about this.)

iii Carbon dioxide that is given to the plant should be labelled with carbon-14. This makes the carbon dioxide radioactive. After a time the glucose that the leaf has made (by photosynthesis) is radioactive. This shows that the carbon used to make the glucose has come from the carbon dioxide.

iv The chloroplasts of the palisade mesophyll cells. The reaction takes place in any green cells of the plant, but most of the photosynthesis occurs in the palisade mesophyll cells.

What are limiting factors?

The four factors (light, chlorophyll, carbon dioxide and water) and temperature affect the rate at which plants photosynthesise. This is very important to commercial plant growers. If they can make photosynthesis occur faster the yield of plants increases, and so do their profits.

In a process like photosynthesis, which depends upon a number of factors, if any one of these is in short supply then the rate of photosynthesis is less than a maximum. The factor that is in short supply is called a limiting factor.

Light Intensity

Commercial growers use greenhouses to encourage the maximum amount of light to reach the plants. In general, the brighter the light the faster the rate of

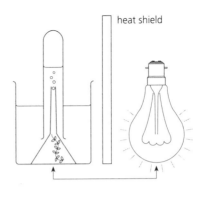

heat shield

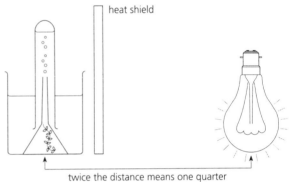

heat shield

twice the distance means one quarter the light intensity reaches the plant

Fig 10

photosynthesis. In the early morning, or on a dull day, light may be a limiting factor.

If the light is very bright the rate of photosynthesis may slow down, as plants are damaged by ultraviolet rays.

The intensity of light is inversely proportion to the square of the distance between the plant and the light source.

light intensity α $1/(distance)^2$

Distance = 12cm	Distance = 24cm
Light intensity	Light intensity
α $1/12^2$	α $1/24^2$
$= 1/144 = 0.00694$	$= 1/576 = 0.00173$
$= 6.94 \times 10^{-3}$cm	$= 1.73 \times 10^{-3}$cm

Type of light

Sunlight, called white light, is made up of all wavelengths of the spectrum.

Fig 11 shows that the chlorophyll absorbs red and blue light. The chlorophyll reflects the green light. (This is why leaves look green). The type of light is therefore a limiting factor – the absence of red and blue light reduces photosynthesis. Light manufacturers produce bulbs that enhance red and blue wavelengths for commercial greenhouses.

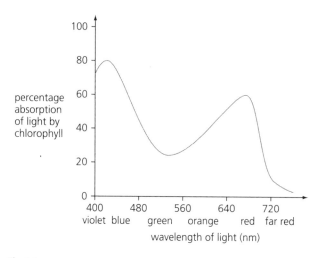

Fig 11

Carbon dioxide

Methane is burnt in many greenhouses and this increases the percentage of carbon dioxide in the air, as well as providing warmth. In general, the rate of photosynthesis increases with the amount of carbon dioxide in the air. The average amount of carbon dioxide is about 0.03%. Insufficient carbon dioxide in the atmosphere will limit photosynthesis.

Temperature

Increasing the temperature by about 10°C doubles the rate of many chemical reactions. Photosynthesis is a chemical reaction and it is affected by temperature just the same as other reactions. However, above about 40°C the enzymes involved in photosynthesis are denatured (see p 11) and the plant is damaged. Thus temperature is a limiting factor for photosynthesis – the reactions are slow if it is too cold and the enzymes are destroyed if it is too hot.

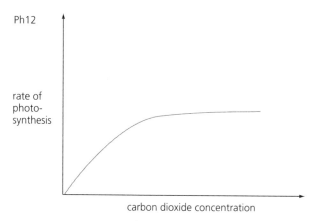

Fig 12

Water

A lack of water affects the plant in many ways, rather than just having a direct effect on photosynthesis. However, a wilting plant may photosynthesise at only half the rate of when it has sufficient water.

Chlorophyll

Insufficient chlorophyll can act as a limiting factor. The plant therefore needs a sufficient supply of magnesium, the element at the centre of the chlorophyll molecule. Remember that in a variegated plant the 'white parts' cannot make starch.
(see p 31 – Mineral salts and healthy plant growth.)

QUESTION

a Why do green plants grow better in red or blue light than they do in green light?
....
.... (1 mark)
b Why do many gardeners use additional lighting?
....
.... (1 mark)
c Name two substances that plants need for photosynthesis.
1 ....
2 .... (2 marks)
d What else might increase the rate of photosynthesis?
.... (1 mark)
[MEG]

ANSWER

a Green plants cannot absorb green light. They reflect green light and so cannot use it for photosynthesis.
You must give enough detail – 'because they have green chloroplasts' is too vague.
b This increases the rate of photosynthesis, so the plants grow more quickly.
c Any two of water, carbon dioxide and chlorophyll.
You could also name a specific mineral such as magnesium or 'phosphate', but you cannot say light – it is not a substance!
d An increase in any of the following: temperature, carbon dioxide, light, chlorophyll and water.
You must make sure that you say increase and not, for example, just 'light. This is not specific enough.

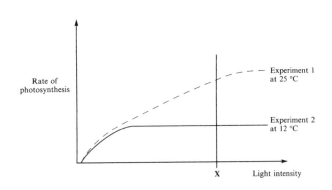

Fig 13

QUESTION

The graphs above show the effect of changes in the light intensity on the rate of photosynthesis of the same plant. The plant was at different temperatures in each experiment. All other conditions were the same.

What factors were limiting (controlling) the rate of photosynthesis at light intensity X?

	In experiment 1	In experiment 2
A	light	temperature
B	light	light
C	temperature	temperature
D	temperature	light

[SEG 1994]

ANSWER

A

The leaf

Just as we have organs which do specific jobs (e.g. the heart pumps blood) so do flowering plants. All cells which contain chlorophyll can carry out photosynthesis, but the leaves are the organs that are adapted for this function.

How are the leaves adapted for photosynthesis?

plants, given the chance, grow towards the light

the leaves themselves are arranged so that they do not shade each other

the total surface area of the leaves on a plant is large

the veins in the leaves help to hold the leaves up so they catch the light

Fig 14

What does the outside of the leaf indicate about photosynthesis?

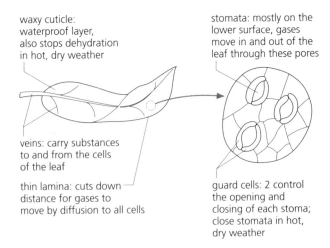

waxy cuticle: waterproof layer, also stops dehydration in hot, dry weather

veins: carry substances to and from the cells of the leaf

thin lamina: cuts down distance for gases to move by diffusion to all cells

stomata: mostly on the lower surface, gases move in and out of the leaf through these pores

guard cells: 2 control the opening and closing of each stoma; close stomata in hot, dry weather

Fig 15

What does the inside of the leaf indicate about photosynthesis?

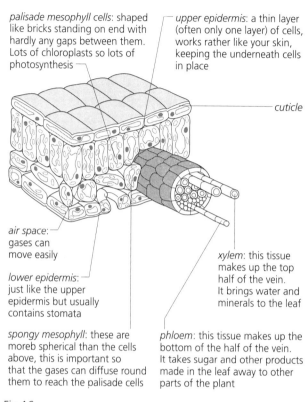

palisade mesophyll cells: shaped like bricks standing on end with hardly any gaps between them. Lots of chloroplasts so lots of photosynthesis

upper epidermis: a thin layer (often only one layer) of cells, works rather like your skin, keeping the underneath cells in place

cuticle

air space: gases can move easily

lower epidermis: just like the upper epidermis but usually contains stomata

xylem: this tissue makes up the top half of the vein. It brings water and minerals to the leaf

spongy mesophyll: these are moreb spherical than the cells above, this is important so that the gases can diffuse round them to reach the palisade cells

phloem: this tissue makes up the bottom of the half of the vein. It takes sugar and other products made in the leaf away to other parts of the plant

Fig 16

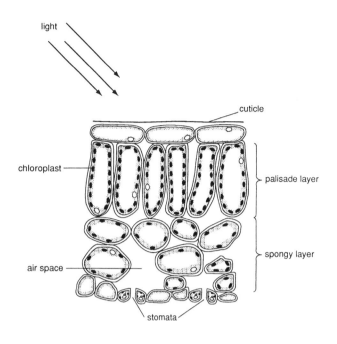

light

cuticle

chloroplast

palisade layer

air space

spongy layer

stomata

Fig 17

QUESTION

Leaves are organs of photosynthesis. They come in all shapes and sizes but all of them are adapted to absorb as much light as possible.

a Give one way in which leaves are adapted to absorb light.

....
.... (1 mark)

b Fig 17 shows a cross-section through a leaf. Explain the following observations:

   i The cuticle is transparent.

....
.... (1 mark)

   ii Most chloroplasts are found in the palisade layer.

....
.... (1 mark)

   iii Air spaces are found mostly in the spongy layer.

....
.... (1 mark)

iv What is the substance in the chloroplasts which absorbs light?

....
.... (1 mark)

c Explain how each of the following affects the rate of photosynthesis in a potted plant.

   i Moving it nearer the window.

....
.... (1 mark)

   ii Moving it to a colder room.

....
.... (1 mark)

d Complete the following word equation for photosynthesis.

                    sunlight
.... + water   →   glucose + ...

(2 marks)
[MEG]

ANSWER

a In the palisade layer there are many chloroplasts in the cells, these absorb light.

b *The question asks you to* explain *the observations, make sure you do not just* describe *them!*

   i The transparent cuticle allows the light to pass through. The light needs to pass into the palisade layer where it is absorbed by the chloroplasts.

   ii The palisade layer is close to the top of the leaf. It is here that the light is absorbed.

iii Carbon dioxide needed for photosynthesis
passes into the leaf through the stomata.
This diffuses through the air spaces to the
palisade cells.

c chlorophyll

d i Moving the plant near the window increases
the intensity of the light so this increases the
rate of photosynthesis.

ii Moving the plant to a colder room decreases
the rate of the chemical reaction in
photosynthesis.

e carbon dioxide, oxygen.

What does the plant do with the glucose that it makes?

It is:

- transported to other parts of the plant in the form
  of sucrose.
- used in respiration, to provide the plant cells with
  energy for carrying out other chemical reactions.
- turned into insoluble starch as an 'energy store'.
- turned into fats and oils as an 'energy store'.
- used to make cellulose cell walls.
- used (along with nitrogen and sulphur) to make
  amino acids and then proteins, which the plant
  needs for growth and repair.

QUESTION

*This question, like many questions about
photosynthesis, also asks about respiration. If you need
to revise this topic look on p 47 to p 50.*

Fig 18 shows a vertical section through a leaf.

a i What gas is represented by X? (1 mark)
ii What gas is represented by Y? (1 mark)

b The cells in the diagram below respire. Name two
substances, made by the plant, that are used in the
process of respiration.
i .... ii .... (2 marks)

c State one way that plants use the energy released
during respiration. (1 mark)

d State two ways that mammals use the energy
released in respiration.
i .... ii .... (2 marks)

e Fig 19 shows the average size of the leaves of
plants of the same age. Some had grown in the
shade and some in the light.

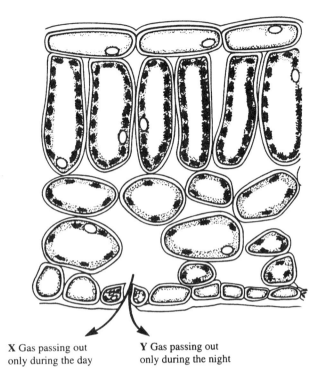

X Gas passing out   **Y** Gas passing out
only during the day   only during the night

Fig 18

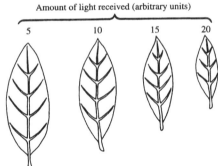

Amount of light received (arbitrary units)

5   10   15   20

Diagrams are drawn to the same scale.

Fig 19

Explain these observations (2 marks)

....
....
....
....

[WJEC]

ANSWER

a i oxygen
ii carbon dioxide

b oxygen and glucose

c for growth

d for growth, for movement

e The less light the leaves get the bigger they
become.
They will have more chloroplasts to absorb the light.

QUESTION

State three ways the plant uses glucose which is made in the leaf. (3 marks)

1 ....
....

2 ....
....

3 ....
....

Part question [SEG 1994]

ANSWER

There are many ways you could include here but notice the question asks you how *the plant* uses *the glucose.*

- The glucose can be converted into starch as an energy store.
- The glucose can be converted into cellulose to make cell walls.
- The glucose may be used as a fuel in respiration to provide energy for the cell's activities.
- The glucose may be needed, along with nitrogen, to make proteins so that the plant can grow.

Mineral salts and healthy plant growth

Green plants make glucose by photosynthesis. Glucose contains the elements carbon, hydrogen and oxygen. These three elements make up starch, fats and oils and no additional elements are needed to make these substances. To grow, plants need proteins. These contain the elements carbon, hydrogen and oxygen *plus* nitrogen and sulphur. These and other elements which the plant needs for healthy growth are taken in from the soil. They are called mineral salts. (Mineral because they are not taken directly from living things, and salts because they are found in the soil as compounds called salts, for example nitrates (see p 144).

The following diagrams illustrate why plants need these elements. By looking at unhealthy plants it is possible to spot which elements they are missing. These plants are said to suffer from mineral deficiency *diseases*.

The mineral salts which plants take from the soil need to be replaced. This happens naturally if the plants die and rot. However, in agriculture the plants are removed; for example, a sugar beet crop is harvested to provide sugar. If the field is to be used again for a similar crop then fertilisers need to be added to replace the lost minerals. The most common type is N.P.K., which contains nitrogen (N), phosphorus (P) and potassium (K) – the most important minerals for plant growth.

QUESTION

Some pond plants were not growing well. They were thought to be suffering from nitrate deficiency.

No nitrogen	No phosphorus	No potassium	No calcium	No iron	No magnesium
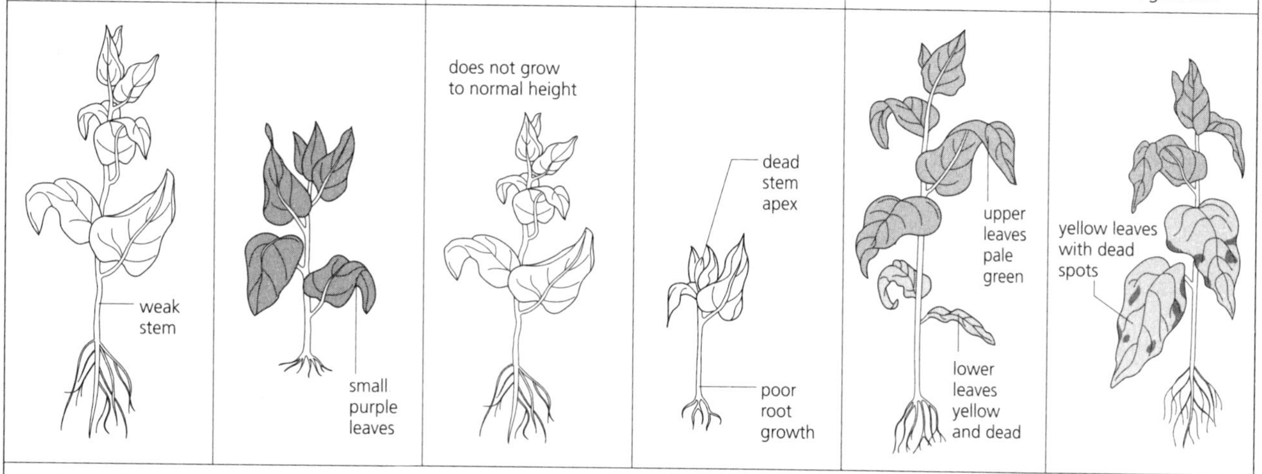 weak stem	small purple leaves	does not grow to normal height	dead stem apex; poor root growth	upper leaves pale green; lower leaves yellow and dead	yellow leaves with dead spots
Used to make					
proteins and nucleic acids	ATP (energy 'rich' molecule – important in photosynthesis and respiration)	proteins and cell membranes	'glue' between cell walls	enzymes to make chlorophyll	chlorophyll molecule

Fig 20

a How might the deficiency have been observed?

b What does the plant need the 'nitrate' for?

ANSWER

a Weak plant, particularly the stem.

b To provide the nitrogen that is needed to make proteins. *Nitrogen is also needed to make DNA.*

QUESTION

A new plant fertiliser is being advertised which is particularly rich in magnesium and calcium. In a plant what are the following used for:

a calcium?

b magnesium?

ANSWER

a Calcium is needed to make the substance that helps the cells to 'stick together'.

b Magnesium is part of the chlorophyll molecule and so is very important for photosynthesis.

QUESTION

a Plants need mineral salts for healthy growth. Give the chemical names of two types of mineral salts.

1 ....

2 .... (2 marks)

b A farmer wants to increase his yield by sensible use of fertilisers. The graph shows how the mass of crop produced from a field depends on the quantity of nitrogen used.

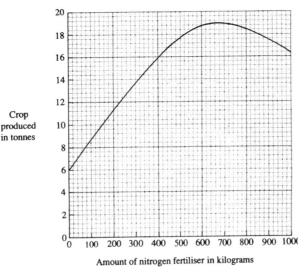

Crop produced in tonnes

Amount of nitrogen fertiliser in kilograms

Fig 21

What is the maximum mass of crop that could be produced by using nitrogen fertilisers on the field? (1 mark)

.... tonnes

c Many of the chemicals in fertilisers dissolve in water. When it rains, some of the fertiliser is washed out of the soil into rivers and streams. What effect does the fertiliser in the river water have on the river plants:

i Immediately or in the short term; ....

.... (1 mark)

ii In the long term? ....

.... (1 mark)

Part question [SEG 1994]

ANSWER

a *This is quite tricky. The question asks you for two types of mineral salts, so it expects you to name:* nitrates, or phosphates or sulphates. *Just giving* nitrogen *is not sufficient.*

b 19 (tonnes)

c i The plants will grow more or they will grow more quickly.

ii The oxygen in the river will be reduced, the plants in the river will die and the river will be choked with dead plants. These will decompose due to the action of bacteria.

Many questions about minerals involve the 'bad' effects of fertilisers.

Nutrition

Why do we need food?

All animals need food. Remember that nutrition is one of the seven characteristics of life. The term nutrition is really just another word for feeding. Thinking about what the food is needed for makes it easier to work out which sorts of food are needed.

Other words related to feeding that you may come across:
Nutrient: a food substance, for example carbohydrate.
Nutritional: used to describe a food which is rich in a nutrient, for example protein.

1 As a fuel

The cells in your body are carrying out a large number of chemical reactions as you read this. In

The essential raw materials that our body needs

nutrient	examples of food source	use in body
carbohydrate starch – most common carbohydrate	bread, potatoes, pasta	provides energy
sugar – many types	fruit – contains fructose or glucose sucrose – added to tea or coffee	provides energy
cellulose – contained in all plant cell walls	any plant	dietary fibre (roughage), helps prevent constipation as it keeps food moving in the gut
fat – some are saturated and increase blood cholesterol level, but polyunsaturates decrease this level	butter, olive oil, peanuts	provides energy and warmth
proteins	milk, eggs, meat	for growth, repair and manufacture of enzymes
vitamins and minerals – the body needs quite a variety of particular substances, some important ones are: sodium	salt	to maintain nerves and muscles, but too much can cause high blood pressure
calcium	bread, cheese, milk	to maintain bones and teeth and also for blood clotting; rickets is a deficiency disease caused by lack of calcium
iron	red meat and green vegetables	to make haemoglobin; without it anaemia may result
iodine	salt and sea foods	to make the hormone thyroxine which increases the rate of metabolism; without it reactions are slow and the thyroid may swell (goitre)
vitamin A	carrots, fish liver oil	to see in dim light
vitamin B – a group of vitamins	cereals and yeast	for respiration
B1 (thiamine)	cereals and yeast	for nerves and muscles; without it beri-beri may occur
B2 (riboflavin)	cereals and yeast	for general growth, healthy skin
vitamin C – this is destroyed by cooking	fresh spinach and citrus fruit	for tissues lining body cavities; without it scurvy may occur
vitamin D	fish products, but is also made in skin as UV light is absorbed	to enable bones and teeth to absorb calcium

every cell, food is being oxidized (see p 146) to release the energy needed for these reactions. In fact, most of the food you eat is used in this way.

2 As building materials

Some of your food is used to actually build and repair your body. Although adults have stopped growing, they still need to repair and replace worn out cells.

3 To maintain a healthy body

Some of the activities in the body need particular substances. Although only small amounts of these are needed, they are very important.

A balanced diet

A balanced diet is one that contains all the necessary nutrients in the correct proportions. No individual food contains everything the body needs and there are different ways of achieving a balanced diet. When analysed the diet should contain these seven essential raw materials:

carbohydrates
fats
proteins
minerals
vitamins
dietary fibre (roughage)
water

Water

Water is an essential part of the diet. It is needed to enable substances to be carried round the body. Many of the reactions occurring in cells can only occur in an aqueous solution. Although you could live for a month without food, you would die after a few days if you did not have any water.

Choosing a balanced diet

When deciding if a diet is balanced you need to do more than check that it has the necessary seven raw materials. Everyone is different! Chemical reactions in different people work at different rates. This is called the metabolic rate. A person who seems to eat all the time and yet stays slim may have a high metabolic rate. In extreme cases this may be a symptom of an over-active thyroid gland. Some important considerations are:

Age – A young person who is still growing needs more protein per unit mass than an adult who only needs protein to replace and repair cells.

Activity – If you have a lot of exercise, you will need more carbohydrates and fats in your diet to provide the energy. However, if you have a 'high energy' diet and do not exercise, the energy is stored as fat.

Sex – In general, males need more energy from their diet than females. A 15 year old girl needs about 10,000 kJ, but a 15 year old boy needs about 12,000 kJ.

Food tests

You can carry out simple tests to find out which foods contain different nutrients.

food type	summary of test	positive result
starch	add iodine solution	blue-black colour
sugars	add dilute hydrochloric acid to mashed food in water, heat gently for 1 min. Add dilute sodium hydroxide to neutralise. Add Benedict's solution. Heat for 1 min.	green or brown precipitate
fats	add the mashed food to ethanol, shake vigorously. Add water – or more simply rub the food on a piece of paper.	cloudy mixture greasy mark
proteins	add copper(II) sulphate solution and sodium hydroxide solution to mashed up food in water, mix and wait a few minutes.	violet colour

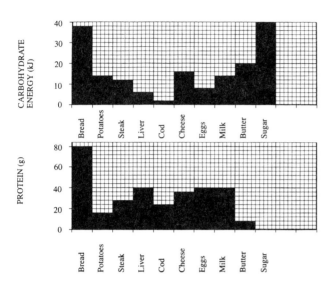

Fig 1

There are other factors that might be important too: for example, is the person pregnant, recovering from illness, living in a cold country? In each case you need to think of the bodily needs and how the diet can meet them.

QUESTION

The bar charts above show the contents of various foods which were bought for the same amount of money.

Use the bar charts to answer the following questions:

a Which food contained the most:
   i protein; .... ii energy? .... (2 marks)
b Name a food which contains no protein. (1 mark)
c In terms of value for money, which food would you choose (bread, steak or cod) to provide energy and protein? Give reasons for your answer. (1 mark)
   ....
   ....
d Name two other classes of food which are necessary for a balanced diet. (2 marks)
   i .... ii ....

[WJEC]

ANSWER

a i bread; ii sugar
c bread; it has the most energy (or carbohydrate) and protein
d fat, vitamins, minerals
   It is probably best not to include dietary fibre and water as these are not strictly 'classes of food'.

Vegetarian diets

These diets are based on plants, but may include some animal products such as milk and eggs to provide essential amino acids. Proteins are synthesised from about 23 amino acids in the body. The body can only make some of the amino acids it needs. Others must be included in the diet, hence their name essential amino acids. Without these the body is unable to make essential proteins. Strict vegetarians, called vegans, do not include animal products in their diet and need to supplement their diet to provide these amino acids.

Low-cholesterol diet

Cholesterol is an important part of all cells and so it is essential to have some in the diet. However, some people have high levels of cholesterol in their blood. This can increase the risk of heart disease as cholestol is known to be deposited along the lining of arteries. Simply reducing the cholesterol in the diet by cutting down on 'high cholesterol foods' such as egg yolks does not always reduce the blood cholesterol level. Changing the type of fat in the diet, as shown in the table, is more effective.

Reduced-salt diet

Most of us have too much salt in our diet. We do need a small amount, but most of us have about two teaspoons a day! Too much salt can lead to raised blood pressure and this in turn can lead to an increased risk of a heart attack. People suffering from high blood pressure are often advised to watch – and try to reduce – the amount of salt in their diet.

QUESTION

The following is taken from a 25g packet of potato crisps.

	NUTRITION	
	per 25 g packet	per 100 g
ENERGY	560 kJ	2240 kJ
PROTEIN	1.5 g	6 g
CARBOHYDRATE	12 g	48 g
FAT	9 g	36 g
FIBRE	1 g	4 g
SALT	0.5 g	2.0 g

Fig 2

a How much energy is provided by 25g of crisps?
.... (1 mark)

b The recommended daily amount of fibre is 28g.
How many 25g packets of crisps provide this
much fibre? Show your working. (2 marks)

c Crisps contain large amounts of fat and salt. What
are the dangers to health of eating.
  i too much fat? (1 mark)

....

....

  ii too much salt? (1 mark)

....

....

d Which important group of nutrients is missing
from the list given on the crisp packet? (1 mark)

....

[MEG]

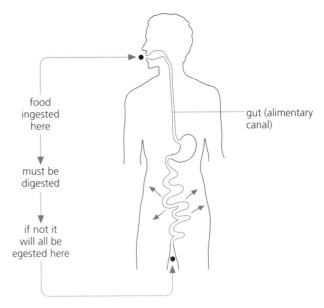

Fig 3

ANSWER

a 560 kJ (*Don't forget the units, if you do you might
lose the mark!*)

b 28 packets (*Do show the working – you will get
some credit for a correct method, even if you get
the answer wrong.*)

c i *your answer should indicate one of the following:*
    – that fat can cause problems for circulation of
      the blood in the coronary arteries, and may
      eventually result in a heart attack;
    – that the fat may be stored in the body and
      make it difficult to move around, or may
      increase the risk of arthritis;
    – may lead to the development of diabetes in
      some people.
  ii It may lead to high blood pressure (and an
    increased risk of heart disease).

d vitamins (*Notice salt is in the list so 'minerals' is
not correct.*)

How does food get to the cells?

The gut is a very long muscular tube. It is about ten metres
long and if the food did not pass through the wall it would
all come out at the other end (correctly called the anus).
After the food has been ingested, or taken in, the main
function of the gut is to digest the food. Put simply,
digestion is the breaking down of food into simple
molecules that will pass through the gut wall into the
blood. The regions of the gut are adapted so that the
processes of digestion are carried out efficiently.

Once the food has been digested, it is absorbed into
the blood and then assimilated, or used for different
functions in the cells. Any undigested food is
expelled from the body as waste during the process
of egestion.

How food is moved along the gut
Food is moved along by peristalsis. This occurs
when muscles in the gut wall contract. The gut
wall contains two layers of muscle fibres (see
below). These work in conjunction with one
another. By contracting at right angles with one
another they bring about peristalsis – waves
of contraction which pass along the gut,
pushing the food along.

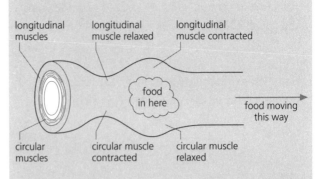

Fig 4 Peristalsis

Contraction of the longitudinal muscles, where the food
is present, shorten the distance that the food is moved.
The circular muscles contract behind the food to push
the food forwards. These two sets of muscles work in
pairs; when one set is contracted the other set is
relaxed. They are said to be antagonistic.

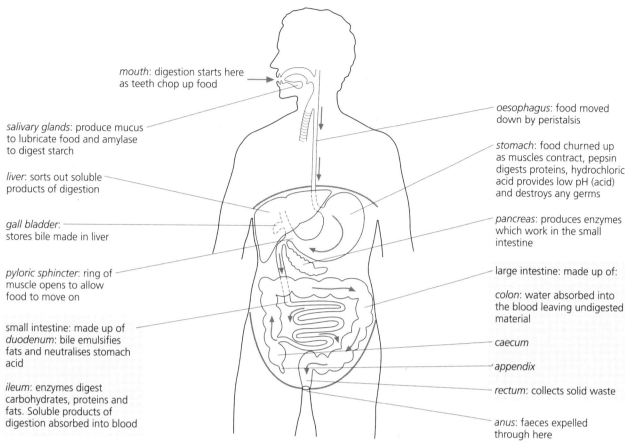

mouth: digestion starts here as teeth chop up food

salivary glands: produce mucus to lubricate food and amylase to digest starch

liver: sorts out soluble products of digestion

gall bladder: stores bile made in liver

pyloric sphincter: ring of muscle opens to allow food to move on

small intestine: made up of duodenum: bile emulsifies fats and neutralises stomach acid

ileum: enzymes digest carbohydrates, proteins and fats. Soluble products of digestion absorbed into blood

oesophagus: food moved down by peristalsis

stomach: food churned up as muscles contract, pepsin digests proteins, hydrochloric acid provides low pH (acid) and destroys any germs

pancreas: produces enzymes which work in the small intestine

large intestine: made up of:

colon: water absorbed into the blood leaving undigested material

caecum

appendix

rectum: collects solid waste

anus: faeces expelled through here

Fig 5 What happens to food between the mouth and the anus

Digestion

1 Physical digestion

Chewing in the mouth and the churning up of the food as it moves along the gut, in particular during the six or so hours that it is present in the stomach, break up the large pieces of food and mix them with the digestive juices. This is called physical digestion and does not involve any chemical reactions. It is very important in increasing the surface area of the food. Teeth are particularly important in this process. There are 32 teeth in a full adult set. Nearest the front of the mouth are the incisors (8), which have sharp edges for cutting food. Next are the canines (4) which are larger and more pointed for tearing at food. The back teeth are made up of the pre-molars (8) and molars (12), which have flattened surfaces for crushing and grinding food.

2 Chemical digestion

When the food has been turned into a semi-liquid state, a number of different chemical reactions take place. These break down the large molecules in the food so that the smaller molecules produced can pass through the gut wall into the blood, and then be transported to where they are needed.

The reactions involve digestive enzymes that are produced by glands in the gut wall (see p 11 for general information about enzymes).

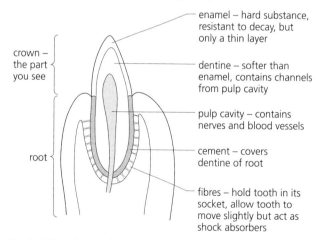

crown – the part you see

root

enamel – hard substance, resistant to decay, but only a thin layer

dentine – softer than enamel, contains channels from pulp cavity

pulp cavity – contains nerves and blood vessels

cement – covers dentine of root

fibres – hold tooth in its socket, allow tooth to move slightly but act as shock absorbers

Fig 6 What the inside of a tooth looks like

The table gives details of the main enzymes of the gut. Notice how different enzymes work best at different pHs.

Main enzymes of the gut

name	where made	where it works	pH	substrate	product	absorbed products
digesting starch amylase	salivary glands	mouth	7	starch	maltose	
	pancreas	small intestine	7	starch	maltose	
maltase	wall of small intestine	small intestine	8.5	maltose	glucose	can be absorbed into the blood
digesting sucrose sucrase	wall of small intestine	small intestine	8.5	sucrose	glucose and fructose	can be absorbed into the blood
digesting proteins pepsin	wall of stomach	stomach	2.0	protein	polypeptides	
trypsin	pancreas	small intestine	7.0	protein	peptides	
peptidases	wall of small intestine	small intestine	8.5	peptides	amino acids	can be absorbed into the blood
digestion of fats lipase	pancreas	small intestine	7.0	fat	fatty acids and glycerol	can be absorbed into cells of the villi

QUESTION

a Peanuts are seeds that we eat. We have to digest the peanut if we want to make use of the proteins that it contains.

   i Why do we need proteins in our diet? (1 mark)

....

  ii Explain why food has to be digested. (2 marks)

....

....

....

....

....

iii What is the final breakdown product of all proteins? (1 mark)

....

Part question [SEG 1994]

ANSWER

a i *The following would be suitable answers:* growth, repair, make enzymes

ii *You need to explain that:*
  Large molecules need to be made smaller and soluble *so that* they can be absorbed through the wall of the small intestine (or villi) into the blood. *Notice there are 2 marks here.*
iii amino acids

QUESTION

Experiments were carried out to investigate the action of two enzymes at different pH values. The enzymes were pepsin (a protease) and amylase. All experiments were carried out at 37°C for 20 minutes. The results are shown on the graph below.

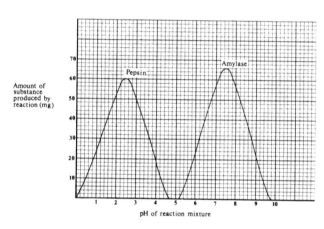

Fig 7

a How much substance was produced in the pepsin – controlled reaction at pH 3? (1 mark)
.... (mg)

b At which pH values were 60mg of substance produced by:
  i pepsin; ....
  ii amylase? .... (3 marks)

c Name the enzyme which works best in acid conditions. (1 mark)
....

d Scientists were searching for an enzyme to remove lipids (fats and oils) from clothes to make Zappo, a new biological washing powder.
  i Name an enzyme which could be added to the washing powder to remove fat stains. (1 mark)
....

  ii Which substances would be produced as the enzyme digests fat? (2 marks)
  1 ....
  2 ....

iii Why should washing powder containing this enzyme not be used at high temperatures?

(1 mark)
[ULEAC]

ANSWER

a 50 (*Note this question gives you the units already – but you will need to check this carefully*)
b i any answer in the range 2.4–2.6
   ii 7.1 and 7.8 (*Notice that there are two answers here – hence 2 marks*)
c pepsin (*But protease is also correct.*)
d i lipase (*Don't get confused because the question now talks about washing powders!*)
   ii glycerol and fatty acids (*The order is not important here.*)
   iii *You need to show that you understand that* the enzyme is denatured or the active site cannot function, *so* the washing powder will not work at the higher temperature or the fatty stains will not be removed from the clothes at the higher temperature. *There are two marks here so you must give a good explanation.*

Important liquids in the gut

Mucus – this is produced from the inner lining of the gut. It acts as a lubricant, helping the food to pass along easily. It also prevents the enzymes of the gut digesting the actual gut!
Hydrochloric acid – this is produced by glands in the wall of the stomach. It provides the pH needed for the pepsin to work. It also kills germs which happen to reach the stomach.
Bile – this is produced by the liver and stored in the gall bladder. It does not contain enzymes. It is important in emulsifying fat, that is converting large particles into smaller droplets so that the enzyme lipase can break down the fat. Bile also neutralises any acid that leaves the stomach.

Absorption

The soluble end products of digestion, including glucose, amino acids, fatty acids and glycerol are absorbed at the ileum (part of the small intestine). It is well adapted to carry out its function of absorption. Its inner surface contains a large number of finger-

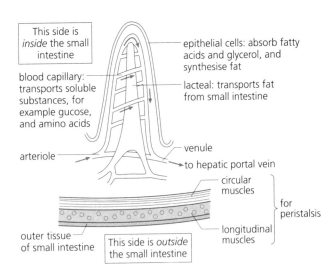

Fig 8

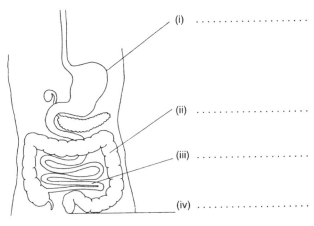

Fig 9

like projections called villi. Each one of these villi has a number of projections covering the surface called microvilli. The total surface area of the ileum is probably about as big as your bedroom floor!

After the small intestine

Nutrients needed by the body are absorbed into the blood at the small intestine. However, the fluid that enters the large intestine contains a lot of water. The body cannot afford to lose all this water. As the waste moves along the colon (part of the large intestine), water is absorbed and the waste becomes more and more solid. This solid waste (called faeces) is passed to the rectum where it is stored. Periodically, a reflex action causes the ring of muscle to open and the waste is lost through the anus in the process of defaecation. Also in the large intestine, a number of bacteria feed on the undigested waste. These synthesise some amino acids and vitamin K which are absorbed into the blood.

QUESTION

a Fig 9 is a diagram of the human digestive system. Label the diagram. (4 marks)

b Write down one job that the large intestine does. (1 mark)

[MEG]

ANSWER

a   i stomach

   ii large intestine or colon

   iii small intestine or ileum

   iv anus – you could put 'anal sphincter muscle'

b *any of these:* absorbs water from the undigested food; stores faeces; carries faeces to the anus

What happens to the absorbed food?

The soluble food molecules are taken to the liver, via the hepatic portal vein, to be sorted. Fatty acids and glycerol are not taken to the liver – they enter the blood via the lymph system (see p 55).

Glucose

This is taken to the cells to be used in respiration to provide energy. Any glucose which is surplus to the needs of the body is stored as glycogen, either in the liver or in the muscles.

Amino acids

These are used in the cells to make new proteins. Any amino acids that are not needed for this are de-aminated in the liver, i.e. they are turned into urea (see p 13–14 for more details).

Fatty acids and glycerol

These are stored as fat, an important energy source for the body. If the fat is stored under the skin it provides insulation. Some fat is stored around important organs, for example the heart and kidneys, to protect them.

Some fat is used in making membranes in cells.

Revision sheet

Some important biological ideas

1 Label the parts of this animal cell and give a function of each.

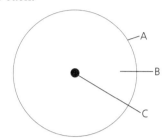

Fig 1

2 Give three structures found in a plant cell not found in an animal cell.

a _____

b _____

c _____

3 Match up these pairs to show how substances move into and out of cells:

Diffusion   Requires energy

Osmosis   From a high concentration to a low concentration

Active transport   Involves the movement of water and needs a partially permeable membrane

4 The seven living processes are:

a _____   b _____

c _____   d _____

e _____   f _____

g _____

5 How is nutrition different in plants and animals?

6 For a process to be described as excretion where must the waste products have come from?

7 What word is used to describe all the chemical reactions that occur in an organism to make it 'work'?

Photosynthesis

1.

a Write the chemical equation for photosynthesis.

b Where does the plant get each raw material from?

c Is it an endothermic or exothermic reaction?

2 Give 2 ways of testing whether a plant is carrying out photosynthesis.

3 What experiment would you do to be sure that each of these is needed for photosynthesis:

carbon dioxide?

light?

chlorophyll?

4 What substance can be used to:

• increase the carbon dioxide around a plant?

• absorb carbon dioxide from around a plant?

5 Label this section through a leaf and give the function of each part:

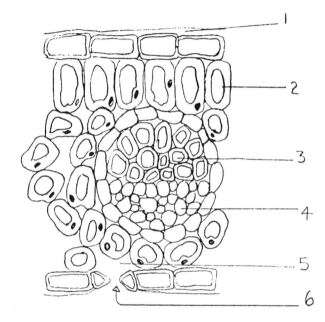

Fig 2

6 Why does a plant need:

nitrogen?

calcium?

magnesium?

Nutrition

1 Give 7 requirements of a balanced diet.

2 Give 3 reasons why the body needs food.

3 Give the meaning of each of these terms, and say which parts of the digestive system are most involved in each process:

a mechanical digestion

b chemical digestion

c absorbtion

d egestion

4 Enzymes break up large food molecules into smaller ones. Complete this table;

Type of food	Type of enzyme	End product to be absorbed
Protein		
Starch		
Fat		

5 a Where are villi found?
   b What is their function?
   c How are they adapted to be 'good at their job'?

Revision sheet answers

Some important biological ideas

1 A Cell membrane; keeps cell contents in place; selective barrier to cell
   B Cytoplasm; chemical reactions of the cell occur here
   C Nucleus; controls and co-ordinates the cell's activities
2 Cellulose cell wall, vacuole, chloroplasts
3 Diffusion – from a high to a low concentration
   Osmosis – involves the movement of water and needs a partially permeable membrane
   Active transport – requires energy
4 Movement, Respiration, Sensitivity, Growth, Respiration, Excretion, Nutrition
5 Plants synthesise (make) their food by photosynthesis, animals get their food from plants and other animals.
6 The waste products must have come from processes carried out in cells.
7 Metabolism

Photosynthesis

1 a water + carbon dioxide → glucose + oxygen
   (*You could have carbohydrate instead of glucose.*)
   You could also write 'light' and 'chlorophyll' on the arrow.
   b Water comes from the soil, carbon dioxide comes from the air.
   c It is an endothermic reaction, i.e. *energy is taken in during the reaction.*

2 To test a plant for photosynthesis you need to describe:
   • a starch test in the leaves. Describe all the stages (with reasons). Do not forget to say how you de-starch the plant first.
   • the collection of oxygen from a water plant.
   • using a water plant and hydrogencarbonate indicator.
3 To show that:
   carbon dioxide is needed in photosynthesis you need to remove the carbon dioxide from around the plant – using sodium hydroxide solution.
   light is needed in photosynthesis, either place the whole plant in the dark or cover up a part of a leaf.
   chlorophyll is needed in photosynthesis – use a white part of a variegated leaf.
   In all 3 cases you need to describe how you would do a starch test and obtain the result.
4 Sodium hydrogencarbonate increases the carbon dioxide around a plant. Sodium hydroxide removes the carbon dioxide from around the plant.
5
   1 cuticle – protects the leaf from damage by micro-organisms, reduces water loss.
   2 palisade mesophyll cells – contain many chloroplasts and form the main region where photosynthesis takes place.
   3 xylem – brings water to the leaf from the roots.
   4 phloem – carries soluble food to the rest of the plant.
   5 air space – allows gases to diffuse to the cells of the leaf, for example the carbon dioxide needed in photosynthesis.
   6 stomata – control the movement of gases into and out of the leaf.
6 A plant needs:
   nitrogen to make proteins (and DNA).
   calcium to make cell walls; actually the material between the cells walls of adjacent cells.
   magnesium to make chlorophyll.

Nutrition

1 Carbohydrates, proteins, fats, water, minerals, vitamins, fibre (roughage)
2 The body needs food:
   – as a fuel
   – to build cells
   – to enable the body to be healthy

3 *Mechanical digestion* – chopping large pieces of food into smaller pieces. Occurs in mouth and stomach.
Chemical digestion – chemical reactions which turn large molecules into small (soluble) ones. Occurs in mouth, stomach and small intestine.
Absorption –where soluble food is taken into the blood. Occurs at the small intestine.
Egestion – the removal of solid undigested waste as faeces. Occurs at the anus.

4 Protein is digested by proteinases and turned into amino acids. Starch is digested by amylase and turned into glucose.
Fat is digested by lipases and turned into fatty acids and glycerol.

5 a Villi are found in the small intestine.
b They absorb digested food into the blood (and lacteals).
c They are 'good at their job' because they:
have a large surface area.
are well supplied with blood.

Student Answer with Comments

A green plant was placed in a dark cupboard and, after 24 hours, some of the leaves were tested for starch. No starch was found in any leaf. The same plant was then placed in sunlight, but one leaf, Q, was treated as shown in the diagram below. After a further 24 hours leaves P and Q on the plant were tested for starch.

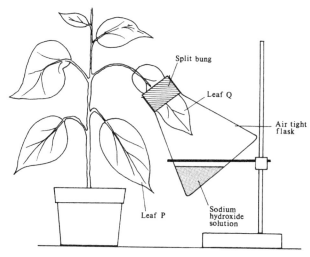

Fig 3

a i Explain why no starch was found in the leaves after the plant had been in the cupboard for 24 hours.

Without sunlight photosynthesis can't take place, so starch is produced. ✗No
Do watch this – a small slip has lost you the mark. (1)

ii What was the purpose of the sodium hydroxide solution shown in the diagram?
To remove carbon dioxide from the air in the flask (a good explanation) ✓ ① (1)

b i Name the substance found only in green leaves which helps plants to make starch
Chlorophyll ✓ ① (1)

ii Name the gas produced by green leaves when they make glucose for starch production.
Oxygen ✓ ① (1)

c The diagrams show the results of starch tests on discs taken from leaves P and Q. The diagrams also indicate the parts of the leaves from which the discs had been taken.

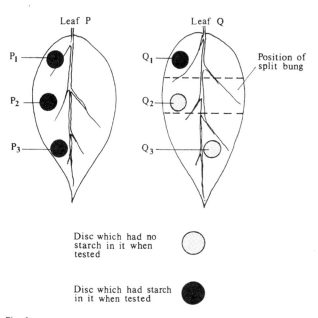

Fig 4

i Explain the reason for the difference between discs P3 and Q3.
Photosynthesis has taken place at P3, so starch is present. Q3 photosynthesis has not taken place, because it is in the flask with no CO^2. ✓ ②
CO_2 not CO^2, otherwise good.
It is important to give the reason. (2)

ii Explain the reason for the difference between discs P2 and Q2.

Photosynthesis has taken place at P2, so starch is present. ✓ Q2 was covered by the bung so no light or CO^2 could get to the leaf. So photosythesis could not take place, and no starch is made. ✓ ②

Yes – no light can get to Q_2 – it is a reasonable assumption to think that no CO_2 would get in a split bung ... but a little would be there.

d The diagrams below show the method used to test the leaf discs for starch. The discs were transferred in the direction of the arrows.

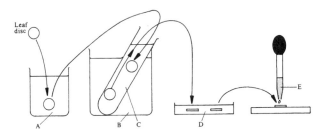

Fig 5

Which of the liquids, A, B, C, D or E, in the diagram is

i iodine solution; E ✓ ① .... (1)

ii used to kill the leaf discs; C ✗ .... (1)
    No! "A" the boiling water kills the leaf discs.

iii used to decolourise the discs? D ✗ .... (1)
    No. "C" – boiling alcohol decolourises the discs.

$8/11$ (Total 11 marks)
(ULEAC)

An exam question for you to try

QUESTION

The amount of nitrogen combined as compounds in the body is kept constant by a number of processes. Nitrogen is present in cells mostly as amino acids. If amino acids are present in excess they are deaminated. This results in the removal of nitrogen, which is excreted in urea.

a i What name is given to the process which keeps conditions and substances at a constant level in the body?
    .... (1 mark)

ii Why are amino acids necessary in the body?
    .... (1 mark)

iii Explain how the body obtains the amount and variety of amino acids that it requires.
    ....
    ....
    ....
    ....
    ....
    ....
    .... (4 marks)

b The daily excretion of nitrogen compounds from two people is shown in the table below.

Quantity	Person X	Person Y
Urea nitrogen	14.70g	2.20g
Uric acid nitrogen	0.18g	0.09g
Ammonia nitrogen	0.49g	0.42g
Creatinine nitrogen	0.58g	0.60g

i Explain, with reasons, how the diet of person X differs from that of person Y.
    ....
    ....
    ....
    .... (2 marks)

ii If anabolic steroids drugs are taken, the nitrogen balance in the body is disturbed. As a result, the intake of nitrogen compounds greatly exceeds their excretion. What effect could taking these drugs have on the body?
    ....
    .... (1 mark)
    [SEG 1994]

Answer

a i Homeostasis. *This is an important process, you might be asked about it in any topic (see p 74–80 for more details).*

ii To make proteins.

iii Proteins are made up of amino acids.
    The body obtains its supply of amino acids by eating a range of foods containing proteins such as meat, beans, fish.
    In the gut the proteins are digested by proteinases to form amino acids which are

absorbed into the blood at the villi.

The body can make some amino acids that it needs. Others must be taken in, in food – these are called essential amino acids.

These amino acids are built up by cells to form the different proteins that the body needs, but the question does not actually ask for this.

b   i Person X has more protein in his or her diet. This can be deduced from the table because a higher mass of 'urea nitrogen', 'uric acid nitrogen' and 'ammonia nitrogen' is excreted by person X.

   ii Anabolic steroids are taken to help increase the size of the muscles. Excess amino acids cannot be stored in the body and may lead to damage of the liver and/or kidneys.

3 Transporting substances to cells

Transporting substances to cells	Midland (MEG)				Northern (NEAB)		London (ULEAC)				Southern (SEG)		Welsh (WJEC)
	Own	Nuffield	Salters	Suffolk	Co-ordinated	Modular	Modular GASP	Combined	Co-ordinated	Modular	Double	Modular	Co-ordinated
BREATHING AND RESPIRATION													
The importance of respiration	✓	✓	✓	✓	✓	✓	✓	✓	✓	✓	✓	✓	✓
Gaseous exchange	✓	✓	✓	✓	✓	✓	✓	✓	✓	✓	✓	✓	✓
Anaerobic respiration	✓	✓	✓	✓	✓	✓	✓	✓	✓	✓	✓	✓	✓
Smoking	✓	✓	✓	✓	✓	✓	✓	✓	✓	✓	✓	✓	✓
CIRCULATION													
The importance of a circulatory system	✓	✓	✓	✓	✓	✓	✓	✓	✓	✓	✓	✓	✓
The heart	✓	✓	✓	✓	✓	✓	✓	✓	✓	✓	✓	✓	✓
Blood vessels	✓	✓	✓	✓	✓	✓	✓	✓	✓	✓	✓	✓	✓
Diseases of the circulatory system	✓	✓					✓	✓	✓	✓	✓	✓	✓
Blood	✓	✓	✓	✓	✓	✓	✓	✓		✓	✓	✓	✓
The lymph system		✓	✓				✓						
THE MOVEMENT OF SUBSTANCES IN PLANTS													
Why substances need to move in plants	✓	✓	✓	✓	✓	✓	✓	✓	✓	✓	✓	✓	✓
Plants and water	✓	✓	✓	✓	✓	✓	✓	✓	✓	✓	✓	✓	✓
Stomata	✓	✓	✓	✓	✓	✓	✓	✓	✓	✓	✓	✓	✓
The transport of sugar in a plant	✓	✓					✓	✓		✓	✓	✓	

Breathing and Respiration

Why do we need respiration?

The vast number of chemical reactions that take place in your cells need a continual supply of energy. They get this energy from the food that you eat, but just taking in the fuel is not enough. Oxygen is needed to react with the fuel, which is mainly glucose, in order to release the energy. This important process is called respiration. (As the process uses oxygen it is more correctly called aerobic respiration.) Your cells are respiring as you sit and read this. The process can be summarised in an equation:

glucose + oxygen → carbon dioxide + water (+ energy)
$C_6H_{12}O_6 + 6O_2 \rightarrow 6CO_2 + 6H_2O$ $\Delta H = -2802kJ$

The glucose and oxygen are the reactants and the carbon dioxide *and the water are the products in the reaction*

QUESTION

You may need to look at photosynthesis on p 23 to p 31 before you try this one.

Respiration and photosynthesis are two important life processes. The table compares these two processes. Complete the gaps in the table by choosing suitable words from the selection in brackets in the first column.   (4 marks)

Activity	Photosynthesis	Respiration
Takes place in … (animals/plants/ animals and plants)		
Takes place during the … (day/night/day and night)		
Carbohydrates are … (made/used up)		
Carbon dioxide is … (given out/taken in)		

Fig 1

ANSWER

PHOTOSYNTHESIS	RESPIRATION
plants	animals and plants
day	day and night
made	used up
taken in	given out

What is the difference between respiration and breathing?

Respiration is the chemical reaction that takes place to provide cells with the energy they need. The important point to remember is that respiration happens in every cell of your body all the time. Breathing describes the movements of the chest which enable you to take oxygen into the blood and to get rid of the waste products of respiration. Your circulatory system (see p 51–52) moves the reactants and products to the cells that are respiring.

What is gaseous exchange?

When the air that you breathe in reaches the inner surfaces of the lungs, some of the oxygen from the air passes into the blood. Carbon dioxide moves from the blood into the air. This is called gaseous exchange and the gases move like this due to the process of diffusion. For this process to be efficient it is important that the blood and air meet over the biggest possible surface area and that the thickness of the wall that the gases have to cross is small. The air sacs (alveoli) of the lungs are well adapted for this function.

To test for carbon dioxide
- add the gas to limewater; if it turns cloudy the gas is carbon dioxide.
- use hydrogencarbonate indicator which turns from orange to yellow if carbon dioxide is present (more sensitive than the limewater test).

To test for the presence of water
- use cobalt chloride paper; this is blue when dry and turns pale pink if water is present.

[SEG]

Gases involved in gaseous exchange

gas	inspired air (going to lungs) %	alveolar air (in the air sacs) %	blood going to alveoli %	blood leaving the alveoli %	exhaled air (air leaving the lungs)
oxygen	21	13	11	19	16
carbon dioxide	0.03	5	58	50	4

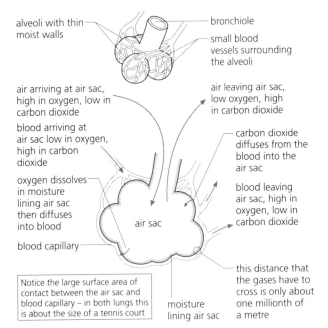

Fig 2 Gaseous exchange in the alveoli

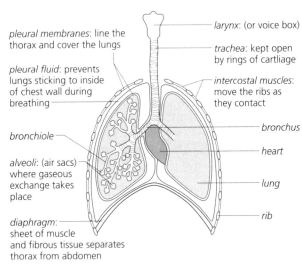

Fig 3 Structure of the thorax

How the air gets down to the alveoli

The chest (or thorax) is the part of your body concerned with getting the air right down into the furthest alveoli.

If you breathe in deeply you will realise that the volume of your thorax (chest) has increased. Your ribs and diaphragm have moved to cause this. As the volume of the thorax increased so the pressure inside the chest decreased and this caused air to go into the lungs. In other words, you breathed in, or inhaled. Inhaling is an active process.

Breathing out is brought about by the reverse happening. The volume of the thorax is decreased and the pressure is increased so that air is forced out of the lungs. You have breathed out, or exhaled. Exhaling requires less effort than inhaling. Much of the air is actually forced out as the muscles and lung tissue return to their relaxed state.

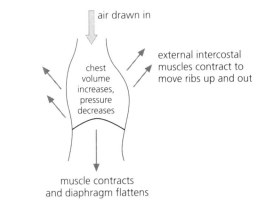

Fig 4 Inhaling

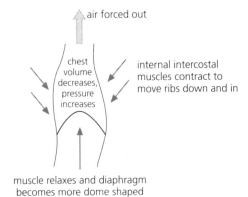

Fig 5 Exhaling

Respiration without oxygen

Muscle cells carry out quite a lot of respiration to supply the energy needed for their contraction. Sometimes, your blood cannot transport the oxygen to the cells fast enough; you notice this when you have been exercising and your muscles ache. This is due to the build up of lactic acid in the cells. Respiration has still occurred, but it has been respiration without oxygen – called anaerobic respiration. Less energy has been released than in 'normal' respiration using oxygen. This can be summarised in an equation:

glucose $\rightarrow$ lactic acid + (energy)

$$C_6H_{12}O_6 \rightarrow 2C_3H_6O_3 \quad \Delta H = -115kJ$$

After you have stopped exercising, you breathe deeply. The lactic acid is slightly poisonous and needs to be removed. Panting takes in extra oxygen to breakdown the lactic acid to carbon dioxide and water – this is called repaying the oxygen debt.

Smoking

People who smoke usually inhale the smoke. This then travels down into their alveoli and on the way affects tubes that it passes through.

1 The trachea and bronchi are lined with goblet cells which produce mucus. Tiny hairs, called cilia, beat to move this mucus upwards to remove any particles which otherwise might harm the alveoli. Smoking paralyses the cilia.
2 More mucus is made and smokers often cough to remove this sticky phlegm. Chronic bronchitis can result if the tubes become infected. Continual coughing damages the alveoli and reduces the surface area for gaseous exchange, hence smokers often get out of breath easily. This can cause emphysema.
3 Carbon monoxide in the smoke combines with the haemoglobin of the blood in place of the oxygen. This reduces the amount of oxygen that the blood can carry.
4 Tar collects in the lungs. This contains carcinogens, or cancer causing substances. Smoking has been associated with lung cancer.
5 Nicotine is an addictive drug in cigarettes. It increases blood pressure and makes the blood clot more easily, and hence can lead to heart disease.

QUESTION

Bronchitis is an infection of the bronchial tubes which lead to the lungs.

a

Fig 6

What general pattern is shown by this information?

.... (1 mark)

b The diagrams show the effects of cigarette smoke on small hairs called cilia in the bronchial tubes.

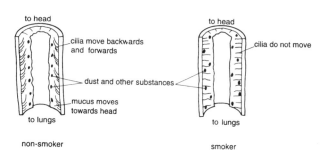

Fig 7

i What effect does cigarette smoke have on the movement of mucus?

....

.... (1 mark)

ii Suggest why smokers tend to cough more than non-smokers.

....

....

....

.... (2 marks)

iii Smokers are sometimes short of breath. Suggest how smoking affects the lungs to cause this.

....

....

....

.... (2 marks)

c We take air into our bodies so that we can respire.
 i Where does respiration take place?

.... (1 mark) ii Why do we respire?

....

.... (1 mark)

[MEG]

ANSWER

a In men, the more cigarettes smoked per day the more likely they are to suffer from bronchitis.

b i The mucus cannot move (up to the throat).

   ii The cilia and mucus cannot move the particles in the smoke out of the bronchial tubes. Smokers tend to cough to try and remove these.

   iii Tar and chemicals in the smoke tend to be deposited as a lining to the alveoli of the lungs. This means that gaseous exchange is less efficient and so less oxygen is absorbed.
Do not say vague things such as: 'The lungs get clogged up or blocked with tar.'

c i Respiration takes place in the cells of the body.
Do not say 'lungs'; this is where gaseous exchange takes place, but energy from respiration is needed in all the cells of the body.

   ii To provide energy for the activities of the cells.

Respiration and plants

Plants are living organisms and need to respire to provide their cells with energy. It is a bad mistake to think that plants only respire at night because during the day they are carrying out photosynthesis. Plants respire all the time, just like you. It is, however, easier to be aware of the process at night when photosynthesis is not being carried out. Although plants do not run around they need energy for other processes; for example, to take in minerals from the soil by active transport (see p 22).

Respiration and micro-organisms

Many micro-organisms can live successfully in places where there is no oxygen. They carry out anaerobic respiration. The baking and brewing industry make use of the fact that yeast carries out this process. When yeast respires in this way, ethanol (a type of alcohol) and carbon dioxide (rather than the lactic acid produced in humans) are formed. The process is called fermentation.

glucose → ethanol + carbon dioxide (+ energy)
$C_6H_{12}O_6 \rightarrow 2C_2H_5OH + 2CO_2$ $\Delta H = -68kJ$

QUESTION

Fig 8

Beer and wine are produced by fermentation. Describe, in as much detail as you can, what happens during this process.

....

....

....

....

....

.... (4 marks)

[NEAB]

ANSWER

You need to include these points in your answer:
An enzyme in yeast breaks down sugar. When this happens carbon dioxide and alcohol are produced.
(It is the alcohol that is the important product in making beer and wine. Carbon dioxide is the important product in bread making.)

Circulation in the body

Why do we need a circulatory system?

Your cells are similar to factories. They carry out a number of processes (chemical reactions) for which they need raw materials (reactants) and produce manufactured goods (products). Just as it is essential that a factory has a good transport system to carry these materials, the same is true for your body. In very tiny organisms these materials can move by diffusion (see p 20), but in larger organisms – like you – a transport system is essential. This is the blood (or circulatory) system. The flow of materials is maintained by the pumping action of the heart. Compared to some other animals your circulatory system is quite complex. The blood travels through

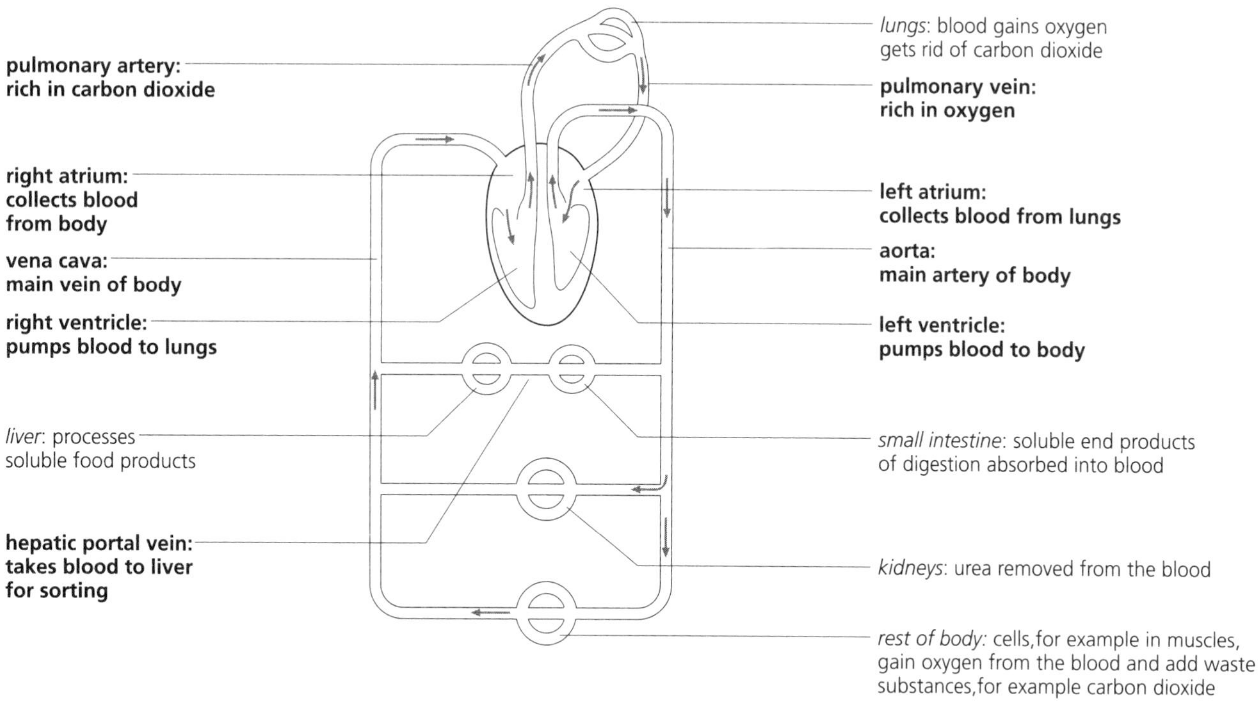

pulmonary artery:
rich in carbon dioxide

lungs: blood gains oxygen
gets rid of carbon dioxide

pulmonary vein:
rich in oxygen

right atrium:
collects blood
from body

left atrium:
collects blood from lungs

vena cava:
main vein of body

aorta:
main artery of body

right ventricle:
pumps blood to lungs

left ventricle:
pumps blood to body

liver: processes
soluble food products

small intestine: soluble end products
of digestion absorbed into blood

hepatic portal vein:
takes blood to liver
for sorting

kidneys: urea removed from the blood

rest of body: cells, for example in muscles,
gain oxygen from the blood and add waste
substances, for example carbon dioxide

Fig 1 The circulatory system

the heart twice as it makes a complete circulation of the body. On one circuit the blood is pumped from the heart and takes oxygen to the cells, and on the other circuit the blood is pumped from the heart to the lungs where it picks up a fresh supply of oxygen.

Remember one of the most important processes taking place in the cells is respiration, which provides the energy for all the other reactions.

The heart

The heart pumps blood through some 130,000 km of pipes, which means it must be able to force the blood a long way. The ventricles making up the lower part

of the heart are very muscular. The left ventricle has the thickest wall as it has to pump blood as far as your big toe, while the right ventricle only has to pump the blood as far as the lungs. The top part of the heart is adapted for collecting blood. The right atrium collects deoxygenated blood from the body and the left atrium collects oxygenated blood from the lungs.

The atria are sometimes called auricles.

How the heart works

Cardiac muscle which makes up the heart is unlike any other muscle in the body – it can contract

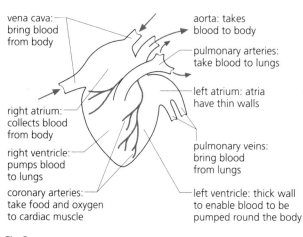

vena cava:
bring blood
from body

aorta: takes
blood to body

pulmonary arteries:
take blood to lungs

left atrium: atria
have thin walls

right atrium:
collects blood
from body

right ventricle:
pumps blood
to lungs

pulmonary veins:
bring blood
from lungs

coronary arteries:
take food and oxygen
to cardiac muscle

left ventricle: thick wall
to enable blood to be
pumped round the body

Fig 2a

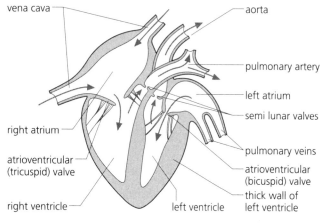

vena cava

aorta

pulmonary artery

left atrium

semi lunar valves

right atrium

pulmonary veins

atrioventricular
(tricuspid) valve

atrioventricular
(bicuspid) valve

thick wall of
left ventricle

right ventricle

left ventricle

Fig 2b

rhythmically without getting tired. It beats about 70 times a minute. As the heart contracts, the blood is forced through the arteries. This movement can be felt as a pulse. Your pulse rate tells you how fast your heart is beating in different circumstances.

The heart has its own built in device for controlling the contraction of the heart muscle. This is a patch of tissue in the right atrium, commonly called the pacemaker. Both nervous and hormonal messages can change this rate however (see p 65).

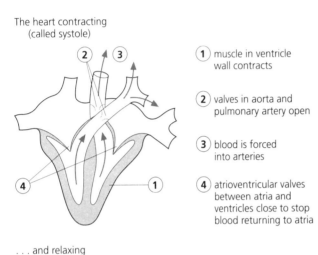

The heart contracting (called systole)

1. muscle in ventricle wall contracts
2. valves in aorta and pulmonary artery open
3. blood is forced into arteries
4. atrioventricular valves between atria and ventricles close to stop blood returning to atria

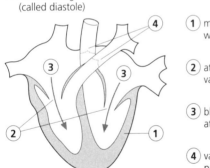

. . . and relaxing (called diastole)

1. muscle in ventricle wall relaxes
2. atrioventricular valves open
3. blood flows from atria to ventricles
4. valves in aorta and pulmonary artery close

Fig 3 The heart contracting … and relaxing

QUESTION

a What is the main job of the circulatory system?

....

.... (1 mark)

b The diagram below shows a section through a human heart.

   i Name the parts labelled A and B.

   A..

   B..

   ii On the diagram, draw arrows to indicate the direction of blood flow into, through and out of the left side of the heart. (3 marks)

iii Explain, as fully as you can, how blood is forced to flow in this direction.

....

....

....

.... (2 marks)

[NEAB]

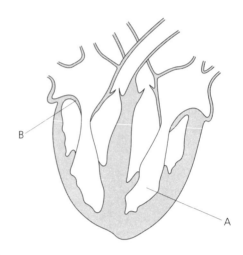

Fig 4

ANSWER

a Transports (carries) materials around the body. *Notice the word* main *in the question – give a general answer here.*

b i A is the left ventricle, B is the tricuspid valve. *You will need a way of remembering that the tricuspid valve is on the right – RT perhaps (RT as short for right, R for right, T for tricuspid).*

   ii *3 marks are allowed for this, so try and show the blood flow through all of the left side of the heart:*

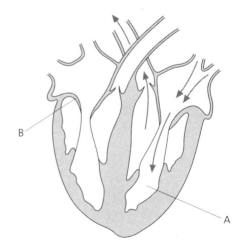

Fig 5

iii *Only 2 marks are allowed here, but try and describe the movement of the blood as you have indicated above:*

Muscle in the ventricles relaxes and blood flows into the ventricle from the atrium, through the open bicuspid valve.

As the muscle in the ventricle contracts, the valves between the ventricle and atrium close.

The blood is forced through the open semi-lunar valves into the aorta to go round the body.

QUESTION

Fig 6 shows a section through the heart.

a The cardiac muscle around the left ventricle is thicker than that around the right ventricle. Why should this muscle be thicker?

....

.... (1 mark)

b When a person is running, the rate of heart beat increases.

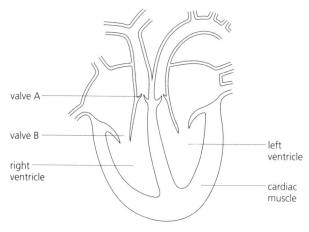

Fig 6

Explain the effects of this change.

....

....

....

.... (3 marks)

[ULEAC]

ANSWER

a The left ventricle has to force blood all round the body but the right ventricle has only to force blood to the lungs. *You need to compare the two ventricles here as the question asks about the left and right ventricle.*

b The cells need to release more energy.

Therefore they need more glucose and oxygen.

Therefore the blood needs to be carried to the cells more quickly to provide this.

Also the waste carbon dioxide and 'heat' need to be removed from the cells more quickly.

Notice there are three marks, so you need to explain three points. Just saying 'the muscles are working harder' is not explaining in sufficient detail.

Blood vessels

The term blood vessels includes all the tubes that carry blood around the body. There are three main types of these:

arteries which have thick muscular walls and carry oxygenated blood away from the heart under high pressure.

veins which have much thinner walls and carry de-oxygenated blood back to the heart under low pressure. Muscles, in the legs for example, contract to move this blood back to the heart.

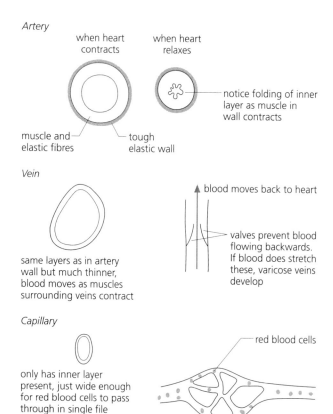

Fig 7 Blood vessels

capillaries which only have a single cell layer to their walls, and are very narrow. These are found in a network. Their features allow the maximum time for diffusion of materials to and from the cells of the body. Capillaries link small arteries (arterioles) to small veins (venules).

The circulatory system and disease

Atheroma (Hardening of the arteries)

Cholesterol (see p 35) may build up inside the blood vessels, making them less efficient at transporting blood. If this occurs in the coronary arteries it may lead to angina (a chest pain). This can occur if the person puts more strain on the system than normal, for example walking up stairs.

Coronary thrombosis (Heart attack)

This occurs when one of the coronary arteries develops a blood clot, possibly due to atheroma. The heart muscle in that region cannot get the oxygen it needs and so the tissue in that area dies. If this damage is localised then a by-pass operation might be possible to re-route the circulation by grafting in a blood vessel, usually from a leg.

Stroke

This is caused when a blood clot occurs in one of the blood vessels taking blood to the brain. The cells of the brain will die if they are without oxygen for a few minutes. A stroke may result in a speech defect, the loss of use of one side of the body, or in more severe cases, death.

Pacemaker

Should the heart's pacemaker fail to work properly a small electronic device can be implanted into the chest to take over this function.

What is blood?

About a tenth of your weight is made up of blood. You have about 5–6 litres of blood. In fact it is mostly water. It is one of the most important tissues of the body.

The following diagram summarises the main components of the blood and how important each is to the body.

This word equation is worth remembering:

$$\textit{Haemoglobin} + \textit{oxygen} \underset{\underset{\textit{cells}}{\leftarrow}}{\overset{\overset{\textit{lungs}}{\rightarrow}}{}} \textit{oxyhaemoglobin}$$

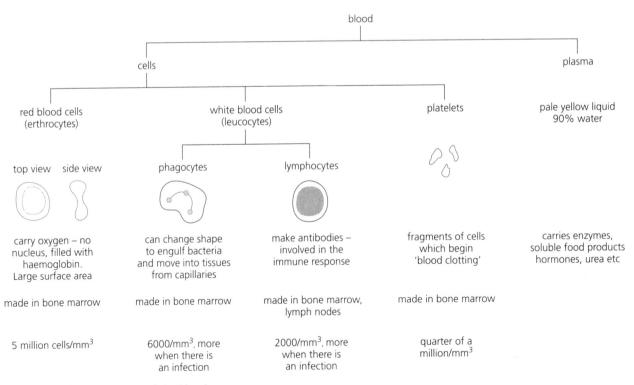

Fig 8 The main components of the blood

QUESTION

The main function of red blood cells is

A clotting
B killing invading bacteria
C transporting food
D transporting oxygen (1 mark)

[SEG 1994]

ANSWER

D.

QUESTION

a The diagram below shows a white blood cell.

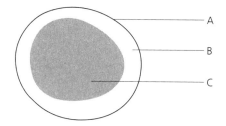

Fig 9

Name the parts labelled A, B, and C, on the diagram
A ....
B ....
C .... (3 marks)

The lymph system

At the capillaries, some of the liquid leaves the blood and surrounds the cells. This carries substances to the cells and waste from the cells dissolves into it. This is called intercellular or tissue fluid. It eventually drains into lymph capillaries. These carry the lymph, as it is now called, away from the body cells and return it to the veins. In this way the volume of the blood is maintained. Your lymph system has another important function. If you are unwell a doctor may wish to check the 'glands' in your neck. These lymph glands contain phagocytes and lymphocytes. If these glands are swollen, they indicate that your body's defence system is in operation and doing its best to fight any germs that have built up in these lymph glands.

b Give two ways in which white blood cells protect us from disease
1 ....
....
2 ....
.... (3 marks)

[NEAB]

ANSWER

a A cell membrane
B cytoplasm
C nucleus
b engulf bacteria, produce antibodies

(See p 82 for more details of the immune response.)

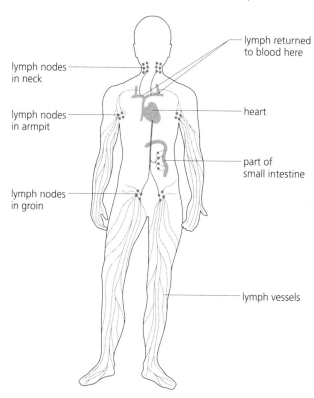

Fig 10 Simplified diagram of lymph system

The movement of substances in plants

Why do substances need to move in plants?

Just as in animal cells, a large number of chemical reactions take place in plant cells all the time. Reactants need to be taken to the cells and in many cases the products of the reaction are taken out of the cell to be used elsewhere. Humans have a blood system, in which the heart beats to circulate the

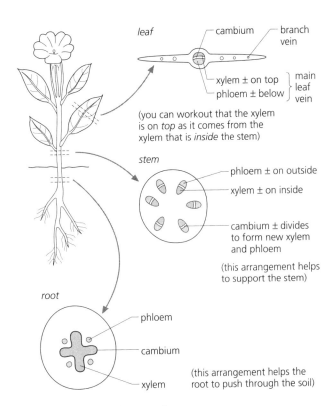

Fig 1 Vascular bundles in a plant

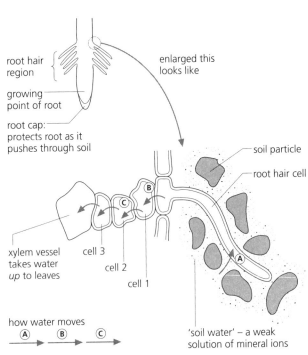

Fig 2 Diagram of a section of a root to show how water is taken in from the soil

materials around the body. Plants do not have a single system like this. Water and food both need to be moved around, and flowering plants such as the geranium have two different sets of tubes for this – xylem for carrying water and minerals, and phloem for carrying food, mainly in the form of sugar. These tubes are grouped together in vascular bundles.

Why is water so important to plants?

Water is essential for a cell if it is to carry out a range of different chemical reactions. However, compared to a human a plant has two additional reasons for needing water :

- as a raw material in photosynthesis.
- to help support the plant (humans have bones which hold their bodies upright).

How do plants take in water?

You know that if a potted indoor plant is not watered it wilts and dies. This indicates that plants take in water via their roots. The roots of a plant may spread out in the soil as much as the branches of the stem. Besides anchoring the plant in the soil, the roots' large surface area ensures that the plant can take in

water efficiently. Tiny hairs (called root hairs) just behind the tip of each branch of the root have precisely this function.

Water moves into the root by osmosis (see p 20). The concentration of the cell sap in the root hair cell is greater than the concentration of the 'soil water'. This means that:

- Water enters the root hair cell. (arrow A)
- Once this has happened the concentration of the cell sap in the root hair cell is weaker than the concentration of the cell sap in cell 1. Water therefore moves into cell 1. (arrow B)
- This makes the concentration of the cell sap here weaker than in cell 2 so water moves into cell 2 by osmosis. (arrow C)

Eventually, the water reaches the middle of the root, where it moves up to the leaves in the xylem.

QUESTION

The drawing shows a sectional view of a root hair on a root in some soil.

a One of the jobs of a root hair is to take in water from the soil.
   State one feature of the structure of the root hair.
   Explain how it helps the root hair to take in water.
   (2 marks)

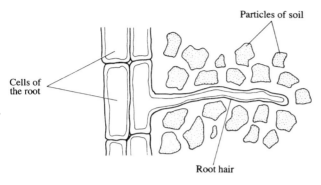

Fig 3

Feature ....
....
How it helps ....
....

b Describe in detail how water passes from the soil
into the root hair.   (4 marks)
....
....
....
....
....
....
....
....
....

[SEG 1994]

ANSWER

a *There are several features that you could give here
but you must make sure that you describe how that
feature helps!*
For example:
It has a large surface area which helps the cell take
in water more quickly.
It has thin cell walls which help the cell take in
water more easily.
It can reach for a long distance between the
particles of the soil so that it can take in water
from a large area.

b *You must be careful here that you describe what
happens in a logical sequence. You must also be
careful to add detail to the answer and not give a
very vague answer, such as: 'the water moves into
the cell through the cell wall.'*
The solution inside the vacuole of the root cell
is more concentrated than the soil water. The cell
membrane is selectively (or semi-) permeable.
Water moves from the less concentrated solution

outside the root hair cell into the cell vacuole by
osmosis. Once inside this cell, it is now weaker than
the next cell inside it. The above process repeats
itself, until the water has moved into the root of the
plant.

How is the water transported around the plant?

Once in the centre of the root the water moves inside
cells which make up the xylem tissue. These cells are
well adapted for their function. They are very long
empty tubes formed from several cells joined
together. There is no living cytoplasm in these tubes
so the cells are 'dead'. The walls are strengthened
with lignin which aids in the support of the plant.
Xylem tissue forms wood in older plants. The general
direction of the water movement in a plant is
upwards. Before reaching and after leaving the
xylem, water moves from cell to cell by osmosis.

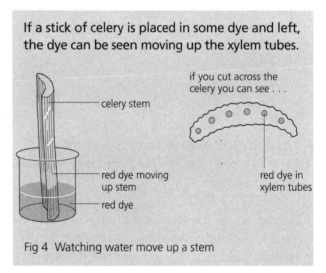

If a stick of celery is placed in some dye and left,
the dye can be seen moving up the xylem tubes.

Fig 4 Watching water move up a stem

Why does water move upwards in the stem?

The lower surface of the leaf contains many stomata.
These allow gases to diffuse in and out of the leaf
during photosynthesis. Water also evaporates from
these; a sunflower plant could easily lose a litre of
water a day. The evaporation of water from a plant is
called transpiration. As water is lost from the leaves
more is taken up from the roots. This continuous
movement of water is called the transpiration stream.
The water is 'pulled up' the plant faster in the light,
when the stomata are open for photosynthesis, and

when the atmosphere is particularly good for drying – i.e. windy and hot.

QUESTION

A shoot was cut from a plant and immediately put in a beaker of red dye. (The dye was harmless to the plant). After 1.5 hours the shoot was removed from the dye and sections taken to see where the dye had moved to in the shoot.

a   Which tissue took up a lot of the dye?

.... (1 mark)

b   What process caused the dye to move up the shoot?

.... (1 mark)

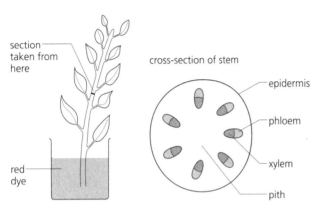

Fig 5

c   The dye solution had moved 40 cm up the shoot. Give, with units, the average rate of movement of the dye solution.

.... (2 marks)

d   Another shoot, from the same plant, was put in the dye solution at the same time, under identical climatic conditions. It was found that dye had travelled 70 cm up this shoot in the same time. Give one factor which could have accounted for the different rate of movement of the dye.

.... (1 mark)

e   Give one reason why the student would have to be careful when using the data from these experiments when coming to a conclusion about the movement of water in a plant shoot.

.... (1 mark)

ANSWER

a   Xylem.

b   Transpiration

c   26.6cm/hour

d   The second shoot may have had more leaves. *Be careful here; the question tells you that the climatic conditions were identical in both cases, so you cannot say things like: 'it was more windy'.*

e   It is difficult to draw firm conclusions when only two shoots are used, particularly when these give such different answers for the rate of movement of water in the shoot.

How do the stomata work?

The water moves from one mesophyll cell to the next by osmosis, in a similar way to that in which water moves across the cells in the root. Water evaporates from the wall of the cells which surround the substomatal air space. Once in this space the water vapour leaves the stoma by diffusion into the air surrounding the leaf, which has a lower water vapour content – unless of course it is raining!

The guard cells determine whether the stomata are open or closed. They can be thought of as two sausage shaped cells that are joined to form a hoop. If they are turgid (full of water) they move apart and the stoma between them is open. If the guard cells are flaccid (low in water content) they move together and the stoma closes.

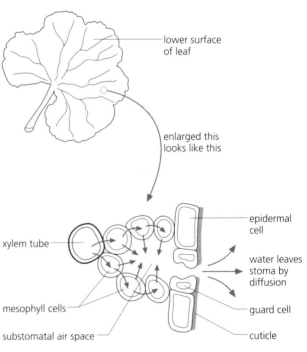

Fig 6 Diagram to show how water leaves a stoma

stoma open

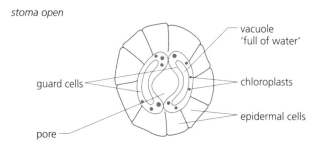

stoma closed

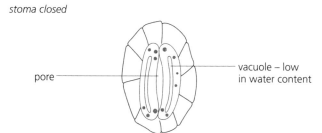

Fig 7 The way in which guard cells control the size of the stoma

If cobalt chloride paper is fixed to a leaf by glass slides to make an airtight seal, the loss in water from the stomata can be detected. The dry blue paper changes to pale pink as it becomes moist. This happens on the bottom of a leaf more quickly than the top, where the cuticle is thicker.

QUESTION

The following information is taken from a plant label.

Rubber plant

This plant has shiny attract leaves.
The upper surface of the leaves can be lightly sprayed
with wax furniture polish to keep them shiny.
Do not overwater. Keep in a cool place.

A gardener wanted to find out what would happen if some of the wax polish was accidentally sprayed on the under surface of a leaf. Four leaf discs of the same size were cut from a leaf. Three of these were sprayed with wax polish in different ways. The fourth disc was left as a control. All four discs were then weighed and reweighed 48 hours later. The results of the experiment are shown in the table below.

a Why did the discs lose mass?

....
.... (1 mark)

b Account for the difference in loss of mass for discs B and C.

....
....
.... (2 marks)

c The instructions state that the plant should be kept in a cool place. Suggest why this is good advice.

....
....
....
.... (2 marks)

[MEG]

ANSWER

a The discs lost water.
   You could explain that transpiration had taken place.

b There are most stomata on the lower side of the leaf. Water is lost through the stomata. In B the stomata are blocked so that the *disc B* lost less water than disc C.
   This is a comparison question. You must make sure that the examiner knows which discs you are talking about. Do not just say 'they have more stomata'.

c In a cool place the plant will need less water because there will be less evaporation.

	disc A	disc B	disc C	disc D
	disc sprayed on both surfaces	disc sprayed on lower surface only	disc sprayed on upper surface only	not sprayed
mass / g at start	3.3	3.2	3.2	3.1
mass / g after 48 hours	3.2	3.0	2.6	2.4

Why is sugar needed by the plant?

Every cell of the plant requires sugar in the form of glucose for respiration, to provide the energy needed to carry out the activities of the cells.

How does the plant get its sugar?

Unlike animals, plants manufacture their own glucose in their leaves by the process of photosynthesis (see section 2). This must be transported away from the leaves to other regions of the plant. This movement is generally downwards, but sugar is also needed by young leaves and buds developing into flowers.

How is sugar transported around the plant?

The sugar is moved in tubes which make up the phloem tissue. Unlike xylem tubes, these are living and the transport of food needs energy (provided by respiration). Phloem is the outside tissue in the vascular bundles (see fig 1) and makes up the bark in older stems.

In the 1700s Stephen Hales showed the importance of phloem to a tree.

bark (phloem) removed

after some time

bulge as food cannot pass down the tree in the phloem

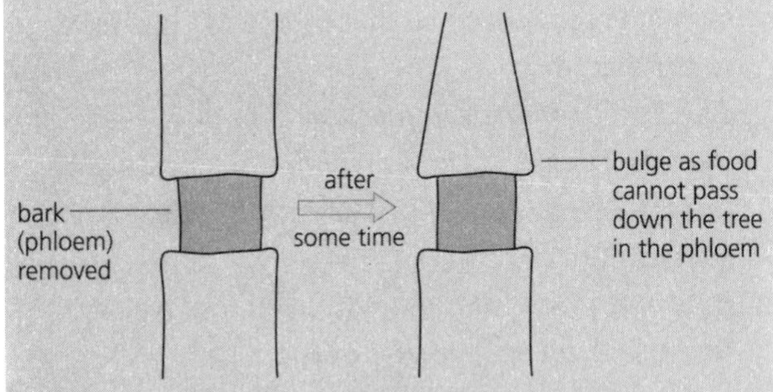

Fig 8 Evidence of the importance of phloem to a tree

You may have seen young trees planted with protective collars around the base. These deter squirrels and deer from damaging the bark, and so killing the tree by starving the roots of glucose.

Breathing and respiration

1 How is respiration different from breathing?
2 Give the word equation for aerobic respiration.
3 a What happens at the alveoli?
   b How does this happen?
4 What happens in your thorax when you:
   a inhale
   b exhale
5 a When do you respire without oxygen?
   b Where might this happen?
   c How would you know this was happening?
6 Give 3 ways that smoking might damage the body.
7 a Write a word equation for respiration in plants.
   b When do plants respire?

Circulation

1 a Give 3 differences in structure between arteries and veins.
   b What is the main difference in function between arteries and veins?
2 a Label this diagram of the heart.

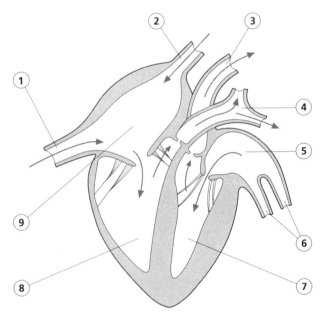

Fig 1

   b Describe how it works to pump blood round the body.

3 Label this simple diagram of the circulatory system.

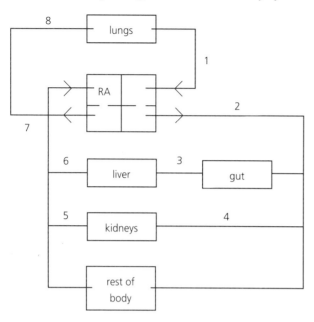

Fig 2

4 What are the functions of:
   a red blood cells?
   b white blood cells?

Movement of substances in plants

1 Give two additional reasons why plants need water (in addition to the reasons why animals need water!).
2 Name the process by which water enters a root.
3 Which tissues carry:
   a glucose
   b water
   in a plant?
4 a What term is used to describe the loss of water from plant leaves?
   b Where in the leaf does most of this occur?
   c Give some factors that would increase the loss of water from a plant.
5 a Why does a plant need glucose?
   b How does a plant obtain its glucose?

Revision sheet answers

Breathing and respiration

1 Breathing is the process whereby air is taken into and out of the lungs, whereas respiration takes place in all the cells of the body. It is the name given to the chemical reaction where energy is released as glucose reacts with oxygen.
2 glucose + oxygen → water + carbon dioxide
                            (+ energy)
3 a Gaseous exchange.
   b Oxygen diffuses into the blood and carbon dioxide diffuses from the blood.
4 a Inhale : ribs go up and out, diaphragm goes down.
   b Exhale : ribs go down and in, diaphragm goes up.
5 a When there is a shortage of oxygen, at the cells.
   b In the muscles during exercise.
   c The muscles ache due to the build up of lactic acid.
6 Cilia stop working in the trachea and bronchi, mucus builds up (smoker's cough may result), carbon monoxide reduces the amount of oxygen the blood can carry, tar lines the alveoli, nicotine becomes addictive.
7 a glucose + oxygen → water + carbon dioxide
                            (+ energy)
   b All the time!

Circulation

1 a Arteries have thicker walls, arteries have a folded inner lining, veins have valves.
   b Arteries carry oxygenated blood under pressure, veins carry de-oxygenated blood under low pressure.
2
a 1 – vena cava
  2 – vena cava
  3 – aorta
  4 – pulmonary artery
  5 – left atrium
  6 – pulmonary vein
  7 – left ventricle
  8 – right ventricle
  9 – right atrium
b The ventricles contract, the thicker-walled left ventricle pumps the blood to the body and the thinner-walled right ventricle pumps the blood to the lungs.
3
  1 – pulmonary vein
  2 – aorta
  3 – hepatic portal vein
  4 – renal artery

5 – renal vein

6 – hepatic vein

7 – vena cava

8 – pulmonary artery

4 a Carry oxygen to the cells, the oxygen combines with the haemoglobin to form oxyhaemoglobin.

  b Engulf bacteria, make antibodies – involved in the immune response.

Movement of substances in plants

1 For support and as a raw material for photosynthesis.

2 Osmosis

3 a Phloem carries glucose.

  b Xylem carries water.

4 a Transpiration

  b The lower surface of the leaf has most stomata, so there is most transpiration here.

  c Wind, increase in light intensity, reduction in humidity, increase in the number of leaves on the shoot.

5 a To provide energy (during the process of respiration).

  b It synthesises its own glucose in the process of photosynthesis.

Student Answer with Comments

The diagram shows the human respiratory system.

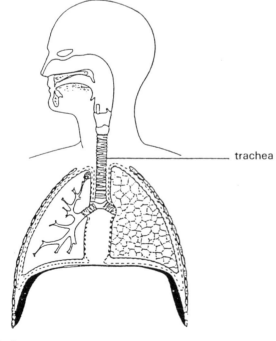

trachea

Fig 3

a The trachea produces mucus. What is the job of this mucus?

  Mucus is there to trap dust particles you ✓ ①
  breath in (1)

b Name the type of cell that produces mucus.
  Goblet cells ✓ ① (1)

c Cigarette smoke contains substances which stimulate mucus secretion (phlegm) which causes a persistent cough.
  Explain how the production of too much mucus reduces the efficiency of the lung.
  If too much mucus is produced it will line the
  trachea too thickly and restrict the path that air
  has to go through thus reducing the efficiency of
  the lung. ✓ ① (2)

The question asks about the lung! The mucus accumulates in the bronchioles, which then reduces air flow and efficiency of the lung.

d Structures called cilia remove mucus. Where, in the respiratory system, would you find cilia?
  You would find them on the inside of the trachea.
  ✓ ① (1)

Good, they are not *inside the bronchioles!*

e How do the cilia remove mucus?
  The cillia are constantly moving and push mucus
  upwards. ✓ ①
  (1)

Watch spellings: Cilia

f What is the effect of cigarette smoke on the cilia?
  The cigarette smoke gradually kill the cillia.

Don't use the word "kill" if you can help it – better to say "destroys them" or "stops them moving"

g Explain why smokers find great difficulty in giving up the habit.
  The nicotine in the cigarette is addictive and also
  the smoker thinks that they calm them down and
  relaxes them. ✓ ② (2)

h Carbon monoxide is a major constituent of cigarette smoke. Explain why it reduces oxygen availability to the cells of the body.
  Carbon monoxide combines with the hemaglobin
  in the blood even better than the O_2. Because of ✓
  this less oxygen can be carried round the body in
  the blood. ✓ ② *watch: haemoglobin* (2)

j Give one other adverse effect of smoking on health.
  lung cancer. ✓ ① (1)

(MEG)
10/12

An exam question for you to try

The diagram below represents a white blood cell releasing antibodies in the blood. To defend the body, antibodies bind to foreign particles called antigens that are made by microbes.

a i With which antigen will the antibodies bind?

.... (1 mark)

   ii Explain your answer to (i)

....

.... (1 mark)

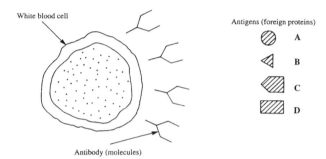

Fig 12

b Besides using antibodies, state two other methods that white blood cells use to defend the body against invading microbes.

i ....

ii .... (2 marks)

c When a mammal is injected with tetanus bacteria, certain white blood cells in the animal produce antibodies against the bacteria. If a sample of the animal's blood is then removed and allowed to clot, a fluid called serum is obtained when the clots are removed. Explain how this serum might help a human suffering from the effects of the tetanus bacteria.

....

....

....

.... (3 marks)

[WJEC]

Answer

a i C

   ii The shape of the antigen matches that of the antibody

b The white blood cells can engulf the bacteria; white blood cells can produce antitoxins (*see p 81 for more help on this*).

c The serum contains antibodies. These can react with the tetanus antigens which have been made by the tetanus bacteria.

4 Response in organisms

Response in organisms	Midland (MEG)				Northern (NEAB)		London (ULEAC)				Southern (SEG)		Welsh (WJEC)
	Own	Nuffield	Salters	Suffolk	Co-ordinated	Modular	Modular GASP	Combined	Co-ordinated	Modular	Double	Modular	Co-ordinated
CO-ORDINATION													
The nervous system	✓	✓	✓	✓	✓	✓	✓	✓	✓	✓	✓	✓	✓
The eye	✓	✓	✓	✓	✓	✓	✓	✓	✓	✓	✓	✓	✓
Eye defects	✓	✓	✓	✓	✓	✓	✓	✓	✓	✓	✓	✓	✓
The brain	✓	✓	✓	✓	✓	✓	✓	✓	✓	✓	✓	✓	✓
The reflex arc	✓	✓	✓	✓	H	H	H	H	H	✓	✓	✓	H
The hormonal system	✓	H	✓	✓	✓	✓	H	✓	✓	✓	✓	✓	✓
Co-ordination in plants	✓	H	✓	✓	✓	✓	H	H	✓	✓	✓	✓	✓
HOMEOSTASIS													
The importance of homeostasis	✓	✓	✓	✓	✓	✓	✓	✓	✓	✓	✓	✓	✓
Controlling body temperature	✓	H	✓	✓	H	✓	✓	✓	H	✓	✓	✓	H
Controlling water content	✓	✓	✓	✓	✓	✓	✓	✓	✓	✓	✓	✓	✓
Controlling the amount of sugar in the blood	✓	H	✓	✓	H	H	H	✓	H	H	✓	H	H
Controlling breathing rate	H	H	✓	✓	✓		H		✓	H	✓	H	✓
Keeping the body healthy	✓	✓	✓	✓	✓	✓	✓	✓	✓	✓	✓	✓	✓

Co-ordination

Why is co-ordination so important?

If the systems in the body were not co-ordinated, the body could not function efficiently and there could be complete chaos. For example, imagine that you are running. Your cells need more oxygen to provide the energy that is needed. If your breathing rate decreased and your heart rate fell, then sufficient oxygen could not reach the cells and carbon dioxide would build up in the tissues, which could be very harmful. Sensitivity (or irritability as it may be called) is one of the seven processes of life. Humans, like other animals, have two co-ordination systems:

- the nervous system, which uses an electrical system for fast responses concentrated more or less in one area.
- the hormonal (or endocrine system) which uses a chemical system for slower and more 'spread out' responses.

Co-ordination which involves either of these two systems has three different components:

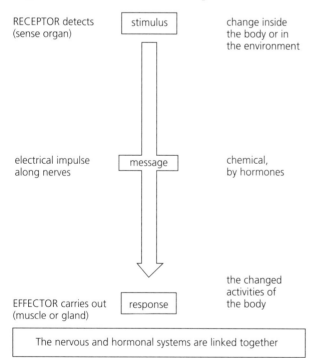

Fig I Characteristics of the co-ordination systems

The Nervous system

Your nervous system contains many billions of highly specialised cells which work together, enabling the body to respond to a stimulus in a

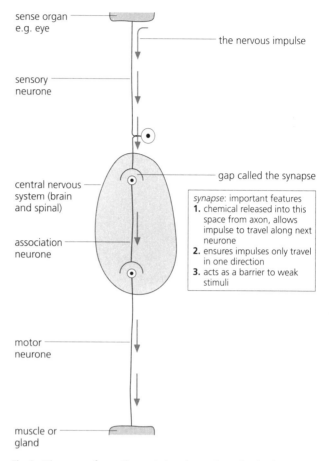

Fig 2 Diagram of a pathway taken by an impulse in the nervous system

fraction of a second. The main parts of the nervous system which carry the impulses are concentrated in the centre of the body – the brain and spinal cord. They make up what is known as the central nervous system. This co-ordinates and controls the activities of the body that involve nerves. Joining this region are many nerves which carry impulses to and from the extremities of the body. The cells which carry the impulses are called neurones. Sensory neurones carry messages in from the sense organs to the central nervous system for processing. Motor neurones carry the processed messages out to the muscles or glands in response to the initial stimulus.

QUESTION

The increase in the heart-beat is a response to a stimulus. For this response suggest:

i the stimulus..

ii the co-ordinator...

iii the effector .... (3 marks)

[NEAB]

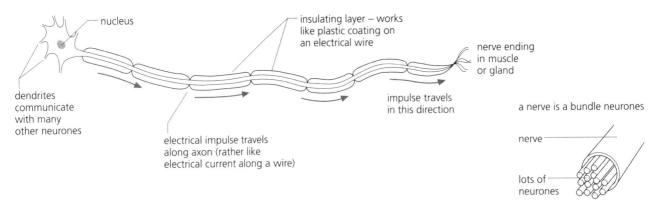

Fig 3 A neurone

ANSWER

i An increase in the carbon dioxide concentration of the blood.
ii The brain or central nervous system.
iii Muscles of the heart.

What does a neurone look like?

In common with other animal cells, the neurone has a nucleus, cytoplasm and a cell membrane. Unlike other cells, the cytoplasm around the nucleus is elongated to allow the cell to communicate with other neurones, receptors or effectors.

One part of the cytoplasm is elongated even further (the axon), to enable an impulse to be carried a long distance.

The eye as a sense organ

The function of the eye is to see, but what exactly does that mean? The sense cells of the eye (in the retina) detect light of various wavelengths and turn this into electrical impulses. These are then taken to the brain (via the optic nerve) so that an accurate image can be formed.

There are more rods than cones in the eye.

QUESTION

We see things when light from an object enters the eye. The light is focused to give an image on the retina. The retina contains millions of light-sensitive cells.

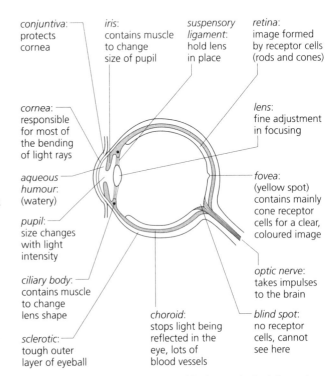

rods: are sensitive to low light intensities but can't give information about colour
cones: mostly used in bright light (daylight) and give information about colour

Fig 4 Side view of the eye

Name the two types of light sensitive cell found in the retina and state what job each type does.

cell type 1 .... what it does ....
....
cell type 2 .... what it does ....
....(4 marks)
[MEG]

ANSWER

Rods – work in low light intensities and are used to see at night when the light is poor.
Cones – give information about colour.

Looking at close objects

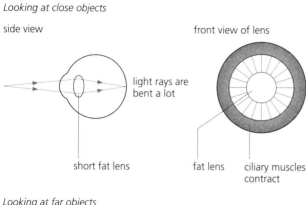

Looking at far objects

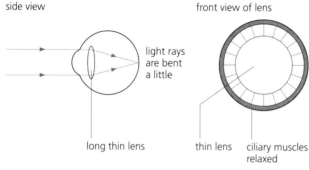

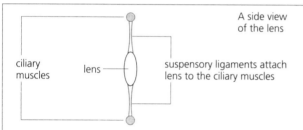

Fig 5 How the eye focuses

Light rays are refracted (bent) as they meet the curved cornea at the front of the eye. The shape of the lens can be adjusted by the ciliary muscles, so that the light rays are focused on the retina. This is called accommodation.

QUESTION

The diagram in Fig 6 shows a section of the eye. Which of the numbered parts helps to focus light on to the retina?

A 1 and 2
B 1 and 3
C 2 and 3
D 2 and 4

ANSWER

A

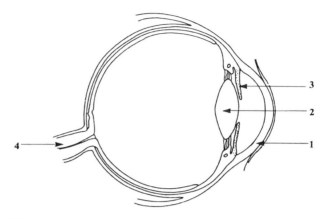

Fig 6

[SEG 1994]

QUESTION

Which describes the path of a light ray through the eye?
A Cornea → Pupil → Lens → Retina
B Cornea → Lens → Retina → Pupil
C Pupil → Cornea → Lens → Retina
D Pupil → Lens → Retina → Cornea

[SEG 1994]

ANSWER

A

The amount of light entering the eye is controlled by the muscles of the iris (the coloured part of the eye). These work as an opposing pair (antagonistic) and are an example of a reflex action (see below).

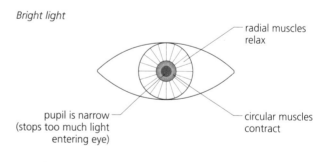

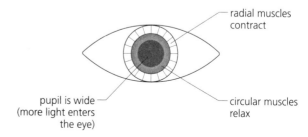

Fig 7 How the iris responds to light intensity

Eye defects

Defect	Cause	Solution – if any
Detached retina: partial blindness	hole in retina, could allow fluid to lift retina from choroid	Laser beam fixes retina in place around the hole
Long sight (hypermetropia): can focus on distant objects	eyeball too short or lens does not bend light rays enough – so light rays focus behind retina	wear glasses with converging lenses which bend light rays in more before they reach the cornea
Short sight (myopia): can focus on near objects	eyeball too long or lens bends light rays too much – so light rays focus in front of retina	wear glasses with diverging lenses which bend the light rays out before they reach the cornea.
'Old sight' (presbyopia): can focus on far objects more easily	lens becomes less elastic, cannot change shape so easily	wear glasses as in long sight, bifocals or varifocals
Cataract: vision gradually gets worse	lens becomes cloudy, light cannot get through	operation to remove lens, which may be replaced by acrylic lens
Astigmatism: cannot focus on vertical and horizontal planes at the same time	curvature of the lens is irregular	wear glasses with cylindrical lenses, which change the focal length of vertical or horizontal plane
Colour blindness: often cannot distinguish red-green shades	absence of appropriate 'colour' genes in X chromosome (see p 99)	None

The brain
This is the expanded 'top' part of the spinal cord. It contains millions of neurones, each one of which is connected to thousands of others. This makes the brain efficient as a co-ordination centre, but the human brain also has many other important functions.

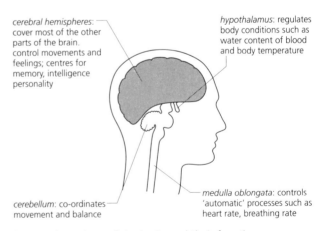

cerebral hemispheres: cover most of the other parts of the brain. control movements and feelings; centres for memory, intelligence personality

hypothalamus: regulates body conditions such as water content of blood and body temperature

cerebellum: co-ordinates movement and balance

medulla oblongata: controls 'automatic' processes such as heart rate, breathing rate

Fig 8 Main regions of the brain and their functions.

What is a reflex action and why is it important?

If you have ever touched a hot object, you no doubt moved your hand away before you thought about what was happening. This is an example of a reflex action – a very fast, automatic response to a stimulus which does not involve your brain thinking about it.

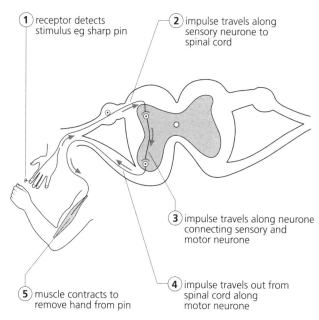

① receptor detects stimulus eg sharp pin

② impulse travels along sensory neurone to spinal cord

③ impulse travels along neurone connecting sensory and motor neurone

④ impulse travels out from spinal cord along motor neurone

⑤ muscle contracts to remove hand from pin

Fig 9 How a reflex action works

Often, a reflex action protects the body from damage. The route taken by the impulse in this process is called a reflex arc. Reflex arcs are very important to the body. They enable the body to respond to potentially dangerous changes in the external environment. Reflex arcs also allow the body to adjust to internal changes. Many of the mechanisms involved in homeostasis, e.g. responding to too much carbon dioxide in the blood by increasing the breathing and heart rates, involve reflex actions.

QUESTION

When a reflex action takes place, it can be summarised as follows:

1 Stimulus → 2 Receptor → 3 Co-ordinator → 4 Effector → 5 Response.

a Give an example of a reflex action and describe it in terms of 1–5 above.
   Example ....
   Description ....
   ....
   ....
   .... (5 marks)

b Complete the table below to show two differences between *reflex* actions and *learned responses*.

Reflex actions	Learned responses
i	i ....
ii	....
....	ii ....
....	....

[WJEC]

ANSWER

a *There are many examples you could give here. As there are 5 marks you could expect to be given one for the example and four for the description.*
   Example: Taking your hand away from a hot object.
   Description: Nerve endings in the skin respond to heat.
   Impulses pass along the sensory neurones to the spinal cord.
   In the grey matter in the spinal cord, intermediate neurones transmit the impulses to motor neurones.
   Impulses pass along the motor neurones.
   Muscles (the effector) contract to move the hand away from the heat.

b Reflex actions, many to chose from here:
   Shouting out when you stand barefoot on a drawing pin.
   Blinking.
   Pupils getting smaller in bright light.
   Swallowing.
   Learned responses, many to chose from here:
   You put your coat on before going out on a snowy day.
   You begin to pack your books away when the school bell rings.
   You turn off the television when your parents come into the room.
   Writing.

The hormonal system

Where a response to a stimulus is relatively slow and more than one part of the body is involved, it is likely that hormones rather than nerves are involved. Many processes in the body are controlled by hormones. A hormone is a chemical substance made in an endocrine gland and added directly (or secreted) into the blood, i.e. it does not go via a tube or duct. (Hence another term for endocrine gland is ductless gland.) Another characteristic of a hormone is that it is made in one part of the body but used in another.

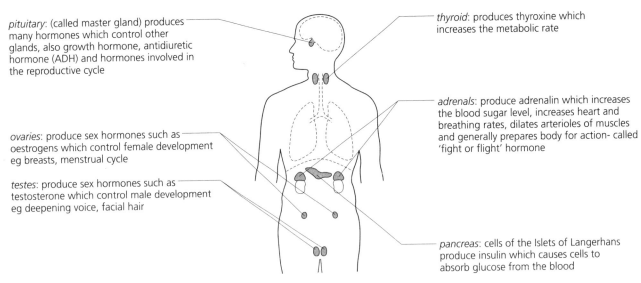

pituitary: (called master gland) produces many hormones which control other glands, also growth hormone, antidiuretic hormone (ADH) and hormones involved in the reproductive cycle

thyroid: produces thyroxine which increases the metabolic rate

adrenals: produce adrenalin which increases the blood sugar level, increases heart and breathing rates, dilates arterioles of muscles and generally prepares body for action- called 'fight or flight' hormone

ovaries: produce sex hormones such as oestrogens which control female development eg breasts, menstrual cycle

testes: produce sex hormones such as testosterone which control male development eg deepening voice, facial hair

pancreas: cells of the Islets of Langerhans produce insulin which causes cells to absorb glucose from the blood

Fig 10 The main endocrine glands and their hormones

The pituitary gland, situated under the brain and connected to it, is often called the 'master gland' because it controls the activities of the other glands. See p 78–79 for further details of insulin and the treatment of diabetes.

QUESTION

The diagram below shows some of the organs of a man.

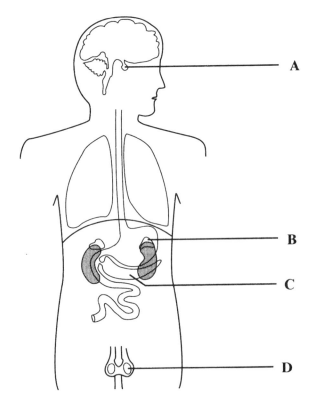

Fig 11

Which organ, A, B, C or D, produces a hormone that stimulates growth?

[SEG 1994]

ANSWER

A

QUESTION

The graphs below show how the amount of a hormone in the blood and the thickness of the lining of the uterus change during the menstrual cycle.
The hormone is:

A adrenaline

B growth hormone

C oestrogen

D testosterone

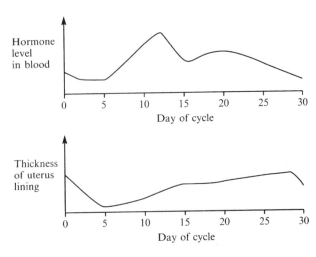

Fig 12

[SEG 1994]

ANSWER

C

The sex hormones

Secretions from the pituitary gland begin puberty (or adolescence). Hormones stimulate the testes and ovaries to produce sex hormones. Apart from being responsible for the visible changes associated with puberty, such as an increase in male body hair and bust development in females, the sex hormones are involved in a number of processes associated with reproduction.

In the male

Sperm production in the male begins at puberty and continues throughout life. This process requires the action of a pituitary hormone and testosterone, a hormone produced in the testes.

In the female

The process of producing ova (eggs) in a female also begins at puberty. Normally only one egg is produced each month (hence the term 'period'). This involves changes in the reproductive system which are controlled by the hormones oestrogen and progesterone.

A hormone from the pituitary stimulates the follicle (in the ovary) to develop. This contains the ovum. The hormones oestrogen and progesterone from the ovary prepare for implantation of the fertilised ovum by ensuring that the lining of the uterus is thick with a good blood supply. Once the ovum is released at about day 14 two different events can happen:

If the ovum is not fertilised: the corpus luteum is formed from the 'old follicle'. Eventually, around day 24, this begins to degenerate, causing a decrease in the amount of oestrogen and progesterone. This in turn allows the secretion of pituitary hormone, causing another follicle to develop. And so the cycle continues.

If the ovum is fertilised: The corpus luteum does not break down. This means that the levels of oestrogen and progesterone remain high and so the lining of the uterus remains thick. The high levels of these hormones mean that no more follicles can begin to develop and so no more ova will be available for fertilisation.

Using knowledge of the sex hormones to help infertility.

If the female fails to ovulate (produce an ovum) then 'a fertility drug' may be given. This works on the pituitary, increasing the level of the hormone which stimulates the development of the follicle. The exact timing of the dose must be related to the menstrual cycle, so that it is taken when it is most likely to cause the follicle to release an ovum.

Similarly, if it is found that the male fails to produce sufficient sperm, a drug may be taken to stimulate the pituitary to release more of the follicle stimulating hormone. In this way the sperm count of the male can be increased.

Using knowledge of the sex hormones to prevent pregnancy

If increased levels of the hormones oestrogen and progesterone are in the blood, the pituitary cannot release the hormone which stimulates the follicle to develop. Therefore there is no ovum present to be fertilised by sperm. All types of oral contraceptives, commonly called 'the pill', contain progesterone. Some also contain oestrogen. If these are taken as prescribed (normally for 21 days of each menstrual cycle) then the normal menstrual cycle is disrupted and fertilization of an ovum is unlikely to occur.

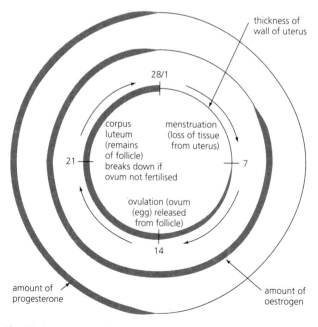

Fig 13 A summary of hormones in the menstrual cycle

QUESTION

Oestrogen and progesterone are hormones secreted by the ovaries during the menstrual cycle. Their effects are extremely complex and not completely understood. Changes in oestrogen and progesterone levels are shown in diagram Y. Changes in body temperature are shown in diagram Z.

Diagram **X**

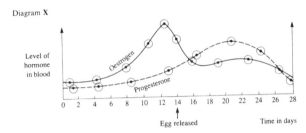

Diagram **Y**

Diagram **Z**

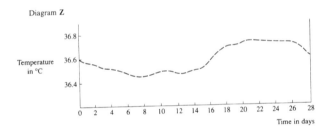

Fig 14

a   i   How are the hormones transported from the site where they are produced to the organs which they affect?

....
....(2 marks)

   ii   Why does the lining of the uterus become thickened for part of the month?

....
....(1 mark)

   iii   What would happen to the level of progesterone if a woman became pregnant?

....(1 mark)

b   i   Is the rise in body temperature starting on day 15 due to the secretion of oestrogen and progesterone? Give a reason for your answer.

....
....(1 mark)

   ii   Explain how the rise in body temperature can be used as a means of contraception.

....
....
....(1 mark)

c   A synthetic oestrogen ethynyl oestradiol is used (together with small quantities of a synthetic progesterone) to make a contraceptive pill. Natural oestrogen, a fat, can be made in large quantities and could be used as a contraceptive. However, ethynyl oestradiol is much more effective when taken orally. The pill prevents ovulation and causes the mucous lining of the cervix to become thick and sticky.

   i   Suggest why natural oestrogen is not very effective when taken orally.

....
....(1 mark)

   ii   Explain how the pill acts as a contraceptive.

....
....
....
....(2 marks)

[SEG 1994]

ANSWER

a   i   Hormones are transported by the blood, in the plasma. *Notice there are two marks here – there are not two different points to make, so you will need to include more detail to get the second mark.*

   ii   It prepares for the fertilised egg to be implanted. If the fertilised egg is implanted, tissue from this and the uterus form the placenta. *(More details on p 92).*

   iii   It would remain high.

b   i   The rise in temperature is due to the secretion of progesterone. The temperature graph shows the same pattern as the progesterone graph, but not the same pattern as the oestrogen graph.

   ii   The rise in body temperature indicates when the egg is released. This is known as the 'fertile' period. Intercourse at this time could result in the egg being fertilised.

c   i   Natural oestrogen is a fat and is digested by enzymes in the digestive system.

   ii   The pill prevents an egg being released. It also makes the mucus in the cervix sticky, so that any sperm would find it difficult to get past the cervix. *Be careful with a question like this – you must do more than just repeat the information given in the question.*

Do plants have hormones?

Plants do have chemicals which are involved in co-ordination. However, unlike hormones in animals they are often used where they are made. These substances include auxins – often called plant growth substances, which gives a clue to their usefulness. Auxins are produced at the tip of the shoot of the plant and are thought to move away by diffusion. Small amounts of auxins are made in the roots. Auxins:

- Increase growth just behind the tip of the shoot. (They are used in weedkillers to make plants grow so fast that they lose water by transpiration which cannot be replaced fast enough, so they shrivel up … and die.) *It is appropriate to use 'die' in this case but do think twice before using it in any answer – it is usually too vague.*
- In *very low* concentrations increase the growth of the root just behind the tip.
- Promote the growth of roots from cuttings. (They are used in hormone rooting powder.)
- Promote the growth of fruit.
- Promote the growth of the main shoot rather than side shoots. (Removing the main shoot – called 'pinching out' – encourages the side shoots to grow and a bushy plant to develop.)

How do plants respond to light and gravity?

Auxins are involved in a plant's response to light and gravity. These responses are called tropisms. The response to light is called phototropism and the response to gravity is called geotropism.

Phototropism

Auxin accumulates on the side of a shoot away from the light source. This produces greater cell growth so the plant grows towards the light. This is called positive phototropism.

Geotropism

Auxin accumulates on the underside of a root that is growing horizontally. In roots a high concentration of auxin inhibits cell growth, so the cells on the top surface grow more and the root bends downwards. This is called positive geotropism.

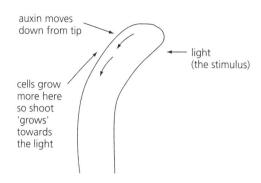

Fig 15 Phototropism in a shoot

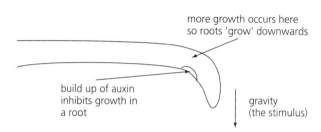

Fig 16 Geotropism in a root

QUESTION

A scientist used three identical plants for an experiment on auxins.
Plant A was untreated and used as a control.
Plant B had its growing tip removed and the cut surface was wiped with a smear of petroleum jelly (vaseline).
Plant C had its growing tip removed and the cut surface was covered with a smear of petroleum jelly containing auxin.

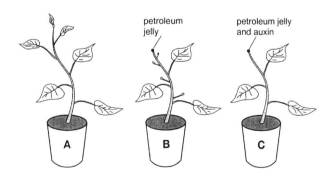

Fig 17

a i Describe how the appearance of plant B differed from plant A.

  .... (1 mark) ii Suggest one effect of auxin which can be deduced from this experiment

....

....

.... (1 mark)

iii How does this experiment support the hypothesis that auxins are made in the growing tip of the plant? Explain your answer.

....

....

.... (2 marks)

b Auxins can be sprayed as selective weedkillers. When sprayed on plants, they encourage the growth of stems and leaves whilst preventing the normal growth of roots.

When sprayed on a lawn in dry weather, broad leaved weeds such as dandelions and daisies grow rapidly, then wilt and die.

Grasses have narrow, vertical leaves and appear unaffected by the auxin spray.

i Suggest how most of the auxin in the spray enters the plants. Give a reason for your answer.

....

....

....

....(2 marks)

ii Explain why these auxins cause the weeds to shrivel up and die.

....

....

....

....(2 marks)

[MEG]

ANSWER

a i Plant B has side branches which have grown from buds.

ii When present auxin prevents side branches growing.

iii The only difference between A and C is that C has the shoot tip replaced by petroleum jelly and auxin. The tip must have the same effect as the petroleum jelly and the auxin. In B there is no tip and no auxin, but side branches have been able to grow in this plant.

b i The spray is likely to have entered through the leaves. It is most likely to enter through the stomata on the under surface as the top surface of the leaf is covered by an impermeable cuticle.

ii The leaves of the plants grow much more than normal, so there is a much greater water loss from the leaves than normal. The plants cannot take up sufficient water to maintain this loss, so the plants wilt and die.

Homeostasis (self regulation in the body)

Why is homeostasis necessary?

You will be aware of the seven processes which are common to living organisms (see p 10). But just being able to carry out those processes does not necessarily enable you to survive. You must be able to maintain your body in a steady state. For example, reactions in cells work best at a certain temperature – if the enzymes controlling them became too hot they would be denatured and would not work at all. As a result you could die. The term homeostasis is used to describe the ways in which the body is able to maintain this constant internal environment. By being able to control how your body works you are quite independent of the environment around you.

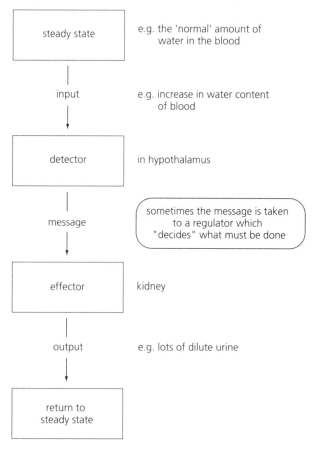

Fig 1 A model of a homeostatic mechanism

How homeostasis operates

If no changes occurred in the body there would be no need for mechanisms to deal with variations. But this is not the case. Conditions in the body do alter. For example, you may drink a lot on one day. This would increase the water content of the blood, unless something was done about it. Changes like this start the homeostatic process dealing with water content. All the separate components in the system must be linked together to bring about changes which return the body to its steady state. Fig 1 shows how a control system works in homeostasis.

An important idea behind the working of a mechanism like this is negative feedback. This means that if the system is disturbed (in this case the amount of water in the blood rises), then the body operates in such a way as to restore the steady state (in this case the kidney produces lots of dilute urine to expel the excess water). It helps to think about other homeostatic mechanisms in the body in terms of this model.

Controlling body temperature

The cells in the body release energy during respiration. As much as 70% of this is 'heat'. Humans (being mammals) and birds are able to regulate the amount of heat lost so that there is a balance and the temperature of the body remains constant. In humans it is maintained at about 37°C. The body must know when to adjust the thermostat. The thermostat is situated in the hypothalamus (see p 70) and monitors blood temperature. It also

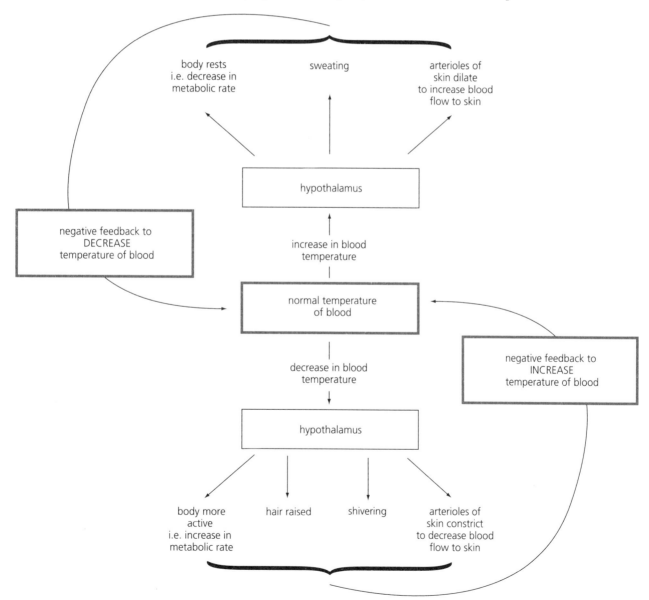

Fig 2 A summary of the control of body temperature

receives messages about the external temperature from the skin.

The skin is very important in temperature control. Three factors affect heat loss from the skin:

1. *Sweat.* This is a watery liquid produced by glands in the skin. You normally lose just under a litre a day of sweat, but in a hot, dry environment this can increase by up to twelve times. Energy is taken from the body as the sweat evaporates and this lowers the body temperature.
2. *Arterioles.* In the skin the arteries branch into many tiny arterioles. These have muscular walls which can contract to change their internal diameter. This happens when it is cold (called constriction). This reduces blood flow in the skin and so the blood is less likely to be cooled by the cold air around the body.
3. *Insulation.* The hairs of the skin are operated by muscles. When it is cold, the muscles contract to raise the hairs. This increases the layer of insulating air that is trapped next to the skin.

QUESTION

To keep us cool on a hot day our skin goes red and we sweat. Explain what happens in each of these actions to help us keep cool.

    i Our skin goes red.

        ....

        ....

        ....(2 marks)

    ii We sweat

        ....

        ....

        ....(2 marks)

                  Part question [SEG 1994]

ANSWER

    i The arterioles near the surface of the skin dilate. In this way the arterioles contain more blood. This gives out more heat than normal. *Saying that the arterioles move nearer the surface of the skin is wrong! Also, be careful that you do not just copy out the information that is given in the question.*
    ii As the sweat evaporates, energy (heat) is taken from the skin. *Look up energy and change of state on p 152 if you need more help here.*

Controlling water content

Like plants, animals have problems in obtaining water, keeping what is needed and getting rid of any extra that has been taken in. It is important that body fluids contain the correct amount of water. This is particularly important in the blood. If there was insufficient water and the blood became too concentrated, the red blood cells would shrink as they lost water by osmosis. If the blood was too dilute the red blood cells would swell up and eventually burst. (Cell walls in plants prevent this happening.) The kidneys are the organs which control the water content of the body. Humans, like other animals, have to get rid of waste substances containing nitrogen (from proteins), as they are toxic to the body. These need water to remove them. This is another function of the kidneys (see p 13).

Some factors likely to lead to a change in urine output

Factor	Effect on urine output
hot day	less urine, concentrated urine – water lost from body in sweat
diet high in protein	less urine, concentrated urine
drinking a lot of water	more urine, dilute urine
eating very salty food	less urine, more concentrated

Diuretics – are commonly known as 'water tablets'. They are taken by patients who retain too much water in their bodies. These tablets *increase* the output of urine. So, an *anti-diuretic* (e.g. ADH) means *less urine* is produced and more water is retained. In other words *ADH is secreted when the body needs to keep water.*

QUESTION

Some volunteers took part in an investigation. Their urine was collected and measured over two five day periods, one in the summer and one in the winter. During the period of each investigation the volunteers were kept on the same diet and the same level of activity. The results of the investigation are shown in the table on the next page.

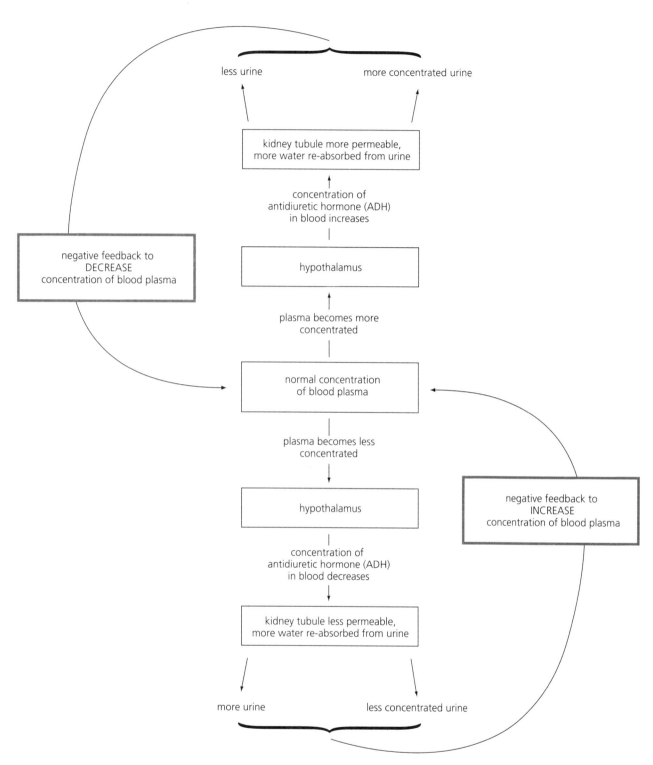

Fig 3 A summary of the control of water content

	Summer sample	**Winter sample**
Volume of urine per person per day.	990 cm^3	1470 cm^3
Colour of urine	dark yellow	pale yellow

Using your knowledge of the function of the kidney, give an explanation which would account for the data in the table.

....
....
....
....
....
....
....(6 marks)
[ULEAC]

ANSWER

This sort of answer needs careful planning. You have 6 marks available and the question asks for an explanation! There are several points to include such as:

– The volunteers drank the same amount of water in summer and winter.
– The concentration of the blood should remain constant, so the same amount of water must be lost by the body both in summer and in winter.
– In the summer the body loses water in sweat (sweating is needed for cooling), so less needs to

be lost in the urine. This accounts for the lower volume of urine produced in the summer.
– As there is less water in the urine in the summer, it is more concentrated. This accounts for the dark yellow colour.

Controlling the amount of sugar in the blood

The amount of glucose in the blood is an important factor influencing the two centres in the hypothalamus, causing the body to either eat food or refrain from eating! Glucose, being a carbohydrate, is taken from the small intestine to the liver in the hepatic portal vein. It is not needed to provide energy immediately, so is mostly stored as insoluble glycogen, either in the liver or muscles. Excess or insufficient glucose in the blood affects the overall concentration of the blood and causes an osmotic effect on the red blood cells (see p 21). When cells need glucose to provide energy during respiration, glycogen is turned back into glucose, which is then taken round the body in the blood. The uptake of glucose by cells is controlled by the hormone insulin which is produced in the pancreas.

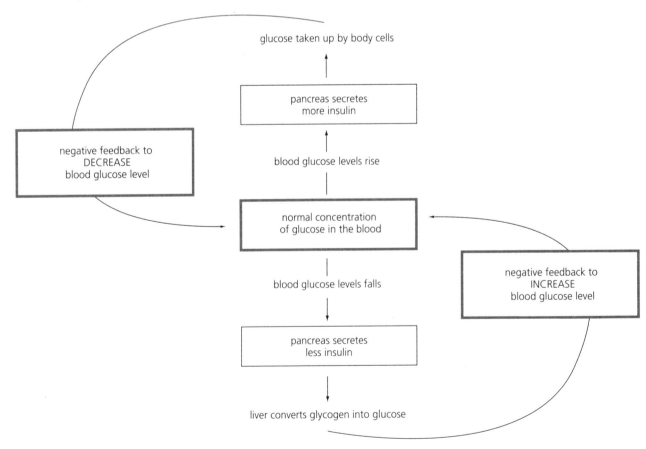

Fig 4 A summary of the control of blood sugar content
Note: Glucagon is the hormone which controls the change from glycogen into glucose by the liver.

Diabetes
If the pancreas produces too little insulin, the amount of glucose in the blood continues to rise. This causes the person to be thirsty, to produce more urine than normal and to lose weight. The condition is called diabetes and can be detected by the presence of glucose in a urine sample, as the body attempts to get rid of the extra glucose. People suffering from diabetes need to control the amount of glucose in their diet and to monitor their activity so that a balance is achieved. Insulin must be taken to control the level of sugar in the blood. As insulin is a protein, which would be digested if it were taken by mouth, it must be injected through the skin. Once injected, it enables the body to turn excess glucose into glycogen and so reduce the level of glucose in the blood.

QUESTION

The diagram summarises the homeostatic mechanism for controlling blood sugar level.

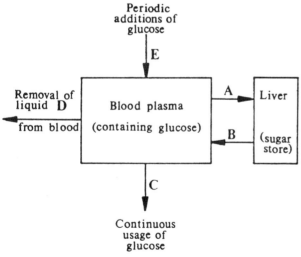

Periodic additions of glucose

E

Removal of liquid **D** from blood

Blood plasma (containing glucose)

A → Liver

B ← (sugar store)

C

Continuous usage of glucose

Fig 5

a What is meant by the term homeostasis?
....
....(2 marks)

b In what form is glucose stored in the liver?
....(1 mark)

c Two hormones control the storage of glucose. One controls change A. The other controls change B which releases glucose back into the blood.

i Name the hormone which controls change A.
....(1 mark)

ii Name the hormone which controls change B.
....(1 mark)

d The glucose level in the blood is constantly monitored. Which organ carries out the monitoring?
....(1 mark)

e i Which process continuously uses up glucose from the blood plasma at C?
....(1 mark)

ii Which process periodically adds glucose to the blood at E?
....(1 mark)

f i If the control mechanism fails then excess glucose in the blood is lost via liquid D. What is liquid D?
....(1 mark)

ii Suggest ONE reason why excess glucose may be present in the blood. Explain how this condition could be controlled.
....
....
....(3 marks)
[ULEAC]

ANSWER

a Homeostasis is how the body maintains the constant internal environment.

b Glycogen.

c i Insulin.

ii Glucagon.

d Pancreas (*this responds directly to glucose*).

e i Respiration (*to provde the body with energy*).

ii Absorption (*from the villi of the small intestine*).

f i Urine.

ii The person may suffer from diabetes. This means that the pancreas does not produce sufficient insulin. Glucose can not be stored as glycogen, for example in the liver. The person needs insulin usually given by injections or a special 'gun'.

Notice the question asks how the condition can be controlled – do not overlook this part.

QUESTION

The following flow diagram demonstrates the principle of negative feedback to maintain the balance of materials in the body.

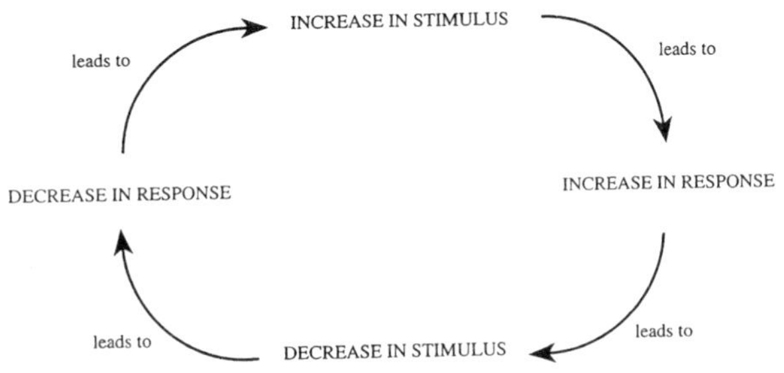

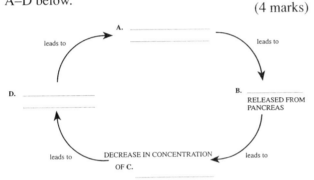

Fig 6

Complete the following flow diagram to show how the production of a hormone by the pancreas demonstrates negative feedback. Fill in the blanks A–D below.

(4 marks)

Fig 7   [WJEC]

ANSWER

A   Increase in the amount of glucose in the blood.
B   Insulin (released from pancreas).
C   Decrease in the amount of glucose in the blood (converted to glycogen).
D   Reduction in the amount of insulin released from the pancreas or increase in the amount of glucagon.

Controlling the breathing rate

When you are active, for example during running, the cells of the muscles need more oxygen. You breathe more quickly and deeply to take in this oxygen. This is controlled by the amount of carbon dioxide in the blood.

Keeping the body healthy

The body is not healthy if changes cause damage to the systems which work together in the body. Any such change is called a disease.

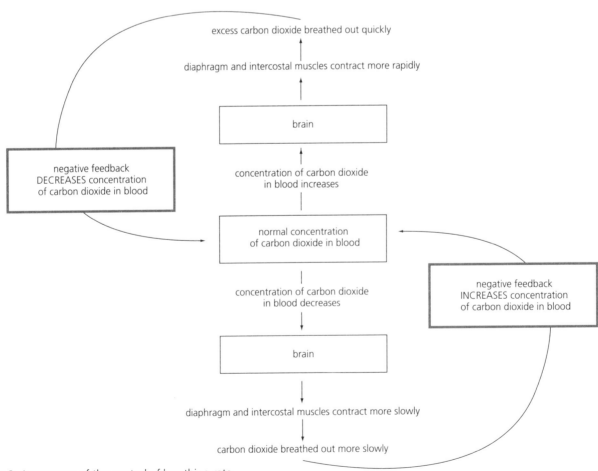

Fig 8 A summary of the control of breathing rate

Diseases can be caused by:
Not eating a balanced diet (see p 34)
Genetic causes (see p 99–101)
Hormonal causes (see p 69 and 79)
Micro-organisms

Defending the body from micro-organisms

To cause disease micro-organisms must enter the body. The body has two lines of defence. These can be thought of as front line defence and a back up system.

Front-line defence

a Skin
This is a barrier between the inside of the body and the environment. It contains the waterproof protein keratin, which stops the skin becoming dry and cracking, which would allow micro-organisms to enter. Sweat, produced by glands in the skin, is an antiseptic.

b Lining of the respiratory system
Mucus and cilia lining the tubes trap micro-organisms (see p 48–49).

c Lining of the digestive system
Any micro-organisms which reach the stomach are destroyed by the acid environment.

The back-up system

If micro-organisms get beyond the front-line defence they meet the blood and lymph defence systems.

a White blood cells
Phagocytes and lymphocytes are the two main kinds of white blood cells involved.

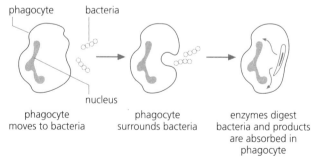

Fig 9 How phagocytes destroy micro-organisms

b Platelets
These fragments of red blood cells (see p 54) are involved in forming a blood clot. In combination with fibres of fibrin they form a mesh, which enables a cut to be sealed over. This stops the entry of micro-organisms. Phagocytes and lymphocytes may also move to this area to fight any infection that has entered.

c Lymph nodes
Lymphocytes, produced in the lymph nodes, manufacture antibodies which are important in giving the body immunity.

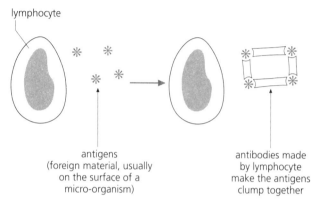

Fig 10 How lymphocytes destroy micro-organisms

Note: Other antibodies may cause the micro-organisms to burst, or stick to the surface of the micro-organisms.

Some micro-organisms release harmful substances called toxins. If this happens the antibodies produce antitoxins to render the harmful substances harmless.

Each antigen needs a specific antibody to deal with it.

QUESTION

a Explain how diseases caused by bacteria are usually treated by doctors.

....
....(2 marks)

b Explain, as fully as you can, how white blood cells protect us from disease.

....
....
....
....
....
....
....
....
....
....
....(5 marks)
[NEAB]

ANSWER

a Doctors prescribe antibiotics which kill the bacteria.

b Phagocytes, a type of white blood cell, are able to change their shape. They are able to leave the blood and move between the cells of the surrounding tissues. Bacteria, or other disease-forming micro-organisms, are surrounded by the phagocytes, which then digest the organisms. Lymphocytes recognise antigens in the blood stream. The lymphocytes then produce antibodies which react with the specific antigens.

The antibodies may release a chemical substance called an antitoxin which reacts with any toxins present. These toxins may have been produced by a disease-forming organism, such as a bacterium.

What is immunity?

To be immune from, for example, chicken pox, means that you are protected from it. Either you are immune because you acquired some immunity from your mother (this only lasts for a short time after birth), have had the disease previously, or have had an injection to prevent you suffering from the disease.

Immunity acquired from your mother

Antibodies enter the foetus via the placenta.

Immunity due to having had the disease

Your body makes antibodies when you have a particular disease – for example, mumps. The lymphocytes 'remember' how to make these antibodies, so if the micro-organism causing mumps tries to invade the body again it is immediately destroyed. This type of immunity can last for a very long time. (This doesn't work for 'flu or colds because each time you catch a cold or 'flu it is caused by a different strain of virus.)

Immunity due to having had an injection

If the body is injected with a small amount of antigen (from the disease-forming micro-organism) the body responds by making antibodies to destroy it. This gives the body immunity against the actual disease. The antigen is either a dead or weakened form (as used against polio) or altered so that it does not stimulate the disease (as in anti-tetanus vaccines).

What is the difference between drugs and medicines?

A drug is any substance which has an effect on the body. Most drugs are used as medicines. They may prevent the body getting a disease (for example, anti-tetanus vaccine), treat the symptoms of a disease (antibiotics like penicillin) or help the body withstand the effects of the disease (for example, aspirin which relieves pain).

The following table gives details of drugs that do not have any medical use for the body.

There is more about tobacco and the body on p 49.

name	some effects on the body
alcohol	sedative
solvents – glue, lighter fuel	hallucinogen; damage to respiratory system
heroin	sedative
cannabis	hallucinogen
cocaine	stimulant
LSD	hallucinogen
caffeine – in tea, coffee	stimulant
tobacco	stimulant

Terms connected with drugs

Addictive – drug which a person may become dependent upon.

Analgesic – relieves pain (often called painkiller).

Antibiotic – substance which kills or stops bacteria or fungi growing. Some of these are now synthetic.

Hallucinogen – a drug causing a person to hallucinate, that is to see things that are not there.

Prophylactic – medicine taken to stop the body suffering from a specific disease.

Sedative – drug which 'slows down' the activity of the nervous system.

Stimulant – drug which 'speeds up' the activity of the nervous system.

Tranquiliser – drug which has a calming effect, a sedative.

Withdrawal symptoms – any symptoms that result when a person stops taking an addictive drug.

QUESTION

The table shows the effect of different amounts of alcohol on a man's body.

Number of alcohol units the man has drunk.	Blood alcohol level mg/ 100cm³.	The effect on the body.
2	30	feeling good, no cares
4	60	some loss of muscle control
6	90	serious loss of muscle control
14	300	unconscious

a A man has 75mg of alcohol per 100cm³ blood. His body can break down 1 unit of alcohol per hour.
   How long will it take to completely break down the alcohol? Show your working.

   ....
   ....
   ....hours (3 marks)

b In England it is illegal to drive with more than 80mg alcohol in 100cm³ blood. What effect does this level have on the body?

   ....
   ....(2 marks)
   [NEAB]

ANSWER

a The body can break down 1 unit of alcohol per hour (*given in the question*).
   2 units of alcohol represent 30mg/100cm³ of alcohol in the blood, that means that 1 unit is 15mg/100cm³ (*worked out from the table*).
   So, if the man has 75mg of alcohol per 100cm³ blood, this means it will take him:
   75/15 hours to break this amount down = *5 hours*

b There will be quite serious loss of muscle control. (*80mg is close to 90mg, 90mg in 100cm³ means 'serious loss of muscle control'.*)

QUESTION

Prostaglandins are produced when the body is cut, burned or becomes infected. They are released into the blood. They raise the temperature of the affected area, and nerve endings are stimulated, causing irritation.

a Explain why prostaglandins can be described as acting like hormones.

   ....
   ....
   ....
   ....
   ....(3 marks)

b Aspirin, codeine and paracetamol are all pain relievers.
Aspirin stops production of prostaglandins. It also reduces the blood's ability to form clots.
Codeine blocks the nerve impulses inside the brain and central nervous system. It can cause drowsiness and may be habit-forming.
Paracetamol stops the production of prostaglandins in the brain rather than at the site of injury. Too much paracetamol can cause liver damage.
Aspirin is given to people who have suffered a heart attack.

   i Explain why this might reduce the chances of another heart attack.

   ....
   ....
   ....(2 marks)

Information on the active ingredients of four brands of pain reliever is shown in the table.

brand	ingredient		
	Aspirin	Codeine	Paracetamol
Veganin	✔	✔	✔
Solpadeine		✔	✔
Panadol			✔
Dispirin	✔		

✔ = present

Fig 11

Arthritis is a long term condition which causes pain in joints.

ii Use the information to suggest which brand sufferers should take. Explain your choice.

....
....
....(2 marks)

c Explain why a rise in body temperature may sometimes speed up or sometimes slow down recovery after infection.

....
....
....
....
....
....
....
....(4 marks)
[MEG]

ANSWER

a They are produced in one area of the body and act in another.
They are carried by the blood. *(Look on p 69 if you need reminding about hormones.)*

b i A heart attack occurs when one of the coronary arteries supplying the heart muscle develops a blood clot. If this happens the tissue in this area cannot get the oxygen it needs and the muscle is unable to function. Aspirin is a drug which reduces blood clots, making the chance of more blocked coronary arteries less likely.

   ii Dispirin should be taken as a pain reliever. Codeine may be habit forming and paracetamol can cause liver damage. Both these ingredients are in the other brands. As arthritis is a long term condition these factors are important.

c *Speeding up recovery*: if the body temperature is raised the chemical reactions in the body will be faster (faster metabolic rate), energy production in cell respiration may be faster and help to aid recovery.

Slowing down recovery: if the temperature is raised then there is likely to be more sweating and liquid will be lost from the body in this way. The patient may become dehydrated.

Revision sheet

Co-ordination

1 a What are the two co-ordination systems in the body?
  b How do they differ from each other?
2 When considering the nervous system, describe each of these:
  a stimulus
  b receptor
  c sensory neurone
  d co-ordination centre
  e motor neurone
  f effector
3 What are the characteristics of a reflex action?
4 What is a hormone?
5 Why might an auxin be called a plant hormone?
6 How do plants 'grow' towards the light?

Homeostasis

1 What is homeostasis?
2 What is meant by negative feedback?
3 Describe 3 changes in the skin which help to keep the body warm.
4 Which organ of the body controls the water content of the body fluids?
5 What causes diabetes?
6 Which gas, in the blood, is the trigger that causes the rate of breathing to change?
7 Which cells in the blood 'fight bacteria'?
8 What does 'to be immune' mean?
9 What do the following terms mean:
  a drug
  b stimulant
  c sedative

Revision sheet answers

Co-ordination

1 a Nervous system and hormonal system.
  b Nervous system – messages are in the form of electrical impulses, fast response, usually concentrated in one area.
  Hormonal system – messages are in the form of chemical substances, slower response than nerves, response usually more 'spread out'.

2 a Stimulus – change in the internal or external environment detected by a sense cell.
  b Receptor – detects the stimulus, often receptors are grouped into sense organs.
  c Sensory neurone – carries the impulse *in* to the central nervous system.
  d Co-ordination centre – the central nervous system (brain and spinal cord) which processes the messages.
  e Motor neurone – carries the impulse *out* from the central nervous system.
  f Effector – the muscle or gland which responds.
3 A reflex action is a fast, automatic response to a stimulus.
4 A hormone is a chemical substance which is made in an endocrine gland. It is made in one part of the body and taken to another part (where it 'works') by the blood.
5 An auxin might be called a plant hormone because it is a chemical substance involved in co-ordination in a plant. *(Unlike human hormones auxins 'work' where they are made.)*
6 Auxin builds up on the side of the shoot away from the light. Here it stimulates the growth of cells so that the plant grows towards the light.

Homeostasis

1 The changes occurring in the body which enable it to maintain its constant internal environment.
2 If a condition in the body increases, for example the temperature of the blood, then the body carries out adjustments to reduce the temperature until the normal temperature exists again.
3 a Constriction of arterioles in the skin, which reduces the heat loss from the skin by convection and radiation.

  b Hair being erected, as the muscles operating the hairs contract. This increases the thickness of the insulating layer of air next to the skin.
  c The skin does not sweat, so energy is not taken from the blood to evaporate the sweat.
4 The kidney.
5 In diabetes, the pancreas does not make insulin. Insulin is a hormone which controls the conversion of glucose to glycogen (at the liver). The level of glucose in the blood remains high. Diabetes is detected by the presence of glucose in the urine.
6 Carbon dioxide.
7 Phagocytes – engulf bacteria.
  Lymphocytes – produce antibodies (to counteract antigens which may be present on the bacteria) and antitoxins (to counteract toxins which may be made by the bacteria).
8 If you are immune to a disease, you are protected from catching the disease. You may have had the disease before or had an injection to prevent you catching the disease.
9 a Drug – substance which has an effect on the body.
  b Stimulant – 'speeds up' the activity of the nervous system.
  c Sedative – 'slows down' the activity of the nervous system.

Student Answer with Comments

The table below shows the water and glucose content of the blood plasma and the urine of three people.
A and C are not diabetic. B is diabetic.
C had been given a small drink containing 10g of glucose 30 minutes before the information was collected.

Substance (g/dm³)	A (non-diabetic)		B (diabetic)		C (non-diabetic)	
	Blood plasma	Urine	Blood plasma	Urine	Blood plasma	Urine
Water	911	960	912	958	910	961
Glucose	1	0	1.8	0.4	1.9	0

a Explain why the glucose content of the blood plasma and urine are different in A and B.

The diabetic would have a higher glucose content in the blood plasma and urine, this is because the kidneys are not absorbing the correct content of fluids. ✓ ①

(2 marks)

Too vague to say this, you must say that the kidney does not therefore absorb the glucose, or discuss lack of insulin in a diabetic.

b Explain why A and C had the same amounts of glucose in their urine but different amounts of glucose in their blood plasma.

'C' had been given a drink containing 10g of glucose 30 mins before the information was collected, so it is very possible that the glucose is still being absorbed at this time. ✓ ②

(3 marks)

(This implies the level in the blood is still high.)
3 marks so also explain that glucose is reabsorbed by the kidney in both A and C

c What causes diabetes?

Diabetes is caused by the malfunction of the kidneys, which in turn causes extra sugar in the blood. ✗

(2 marks)

Ugh – a common mistake!
The pancreas of the body cannot produce insulin (or enough) insulin so there is a high level of glucose in the blood. This is not converted into glycogen (as a 'store'), ... due to the absence of the hormone insulin.

d A person quickly drank one litre of water on Thursday. Samples of urine were collected for approximately four hours after drinking. The room temperature was 20°C.
The procedure was repeated on Friday when the room temperature was 30°C.
The results are shown in the graph.
Explain the differences in the amount of urine collected on Thursday and Friday.

The amount of urine that was collected on Thursday was more than Friday because their room temp was 20°C, whereas on Friday the temp was 30°C so the person needed more liquid to avoid dehydration. ✓ ①

(3 marks)

to retain? You must be clearer!!

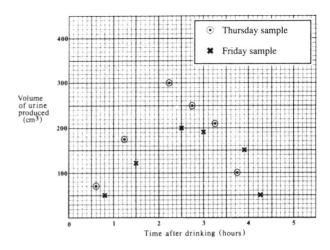

As less urine was produced on Friday, the concentration of anti-diuretic hormone (in the blood) would be increased. Include this as you can work it out! Also as it was hotter, the person would be sweating more.
Watch out for questions like this – there are three 'explains' here!!

⁴/10
(Total 10 marks)
[ULEAC]

An exam question for you to try

The graph shows the changes in blood temperature before, during and after exercise by a human.

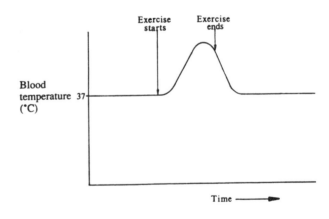

a i The rise in temperature shows that extra heat is being released within the body during the period of exercise. Which cellular process releases this heat?

.... (1 mark)

ii If the body becomes overheated, a number of body mechanisms which increase heat loss can be activated. The rise in temperature will be monitored to allow this. Where in the body is the rise in blood temperature monitored?

....(1 mark)

iii The main effectors which control the temperature of the body are in the skin. How are they controlled?

....

....

....(2 marks)

b Identify the main mechanism which will act to reduce blood temperature when it rises above normal and give a brief explanation of each mechanism.

....

....

....

....

....

....

....

....

....(7 marks)

[ULEAC]

Answer

a   i Respiration.

ii Hypothalamus *(this is more accurate than 'brain').*

iii Impulses pass along the motor neurones from the central nervous system.
(This would be true for effectors in any part of the body.)

b *7 marks are a lot here, it will be easy to get three or four but think carefully and make sure that you explain how each mechanism works to get full marks.*

– Arterioles near the surface of the skin dilate (their diameter increases), in this way they can carry more blood. This is cooled by the air moving over the skin.

– Sweat is formed. As this evaporates from the skin, energy (heat) is taken from the body and the temperature of the body is lowered.

– The hairs on the skin lie flat. In this way there is no thick layer of air trapped next to the skin to act as an insulating layer.

Continuing life

Continuing life	Midland (MEG)				Northern (NEAB)		London (ULEAC)				Southern (SEG)		Welsh (WJEC)
	Own	Nuffield	Salters	Suffolk	Co-ordinated	Modular	Modular GASP	Combined	Co-ordinated	Modular	Double	Modular	Co-ordinated
REPRODUCTION AND INHERITANCE													
Asexual reproduction	✓	✓	✓	✓	✓	✓	✓	✓	✓	✓	✓	✓	✓
Sexual reproduction in plants	✓	✓	✓	✓	✓	✓	✓	✓	✓	✓	✓	✓	✓
Sexual reproduction in humans	✓	✓	✓	✓	✓	✓	✓	✓	✓	✓	✓	✓	✓
Inheritance	✓	✓	✓	✓	✓	✓	✓	✓	✓	✓	✓	✓	✓
Replication of DNA	H	H	✓	✓	H	H	H	H	H	H	✓	H	H
Sex linkage	✓	✓	H	✓	H	✓	✓	✓	H	✓	✓	✓	H
Mutations	✓	✓	✓	✓	H	H	H	H	H	H	✓	H	H
Variation	✓	✓	✓	✓	✓	✓	✓	✓	✓	✓	✓	✓	✓
Selective breeding	✓	✓	✓	✓	✓	✓	✓	✓	✓	✓	✓	✓	✓
Genetic engineering	H	H	✓	H	H	H	H	H	H	✓	H	H	H
EVOLUTION													
Evidence for evolution	H	H	✓	H	✓	✓	✓	H	✓	H	✓	H	✓
CLASSIFICATION													
Importance of classification	✓	✓	✓	✓	✓	✓	✓	✓	✓	✓	✓	✓	✓
Classifying organisms	✓	✓	✓	✓	✓	✓	✓	✓	✓	✓	✓	✓	✓

Reproduction and inheritance

Why is reproduction so important?

Organisms do not live forever; therefore reproduction is necessary if a population is to be maintained. Without reproduction the species would become extinct. During reproduction genetic material is passed from the parent to the offspring. In this way characteristics are passed on from generation to generation.

Types of reproduction

There are two types of reproduction.

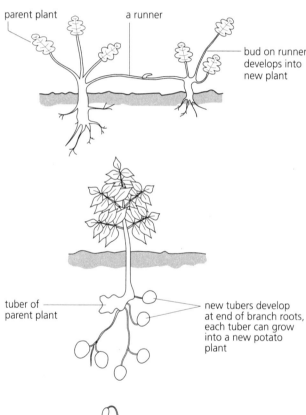

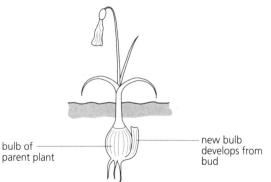

Fig 1 Examples of asexual reproduction in plants (also called vegetative propagation)

Asexual reproduction

- one parent
- no gametes
- identical offspring

Cloning in plants

One of the advantages of this type of reproduction is that the offspring are identical to the parent. These are called clones. They have the same chromosomes, and thus genes, as the parent and each other. Cloning is used commercially to produce plants and plant products, such as palm oil, by a technique called tissue culture.

The oil is used for cooking and making soap and detergents, but the amount of oil in the seeds varies. More profit can be made if the palms that are grown yield a lot of oil. Once a variety of palm with a high yield of oil has been established, further plants are produced which have identical genes to the parent plant. A large number of other types of plants, such as strawberries and potatoes, are also produced using this technique.

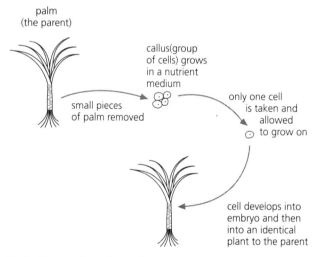

Fig 2 Tissue culture in a palm

QUESTION

a i What is meant by the term tissue culture? Explain how it could be used to grow many genetically identical carrot plants from a single carrot.

....

....

....

....

....

....
....
....
....
....(4 marks)

ii Why are sterile conditions needed for tissue culture?

....
....(1 mark)

b i How can tissue culture be used to maximise the yield of oil from palm oil plants?

....
....(1 mark)

ii Suggest and explain a disadvantage this method has over using seeds for propagation.

....
....
....
....(2 marks)

[MEG]

ANSWER

a i A small piece of the carrot is removed.
A callus (group of cells) is grown in a nutrient medium.
One of these cells is then removed and grown in a nutrient medium.
This cell develops into a carrot that is identical to the parent.

ii So that no micro-organisms such as bacteria or fungi will contaminate the tissue culture.

b i Once a high yielding variety of palm is established, other plants can be produced that are genetically identical to this.

ii As they are all genetically the same, a disease could spread quickly through the plants.
Or;
It is expensive, in terms of labour, to develop plants in this way.

Cloning in animals

Whereas it is possible to grow a plant from any cell, an animal only grows from an egg cell. It is possible to clone animal cells but it is not so simple. The nucleus is removed from the egg cell and a nucleus carrying the desired characteristics inserted in its place. This technique has been carried out in frogs. It is important because it allows researchers to find out more about the way in which the nucleus influences the cell.

Sexual reproduction

– two parents
– gametes which fuse at fertilisation
– offspring not identical

Sexual reproduction in plants

Many plants produce seeds. These are formed as a result of sexual reproduction.

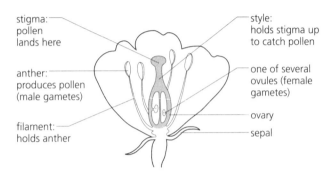

what happens after pollination

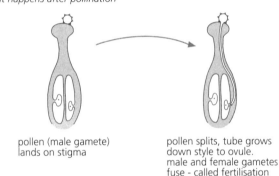

pollen (male gamete) lands on stigma

pollen splits, tube grows down style to ovule. male and female gametes fuse - called fertilisation

Fig 3 The parts of a flower and their role in seed formation

There are two stages in this.
– Pollination, in which the pollen (male gamete) is transfered from the anther to the stigma. Insects carry out this process for most brightly coloured flowers. Flowers that are green (e.g. those of grass and trees) are adapted for wind pollination.

– Fertilisation, in which the nucleus from the pollen tube fuses with the egg cell nucleus inside the ovule. This fertilised egg develops into an embryo. It is in the centre of the seed which usually has the protection of an enlarged ovary. Where this occurs the whole structure is the fruit. The fruit may be adapted for a number of different methods of dispersal. Dispersal is important as it avoids competition for resources such as light, water and minerals, which can be a problem in asexual reproduction.

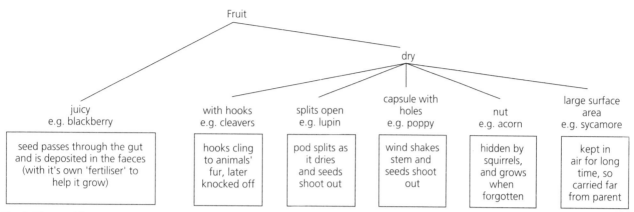

Fig 4 Dispersal key

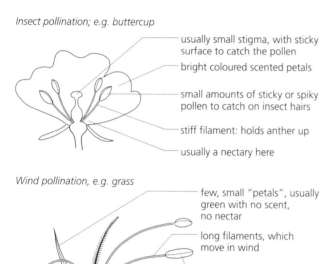

Insect pollination; e.g. buttercup

usually small stigma, with sticky surface to catch the pollen

bright coloured scented petals

small amounts of sticky or spiky pollen to catch on insect hairs

stiff filament: holds anther up

usually a nectary here

Wind pollination, e.g. grass

few, small "petals", usually green with no scent, no nectar

long filaments, which move in wind

lots of small, light pollen: easily carried by wind

large, often fluffy stigma moves in wind to catch pollen

Fig 4 Comparing insect and wind pollination

QUESTION

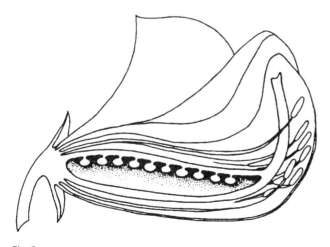

Fig 6

a On the diagram Fig 6:
   i label with the letter P a structure which produces pollen
   ii label with a letter E a structure which produces egg cells. (2 marks)
b Explain what is meant by pollination.

....
....(2 marks)

[NEAB]

ANSWER

a i The anthers – these are on the right of the diagram. *(Make sure your label is accurate and that it does not go to the style.)*
   ii The label should go to the ovary (containing the eggs). *Not the style or the stigma.*
b Pollination is the transfer of pollen from the anthers to the stigma. *Don't give vague answers like – 'from one flower to another'.*

QUESTION

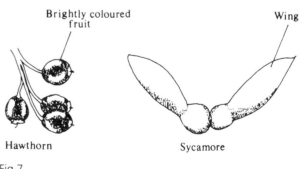

Brightly coloured fruit

Wing

Hawthorn

Sycamore

Fig 7

a Which method of seed dispersal would each plant have?
   1 Hawthorn...
   2 Sycamore .... (2 marks)

b State TWO conditions that seeds need for germination.

....

....(2 marks)

[ULEAC]

ANSWER

a 1 By animals.

   2 By wind.

b You can chose two from: moisture, warmth and oxygen.

Don't be tempted to put light, seeds will germinate in the dark!

Sexual reproduction in humans

Like most other animals, humans reproduce by sexual reproduction. The ovum is fertilised when the nucleus of the sperm joins with the nucleus of the ovum. This takes place in the oviduct (fallopian tube). The reproductive systems of the male and female are adapted to ensure that this process is successful.

Only one sperm enters the ovum and the nuclei from the female and male gametes fuse. This fertilisation results in a zygote (or fertilised egg). The zygote passes down the oviduct to the uterus. By the time it embeds in the uterus wall it is about 7 days old and has undergone a number of cell divisions to form a blastocyst. This develops into the embryo and a surrounding protective amnion, which contains fluid for protection from knocks. A placenta develops

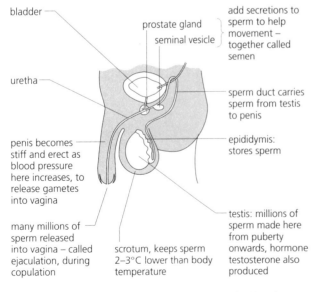

Fig 8 Male reproductive system and its role in fertilisation

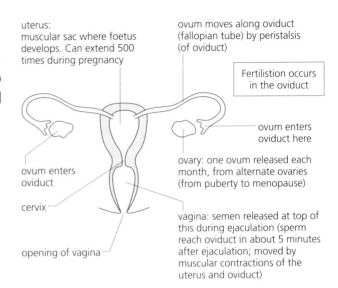

Fig 9 Female reproductive system and its role in fertilisation

from the tissue of the embryo and the wall of the uterus. Through this structure the foetus (the name given to the embryo after 8 weeks) receives nutrients and oxygen from the mother, and passes to the mother waste products of its metabolism such as carbon dioxide and urea. The placenta acts as a barrier and prevents some harmful products passing into the embryo, although it cannot protect the foetus entirely. The virus causing German Measles can cross the placenta and cause damage to the foetus, as can products in the mother's blood from drinking alcohol and from smoking.

The foetus spends 40 weeks in the uterus (called the gestation period). The major organs form within the first twelve weeks and the rest of the time is taken up mainly by growth. Hormones initiate the birth process. Contractions of the uterus push the baby downwards and out of the mother's body. The umbilical cord, which connects the baby to the uterus, is cut and the baby becomes independent. The uterus contracts rapidly and the placenta passes out of the vagina as the afterbirth.

QUESTION

a i The diagram on the next page shows part of the human female reproductive system.

Use F to mark on the diagram the place where fertilisation usually occurs. (1 mark)

  ii Explain how the structure of a sperm enables it to travel from the point of release to F.

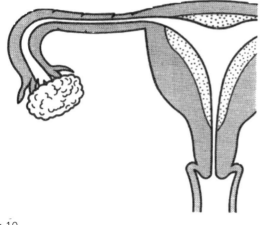

Fig 10

....
....
....
....(2 marks)

b A few weeks after fertilisation, the fertilised egg becomes an embryo which is surrounded by amniotic fluid.

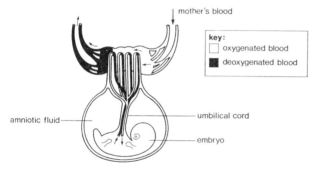

Fig 11

Describe how the oxygen level in the blood of the embryo is maintained.

....
....
....
....(3 marks)

[MEG]

ANSWER

a i This would be in the oviduct (between the ovary and the womb).

   ii The sperm has a long 'tail' which is able to move the cell. This is important in the stages just before fertilisation. The section just behind the head of the sperm is where the energy for this movement is produced. (*Contractions of the oviduct are also important in moving the sperm to the egg.*)

b Oxygen passes from the blood stream of the mother to the foetus, via the placenta. Oxygen enters the blood of the mother at the lungs. The heart (of the mother) pumps this blood round and into the placenta.

What is inheritance?

It may seem obvious to you that you have inherited some of your characteristics, for example eye colour, from your parents. The study of the way in which this happens is called genetics and the units that are responsible for these characteristics are called genes. So, for example, we talk about a 'gene for eye colour'.

What is a gene and how does it determine characteristics?

In the nucleus of each of your cells you have a number of chromosomes. There are 23 pairs in your body cells and 23 single chromosomes in the gametes (the eggs or sperm). Each chromosome is made up of a DNA (deoxyribonucleic acid) molecule.
A gene is a short length of this molecule which has instructions for making a protein or part of a protein.

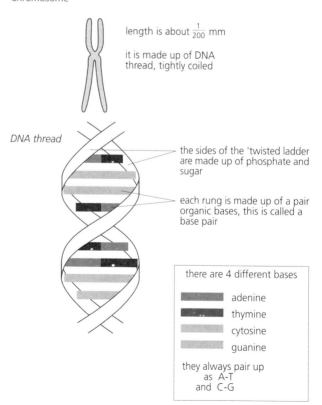

Fig 12 Simplified detail of a chromosome

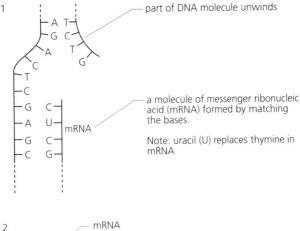

part of DNA molecule unwinds

a molecule of messenger ribonucleic acid (mRNA) formed by matching the bases.

Note: uracil (U) replaces thymine in mRNA

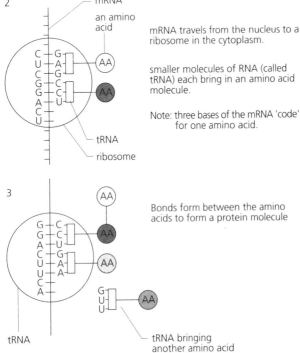

mRNA travels from the nucleus to a ribosome in the cytoplasm.

smaller molecules of RNA (called tRNA) each bring in an amino acid molecule.

Note: three bases of the mRNA 'code' for one amino acid.

Bonds form between the amino acids to form a protein molecule

tRNA bringing another amino acid to the ribosome

Fig 13 How proteins are made in a cell

The chemical reactions which occur in your cells are controlled by enzymes. As enzymes are proteins, the DNA controls the cell and the characteristics you possess by determining which enzymes are made.

QUESTION

The following represents the sequence of bases in part of a DNA molecule.

GTTAACCGAACGGTTAGATGTACATTTAAG

Using the length of DNA shown, how many amino acids can be joined up to form part of a protein?

A 3

B 10

C 15

D 30

[SEG 1994]

ANSWER

B

> Haploid and Diploid
> 23 single chromosomes may be called the haploid chromosome number.
> 23 pairs, that is 46 chromosomes may be called the diploid chromosome number.

QUESTION

The following diagrams show some human cells.

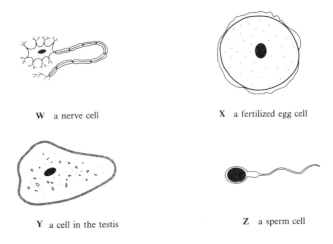

W a nerve cell

X a fertilized egg cell

Y a cell in the testis

Z a sperm cell

Fig 14

Which cells contain the diploid number of chromosomes?

A W, X and Y

B X, Y and Z

C W, Y and Z

D W, X and Z

[SEG 1994]

ANSWER

A

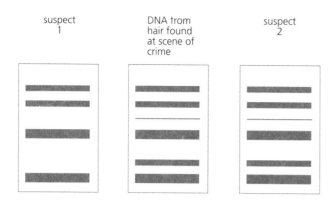

DNA fingerprinting indicates that suspect 2 committed the crime

Fig 15 Genetic fingerprinting

How do chromosomes reproduce themselves?

Before a cell can divide, the DNA in the chromosomes must copy itself. Figure 16 shows how this happens.

How do the cells of the body reproduce themselves?

As your skin, hair and other parts of your body grow, new cells which form must be exactly the same as

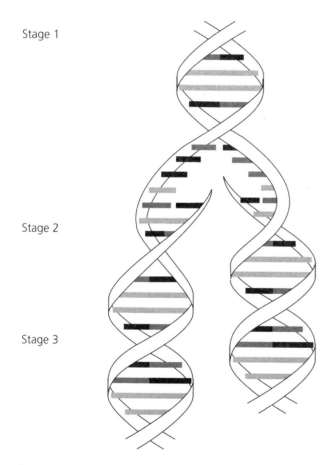

Fig 16 How DNA copies itself

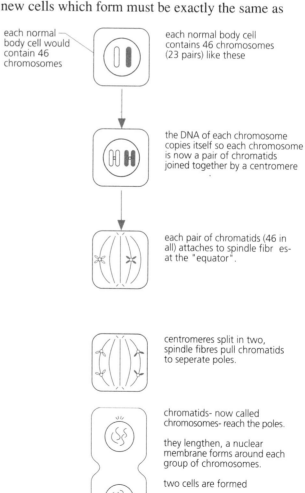

each normal body cell would contain 46 chromosomes — each normal body cell contains 46 chromosomes (23 pairs) like these

the DNA of each chromosome copies itself so each chromosome is now a pair of chromatids joined together by a centromere

each pair of chromatids (46 in all) attaches to spindle fibres at the "equator".

centromeres split in two, spindle fibres pull chromatids to seperate poles.

chromatids- now called chromosomes- reach the poles.

they lengthen, a nuclear membrane forms around each group of chromosomes.

two cells are formed

Fig 17 Mitosis

1   The DNA helix unwinds and the two strands of the DNA separate – rather like a zip unfastening.

2   New bases which are available join up with phosphate and sugar to form two new strands of DNA. The bases match those bases on the original DNA strands, called the templates.

3   The new strands twist around the template strands so that two new DNA helices are formed.

each other and the parent cell. If this did not happen then there would be some very strange effects. Mitosis is the name given to the process when cells divide to make exact copies of each other.

QUESTION

The following diagrams show the main stages in the process of mitosis.

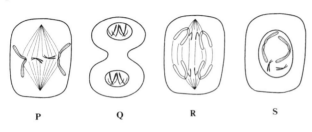

Fig 18

Which one of the following is the correct sequence of events in mitosis?

A $S \rightarrow Q \rightarrow P \rightarrow R$
B $P \rightarrow Q \rightarrow R \rightarrow S$
C $R \rightarrow Q \rightarrow S \rightarrow P$
D $S \rightarrow P \rightarrow R \rightarrow Q$

[SEG 1994]

ANSWER

D

How are characteristics transferred from parents?

Exactly which characteristics you inherit from your parents depends on:

- what happened when the gametes (eggs and sperm) formed.
- what happened at fertilisation.

How are gametes formed?

All the cells in your body are formed by the cell division called mitosis (see above) *except* the gametes. These are produced by the cell division called meiosis. In this cell division the cells that are formed have half the number of chromosomes (23) of the parent (46). (This is obvious if you think about it. If not, at fertilisation the zygote would have 92 chromosomes!) The following diagram shows meiosis in a pair of chromosomes.

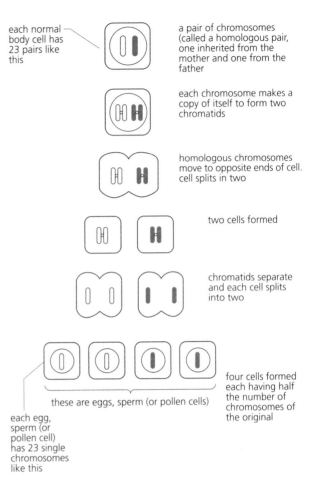

each normal body cell has 23 pairs like this

a pair of chromosomes (called a homologous pair, one inherited from the mother and one from the father

each chromosome makes a copy of itself to form two chromatids

homologous chromosomes move to opposite ends of cell. cell splits in two

two cells formed

chromatids separate and each cell splits into two

these are eggs, sperm (or pollen cells)

four cells formed each having half the number of chromosomes of the original

each egg, sperm (or pollen cell) has 23 single chromosomes like this

NB. "crossing over" between chromosomes also occurs so some genes are 'swapped' between chromosomes- see variation p102

Fig 19 A simplified diagram to show meiosis

What happens at fertilisation?

At fertilisation 23 chromosomes from the sperm cell come together with 23 chromosomes of the egg cell, forming the 23 pairs of chromosomes in the zygote. All the following cell divisions, which turn the zygote into an adult, are by mitosis. (Except of course the cell divisions needed to form eggs and sperm.)

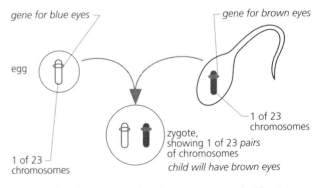

gene for blue eyes

gene for brown eyes

egg

1 of 23 chromosomes

zygote, showing 1 of 23 *pairs* of chromosomes

child will have brown eyes

1 of 23 chromosomes

Fig 20 What happens to the chromosomes at fertilisation

The matching pairs of chromosomes are called homologous chromosomes. The two members of each pair possess genes for the same characteristics, for example eye colour. Genes always work in pairs. The pair of genes may be the same, for example both may produce blue eyes, but one may produce blue eyes and one brown eyes. If the genes are different as in this case, the child actually has brown eyes. The gene for brown eyes is said to be dominant to the recessive gene for blue eyes.

How can we work out which characteristics the offspring will have?

Genes always work in pairs. In the case of eye colour 'brown' is the dominant gene and 'blue' is the recessive gene. An allele is the term given for the blue or the brown 'aspect' of the gene. The term genotype is given to the set of alleles for the character.

A person with the genes BB will have brown eyes
A person with the genes bb will have blue eyes
A person with the genes Bb will have brown eyes
Put simply, if a person has one gene for brown eyes (B) then this is what shows as the characteristic; it is dominant to the gene for blue eyes (b), which is said to be recessive. The outward expression of the gene, that is the blue or brown eyes is called the phenotype. The easiest way to work this out is to draw a table:

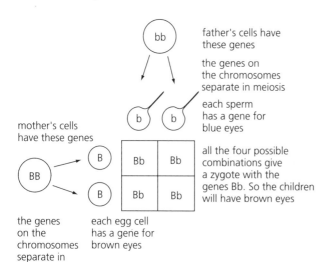

Fig 21 How genes controlling eye colour are inherited – one possibility

In this case both the mother and the father were pure breeds for eye colour. The mother had the genes BB

and the father had the genes bb. They are both said to be homozygous for that characteristic.

The children are said to be hybrids or heterozygous for the eye colour characteristic, as they have the genes Bb.

By using a table, similar to that in Figure 22, it is possible to work out the chances of a child having a certain characteristic – as long as you know the genes of the parents.

From this you can tell that the chances of the child being:

– a pure breed for brown eyes is 25%.
– a hybrid for brown eyes is 50%
– a pure breed for blue eyes is 25%.

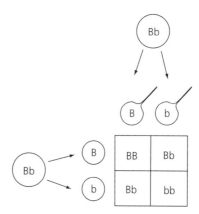

Fig 22 How genes controlling eye colour are inherited – a second possibility

QUESTION

In roses the allele for white-colour (r) is recessive to the allele for red-colour (R).

a   i   What are the two possible genotypes for a red-coloured rose? (1 mark)

Genotype 1...........................Genotype 2...........................

ii   A rose bush with red flowers was self-fertilised. The seeds produced were collected and grown. 25% of these rose bushes produced white flowers. Explain these results, using a genetic diagram.
You will be awarded up to two marks for the clarity of your genetic diagram.

....
....
....
....
....

....
....
....
....
....(5 marks)

b i What is the difference in the number of chromosomes in a normal body cell and the number in a gamete?

....
....(1 mark)

ii Why is this difference in the number of chromosomes necessary?

....
....(1 mark)

Part question [SEG 1994]

ANSWER

a i RR or Rr

ii You could draw either of these diagrams:

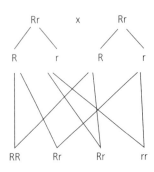

Fig 23

Make sure that you label the genotype of the parents and the gametes clearly. Explain how the rose bushes that form white flowers are due to the double recessive form of the gene for colour in rose flowers. rr make up 25% of the offspring when two hybrid parents are crossed.

b i The number of chromosomes in a human gamete is 23, it is half the number of a normal body cell (46). *Note the question asks you for a difference – you cannot just talk about the number in the gametes without referring to normal body cells.*

ii The cells of the offspring must contain 46 chromosomes. As the gametes fuse at fertilisation, then the gametes must each contain half this number to maintain the human chromosome number after fertilisation.

How do the chromosomes determine the sex of the child?

Each body cell of the human body has 23 pairs of chromosomes. Of these 22 are matching pairs, but the chomosomes in the 23rd pair do not always match. They are called the sex chromosomes.
A female has 22 matching pairs of chromosomes and a pair of sex chromosomes called XX.
A male has 22 matching pairs of chromosomes and a pair of sex chromosomes called XY.
It is the male that determines the sex of the child. Each sperm has 22 chromosomes plus either an X or Y chromosome. The sex of the child depends on whether the ovum is fertilised by an 'X sperm' or a 'Y sperm'. This can also be worked out in a similar genetics table.

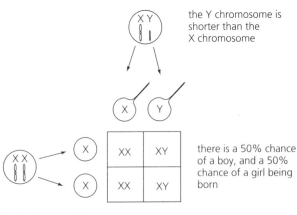

Fig 24 Boy or Girl?

QUESTION

In the human the body cells contain 23 pairs of chromosomes. The sex chromosomes form one of these pairs. The diagram shows the sex chromosomes of female and male individuals.

Sex chromosomes from two individuals

Fig 25

a The sex chromosomes are usually represented by the symbols X and Y.
  i Using these symbols state which sex chromosomes are present in:
  A a female ....
  B a male...(1 mark)

ii State which sex chromosomes could be present in:

A an ovum;..

B a sperm ....(2 marks)

b Use the symbols and a genetic diagram to show how offspring of either sex are formed.

....
....
....(3 marks)

[ULEAC]

ANSWER

a i A Female is XX.
    B male is XY.

ii A X

B X or Y. *Make sure that your answer is clear that these two chromosomes occur in separate sperm cells.*

b A diagram like Fig 24 Boy or Girl, would show how sex is inherited.

Plants and inheritance
The same principles apply to inheritance in plants as to inheritance in humans. If you understand human inheritance you ought to be able to work out what happens in other situations.

Sex-linkage

You may have noticed that more men are colour-blind than women, and that more men suffer from haemophilia than women. This is not a coincidence but is due to sex-linkage. The genes for both these conditions are found on the X-chromosome, not on the Y chromosome, and both genes are recessive. In the male, the recessive gene for either condition can show its effect. In the female both of the X chromosomes would have to carry the recessive gene for the female to suffer from the condition. If the female has one recessive gene and one dominant gene she is said to be a carrier.

Haemophilia is a serious condition in which one of the proteins needed for blood clotting is missing.

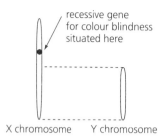

Fig 26 Colour-blindness as an example of sex-linkage

In a male, as there is no equivalent portion on the Y chromosome, the characteristic will appear even though it is recessive.

QUESTION

Red-green colour-blindness is a sex-linked inherited characteristic. The allele (gene) n for colour blindness is recessive to the allele N for normal vision. The allele n is carried only on the X chromosome.

Different combinations of alleles produce different characteristics.

a i Describe the characteristics (phenotypes) produced by these combinations.

(4 marks)

ii In a family, Arthur could not undertand why he was red-green colour-blind when his brother Colin and his parents had normal vision. Use the symbols shown above to explain how this was possible.

....
....
....
....(4 marks)

Fig 27

[MEG]

ANSWER

a   i Female, normal vision
       Male, colour-blind.
  ii Colin and his parents had normal vision. Arthur
     has the recessive colour-blind condition. His
     mother must be a carrier for the colour-blindness
     gene. You could draw a diagram like this:

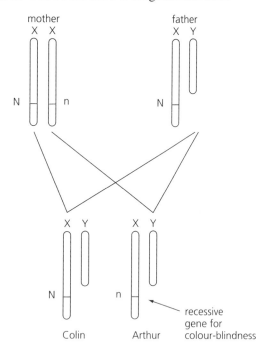

Fig 28

If his mother were a double dominant for normal
vision, NN, then Colin could not be colour-blind.

What is a mutation?

A mutation is a sudden change in the amount or
structure of the DNA of an organism. If this change
happens in the gametes then the change is inherited.
There are two kinds of mutation:

Chromosome mutation

For example, the cell can gain an extra chromosome
when cell division is abnormal. Down's syndrome is
caused in this way.

Gene mutation

For example, there may be change in the order of the
DNA bases. Sickle cell anaemia and cystic fibrosis
are caused in this way.
Mutations are not always bad. They are particularly
important in selective breeding (see below).

What causes mutations?

Any gene can undergo a mutation at any time. This
happens spontaneously and randomly. However, a
number of phenomena are known to increase the rate
of mutation beyond what could be regarded as the
normal rate. Some phenomena which do this are:

– *high energy electromagnetic radiation* such as:
ultra-violet light, X-rays, gamma rays.
– *high energy particles* such as: alpha and beta
particles, neutrons, cosmic radiation.
– *some chemical substances* such as: mustard gas,
certain constituents of tobacco and other drugs,
some food constituents.

QUESTION

The following diagram shows red bone marrow
tissue producing mutant cells which multiply in an
uncontrolled way and become cancer cells.

a If the cell in stage one had 46 chromsomes, how
  many chromosomes are in a cell from stage two?
  ....(1 mark)
b i Between which **two** stages has mutation taken
    place?
    Between stage............and stage ....(1 mark)
  ii What is meant by **mutation**?
    ....
    ....
c Suggest **two** causes of this type of mutation.
  i ....
  ii ....(2 marks)

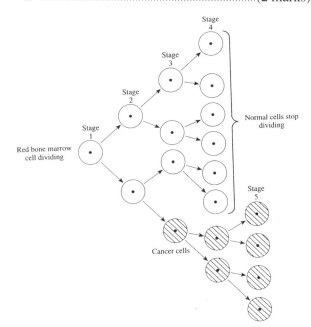

Fig 29

d Sometimes an organism shows a new characteristic as a result of mutation which it then passes on to its offspring.

  i In which type of cell must this mutation have occurred?

  ....(1 mark)

  ii Explain how natural selection may cause the mutation to become common several generations later.

  ....
  ....
  ....
  ....
  ....
  ....(3 marks)

  [WJEC]

ANSWER

a 46

b i Between stage 2 and 3.

  ii A mutation is a change in the DNA of a cell. It might be a change in the amount or the structure of the DNA. It is a sudden change.

c Any two from: high energy electromagnetic radiation (or an example, such as ultra-violet rays); high energy particles (or an example, such as alpha particles); or a named (*suitable*) chemical substance, such as mustard gas.

d i A gamete – egg or sperm.

  ii (*See p 105 if you need more help here.*)

If the mutation causes a favourable characteristic in the organism, this may cause the organism to be better adapted to its environment. These organisms are then more likely to reproduce and pass the favourable characteristics on to their offspring. In this way the mutation may become common after several generations. (This has been seen to occur in the peppered moth.)

QUESTION

a Tomato plants grown by gardeners show a lot of variety in their appearance. Some differences in tomato plants are caused by differences in their genes (genetic cause). Other differences are caused by the conditions in which they are developed (environmental cause). The table shows three effects of these causes on one tomato plant. Show which cause is responsible for each effect by placing a tick (✓) in the correct column.

Effect	Genetic cause	Environmental cause
Colour of petals in flower		
Time taken for tomatoes to ripen		
Resistance to disease		

(3 marks)

b The height to which a tomato plant grows can be affected by both its genes and its environment. Name ONE environmental cause which could affect its height.

....(1 mark)

[ULEAC]

ANSWER

a Colour – genetic.
  Time taken for tomatoes to ripen – environmental.
  Resistance to disease – genetic.

b Any one from: amount of sunlight, amount of water, amount (*or type*) of minerals available to the plant, amount of carbon dioxide (*in a greenhouse this can be controlled*), temperature.

What causes variation?

By variation we mean how the organisms belonging to one species differ in their characteristics. No two organisms are the same, that is they do not have an identical phenotype. Identical twins, which come from the same zygote, have the same genotype (genetic make up) but they are likely to be different in some respect. For example, one might eat more than the other and therefore be larger in width! Therefore variation has two causes – genetic and environmental.

Environmental causes of variation

These can be appreciated easily in plants. A strawberry plant produces new plants by asexual reproduction. However, their growth is very much dependent on the amount of light and water they receive, and the minerals they are able to absorb from the soil.

Genetic causes of variation

Sexual reproduction results in virtually unlimited genetic variation between organisms in a species. The important processes for this are:

• Meiosis
The genes of chromatids of homologous chromosomes 'cross over' and so produce new combinations of genes.
The chromatids are randomly sorted during meiosis and so produce a large number of different combinations of chromosomes in the gametes.

• Fertilisation
The ovum can be fertilised by any one of several million sperm, so the 23 pairs of chromosomes in the zygote are selected randomly.

What is selective breeding?

In any population of animals or plants there is a great variety of organisms. For example, a field of peas will produce plants where the peas are ripe over several weeks. By carefully choosing those that are ripe at the same time and carrying out a breeding programme it is possible to grow a whole field of peas which all ripen at the same time. This is very important to the frozen pea producer who must get the peas from the field to the factory in one journey. Choosing the desired character (in this case peas ripening at the same time), and carrying out such a programme is an example of selective breeding. Such a breeding programme can take many years. Researchers can shorten the time taken if they can increase the speed at which mutations occur. This may be done by subjecting the organism to a phenomenon known to increase the mutation rate, such as X-rays.
In many cases selective breeding leads to improved varieties. If wheat is left lying on a field after the corn has been harvested it is likely to be attacked by the fungus called Eyespot. This fungus then remains in the soil and can attack the crop of wheat planted on the field in subsequent years. A variety of wheat has been produced by selective breeding which is resistant to Eyespot.

What is genetic engineering?

This refers to the processes by which the genetic material of an organism can be changed in the laboratory. Removing a gene from one chromosome and inserting it into another chromosome, in another organism, involves genetic engineering. This in itself is a complex operation. But before this can be carried out, the gene coding for the desired characteristic must be identified. Once inside the 'new' cell the gene can change the function of this cell.

Using bacteria in genetic engineering

1 An enzyme is used to separate genes along the strand of DNA (rather like separating beads of a necklace). This allows the gene which will be transferred to be isolated.

2 A bacterial cell contains a circular strand of DNA called a plasmid. The gene is then 'glued' into this, using other enzymes. This DNA with the 'new' gene is called recombinant DNA.

3 When the cell of the bacteria divides to form daughter cells the 'new' gene replicates as well. This gene can enable the bacterial cell to make proteins that it would not normally make.

Uses of genetic engineering

• Producing insulin – the gene responsible for the production of insulin in humans has been inserted into a bacterium. These cells reproduce rapidly. It is a more satisfactory way of producing insulin than isolating it from the pancreas of animals after slaughter.

• Producing vaccines – in the past many vaccines were produced by growing the pathogen in an animal and then 'harvesting' it for use in humans. Once the gene responsible for a particular disease has been identified, harmless bacteria can be used to produce the vaccine (for example, the vaccine against hepatitis-B).

• Crop improvement – by inserting genes that code for particular proteins, the number of essential amino acids in plants can be increased, thus increasing their nutritional value.

QUESTION

Scientists have found that a type of bacterium living in soil produces a protein which kills insects. Using genetic engineering scientists have been able to develop tomato plants which can also make this protein.

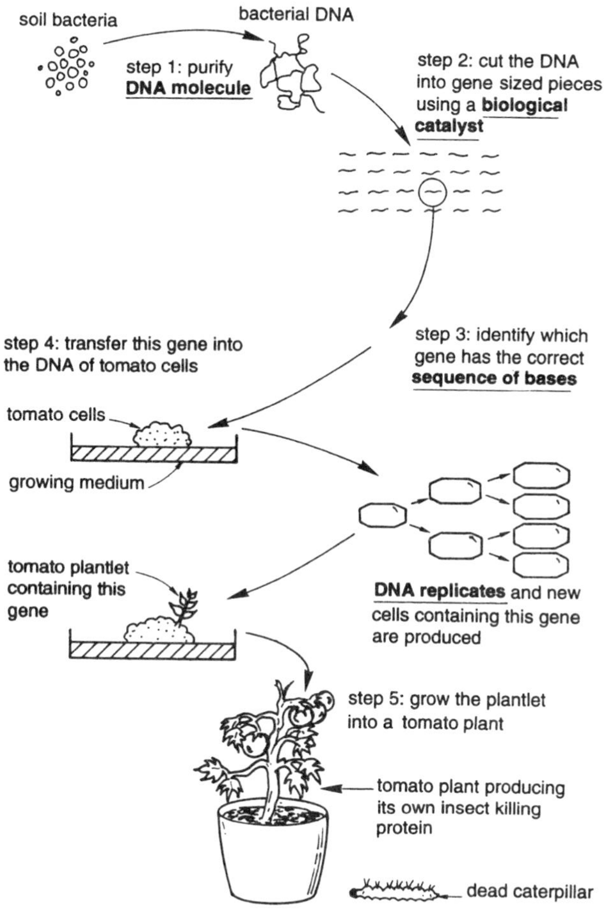

Fig 30

a Explain what you understand by each of the four underlined phrases.

DNA molecule ....

....

....

Biological catalyst ....

....

....

Sequence of bases ....

....

....

DNA replicates ....

....

....(8 marks)

b Suggest why some scientists are concerned about aspects of genetic engineering.

....

....

....

....

....

....

....

....(4 marks)
[MEG]

ANSWER

There is a lot that you could write for each of these answers. You should concentrate on explaining your points clearly. You are unlikely to be expected to explain all of the following for your marks here!

a DNA – This large molecule (which is a double helix) makes up the chromosomes in the nucleus. A gene is a short length of this molecule. A gene has the instructions for making a protein or part of a protein. DNA is said to carry the genetic code because it contains the information to form, maintain and control a living organism.
Biological catalyst – A biological catalyst is an enzyme. Each enzyme is specific – it only controls one reaction. Enzymes are proteins and are denatured by high temperatures; they cannot then operate because their shape is changed and the 'active sites' are not available. Also, enzymes usually only operate within a narrow range of pH.
Sequence of bases – The DNA molecule is made up of four bases, which pair as AT (adenine and thymine) and CG (cytosine and guanine). These are rather like rungs on a ladder. The sequence of bases is important in determining which proteins are made in the cell.
As the DNA replicates, the bonds between the pairs of bases are broken and new bases pair up with the original ones. In this way two identical strands of DNA are formed.

b *Again there are lots of things you could write about here. You should take time to give sufficient detail for the four marks and also give reasons where you can.*
For example:
Much genetic engineering is carried out with bacteria, and there is concern that new and harmful bacteria may be produced.
The natural population of an environment might be changed by the introduction of genetically engineered organisms, for example fish into a river.

Animals being used for experiments in genetic engineering may suffer unduly, for example in the study of diseases such as cancer.

Evolution

What is evolution?

Over millions of years there have been changes in the organisms on Earth. The term evolution is used to describe the change from simple organisms to complex organisms over a long period of time. The first living organisms on the Earth did not have systems adapted for different processes as you do. In some, the whole body was only a single cell. Gradually these simple organisms evolved into the variety of organisms, some quite complex, that are found on the Earth today.

What evidence is there for evolution?

The main evidence for evolution comes from looking at fossils. A fossil is the remains of an organism that has been preserved in sedimentary rock. A fossil is usually the hard part of the organism, such as the shell, but it may also be a cast (or imprint) of the soft parts of the organism. By looking at these fossils there is evidence:

- that many types of animals and plants which lived on the Earth a long time ago are no longer living – they are extinct.
- of how long ago these organism lived.
- of the structure and mode of life of these organisms.
- of how similar (or different) present day organisms are to these extinct ones.

By looking at sedimentary rocks in North America the fossil record of the horse has been constructed. Fig 1 gives details of two aspects of this evolution – changes in height and in the front limbs. Note particularly the changes to the third digit.

How has evolution happened?

Darwin and Wallace are the two scientists credited with suggesting the theory of evolution. Although they worked separately, they based their ideas about evolution on similar thoughts. These can be summarised as survival of the fittest and natural selection.

Survival of the fittest

If you consider most species, there are a lot of offspring and a lot of *variety* between the organisms. For example, plantain plants (which grow on lawns) have different sized leaves.

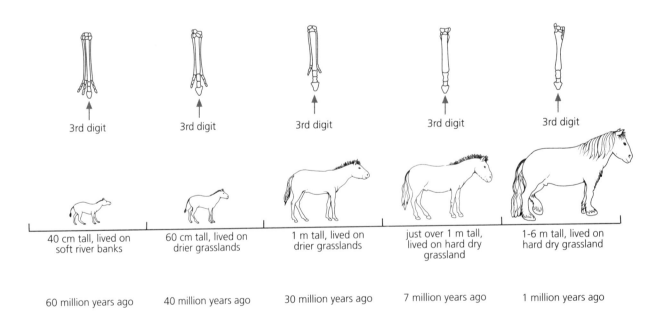

| 3rd digit | 3rd digit | 3rd digit | 3rd digit | 3rd digit |

| 40 cm tall, lived on soft river banks | 60 cm tall, lived on drier grasslands | 1 m tall, lived on drier grasslands | just over 1 m tall, lived on hard dry grassland | 1-6 m tall, lived on hard dry grassland |

| 60 million years ago | 40 million years ago | 30 million years ago | 7 million years ago | 1 million years ago |

height is from shoulder to ground

Fig 1 Evolution of the horse: height and changes in the front limbs

The plants with larger leaves can absorb more sunlight than smaller leaved plants. Those with larger leaves are better *adapted* to the environment than those with smaller leaves.

Those which are better suited to the environment are likely to have the most offspring.

These ideas are often referred to as 'survival of the fittest'. It means that those organisms best suited to their environment are likely to survive.

Natural selection

However, survival of the fittest would not lead to evolution unless these better adaptations were passed on to the offspring. The term 'natural selection' is used to describe this process. In the example above about the plantain, unless the ability to grow bigger leaves is controlled by the genes (rather than the environment) then this feature will not evolve.

QUESTION

List four observations that Darwin and Wallace used as a basis for their theory of evolution.

....
....
....
....
....
....(4 marks)

[MEG]

ANSWER

This question only asks for a list!
Factors which you could include are:

– Organisms produce vast numbers of offspring.
– There is variation between the offspring of the same type.
– Some of these offspring are better suited to their environment than others.
– Some of the variations between the offspring are inherited.

Other points could be included such as:

– Evidence from the fossil record.
– The geographical distribution of species varies.
– Particular structures in some organisms indicate that they had a common ancestor.

This is not the place to discuss mutations in detail.

Mutations and evolution

Before 1850, virtually the whole population of the Peppered Moth, *Biston betularia*, had greyish-white wings. By 1895, 98% of the specimens caught had very dark wings. It is thought that the dark-winged form arose due to a mutation. At this time, in the Midlands and North there was an increase in the number of factories, and hence the amount of soot and smoke in the air. This settled on trees and darkened their trunks. The dark form of the moth was less noticeable to birds that were its predator. It was better adapted to the environment and so more likely to have offspring. See p 100–101 for more details about mutations.

QUESTION

a The Peppered Moth has light-coloured wings 'peppered' with dark spots and bars. In 1850 a dark variety of this moth with almost black wings was discovered in Manchester. After 1850, the dark form rapidly became more and more common so that today, in the Manchester area, the light-coloured variety is rare. The light-coloured variety still continues to thrive in some other parts of the United Kingdom.

  i Suggest how the original dark-coloured variety came into existence.

  ....
  ....
  ....(2 marks)

  ii Explain why the dark-coloured variety has now become the common variety in the Manchester area.

  ....
  ....
  ....(2 marks)

  iii Suggest one reason why evolutionary changes to the Peppered Moth are more rapid than evolutionary changes to the horse.

  ....
  ....(1 mark)

Part question [SEG 1994]

ANSWER

a i There had been a mutation, a change to the genetic material. This change was then passed on to the offspring.

ii The Manchester area is an industrial area. A dark coloured form would be at an advantage as it would be better camouflaged, and less likely to be seen by a predator. As it is better adapted it is more likely to have offspring.

iii The moth has a shorter life cycle; the moth has many more offspring at once than a horse.

How do organisms become extinct?

A species disappears completely when conditions change and the organisms are not well adapted to those changes. For example, the Dodo was a bird native to Mauritius. It was flightless and could not defend itself. European sailors hunted it and their domesticated animals are likely to have hunted its eggs. The Dodo became extinct in about 1700 because its environment changed and it was not well adapted to this.

QUESTION

Read through this information, which is based on an article which appeared recently in a newspaper.

> Cod live for up to twenty years, and reproduce every year once they reach the age of three or four. Records of cod show that, in 1893, half of all female cod did not reach sexual maturity until they were 75cm long. Last year, half of all the females caught were fertile at 50cm. In 1974, no two-year-old females were fertile: last year 10% of two year olds were breeding. However, once a cod reaches a legally netable size, there is 60% chance of it being caught in the mesh of a trawler's net. Only 15% survive to breed at three years; only 5% make it to four.

It seems that cod are evolving to become sexually mature at an increasingly younger age.

Use your knowledge of variation and adaptation for survival to help explain this.

You will be awarded up to three marks if you write your ideas clearly.

....
....
....
....

....
....
....
....
....
....
....
....
....
....
....
....
....
....(9 marks)

[SEG 1994]

ANSWER

There are a lot of marks here. The question indicates that marks are available for a clear answer, so it is worth organising your thoughts carefully before you begin.

Important points to include:
In any population there will be variation.
In this case, there will be natural variation in the age at which the female cod reach sexual maturity.
There is quite a high chance of an older female cod being caught in a net.
Female cod have to be a certain size to be kept from the net.
Assuming that the tendency to mature earlier has a genetic component, those females that mature when they are younger (and smaller) are more likely to pass this tendency on to the next generation. (They will be below the size limit that allows them to be kept from the net.)
This could account for the fact that cod seem to become sexually mature at a younger age.

Classification

Why do we classify organisms?

Ancolie noir-violâtre is a beautiful flower which is found in the Alps. The French name for it is meaningless to anyone that is not a French speaking specialist in alpine flowers. However, the Latin name

Aquilegia atrata would be understood throughout the world. There are just under a million different kinds of animals and over a third of a million different kinds of plants. Each one has been classified and given a scientific name such as that of the plant mentioned above. The name allows us to discuss the correct plant whatever our native language. (This is similar to using formulae for chemical compounds.) It is impossible to study all the characteristics of all the organisms on the Earth. To make the task easier, organisms which are similar are grouped together and then different groups are put together into a larger group and so on. By doing this it is possible to find out about organisms in the detail that you need. An alpine flower specialist may be interested in the species level, but you may only be interested in the fact that they are plants!

Aquilega (notice the capital letter) is the name of the genus and *atrata* (notice the small letter) is the name of the species to which the plant belongs. All the organisms in a species are very similar. There will be some differences between them, due to natural variation, *and* their offspring must be able to breed too. There are many different kinds of plants in the Aquilega genus, (nine others are found in the Alps) but these are not able to breed together. The genus *Aquilegia* is grouped with several other genera in a larger group, called a family, which includes our common buttercup! The families are collected together into an order. The orders are collected together into a larger group called a class. All classes are grouped together into a phylum and these are grouped together into the plant kingdom.

Starting with the biggest grouping and ending up with the scientific name of one organism involves these groups:

Kingdom   Plant
Phylum   Angiospermata
Class   Dicotyledonae
Order   Ranales
Family   Ranunculaceae
Genus   Aquilegia (equivalent to your surname)
Species   atrata (equivalent to your Christian name)

(Some people find it helpful to learn this sentence to help them with this:

<u>K</u>ing <u>P</u>eter <u>C</u>alls <u>O</u>rder <u>F</u>or <u>G</u>eneral <u>S</u>cience)
All living organisms belong to one of five kingdoms.

Kingdom Prokaryotae

These organisms do not have a membrane around the nucleus. It includes bacteria.

Kingdom Protoctista

These are organisms made up of one or a few cells, that do not fit into the animal, plant or fungi kingdoms.

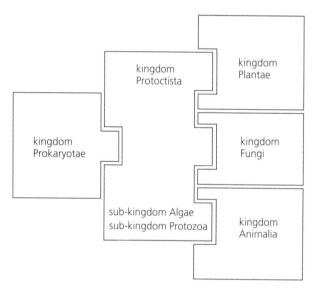

Fig 1 The five kingdoms

Kingdom Fungi

Organisms where the outer wall is not made of cellulose. They do not carry out photosynthesis.

Kingdom Plantae

All the well known plants, such as ferns, mosses, trees, flowers.

Kingdom Animalia

All the well known animals, such as worms, insects, birds and you.

There is not a phylum of invertebrates, it is just the name given to any animal that is not a vertebrate.

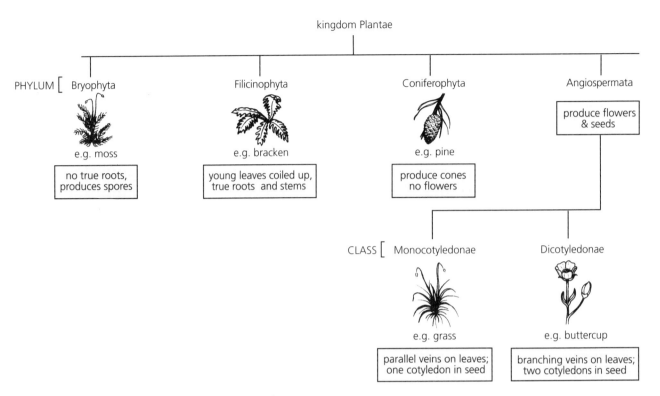

Fig 2 The main taxonomic groups of the Kingdom Plantae

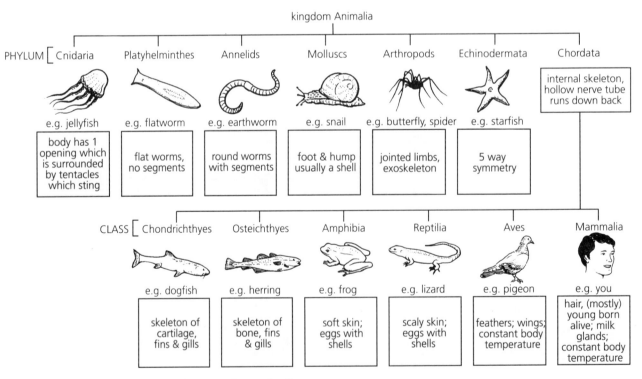

Fig 3 The main taxonomic groups of the Kingdom Animalia

QUESTION

Three small animals are shown in the diagram below.

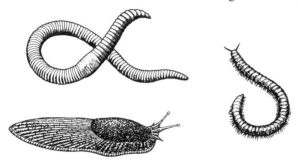

Fig 4

Which word describes all three animals?
Tick the box beside the correct answer. (1 mark)

Amphibian ☐

Annelid ☐

Invertebrate ☐

Vertebrate ☐

Part question [SEG 1994]

ANSWER

Invertebrate.

QUESTION

The table below shows the features of some animal groups. Look at the drawings below the table. Finish this table to match the animal letter with its group name. (5 marks)

features	group name	animal letter
warm blooded fur females produce milk	mammals	
warm blooded wings and feathers beak clawed feet	birds	
breathe using lungs bony scales lay eggs on land	reptiles	
cold blooded smooth moist skin lay eggs in water webbed feet	amphibians	
cold blooded bony scales gills fins	fish	

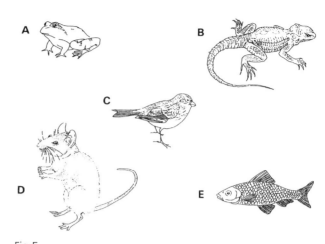

Fig 5

ANSWER

D, C, B, A, E

How do we identify an organism?

To be able to classify an organism, that is to find its correct scientific name, you need to use a key. Keys are usually made up of descriptions of the observable characteristics arranged in contrasting pairs, such as the one in fig 7. By working through it from the top downwards, you should be able to identify the organism.

Using a key

This is *part* of a key to identify animals that are found in freshwater. This section helps to classify small animals without a shell that are less than 5mm long.

1 Body is torpedo shaped, go to 2.
   Body is not torpedo shaped, go to 3.
2 Antennae less than half length of body – *Cyclops*.
   Antennae longer than half the body – *Diaptomus*.
3 Body egg-shaped, movements in water are regular – *Cypris*.
   Body round, eye a black dot, movements in water are jerky – go to 4.
4 Shell with a spine – *Daphnia* (water flea).
   Shell without a spine – *Semicephalus* (water flea).

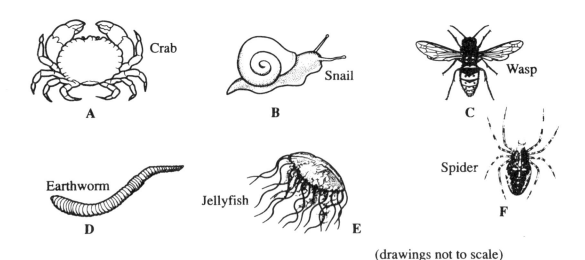

(drawings not to scale)

Fig 6

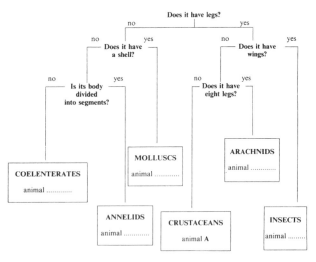

Fig 7

Making a key

This is more difficult than using one. Give yourself plenty of space – remember you need to write two descriptions each time. Work in pencil – you are likely to change the numbers as you make up the key. Look for obvious structural characteristics. For example, 'transparent wings' is better than 'moves fast'. Try and choose characteristics that divide your sample roughly in half each time. When you have finished the key, check it carefully and if possible try it out on somebody else.

QUESTION

The animals in Fig 6 are all invertebrates (animals without backbones). There are many different groups of invertebrates and each of the animals belongs to a different group.

a Use the key in Fig 7 and the information in the drawings to help you to put each animal into its correct group. One has been done for you. (5 marks) The jellyfish and the crab both live in the sea. If they both get washed up on the sand by the tide the jellyfish is less likely to survive than the crab.

b Suggest, with reasons, three features of the body of the jellyfish which make it less likely to survive out of water. (6 marks)

Feature 1 ....
Reason ....
....
Feature 2 ....
Reason ....
....
Feature 3 ....
Reason ....
....

[SEG 1994]

ANSWER

a Coelenterates: animal E.
  Annelids: animal D.
  Molluscs: animal B.
  Arachnids: animal F.
  Insects: animal C.

b Feature 1: The jellyfish cannot move out of water. The jellyfish cannot move under a rock on the beach like the crab can.
  Feature 2: The jellyfish does not have an exoskeleton.
  The crab will be protected by the exoskeleton, the jellyfish is more likely to 'dry up' in the sun.

Feature 3: The jellyfish needs the water to bring it food.

The jellyfish will 'starve' if it is not in water, the crab can go and search for its food and move to a rock pool.

Revision sheet

Reproduction

1 a What are two types of reproduction?
   b How do they differ?
2 Distinguish between pollination and fertilisation in plants.
3 a What is a gene?
   b How does a gene 'work'?
4 What is the difference between mitosis and meiosis?
5 How many chromosomes are there in a human:
   a muscle cell?
   b ovum?
6 A person with brown eyes can be thought of as having a pair of alleles BB.
   a What is their phenotype?
   b What is their genotype?
   c What would be the genotype of someone with blue eyes, if the gene for blue eyes is recessive to brown eyes?
7 What do the following terms mean:
   a mutation?
   b selective breeding?
   c genetic engineering?

Evolution

1 What is meant by the term 'evolution'?
2 What evidence for evolution can we get by studying fossils?
3 What is meant by:
   a variation?
   b survival of the fittest?
   c natural selection?
4 How might organisms become extinct?

Classification

1 a Name the five kingdoms to which all living organisms belong.
   b Place each of these in one of the five kingdoms:

human, mushroom, daisy, salmonella bacterium, amoeba.
2 Fill in the spaces to show the type of divisions between 'Kingdom' and 'Species'
   Kingdom
   ....
   ....
   ....
   ....
   ....
3 What is the definition of a species?
4 What is the species of this organism: Pieris brassicae?

Revision sheet answers

Reproduction

1 a Asexual and sexual reproduction.
   b Asexual – identical offspring to the parent and each other, one parent. Sexual reproduction – offspring different from each other and the parent, two parents, gametes fuse at fertilisation.
2 Pollination – carrying the male gamete to the female gamete.
   Fertilisation – fusion (joining) of the male and female gamete.
3 a A gene is a section of DNA.
   b A gene has the instructions for the production of a protein in the cell. (3 bases of the DNA molecule 'code' for an amino acid.)
4 Mitosis – 2 cells produced from each parent cell; these are identical and contain the same number of chromosomes.
   Meiosis – 4 'cells' (called gametes) produced; these are different from each other and contain half the chromosome number of the parent cell.
5 a Muscle cell – 46 chromosomes/23 pairs.
   b Ovum – 23 chromosomes.
6 a Phenotype – brown eyes.
   b Genotype – BB.
   c Genotype of blue eyes – bb.
7 a Mutation – sudden change in the amount or structure of the DNA.
   b Selective breeding – choosing organisms with desired characteristics and carrying out a breeding programme to obtain offspring with desired characteristics.

c Genetic engineering – the processes involved in changing the genetic material of an organism by human intervention.

Evolution

1 Evolution – used to describe the changes from simple organisms to more complex organisms that have occurred over millions of years.

2 Evidence for evolution from the fossil record:
   – the structure and mode of life of organisms that once lived.
   – the time (in terms of the age of the Earth) when the organisms lived.
   – the structure of the organisms that are now extinct.
   – the similarities and differences between organisms that are now extinct and those that are living.

3 a Variation – how organisms of one species are different.
   b Survival of the fittest – organisms of one species that are well adapted to their mode of life and therefore more likely to have offspring. Natural selection – the processes by which the adaptations (as in 'survival of the fittest') are passed on to the offspring.

4 When the conditions of the environment change and the organisms are not adapted to survive these changes.

Classification

1 a Prokaryotae, Protoctista, Fungi, Plantae, Animalia.
   b Human – Kingdom Animalia.
      Mushroom – Kingdom Fungi.
      Daisy – Kingdom Plantae.
      Salmonella Bacterium – Kingdom Prokaryotae.
      Amoeba – Kingdom Protoctista.

2 Kingdom
   Phylum
   Class
   Order
   Family
   Genus
   Species

3 Organisms in a species are able to breed successfully and their offspring must be able to breed successfully too.

4 brassicae.

Student Answer with Comments

a Domestic animals and cultivated plants can be improved by selective breeding.
   i Describe the process of selective breeding.
   In the process of selective breeding parents with the desired resistances (eg resistance to disease or high milk yields) are bred to form a better more refined offspring. ② (3 marks)

   Yes, important to state desired characteristics. Implies a breeding programme. As there are 3 marks you could stress that the parents must be of the same species.

   ii State **two** characteristics a farmer could improve in his wheat crop by selective breeding.
   Resistance to disease and shorten the length of time needed by the wheat before harvesting. ② (2 marks)

   This is OK, but this depends a lot on the weather – better to say shortening of the length of wheat stalk.

b Tall, high-yielding tomato plants are deliberately crossed with short, disease-resistant tomato plants.

Fig 1

The genotype of the tall plant is **HH** and that of the short plant is **hh**. The dominant allele is **H**.
   i Write down the genotype of the F_1 generation plants.
   Hh ✓ ① (1 mark)

   ii What proportion of the F_1 generation plants would be tall?
   All of them ✓ ① (1 mark)

   iii The F_1 generation plants are allowed to self-pollinate. The seeds from this cross are grown. State and *explain* the probable proportions of tall and short plants in the offspring.

	H	h
H	HH	Hh
h	Hh	hh

As the plants are self-pollinated, one in four of the offspring will be short.

② (3 marks)

You missed the explain – *discuss how tall is* dominant *to short.*

iv The F_1 hybrid plant is very popular with tomato growers.

Suggest **one** reason why commercial tomato growers may prefer to grow F_2 plants rather than the freely-pollinated ones.

In the F_1 generation all the offspring were tall. The growers know all the plants will be tall at F_1 whereas 1 in 4 will be short at F_2

(1 mark)

Why is this an advantage?
Might they have more fruit?

v A gardener grows twelve of the F_1 hybrid seedlings. The seeds are all grown in the same conditions. Eleven of the plants are normal but one has white leaves. Suggest how this could have occurred.

In this plant there is no dominant gene for green leaves. Instead it only has recessive genes for white leaves.

(2 marks)

This answer is not clear – you need to discuss 'a mutation' so that the white plant has been unable to make chlorophyll.

vi Suggest and explain what will happen to the white leaved seedling.

It will die as there is no chlorophyll in its leaves. The chlorophyll is the green substance and is essential in photosynthesis to produce the food for the plant.

② (2 marks)

More correct to say that the chlorophyll absorbs the light.

c Genetic engineers can be successful in changing the characteristics of some plants and animals. Scientists are trying to transfer the nitrogen-fixing ability associated with plants such as peas into other crops such as cereals.

 i Describe how the characteristics of an organism can be changed by genetic engineering.

The genes which ✓ control the characteristics can be changed. The genes are miniscule strips of DNA on the double helix which makes up a chromosome. These strips can be altered by engineers.

① (3 marks)

You've described a gene – not really genetic engineering – a gene from a chromosome in one organism can be removed and placed into a chromosome in another organism.

ii Suggest **two** advantages of having cereal crops which are nitrogen-fixing. ✓

No fertilisers would be needed. When the crop was harvested the soil would be replenished with nitrogen and immediately ready for a new crop.

② ✓ (2 marks)

iii In developing new varieties of plant by genetic engineering, what danger should scientists be aware of and what precautions should they take?

No answer given!

Much genetic engineering involves bacteria – concern that harmful bacteria may be produced. Caution and security during the programme is needed.

$13/23$ (3 marks)
[MEG]

An exam question for you to try

Genetic disorders are caused by certain genes. The genes causing genetic disorders are almost always recessive. One genetic disorder is sickle cell anaemia. In sickle cell anaemia the red blood cells are sickle – shaped and eventually break down. They do this when the amount of oxygen in the blood is lowered. A sickle-shaped red cell and a normal red cell are shown in the diagrams below.
The sickle cell gene has spread in some populations. It started in the black population of Africa, where, now, about 40 per cent of the population have the gene.
Sickle cell anaemia makes people resistant to at least one type of malaria.

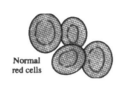

Normal
red cells

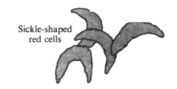

Sickle-shaped
red cells

Fig 2

a   i In what part of the cell are the genes found?

....
....(1 mark)

ii What is meant by a recessive gene?

....
....
....
....(3 marks)

iii The diagram below shows the red cell genes
for a mother and a father.

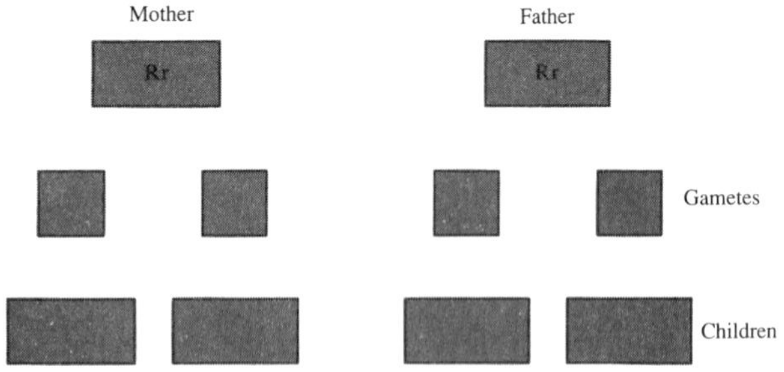

Mother   Father

Rr   Rr

Gametes

Children

Fig 3

The dominant gene for the normal red cells is R.
The recessive gene for the sickle cells is r.

A Complete the diagram above to show the genes
present in the gametes and the children. (2 marks)

B How many of the children will be expected to
suffer from sickle cell anaemia?

....(1 mark)

b   i Suggest why Africans living in high altitudes
may develop the symptoms of sickle cell
anaemia earlier than those living at low
altitudes.

....
....(1 mark)

ii Explain why the gene for sickle cell anaemia is
continuing to spread amongst Africans.

....
....
....(2 marks)
[SEG 1994]

Answer

a   i In the nucleus (or as part of a chromosome or
part of the DNA).

ii The characteristic determined by a recessive
gene is only shown when both genes are
recessive. If there is a recessive gene and a
dominant gene, the characteristic of the
dominant gene will be shown; it 'hides' the
recessive gene. We show a recessive gene by a
lower case letter e.g. b and a dominant gene by
an upper case letter, e.g. B. *(Don't be vague
and write an answer such as : 'It is weaker
than a dominant gene'.)*

iii A Gametes R r   R r
Children RR Rr Rr rr
B 25% or 1 in 4.

b   i There is a lower concentration of oxygen in the
air at high altitudes. This will cause the
formation of sickle cells.

ii If an adult suffers from sickle-cell anaemia, he
or she is less likely to suffer from malaria. This
is an advantage and may allow the adult to
have more children. This would contribute to
the gene for sickle-cell anaemia spreading.

6

Our environment

Our environment	Midland (MEG)				Northern (NEAB)			London (ULEAC)			Southern (SEG)		Welsh (WJEC)
	Own	Nuffield	Salters	Suffolk	Co-ordinated	Modular	Modular GASP	Combined	Co-ordinated	Modular	Double	Modular	Co-ordinated
ECOLOGY													
Important terms	✓	✓	✓	✓	✓	✓	✓	✓	✓	✓	✓	✓	✓
Food chains and webs	✓	✓	✓	✓	✓	✓	✓	✓	✓	✓	✓	✓	✓
Decomposers	✓	✓	✓	✓	✓	✓	✓	✓	✓	✓	✓	✓	✓
Pyramids	✓	✓	✓	✓	✓	✓	✓	✓	✓	✓	✓	✓	✓
NATURAL CYCLES AND ENERGY FLOW													
Carbon cycle	✓	✓	✓	✓	✓	✓	✓	✓	✓	✓	✓	✓	✓
Greenhouse effect	H	✓	✓	✓	✓	✓	✓	✓	✓	✓	✓	✓	✓
Ozone depletion	H	H	✓			H	H			H		✓	H
Nitrogen cycle	✓	✓	✓	✓	✓	✓	✓	✓	✓	✓	✓	✓	✓
Water cycle	✓	✓	✓	✓	✓	✓	✓	✓	✓	✓	✓	✓	✓
Acid rain	✓	✓	✓	✓	✓	✓	✓	✓	✓	✓	✓	✓	✓
Energy flow	✓	✓	✓	✓	✓	✓	✓	✓	✓	✓	✓	✓	✓
Managing food production	H	H	✓	H	H	H	H	H	H	H	H	H	H

Ecology

What is ecology?

Ecology is the study of organisms in their natural environment. It includes ideas about the number of organisms, how they are distributed and how different organisms affect one another. Such a study is important in making judgements about how best to protect the natural environment and also in managing ecosystems. For example, it could help to maximize food production in agriculture or fish farming.

The language of ecology

There are a number of terms that you need to know. Sometimes they seem quite similar so spend some time on really sorting out the differences.

A habitat

This is the place where an organism lives, for example a pond. Each habitat has its own characteristics. These are likely to change during the day and with the seasons, but the variations are likely to be the same each year.

Environment

This means more than just the habitat. It includes the conditions there as well. There are two sorts of conditions (sometimes called environmental factors):

- Physical factors:
  Light intensity, type of soil, temperature, etc.
- Biological factors:
  How other organisms have an effect – e.g. by competing for food, by one organism being a predator, etc.

Population

A population is a group of organisms of the same species (see p 107) living in the same habitat. The size of the population is only likely to be static if the birth rate balances the death rate. Some factors which affect the size of a population are:

- Change in the amount of food – for example, an increase in the harvest mice population is likely after a bumper crop of wheat.
- Arrival of predators in the habitat – for example, seagulls feeding on a different area of shore will reduce the limpet population there.

- Introduction of disease – for example, myxomatosis reduced the population of rabbits.
- Change in some of the physical factors – for example, the growth of algae on the surface of a pond (due to eutrophication) may be so great that light can not penetrate into the pond. Deeper pond weeds then cannot photosynthesise and so die.

These changes in population are never straightforward and often involve competition between organisms (see below).

Community

A number of different populations (of both plants and animals) that live in the same habitat.

Ecosystem

A number of different communities and their environments. For example a seashore could be thought of as an ecosystem, made up of environments associated with the rock pools, rocks and sand, and the area of the beach which is covered by the tides during the day. The organisms in an ecosystem have many links with each other, in terms of the cycles of nutrients and the flow of energy.

What is common about ecosystems?

It does not matter which ecosystem you study. All are likely to have the same basic plan. There will be plants, plant-eating animals (herbivores), animals that eat other animals (carnivores) and decomposers (which break down dead and decaying organic materials). Each organism will be adapted to its own way of life. What is different about different eco-systems is how the organisms are adapted to the physical conditions, and how the organisms in the environment inter-relate with each other.

Food chains and webs

By studying the organisms in an ecosystem it is possible to work out their feeding relationships. The simplest version of this is called a food chain, where each type of organism is eaten by one another. Notice the direction of the arrow; it shows how the energy is transferred in this feeding relationship.
(see p 128)

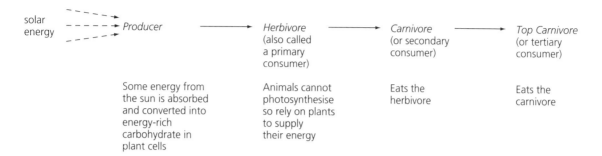

NB. Decomposers operate throughout the food chain to release the nutrients from dead and decaying organisms into the environment

Fig 1 A model for a food chain

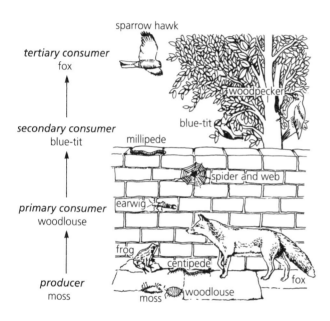

Fig 2 A food chain for a garden showing the trophic levels

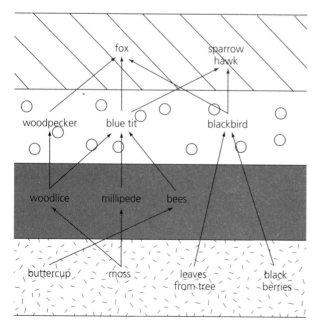

Fig 3 A food web for a garden showing trophic levels

Each different feeding level – producer, primary consumer, secondary consumer and tertiary consumer is called a trophic level.

In an ecosystem it is unlikely that the organisms are linked together in a simple chain like this. For example, when thinking about the wall in Fig 3 you will realise that blue-tits do not just eat woodlice and the woodlice are likely to be eaten by more than just blue tits. Woodpeckers also eat woodlice. If you link up all the organisms to show their feeding relationships, you produce a food web.

The organisms can be divided up into trophic levels as in the food chain.

Where do decomposers fit into food chains and webs?

Decomposers can't really be placed in a food chain or web. They feed on any dead and decaying organisms. As they do so they release nutrients back into the environment. They are particularly important in the carbon and nitrogen cycles (see p 122–125).

Conditions which increase the activity of micro-organisms and therefore speed up the rate of decay are:

- *moisture*: needed for micro-organisms to multiply, and those that have spores need moisture for them to germinate. (The ancient Egyptians made use of this by mummifying the bodies of kings to preserve them. This prevented moisture being present.)
- *warmth*: micro-organisms grow best and therefore reproduce when it is warm. (Freezing food keeps it fresh as microbes cannot reproduce in sufficient numbers to break down the tissues).
- *oxygen*: many micro-organisms need oxygen to respire. Without oxygen they respire anaerobically and form acid as a product. As this builds up the micro-organisms cannot live and decay slows down or is stopped.

A pyramid of numbers

If you could count all the organisms in an eco-system you would find that there were fewer as you went from the producer trophic level to the tertiary consumer trophic level. These numbers can be drawn in a pyramid of numbers where each horizontal bar represents the trophic level and the number of organisms present.

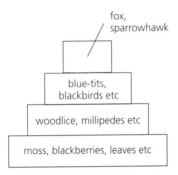

Fig 4 A pyramid of numbers for the garden

Often, however, this is not helpful. For example, in the garden a rose bush is likely to have a large population of aphids. These are consumed by ladybirds which are the prey of a few birds. If a pyramid of numbers is drawn it would not look much like a pyramid, because there is only one rose bush involved.

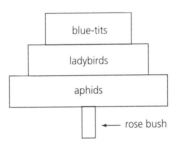

Fig 5 A pyramid of numbers for a rose bush

A pyramid of biomass

In cases like the rose bush mentioned above it is usually more accurate to construct a pyramid of biomass. This shows the total dry mass (so that water doesn't upset the figure) of all the organisms in the trophic level for that habitat. In this case the rose bush would form the longest horizontal bar.
Both the pyramid of numbers and the pyramid of biomass have disadvantages. They are usually constructed at one time in the year and the mass of one of the organisms may vary greatly throughout the

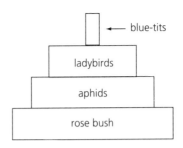

Fig 6 A pyramid of biomass for a rose bush

year. For example it would make a big difference to the mass if it were winter or summer when the mass of a deciduous tree like oak was measured! The most accurate model of a food web in an ecosystem is to construct a pyramid of energy covering the whole year (see p 128).

QUESTION

A community in a woodland consists of oak trees, caterpillars, voles and owls. Many thousands of caterpillars feed on the leaves of a single oak tree. A single vole may eat a hundred caterpillars each day. An owl may eat three voles in one day.
The diagram shows four pyramids of numbers.

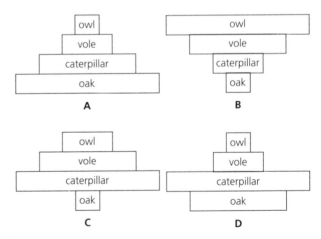

Fig 7

i Which pyramid of numbers is correct for this woodland community?
....(1 mark)

ii What is meant by the term biomass?
....
....
....(1 mark)

iii Draw a pyramid of biomass for the woodland community. (2 marks)

[MEG]

ANSWER

i C

ii It is the mass of the organisms. *If you include the term 'dry mass' this is also acceptable – although in a pyramid of this type it is difficult to obtain the 'dry mass'! Do not name individual species of animals or plants.*

iii *There are 2 marks here and you must make sure that:*

- You draw a pyramid shape for biomass – *the ones in the question are for numbers.*
- That the organisms are in the correct order – *producer at the bottom. You can get the correct order from the other pyramids in the question; for example*

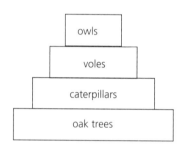

Fig 8

QUESTION

The diagram below shows a food web for a wood.

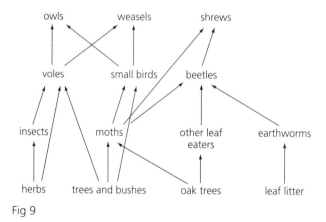

Fig 9

a The diagrams below show a pyramid of numbers and a pyramid of biomass for the same wood.

  i Name one organism from the level labelled X.

  ....(1 mark)

  ii Explain, as fully as you can, why the level labelled Y is such a different width in the two pyramids.

....
....
....
....
....(3 marks)

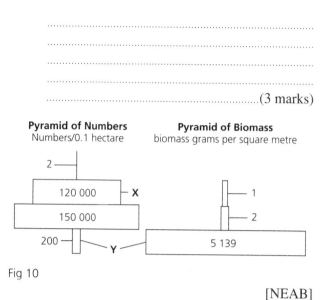

Fig 10

[NEAB]

ANSWER

a i Vole or small bird or beetle.

   ii Oak trees make up a large part of the producer level of the pyramid. There are few oak trees (so in the pyramid of numbers the level is not very wide) *but* their mass is large (so in the pyramid of biomass the level is wide).

Pesticides and food webs

Pesticides in particular may build up in organisms as the trophic level increases. This happens when the pesticides are stable substances and not digested by the organism to which they are applied. The effects of using DDT as an insecticide were noticed about 30 years ago when many organisms not directly sprayed by DDT were affected by it.

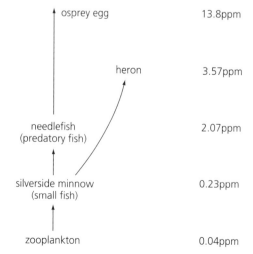

The concentration of DDT is expressed in parts per million; the concentration of DDT that is sprayed was 0.00005ppm

Fig 11 The build up of DDT in food webs

The use of DDT in Britain has been banned since the mid 1960s. Pesticides used today are more specific to the pests that are targeted. Also, they break down more quickly and thus do not build up in food chains.

Prey and predators

Predators eat all or part of other animals, which are called the prey. As you would expect there are usually fewer predators than the prey upon which they feed. The size of the prey population depends upon the amount of food available for them, and this in turn affects the size of the predator population. If the numbers of prey and predators is observed over a period of time, then the populations appear to go in cycles.

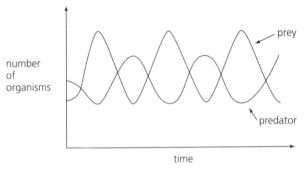

You can always work out which line is which. The highest peaks belong to the **prey** (there will be more of them than the predators) and the peak in the population of the **predators** occurs after the peak in the population of the prey.

Fig 12 A model predator – prey cycle

Predators are usually well adapted for their mode of life. They tend to be fast, quiet in movement and have adaptations for catching and killing their prey. If they are mammals they are likely to have stereoscopic vision. Predators such as the lion may only spend a small part of each day in seeking food. The prey on the other hand may be much slower-moving, and if they are mammals have eyes on the side of their head so that they have a greater field of vision. Herbivorous mammals which are prey, such as the gnu which is preyed on by the lion, tend to spend a large amount of each day in feeding. There is much less energy in a volume of grass than there is in the same volume of gnu!

Biological control using predators

There is much interest in the use of biological control to destroy pests. Natural predators of the pests are used to control their numbers. In the 1880s citrus trees were imported from Australia into America. A scale insect fed on the trees by sucking out the contents from the phloem. The crop of limes, oranges and lemons was much reduced. Ladybird beetles, natural predators of the scale insects, were introduced from Australia and controlled the scale insect infestation. It has been noted that if the population of ladybird beetles declines, for example due to the use of insecticides, then the population of scale insects increases again.

QUESTION

The snowshoe hare lives in the forests of North America. It feeds on the twigs and shoots of shrubs and bushes. It has been hunted for its fur for over 100 years.

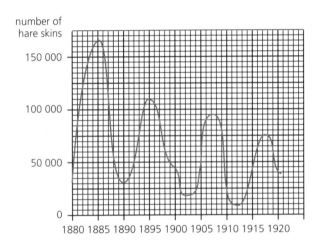

Fig 13

a Describe the way in which the population of snowshoe hares changed between 1880 and 1920.

....

....

....(3 marks)

b i The Canadian lynx lives mainly by preying on the snowshoe hare.

Sketch a line on the graph to show how the population of Canadian lynx may have changed during this time. (2 marks)

ii Suggest two reasons, other than hunting and predation, for the change in the size of the snowshoe hare population during this time.

....

....(2 marks)

[MEG]

ANSWER

a *There are 3 marks here – so look at the graph carefully:*
  - The population is declining.
  - The population is fluctuating, or going up and down.
  - The population is alternately rising and falling every 10 years.
b i *As the lynx is a predator of the snowshoe rabbit:*
    - The population will rise and fall.
    - The rise of the lynx population will follow the rise of the snowshoe rabbit and the fall will similarly follow the fall of the snowshoe rabbit. Your curve should highlight these points.
   ii *There are many suitable answers here. Think of them in terms of competition for food, space and a mate. For example:*
    - Lack of food, competition for food.
    - Competition for a habitat, destruction of the habitat, change in the climate affecting the habitat.
    - Competition for a mate, disease so unable to mate.

How are adaptation and competition important in a habitat?

Adaptation

If you study an ecosystem you will notice how the organisms are adapted to survive there. Each organism has its own characteristics and way of life to enable it to live in that environment. These adaptations may be structural features; for example, the stick insect which resembles a twig and so is less likely to be preyed on by birds. Alternatively, the characteristics may be in lifestyle; for example, bluebells and other woodland plants flower and form seeds early in the spring when the trees have not formed leaves which would prevent the necessary light reaching them for photosynthesis. The adaptation of each individual organism to its habitat is important when considering the abundance and distribution of all the organisms in the habitat.

Competition

Competition in an ecosystem occurs when two or more organisms compete for the same resources that are in short supply. One organism will grow and reproduce more quickly than the other, and in some cases one of the organisms may die. The organisms may be of the same species or of different species. Competition is important in considering the distribution of organisms in a habitat and can have an effect on the survival of whole species (see p 105).

Competition in plants

Plants compete for:
- light
- water
- minerals from the soil

Some plants may compete for an insect to pollinate them, for somewhere to germinate and for carbon dioxide (in a dense crop). Plants rarely compete for space.

Dispersal of seeds is one mechanism for reducing competition between offspring of the same parent (see p 91).

Competition in animals

Animals compete for:
- food
- space (for a territory, shelter from predators, for nesting, for overwintering)
- a mate

An important idea is that no two species can exist together indefinitely in the same community if they occupy the same niche (that is their role in the ecosystem). For example, shags and cormorants are both birds that nest on cliffs and feed by diving for fish in the sea. They are often both seen by bird watchers looking out to sea. They may appear to be in competition but in fact the cormorant nests on broad cliff edges and feeds from the bottom of shallow water. The shag nests on narrower cliff edges and feeds further out to sea on fish from the surface water. Competition between the two is thus much less than it at first appears.

How do communities change?

In any community where there is competition between organisms, whether plants or animals, there will be a change in the community. Imagine a bare rock face. Lichens can colonise the rock as they have few needs. They need few nutrients and can withstand the harsh conditions such as lack of water and temperature fluctuations. After a time, the lichens may well cause some erosion of the rock, soil and humus will be blown against it and settle into crevasses on the rock. Moisture will be retained there. These changing conditions allow mosses to grow. After a time the moss growth may shade out light from the lichens. Further build up of soil encourages other species, such as ferns, to establish themselves. Gradually, animals such as molluscs are able to inhabit this region. Fungi also colonise the area and the breakdown of organic matter increases. This gradual process of change is called succession. It does not go on forever. Eventually a more stable community is formed. In this, when organisms die they are replaced by others of the same sort. This is called a climax community. If the land in this country were left for succession to occur, the climax community would have oak trees as the dominant species.

Natural cycles and energy flow

What is a cycle?

While you are reading this you are breathing out carbon dioxide. This compound contains the element carbon. The very same carbon atoms may have been part of the atmosphere around the Earth millions of years ago! Atoms cannot be created or destroyed; this means that the same carbon atoms have always been in circulation. It is this circulation of carbon atoms, and those of other elements, that is meant by the term cycle. Quite simply, the atoms of the element move round and round, as opposed to a chain where there would be a beginning and an end. When thinking about living things, the important cycles are those of carbon, nitrogen and the compound water.

The carbon cycle

Carbon is a very important element to organisms. All organisms contain carbon; it is part of all carbohydrate, fat and protein molecules. These molecules are so vital to living things that they are sometimes called 'the molecules of life'.
The amount of carbon dioxide in the atmosphere fluctuates about 0.04%. It varies depending on when and where the sample was taken. For example, there would be more carbon dioxide in a sample from a field of wheat during the night when it is respiring,

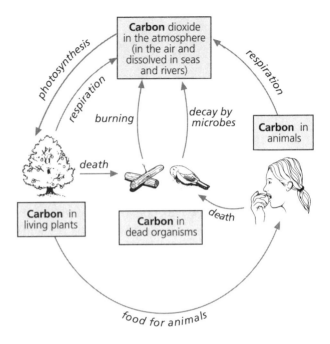

Fig 1 The carbon cycle

than during a bright sunny day when photosynthesis is occurring. It is now thought, however, that the amount of carbon dioxide in the atmosphere is increasing. This change has been called the greenhouse effect. It is thought to be mainly due to the burning of more fossil fuels, such as coal and oil, and the destruction of large areas of forest. These removed carbon dioxide during photosynthesis. Also the increased activity of the microbes produces extra carbon dioxide in the newly cleared soil. The increased amount of carbon dioxide acts as an insulator and stops infra-red radiation escaping from the Earth – hence the name 'greenhouse gas'. It has been suggested that this will cause the polar ice caps to melt, flooding some coastal regions, and that the general change in the climate will turn more of the Earth's surface into desert.

QUESTION

The diagram represents the carbon cycle.

a i Which process is represented by the arrow labelled A?
    ....(1 mark)

   ii Which process is represented by the arrow labelled C?
    ....(1 mark)

   iii What is represented by box B?
    ....(1 mark)

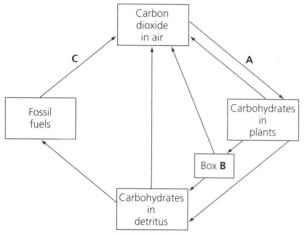

Fig 2

iv Write the letter D clearly alongside an arrow which represents a process brought about by microbes.

....(1 mark)

b The human population has grown enormously over the last 200 years and is still growing. Suggest how the continuing growth can affect the carbon cycle.

....
....
....
....
....(4 marks)

[ULEAC]

ANSWER

a i Photosynthesis.
   ii Combustion.
   iii Carbohydrate in animals.
   iv This should be next to the arrow going from 'carbohydrate in detritus' to 'carbon dioxide in the air'.
b *There are many answers that you could give here. Try to give a reason for each point that you mention. For example:*
   – More energy will be needed *so* more carbon dioxide will be added to the air by combustion.
   – Large areas of plants, for example forests, may be cut down to build new estates of houses, *so* less carbon dioxide will be removed from the air by photosynthesis.
   – Grass may need to be turned into fields of crops for food, which are then harvested. Therefore, less carbon dioxide will be removed from the air by photosynthesis.

– More people means more respiration, and this will increase the carbon dioxide content in the air.

Gases other than carbon dioxide have a 'greenhouse effect' but the mechanism is not straightforward. Important factors are their strength relative to carbon dioxide, the life span of the molecules and their global annual increase.

Gas	strength relative to carbon dioxide	life span of molecules (in years)	global annual increase (%)
carbon dioxide	1	15	0.6
methane	30	20	1
CFCs and halons *	15,000	100	7
dinitrogen oxide	150	150	0.3
tropospheric oxygen	2,000	several weeks	2

* some CFCs have a lifespan of up to 20,000 years

What is the difference between the greenhouse effect and ozone depletion?

Ozone depletion
The composition of the atmosphere is more or less the same wherever you go on the Earth and up to 16km above it. (This assumes that you take a sample of unpolluted air!) There is now evidence that this natural balance is being changed due to the activities of humans, resulting in the so called 'hole in the ozone layer'. Ozone (O_3) molecules are being made and broken up all the time in the stratosphere by natural processes. It is thought that the balance is upset by CFCs (propellants that were used in aerosol sprays), and supersonic aircraft. Gases from these break down the ozone and reduce the amount in the stratosphere, forming the 'hole in the ozone layer'. It is thought that this reduction in ozone may be responsible for the increase in skin cancers.

QUESTION

a The number of vehicles has risen greatly over the last thirty years. If this increase continues in the future, give two ways it could effect the biosphere. (2 marks)

1 ....
2 ....

b Describe two steps which are being taken to reduce pollution from motor vehicles. (2 marks)

1 ....
2 ....

c Large areas of Earth contain forests. Parts of these forests have been destroyed over the past eighty years. Explain the main reasons for this.

....
....
....(2 marks)

d In the future, the biosphere may well change as a result of the 'Greenhouse' effect.

  i Describe and explain the cause of the 'Greenhouse' effect.

  ....
  ....
  ....(2 marks)

  ii Give two possible results of the 'Greenhouse' effect and, for each, explain how the lives of future generations might be affected. (4 marks)

  1 ....
  ....
  ....
  2 ....
  ....
  ....

[SEG 1994]

ANSWER

a *Although the question asks you to* give *two ways, you ought to explain how each would affect the biosphere.* There are many answers, for example:
  – Nitrogen oxides in the exhaust would lead to more acid rain.
  – More roads would need to be built and this would destroy some habitats.
  – More exhaust fumes could result in more asthma or lung diseases.

b *There are many answers here, for example:*
  – Ensuring that all new cars use lead free petrol.
  – Ensuring that all new cars have catalytic converters.
  – Carrying out research into fuels that produce less pollution than petrol.
  – The MOT test now tests vehicles to ensure that the exhaust emissions meet regulations.

c *There are many answers here, for example:*
  – The land is used for growing crops.
  – The land is used to build new estates of houses or to build roads.
  – The wood from the trees is used as fuel or to make paper.
  It would also be correct to explain that the increase in the population has meant that more forests need to be cut down.

d i *A common mistake is to mix up the* greenhouse effect *and destroying the* ozone layer – *make sure that you know the difference! There are only 2 marks available so you must explain the important points clearly and concisely.* For example:
  – There has been a build up of carbon dioxide (due to the burning of fossil fuels) and deforestation, which means that there are not so many trees to remove the carbon dioxide during photosynthesis.
  – Other gases such as methane and dinitrogen oxide also have a 'greenhouse effect'.
  – These gases act as an insulator around the Earth and prevent infra-red radiation escaping from the Earth.

  ii *Make sure that you explain the effect of each of the changes that you mention.*
  There are many suitable answers, for example:
  – The sea level may rise; this will make many people in low lying coastal areas homeless, and cause an increased population in those areas of the country not affected.
  – The climate of this country will be more tropical, and pests that are now only found in warmer countries will come to this country.
  – Pests (of crops) that are normally killed by cold weather will not be destroyed and may eat more of the crops.

The nitrogen cycle

Nitrogen is an element that is found in all proteins. It is important for growth in both plants and animals. Although about 80% of the air is nitrogen this cannot be used directly by animals and only a few plants can actually take the nitrogen from the air and use it to form proteins. An understanding of the nitrogen cycle is particularly important to agriculture.

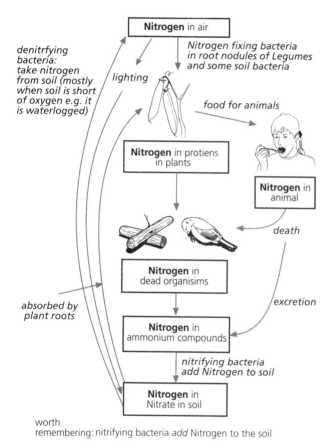

worth
remembering: nitrifying bacteria *add* Nitrogen to the soil

Fig 3 The nitrogen cycle

Humans can affect the nitrogen cycle. Continually growing crops in the same patch of soil removes minerals, particularly nitrogen, from the soil. The crops are removed and the nitrogen in them is used by the consumer. Only in the unlikely event of the crops being 'ploughed in' would the nitrogen be returned to the soil. One way of ensuring that there is sufficient nitrogen in the soil is to add fertiliser to the soil. If too much fertiliser is added then some of it will leach from the soil and increase the nitrogen content of the water into which it drains. This causes algae and pond weed at the surface to grow rapidly and produce a carpet-like effect. Plants below therefore cannot get enough light to carry out

photosynthesis. If this process cannot take place then the deeper plants will die. Decomposers multiply and this reduces the oxygen content of the water. Eventually only anaerobic bacteria will grow in such water. An ever thickening layer of mud forms at the bottom of the pond. This whole process is called eutrophication.

Adding fertilisers to the soil is one way of replacing the nitrogen that has been removed by the previous crop of plants. Other methods include crop rotation where the same type of plant is not grown on the same field continuously. Instead, different crops are grown on a rota system. The rota includes growing a field of clover or peas, and this increases the nitrate level without the use of artificial fertilisers.

The Haber process is an industrial process in which nitrogen is taken from the air and reacted with hydrogen to form ammonia (see p205).

Types of fertiliser

The fertilisers may be organic (either manure or treated sewage) or inorganic (made synthetically). An organic fertiliser improves the structure of the soil as well; it makes the soil less compacted and thus increases the amount of air in the soil, aiding the take up of minerals (see p 22) and also helping the soil to retain water. The nutrients are released slowly. Inorganic fertilisers do not improve the structure of the soil and do not remain in the soil as long as organic fertilisers. They are more likely to cause pollution.

QUESTION

The list below shows five types of organism involved in the nitrogen cycle.

A scavengers
B saprophytes
C nitrogen fixing bacteria
D nitrifying bacteria
E denitrifying bacteria

The table below shows the roles of some organisms involved in the nitrogen cycle. Match the type of organism to each role by writing the correct letter in each box. You may use each letter once, more than once or not at all. The first one has been done for you.

Letter	Organisms and their role in the nitrogen cycle
......C......	Soil bacteria which use nitrogen from the air to make nitrates
....	Larger organisms which eat waste organic material and shred it, increasing the surface area for microbes to act upon.
....	Bacteria which live in the root nodules of pea plants and use nitrogen from the air to help pea plants make protein.
....	Bacteria and fungi which break down dead organic material with enzymes and produce ammonia as a waste product.
....	Bacteria which convert ammonia to nitrate.
....	Bacteria which convert nitrite to nitrate.
....	Bacteria which release nitrogen gas from nitrate.

(Total 6 marks)

[ULEAC]

ANSWER

A
C
B
D
D
E

QUESTION

Leaves fall off trees and become leaf litter. Explain as fully as you can, how the nitrogen from the protein molecules in the leaf litter eventually becomes part of the protein molecules in new leaves. (4 marks)

....
....
....
....
....

[NEAB]

ANSWER

Micro-organisms break down the leaves. The proteins are converted into ammonium compounds. These ammonium compounds are converted into nitrates by nitrifying bacteria. The nitrates can then be absorbed by the roots of the tree. The nitrogen in the nitrate is used by the tree to make proteins. *(It is worth remembering the word nitrifying – look at Fig 3 if you need to sort out the difference between nitrifying and denitrifying bacteria.)*

How do micro-organisms fit into these cycles?

Micro-organisms (known as decomposers) such as bacteria and fungi digest the dead remains and waste products of organisms. As they do this, the minerals are returned to the soil. The minerals are then available for absorption through the roots of plants.

The water (or hydrological) cycle

Just over 70% of the Earth's surface is covered by water and most of this is in the oceans. Only about 3% of the Earth's water is fresh and very little of this is liquid – most is frozen at the poles. Water is very important to organisms:

- chemical substances in cells are dissolved in water.
- reactions in cells take place in water.
- chemical substances are transported around plants and animals in water.
- water is one of the raw materials of photosynthesis.

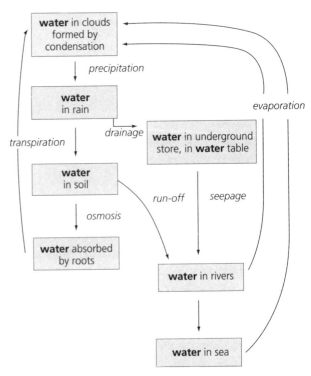

Fig 4 The water (or hydrological) cycle

• more organisms have water as a habitat than air or land.

The movement of water through the environment is therefore very important.

Water evaporates, for example from a river. Water is also returned to the atmosphere by transpiration from plants. It is frequently difficult to separate the two processes and the term evapotranspiration is now used to mean both.

What is meant by 'acid rain'?

All rain is acid. Rain as it falls reacts with carbon dioxide in the air to form carbonic acid (H_2CO_3). This is a weak acid (pH 5.5). It reacts with rocks and buildings containing 'carbonate', for example limestone and causes them to erode. (This is how the underground limestone caverns are formed that pot holers enjoy.) Fuels such as coal and oil (and its products such as petrol) contain sulphur. When these fuels are burnt they produce sulphur dioxide and nitrogen oxides (as well as carbon dioxide and water). When sulphur dioxide and nitrogen oxides react with water in the air they form sulphuric acid and nitric acid. These have a much lower pH (as low as pH2) than carbonic acid, and hence the name 'acid rain' is used to describe rain containing these pollutants.

Some effects of acid rain

• Lakes in rocks such as basalt and granite may have a low pH. Lakes in carbonate rocks such as limestone will be nearer neutral, due to neutralisation of the acid rain.
• As it drains through soil, acid rain dissolves minerals needed for plant growth, such as calcium and iron. This is called leaching. Plants lacking minerals are weakened (see p 31).
• Acid rain in soils dissolves some metals that 'normal' rain cannot, such as cadmium and aluminium. These are toxic to some plants and also build up in food chains.
• Leaves on trees are damaged, and the trees themselves may die as they are unable to photosynthesise.
• Micro-organisms in the soil may be killed, upsetting the natural cycles.

QUESTION

The production of sulphur dioxide in most of Europe has been reduced since 1980. This is shown on the map below, together with planned targets for reduction of sulphur dioxide by the year 2000.

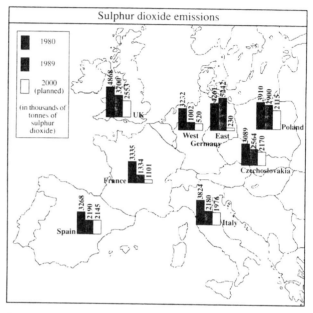

Fig 5

a   i   What percentage reduction in sulphur dioxide production was made by the UK (United Kingdom) between 1980 and 1989?
....
....(1 mark)

   ii Which country was the biggest contributor to acid rain between 1980 and 1989?
....(1 mark)

   iii Name the two countries which are closest to reaching their planned targets for the year 2000. (1 mark)
       1................................   2...

b Give an account of the effects of acid rain on the environment.
....
....
....(3 marks)
[WJEC]

ANSWER

a   i 24%.
   ii East Germany.
   iii Spain and Italy.

b *Some suitable answers:*
   – Reduces the pH of lakes and rivers, which harms the organisms which inhabit them.
   – Dissolves minerals in soil and removes them, so that plants can not absorb them. Calcium is a mineral that is removed in this way.
   – Dissolves minerals that are not soluble in 'normal' rain; these can then be taken in by plant roots. The minerals may be toxic to the plants. One example of such a mineral is aluminium.
   – Leaves on trees may be damaged or fall off and therefore can not photosynthesise.

Is there an energy cycle?

It is not possible to draw an energy cycle like those for carbon, nitrogen and water. However, we can talk about a flow of energy, which enters the ecosystem from the sun and eventually leaves the ecosystem as "heat" – it is more like one way traffic than a roundabout! In an ecosystem all the organisms are kept alive by the sun.

Energy from the sun is trapped by the chloroplasts in the cells of green plants (the producers). This energy is trapped in molecules such as glucose. It might be used by the plant to carry out necessary chemical reactions, or stored in compounds such as starch. If it is stored it is available to consumers in food. The consumers use a certain amount of energy while carrying out their life processes, such as growing. Some will be used in making indigestible structures such as bones and some will be available to animals in the next trophic level (see p 117). This flow of energy through a food web can be represented by a pyramid of energy. The energy content of the organisms at each trophic level is calculated for a year.

The width of the bars represents the energy content of that level. Notice how each trophic level has 'less energy' than the one below.

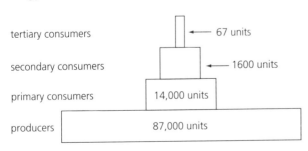

Fig 6 A pyramid of energy

Consider a bull. It does not eat much of the grass in the meadow (he only eats young tasty leaves for example) and is likely to take in 14% of the energy available in the field. About 60% of this passes out into the cow pat! Of the 40% that does get into the blood from the gut, nearly 90% is used to maintain the bull's body temperature and to provide energy in the cells by respiration. Only just over 10% is used to make new cells. If you have been keeping a tally you will realise that less than 1% of the energy in the grass is available to consumers of the bull – us! In energy terms this is very inefficient. Much more energy would have been available if we had been able to eat the meadow grass. Unfortunately this is not possible. Studying the energy flow in an ecosystem is helpful in finding out which organisms are more efficient at converting energy into new material. In this way better crops, in terms of high energy foods, can be investigated. This is particularly important in considering food production in heavily populated areas of the world.

Some examples of how this can be done are:

* Ensuring cows feed on a meadow before grass produces flowers (energy is not then 'wasted' in forming the flowers and seeds).
* Sending young anmals to slaughter before they are old (young anmals turn more of their 'energy' into new cells when they are growing fast, than older ones).
* Exploring the use of rabbits as a larger part of the diet (rabbits convert the same amount of hay into meat as do bullocks, but they do this four times faster).
* Breeding animals and plants which waste less energy (for example, peas grown for freezing have no recognisable leaves on their plants – the peas are important while the leaves are essentially waste in terms of energy).
* Developing more foods based on high protein plant materials, for example soya bean (energy is therefore not lost as the plant protein is converted first into animal protein).

QUESTION

Explain as fully as you can, what eventually happens to energy from the sun which is captured by the plants in the wood.

....

....

....
....
....
....
....
....
....
....
....
....
....
....
....
....(10 marks)
[NEAB]

ANSWER

There are a number of points here – you should try and make sure that you include these points in a logical order:

– Energy is absorbed during photosynthesis.
– Energy is stored in carbohydrates in the cells of the plants.
– Herbivores feed on plants and take in *some* of the energy.
– These herbivores are the food of carnivores which take in *some* of the energy of the herbivores.
– At each stage, some energy is 'lost'; there is progressively less energy in the levels of the energy pyramid as you ascend from producers to top consumers.
– Decomposers break down dead and decaying plant and animal remains and return energy to the environment.

Try and include some examples in your explanations, for example:

• Herbivores use some of the energy they obtained from plants to move about. This cannot then be taken in by carnivores.
• Energy is used in making bones; this energy is not available to predators of these animals.

Managing food production

The sea contains a number of different sorts of fish, for example salmon and herring, which provide food for humans. If these fish are over-harvested then the population will decline and the species will eventually become extinct. This has happened to the salmon industry in Alaska where since 1930 the total catch of salmon has declined. Lessons have been learned and now measures are in place to try and prevent this occurring in all species that are harvested from the seas. For example:

• The mesh size of the net is strictly controlled (so that small fish are not so likely to be caught – the problem with this is that the best size of mesh for one species is unlikely to be the best size for another species).
• A minimum landing size of fish means that young fish cannot be sold.
• The areas of sea that are fished are restricted to avoid breeding areas.
• The number of days that boats are at sea and the season of the year when fishing takes place are restricted, to avoid over-exploiting the resource.
• There is co-operation of countries to provide an international agreement (it is pointless if one country has a set of regulations but these are not followed by all countries with fishing fleets in the area).
• Research is carried out to achieve maximum exploitation without damaging the population.

Revision sheet

Ecology

1 Explain each of these terms:
  a Ecology
  b Habitat
  c Environment
  d Population
  e Community
  f Ecosystem
2 a Organise these into a food chain:
     tadpole   water beetle   pike   pond weed
  b Which one is the producer?
  c Name the tertiary consumer.
  d How is a food web different from a food chain?
  e How do we represent the direction of energy flow in a food chain or web?
3 Explain the difference between a pyramid of numbers and a pyramid of biomass.

4 When considering an ecosystem what is meant by:
 a Adaptation?
 b Competition?
 c Predation?

Natural Cycles and Energy flow

1 a What is meant by the term *cycle* in phrases such as 'carbon cycle' and 'nitrogen cycle'?
 b How are micro-organisms important in these cycles?

2 a Which organisms 'trap' carbon dioxide from the air and build it up into carbohydrates?
 b Which organisms release carbon dioxide into the atmosphere during the process of respiration?

3 Explain the difference between 'the greenhouse effect' and 'ozone depletion'.

4 a Which of the following nutrients contains nitrogen?
 carbohydrates   fats   proteins
 b How do most plants obtain their nitrogen?
 c Which type of bacteria *add* nitrogen to the soil and which type of bacteria *reduce* the nitrogen content of the soil?

5 a How is 'acid rain' different from normal rain?
 b Acid rain causes 'leaching'. What is this?

6 Explain why we talk about 'an energy flow' and not 'an energy cycle'?

Revision sheet answers

Ecology

1 a Ecology – study of organisms in their natural environment.
 b Habitat – where an organism lives.
 c Environment – the habitat and the conditions in it.
 d Population – group of organisms of the same species in the habitat.
 e Community – number of different populations which live in the same habitat.
 f Eco-system – a number of different communities and their environments.

2 a pond weed → tadpole → water beetle → pike
 b Pond weed.
 c Pike.

d Food web is a number of interconnecting food chains.
 e By the arrow.

3 Pyramid of numbers – a way of representing the number of organisms at each trophic level in an ecosystem.
 Pyramid of biomass – a way of representing the (dry) mass of organisms at each trophic level in an ecosystem.

4 a Adaptation – characteristics and mode of life of the organism to suit it to its environment.
 b Competition – two or more organisms that need/desire the same resources that are in short supply.
 c Predation – where one animal (a predator) hunts and kills another animal – the prey.

Natural Cycles and Energy flow

1 a How the atoms of an element (carbon or nitrogen) move round and round through the atmosphere and organisms.
 b Micro-organisms digest the dead remains of organisms and return the elements (in minerals) to the soil.

2 a Plants.
 b All living organisms (includes plants!).

3 Greenhouse effect – increase in the carbon dioxide in the atmosphere, which insulates the Earth.
 Ozone depletion – reduction in the ozone in the atmosphere, CFCs thought to contribute to this.

4 a Proteins.
 b Nitrates from the soil.
 c Adding nitrogen to the soil – nitrifying; reducing nitrogen in the soil – denitrifying.

5 a Acid rain is more acidic; pH of normal rain can be 5.5, for acid rain may be as low as pH 2.
 b When acid rain dissolves minerals such as calcium and iron from the soil, they are not available to plants via their roots.
 c Energy enters an ecosystem from the sun. It is passed through the ecosystem (see food chains and webs) and eventually lost as 'heat'. It is not cycled round in the same way as the element carbon.

Student Answer with Comments

a The diagram shows what happens to 1,000,000 kJ of the Sun's energy falling on a field of grass grazed by a cow.

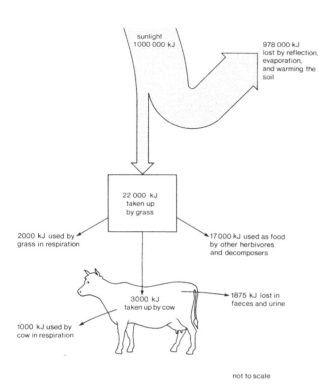

Fig 1

i Of the 1,000,000 kJ of sunlight energy falling on the field of grass grazed by a cow, calculate the percentage which is retained by the cow for growth. Show your working.

3000–1000–187J=12J 12J÷100,000=0.012%

Good, you do need to show your working.

③ (3 marks)

ii Use the information in the diagram to explain why it is more energy efficient for humans to eat plants rather than animals.

Because there is much more energy retained in plants than in animals which eat plants. ✓①

But use some figures from the diagram to explain further!

(2 marks)

b Some of the energy lost from cattle is present in methane gas. Methane is a 'greenhouse gas'. These gases in the atmosphere trap energy. The greater the concentration of greenhouse gases in the atmosphere, the more global warming will occur. This is called the 'greenhouse effect.'

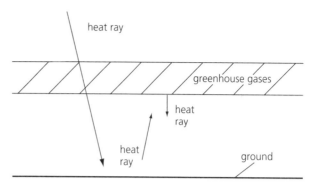

Fig 2

i Explain how the greenhouse effect leads to global warming. A diagram may help to make your answer clear.

The greenhouse gases let the heat rays ✓ *through then bounce off of the earth and they* ✓ *are either reflected or trapped in the gas. This* ✓ *will raise the temperature of the air and thus cause the greenhouse effect.* ✓ ④

(4 marks)

ii Explain why an increase in greenhoues gases in the atmosphere could cause major changes to the environment on Earth.

If the temperature rises too much the ice caps will start to melt, this will raise the level of the sea and we could lose some of the low lying ③ *land over the world. It took an average rise in temperature of 5°C that took us out of the ice age. What another 2 or 3°C will do is unknown.*

11/12 (3 marks)

[MEG]

An exam question for you to try

A paper factory pumps liquid effluent into a river. The effluent contains sugar. The diagram shows changes in water conditions for several kilometers downstream from the factory outflow.

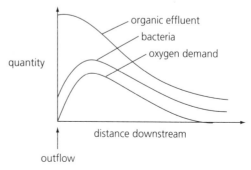

Fig 3

a Explain why there is first an increase and then a decrease in the number of bacteria downstream from the outflow.

....

....

....(3 marks)

b Oxygen demand is the amount of oxygen needed by organisms living in a river.
State and explain how the oxygen demand changes as the number of bacteria in the water increases.

....

....

....(2 marks)

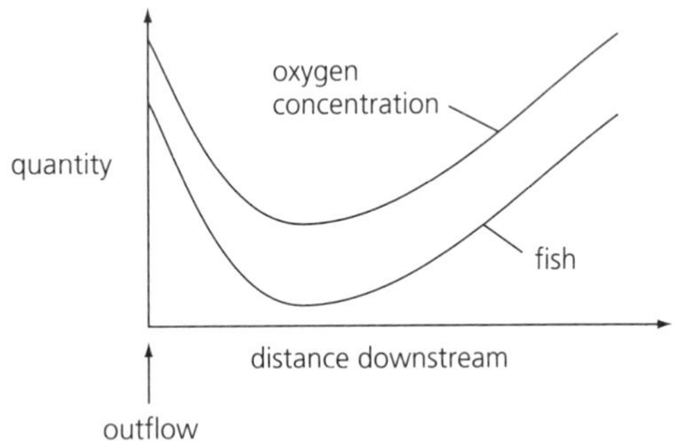

Fig 4

The diagram shows changes in oxygen concentration and number of fish downstream from the outflow.

c Explain why the curve of fish numbers is the same as that of the oxygen concentration.

....

....

....(2 marks)

d The oxygen concentration in the river water increases with distance from the outflow. Suggest two ways in which this oxygen may enter the water.

1 ....

....

2 ....

....

(2 marks)

[MEG]

Answer

a The bacteria feed on the effluent which contains sugar. They reproduce so there are lots of bacteria and these could use up the supply of food. Also the further away the effluent gets from the factory the more diluted it will be by the water.

b As the number of bacteria increases the oxygen demand of the river increases too. The bacteria respire aerobically and need oxygen for this process.

c Fish respire aerobically. The more oxygen there is in the water, as indicated by the oxygen concentration, the more fish are able to survive.

d Oxygen may enter the water by:
   – photosynthesis of plants.
   – The river 'being choppy' and so mixing with the air.

7

Key ideas in chemical processes

Key ideas in chemical processes	Midland (MEG)				Northern (NEAB)		London (ULEAC)				Southern (SEG)		Welsh (WJEC)
	Own	Nuffield	Salters	Suffolk	Co-ordinated	Modular	Modular GASP	Combined	Co-ordinated	Modular	Double	Modular	Co-ordinated
SOME IMPORTANT CHEMICAL IDEAS													
Solids, liquids, gases	✓	✓	✓	✓	✓	✓	✓	✓	✓	✓	✓	✓	✓
Elements, compounds and mixtures	✓	✓	✓	✓	✓	✓	✓	✓	✓	✓	✓	✓	✓
Metals and non-metals	✓	✓	✓	✓	✓	✓	✓	✓	✓	✓	✓	✓	✓
Solutions	✓	✓	✓	✓	✓	✓	✓	✓	✓	✓	✓	✓	✓
Separation techniques	✓	✓	✓	✓	✓	✓	✓	✓	✓	✓	✓	✓	✓
CHEMICAL REACTIONS AND PHYSICAL CHANGES													
Characteristics of chemical reactions	✓	✓	✓	✓	✓	✓	✓	✓	✓	✓	✓	✓	✓
Types of chemical reactions	✓	✓	✓	✓	✓	✓	✓	✓	✓	✓	✓	✓	✓
Acids and bases	✓	✓	✓	✓	✓	✓	✓	✓	✓	✓	✓	✓	✓
Exothermic and endothermic reactions	✓	✓	✓	✓	✓	✓	✓	✓	✓	✓	✓	✓	✓
Bond energies	H	H	H	H	H	H	H	H	H	H	✓	H	H
Kinetic theory	✓	✓	✓	✓	✓	✓	✓	✓	✓	✓	✓	✓	✓
Gas Laws	✓	✓	✓	✓	✓	✓	✓	✓	✓	✓	✓	✓	✓

Some important chemical ideas

There are millions and millions of chemical substances. It's not possible to know everything about all of them but it will be helpful to know about the main ways of grouping them.

Solids, liquids and gases

Matter is the word used to describe all the substances that make up the Universe.

You will also see chemical substances called 'chemicals' or 'substances'.

Solids, liquids and gases are called the three states of matter. Solids, liquids and gases contain particles which may be atoms, molecules or ions (see p 159). Most substances can be either solids, liquids or gases depending upon their temperature and pressure. The following table summarises the important points about each state:

state	example	shape	volume	movement of particles
solid	ice cube	fixed	fixed	vibrate around fixed place
liquid	water	takes shape of container	fixed	particles move at random but still touching each other
gas	water vapour	no fixed shape	no fixed volume	particles move in any direction at very high speed

If a substance changes from a liquid to a solid, for example, when you put water in a freezer to make ice cubes, this is called a change of state. (See p 152 for more details about changes of state.)

Thinking about substances in terms of particles

It is helpful to think of matter as being made up of particles. Knowing how these behave in the different states of solid, liquid and gas will help you to understand the differences between the three states.

solid	liquid	gas
fixed shape / fixed volume / particles vibrate about a fixed place	takes shape of container / fixed volume / particles move around each other	no fixed shape / no fixed volume / particles move in any direction

Fig 1 The three states of matter

See p 159 for details of the different types of particles in substances.

QUESTION

Mary has some calcium carbonate and water in a bottle. The calcium carbonate does not dissolve in the water.

a   i Draw diagrams to show the arrangement of particles in air and water.
The arrangement of calcium carbonate particles is shown. (2 marks)

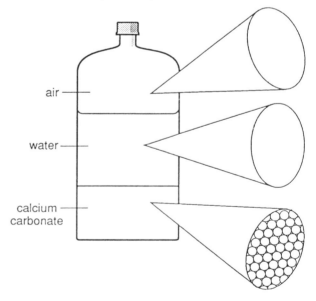

Fig 2

   ii Why is it easier to compress air than water?

....

....(1 mark)

b How could Mary get back some water and dry
   calcium carbonate?

....

....(2 marks)
[MEG]

ANSWER

a i

air   water

Fig 3

*Make sure that you draw the particles the same size
each time (the particles are not bigger in a gas.)
Each particle in the liquid should be touching at least
one other particle.*

   ii The particles in air (a gas) are further apart
      than in water (a liquid).

b Mary needs to filter the mixture to get the water.
   She needs to let the calcium carbonate dry, either
   by leaving it in the air or by warming it gently.
   *The question asks you about the water and dry
   calcium carbonate and is giving two marks. This
   indicates that you need to write about both.*

What is diffusion?

If you burn toast in the kitchen you will soon
smell it in other rooms. Gas molecules move
very fast, and will move to any space that is
available. Molecules from the food have
spread out. This is called diffusion. Important
points about diffusion:

• Diffusion is more noticeable in gases, but it
  can occur in liquids and solids.
• Less dense gases like hydrogen diffuse
  faster than denser gases like carbon dioxide.
Diffusion is important to living organisms
(see p 20).

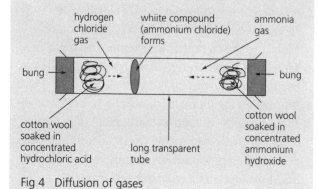

Fig 4 Diffusion of gases

1 The compound is formed in a chemical
  reaction as the two gases diffuse towards
  one another and meet (see Fig 4).
2 The compound forms nearer to the
  hydrochloric acid as ammonia molecules are
  lighter and diffuse faster than hydrogen
  chloride molecules.

What is Brownian motion?

In the example of diffusion shown above, the
molecules of the two gases are being
continually bombarded by the particles
(atoms and molecules) that are in the air. You
may have looked down a microscope and seen
large smoke particles moving in a random
way as they were bombarded by smaller air
particles. This is called Brownian motion.

Pure substances and mixtures

A pure substance is a single substance. All the
substance is the same and it has a sharp melting point
and a sharp boiling point. Many substances that you
see each day are mixtures. Orange juice is advertised
as 'pure' but if you look on the label you may see
that it contains a mixture of substances – water,
sugar, citric acid, natural flavouring and vitamin C!

QUESTION

Which of the following substances are pure?

SUBSTANCE	MELTING POINT (°C)	BOILING POINT (°C)
A	93 to 95.6	265
B	–117	78.5
C	1900	3400
D	–65 to –61.2	65.5

ANSWER

B and C *(the only two with sharp melting and boiling
points).*

Elements, compounds and mixtures

All known substances can be classified into one of these three groups. An element is a substance that cannot be broken down into simpler substances. There are 106 of these elements and 92 of them occur naturally. Each has a symbol – either a capital letter, for example O for oxygen, or a capital and lower case letter like Al for aluminium. (These elements make up the periodic table see p 207.) Elements can be further subdivided into metals and non-metals (see below).

A compound contains two or more elements which have combined together during a chemical reaction. A compound has completely different properties from the elements that it contains. For example hydrogen and oxygen are both colourless gases but they react to form a compound called water.

The word 'properties' sometimes causes students a problem. Example: 'Sulphur is a yellow, non-metallic substance.' This tells you two properties of sulphur – it is yellow and non-metallic.

A mixture can contain any number of different elements or compounds or elements and compounds. A mixture is different from a compound as the substances in it have not been combined during a chemical reaction. Unlike elements and compounds a mixture *does not* have a sharp melting or boiling point. Most substances are mixtures – for example, the air around you, a cup of tea, the ink in your pen, milk, jelly and the lather in the washing machine. Composites are an important type of mixture. Although there are some natural composites, many are designed to use the good properties of the different substances in them. For example: tennis rackets are made from a composite containing graphite (for strength) and plastic (for lightness).

Raw and man-made materials
A raw material is something that occurs naturally.
Much of the chemical industry is involved in using these raw materials to manufacture new and more useful materials. Many of the processes involve chemical reactions. The materials that are made in this way are called man-made.

QUESTION

Copper is an element. The best evidence for this is that it:

A Has been known since 4000 BC.
B Cannot be decomposed.
C Can be obtained by strong heating of copper ore with carbon.
D Forms the compound copper oxide when heated in air.

ANSWER

B
Beware of questions like this, all the answers are true but the only evidence for copper being an element is B.

QUESTION

The use of metals in everyday life depends on their properties. Explain why:

a metals rather than plastics are used to make frying pans; (2 marks)
Reason 1 ....
Reason 2 ....
b man-made fibres rather than metals are used to make ropes; (1 mark)
Reason..
c metals rather than man-made fibres are used for carrying electricity; (1 mark)
Reason..
d ceramics rather than glass are used for heat shields on space craft; (1 mark)
Reason..
[WJEC]

ANSWER

Notice this question uses the phrase 'rather than', you are expected to compare the two materials in each case.

a *Any two of the following would be suitable:*
Metals conduct heat but plastics are insulators.
Metals melt at a higher temperature than plastics.
Metals *(that are used to make frying pans)* do not burn, many plastics do burn.
b *Any one of the following would be suitable:*
Man-made fibres tend to be 'lighter' (less dense) than metals, or man-made fibres do not corrode, but metal ones would. *(Don't say 'rust' as the question says metals and not just iron!)*
c Metals conduct electricity but man-made fibres do not.

d *This is a tricky one as glass and ceramics share a lot of properties.* Ceramics can be made which are stronger than glass. Ceramics used in heat shields are also likely to have good heat insulation properties *(to protect the inside of the space craft).* Ceramics can be made to have higher melting points.

Identifying substances from their symbols and names

Looking at the chemical shorthand. Look for the capital letters:

Na … one capital letter so an element – sodium.

H_2 … one capital letter, so an element – hydrogen (the 2 tells you it is a molecule of two atoms) (see p 164).

NaCl – two capital letters, so its not an element – the compound sodium chloride.

$C_6H_{12}O_6$ – three capital letters, so it is not an element – the compound glucose.

Looking at the name. Look at the end of the name:

sodium chloride ends in **-ide**, the compound is most likely to contain two elements – sodium and chlorine.

sodium chlorate ends in **-ate**, the compound contains oxygen as well as the sodium and chlorine.

QUESTION

a Which of the following does not represent an element?

Cu   CO   Li   Fr

b Which of the following represents a compound?

S_8 Mn   NO   Ba

c What elements are in:

  i hydrogen sulphide

  ii sodium sulphate (VI)

ANSWER

a CO *(two capital letters, therefore two elements).*

b NO *(two capital letters, therefore a compound).*

c i hydrogen, sulphur *(note the -ide).*

  ii sodium, sulphur, oxygen *(note the -ate).*

QUESTION

Choose words from this list to complete the sentences below.

carbonate   chloride   compound   mixture   oxide   solution

a When two elements react, the new substance is called a ....(1 mark)

b The white powder formed when zinc reacts with oxygen is called zinc................................(1 mark)

[NEAB]

ANSWER

a compound

b oxide

Metals and non-metals

All elements can be sorted out into one of two groups: metals or non-metals. They have a number of different physical and chemical properties. The following table shows the main differences between them (at room temperature):

Property	Metal	Non-metal
Physical properties		
State	solid	solid, liquid or gas
Melting and boiling points	high	low
Density	high	low
Strength	good	weak
Malleability	good	brittle
Thermal and electrical conduction	good	poor
Chemical properties		
Reaction with water	may form hydrogen	no reaction
Reaction with acid	may form hydrogen	no reaction
Reaction with oxygen	forms solid oxide, which if soluble forms alkaline solution	forms gaseous oxide, which if soluble forms an acidic solution

Section 11 has more details about metals

It may help to remember that sulphur (a non-metal) as sulphur dioxide contributes to acid rain … non-metals form acidic oxides.

QUESTION

In each of the following cases say whether the element is a metal or non-metal:

A is a yellow solid that forms an oxide which is an acidic gas.

B is a shiny solid which is a good conductor of electricity and gives off hydrogen when steam is passed over it.

C is a dull solid, melting point 98°C and boiling point 885°C. It is a good conductor of electricity and forms an alkaline oxide.

D is a grey, shiny, dense liquid which boils at 357°C. It is a good conductor of electricity.

ANSWER

A Non-metal (*acidic oxide*).

B Metal (*good conductor and forms hydrogen with water*).

C Metal (*good conductor and alkaline oxide*).

D Metal (*grey, shiny and good conductor*).

Solutions

Many of the liquids that you use are solutions. When sodium chloride (common salt) is added to water, it seems to disappear – although it is *still* there. It forms a solution of sodium chloride, which is transparent. The sodium chloride is soluble in the water. In this example the sodium chloride is the solute and the water is the solvent. If you add a little sodium chloride to the water you will make a dilute solution and if you add a lot of sodium chloride you will make a concentrated solution of sodium chloride. Eventually no more sodium chloride will dissolve and some will be left as solid. At this point you will have made a saturated sodium chloride solution. You can dissolve 36g of sodium chloride in 100g of water (at 25°C), but you can dissolve 210g of sugar in the same amount of water. Different substances therefore have different solubilities.

QUESTION

Louise made herself a cup of coffee in an unusual way. Fig 5 shows three stages in what happened. Use the idea of particles to explain these changes. Also explain why they happen so quickly.

....
....(5 marks)

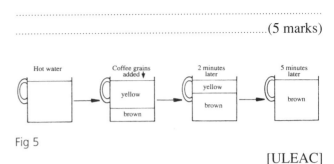

Fig 5

[ULEAC]

ANSWER

This type of question is tricky, there are 5 marks to get! Try and include points such as these:
After the coffee grains are added to the cup, they sink to the bottom. At the bottom the coffee dissolves in the hot water as the particles from the coffee diffuse into the surrounding water. After two minutes more of the water is brown because the particles have spread further from the area of high concentration around the grains into the water higher up the cup where there are no coffee particles. After five minutes the particles from the coffee have diffused through all of the water. This has only taken five minutes because the particles are moving quite fast due to the high temperature.

Suspensions and precipitates

When calcium carbonate (chalk) is added to water you do not get a transparent liquid because the substance does not dissolve. Calcium carbonate is insoluble in water and forms a suspension. During an experiment you may add two solutions and find that you form an insoluble substance. For example, when sodium carbonate solution is added to calcium chloride solution there is a chemical reaction and an insoluble substance, calcium carbonate, is formed. Solid formed in solution as a result of a chemical reaction is called a precipitate.

Solutions and emulsions

When you add some liquids together, for example alcohol and water, they mix completely. They are said to be miscible.
If, however, you add oil and water together they do not mix and the oil sits as a layer on top of the water. The two liquids are immiscible.
If you shake the immiscible mixture of oil and water you can break up the top layer of liquid (the oil) and

spread it through the water. It produces a cloudy liquid that you can not see through (i.e. that is opaque) which is called an emulsion. If you leave the mixture to stand the oil will separate out on top of the water again, unless you add an emulsifier. If you had used vinegar instead of water, egg yolk could be added and you would have made some mayonnaise. The emulsifier in the egg yolk helps the oil and vinegar to mix. One end of the emulsifier molecule is attracted to the oil and the other end to the water in the vinegar.

A foam is a mixture of a gas in a liquid and a gel is a mixture of a liquid in a solid.

QUESTION

a Look at the Table.
It shows four types of mixtures and some examples used in the home.

Type of mixture	Example used in the home
solution	adhesive
foam	shaving foam
gel	hair gel
emulsion	

Complete the Table by giving a suitable example of an emulsion. (1 mark)

b Solvents and detergents can each help to remove stains from clothes.

  i Explain how a solvent removes an oil stain from a cloth.

    ....
    ....(1 mark)

  ii Explain how a detergent helps to clean dirty clothes.

    ....
    ....(1 mark)
                                      [MEG]

ANSWER

a There are lots of answers that you can give here such as milk, salad cream, ice cream, face cream, paint etc.

b i A solvent dissolves the stain.

  ii The detergent molecule has two ends, one which is attracted to the water (hydrophilic) and one

which is attracted to the grease (hydrophobic). *(There is likely to be grease sticking the dirt to the clothes.)* The detergent helps the water to get to the dirt – to 'wet it', so that the dirt is more likely to be removed in washing.

QUESTION

The graph below shows how the solubility of four substances depends on the temperature.

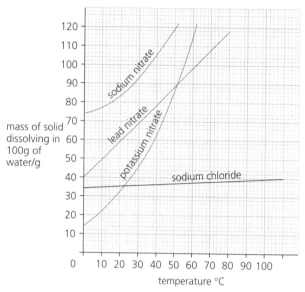

Fig 6

a Which of the four solids is least soluble at room temperature (20°C)?
b Which of these four solids has almost the same solubility in hot and cold water?
c In an experiment Jane made 100g of saturated solution of potassium nitrate at 50°C. She then cooled the solution to 20°C and filtered off the solid. What mass of solid should she obtain?
d Fizzy drinks contain dissolved carbon dioxide gas. When these drinks get warm they go 'flat' and loose their 'fizz'. On the next page sketch the shape of the solubility curve you would expect to get for carbon dioxide, with increase in temperature.
(The starting point has been given for you.)

ANSWER

a Potassium nitrate.
b Sodium chloride.
c 54g *(Find the mass which dissolves at 50°C (86g), then deduct from this the mass that is in solution at 20°C (32g).)*

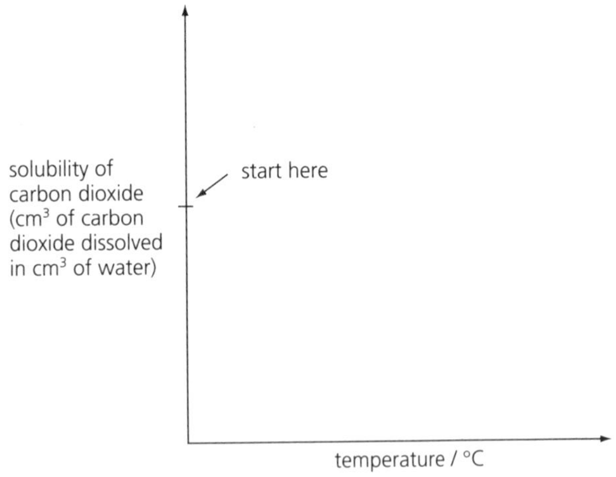

solubility of
carbon dioxide
(cm³ of carbon
dioxide dissolved
in cm³ of water)

start here

temperature / °C

Fig 7

d The curve would go down as the temperature
increased *(gases are less soluble as the
temperature increases, unlike solids).*

Ways of separating substances

Separating insoluble solids from liquids

• Filtering: The smaller solvent molecules pass
through the filter paper and the much larger solid
particles remain on the paper as the residue.

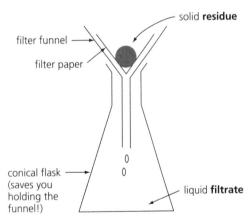

Fig 8 Filtering

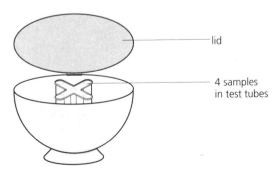

Fig 9 A centrifuge

• Centrifuging: This is used when the solid particles
are small and form a suspension.

Separating soluble solids from solution

• Crystallisation: The solvent evaporates, leaving
the solute to crystallise. The slower the process,
the larger the crystals of solute that are formed.

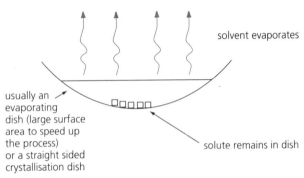

Fig 10 Crystallisation

• Distillation: This method is used if it is more
important to obtain the pure solvent than the solute.

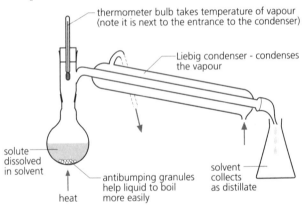

Fig 11 Distillation

Separating different solutes

• Chromatography: Used to separate different
solutes in a solvent.

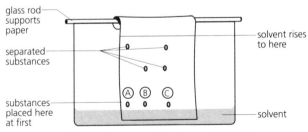

Substances A and B are single substances but substance C is a mixture
containing the solute found in A and the sloute foound in B

Fig 12 Chromatography

*Substances A and B are single substances but substance C is a
mixture containing the solute found in A and the solute found in B.*

Separating liquids

- Immiscible liquids: This method, involving a separating funnel, makes use of the fact that the two liquids do not mix. They form two separate layers.

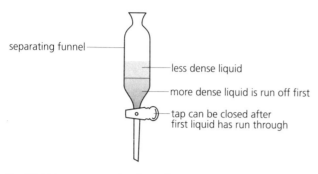

separating funnel

less dense liquid

more dense liquid is run off first

tap can be closed after first liquid has run through

Fig 13 Using a separating funnel

- Miscible liquids: This method, involving fractional distillation, makes use of the fact that the liquids boil at different temperatures.

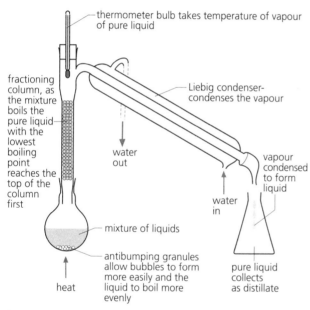

thermometer bulb takes temperature of vapour of pure liquid

fractioning column, as the mixture boils the pure liquid with the lowest boiling point reaches the top of the column first

Liebig condenser-condenses the vapour

water out

vapour condensed to form liquid

water in

mixture of liquids

antibumping granules allow bubbles to form more easily and the liquid to boil more evenly

heat

pure liquid collects as distillate

Fig 14 Fractional distillation

A mixture of propanone and water can be separated in this way. Propanone is the distillate at 56°C (its boiling point). Once this has been collected the temperature rises to 100°C and stays constant while the water is collected as the distillate. The more volatile fraction is always collected first.

QUESTION

This question is about the following everyday substances:

carbon dioxide   cheese   cornflakes   milk
orange juice

a From the list choose
   i one substance which is a solid;
   ....(1 mark)
   ii one substance which is a liquid;
   ....(1 mark)
   iii one substance which is a gas.
   ....(1 mark)

b A little water was left in a glass in a warm room overnight. The next morning there was no water in the glass. Explain what happened to the water particles.
   ....
   ....
   ....(2 marks)
   [MEG]

ANSWER

a i Cheese or cornflakes.
   ii Milk or orange juice.
   iii Carbon dioxide.
b As the water evaporated (turned from a liquid to a gas) the particles in the water moved away from each other. In the gas the particles move faster and in all directions and mix in with the particles of the air.

QUESTION

Making whisky is a complex process. Sugar (in malted barley) ferments in water which has been drained through peat. After the mixture has finished fermenting, it is filtered. The filtrate is a dilute solution of ethanol in water, together with small amounts of 'fusel oils' which colour and flavour the whisky. The whisky is obtained by fractional distillation.

a i Is whisky a compound or a mixture? Give one reason for your answer.
   ....
   ....(1 mark)
   ii Name a process that could be used to separate and help identify the fusel oils. (Note: fractional distillation is not suitable)
   ....(1 mark)

b A small-scale fractional distillation is shown in the diagram below.
   i What is the function of:
   A part X?
   ....
   ....(1 mark)

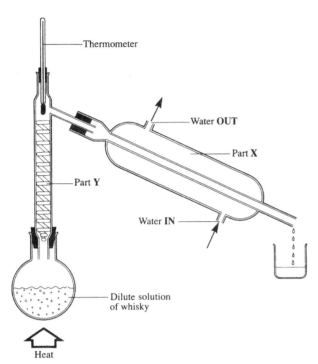

Thermometer

Water **OUT**

Part **X**

Part **Y**

Water **IN**

Dilute solution
of whisky

Heat

(From *Science at Work*, Longman Group UK Ltd)

Fig 15

B the glass spiral (part Y)?

....
....(1 mark)

ii Explain why the dilute solution of whisky can
be concentrated by fractional distillation.

....
....
....
....
....
....(3 marks)

iii The diagram below shows the label from a
small bottle of whisky. The concentration of
the ethanol (alcohol) is shown in two ways. It
is shown as the percentage of alcohol by
volume and as a percentage 'proof'.

HIGHLAND FLING
WHISKY

A blend of finest malt whiskies

40% volume   70° proof

contents 75 cm³

Fig 16

A How many cubic centimetres (cm³) of ethanol are
in the full bottle?

....(1 mark)

B Surgical spirit is a concentrated solution of
ethanol. Suggest two reasons why the government
tries to stop people drinking surgical spirit.

....
....
....
....(2 marks)
[SEG 1994]

ANSWER

a i Whisky is a mixture, because it contains
ethanol, water and small amounts of 'fusel oils'
(and perhaps other substances as well).

ii Chromatography (*notice that the question tells
you that these colour the whisky*).

b i A X is the Liebig condenser which cools the
vapour and turns it into a liquid.

B Y is the fractionating column. As the liquids
in the mixture boil at different temperatures
it helps to separate them. The liquids with
the lowest boiling points reach the top of the
column first.

ii Ethanol and water (both in the whisky) have
different boiling points. The boiling point of
ethanol is lower than that of water. As the
mixture is heated the ethanol fraction will boil
first and be collected. The water will remain in
the flask. This will enable a more concentrated
solution of whisky to be formed.

iii A 30cm³
(*The bottle contains 75cm³ and 40% of this
is ethanol.*)

B Suitable answers would include points such
as:
The government does not charge tax on
surgical spirit.
There may be other more poisonous things
in surgical spirit.
*Avoid vague answers such as: 'People
would die'.*

Chemical reactions and physical changes

What is a chemical reaction?

A large part of the chemical industry is involved in taking substances and converting them into materials that we need (e.g. turning crude oil into drugs, dyes, plastics etc). This involves chemical reactions. Nearly all materials involve chemical reactions in their manufacture.

To decide if a change is a chemical reaction you need to look for:

- new substances being made.
- a transfer of energy (this can mean energy being added or being given out).
- difficulty in getting the starting substances back again.

Note that the total mass before the chemical change will be the same as the total mass after the chemical change. Beware, it is easy to overlook this as quite often some of the substances are gases!

Also, if there is a chemical reaction then it is possible to write a word equation and then a balanced equation. From this it is possible to work out how much of one substance reacts with another substance (see p 180–182).

Useful terms to know about chemical reactions:

Chemical reaction: a change producing new substances and involving an energy change.

Chemical change: another term for chemical reaction.

Permanent change: another term for chemical reaction.

Exothermic: energy is given out during the reaction, for example the substances glow without further heating (see later).

Endothermic: energy is taken in during the reaction (see later).

Reactants: chemical substances we start with.

Products: chemical substances we finish with.

State symbols: these are the part of an equation that shows the state of the reactants and products; whether the substance is a solid (s), a liquid (l), a gas (g) or whether it is dissolved in water (aq). Note, if liquid water is in the equation it is $H_2O(l)$ and not $H_2O(aq)$.

If a solution of sodium chloride is formed this will be NaCl(aq).

Word equation: a way of describing a chemical reaction using words.

Balanced equation: an accurate way of describing a chemical reaction, showing the number of particles of reactants and products involved, so that the amounts of each substance involved can be calculated. (see p 180)

Example one

When green copper carbonate is heated it forms black copper oxide and the gas carbon dioxide.

This is a *chemical reaction*; two new substances have been made. The two *products* are copper oxide and carbon dioxide.

copper carbonate(s) → copper oxide(s) + carbon dioxide(g)

$$CuCO_3(s) \rightarrow CuO(s) + CO_2(g)$$

Example two

Hydrogen is burnt in oxygen to form liquid water. This is a *chemical reaction* as a new substance is made.

hydrogen(g) + oxygen(g) → water(g)

$$2H_2(g) + O_2(g) \rightarrow 2H_2O(g)$$

Example three

Salt is added to melt ice on a path.

This is *not a chemical reaction*. No new substance is formed, the salt just dissolves in the water and it would be easy to get the salt back again by heating the solution until the water evaporates and leaves the salt.

Are there different types of chemical reactions?

There are millions of different chemical reactions but many of them can be grouped into just a few different types. By learning the characteristics of these it will help you to work out what is happening in a reaction you have not met before.

Neutralisation

Adding acid to stop a wasp sting hurting is an example of a neutralisation reaction. A salt is formed when an acid and alkali react. Water is also formed in the reaction.

The general pattern for the reaction is:

acid + alkali → salt + water

It does not matter which acid or alkali you use as reactants, you will always form a salt and water as products.

For example:

hydrochloric + sodium → sodium + water(l)
　acid　　　hydroxide　chloride
　(aq)　　　(aq)　　　(aq)

　HCl　　+ NaOH → NaCl + H_2O
　acid　　　alkali　　salt　　water

Useful terms to know about neutralisation

Acid: A substance which can give H^+ ions to another substance.
Base: The opposite of an acid. It takes H^+ ions away from an acid in a chemical reaction.
Alkali: This is a base which is soluble in water. It contains OH^- ions that react with the H^+ ions of an acid to form water.
Salt: A salt is formed when an acid and alkali react. A salt is an ionic compound (see p 184) that contains a positive metal ion (cation) and a negative ion (anion) that could have come from an acid. (Salts are also produced when an acid reacts with a metal, a compound containing the carbonate ion or a basic oxide – see later).

What is the difference between a concentrated acid and a strong acid?

This is something that many people get confused over.

The concentration of an acid

The label on a solution usually shows the concentration, for example 1 mol dm^{-3} H_2SO_4, or it might still be written as 1M H_2SO_4. The number in front of the M tells you how concentrated the solution is. So 0.1 mol dm^{-3} H_2SO_4 is ten times more dilute than a solution labelled 1 mol dm^{-3} H_2SO_4.

Strong and weak acids

It is possible to have a 1 mol dm^{-3} solution of ethanoic acid and a 1 mol dm^{-3} solution of hydrochloric acid. (Both are said to be molar solutions as they are 1 mol

dm^{-3}; they have the same concentration.) But the ethanoic acid is a weak acid and the hydrochloric acid is a strong acid. This means that if you take 50cm^3 of each of these two acids there would be more H^+ ions in the hydrochloric acid. The hydrochloric acid splits up completely to give H^+ ions but only a few of the ethanoic acid molecules split up to form H^+ ions.

So, for example, if a solution has pH 5 this could be because:

– it is a weak acid
　　or
– it is a very dilute solution of a strong acid.

Some reactions of acids

Apart from reacting with an alkali in a neutralisation reaction, acids have a number of other properties in common.

The reaction of acids and metals

The pattern here is:

metal + acid → salt + hydrogen

Two points to remember:

• Only the more reactive metals (for example magnesium but not copper) follow this pattern.
• Nitric acid often behaves differently from other strong acids.

See section 10 for more details about metals.

The reaction of acids and insoluble metal oxides (or hydroxides)

The pattern here is:

metal oxide + acid → salt + water

The acid is neutralised in this reaction. Insoluble black copper oxide reacts with sulphuric acid to give a blue solution of copper sulphate.

The reaction of acids with metal carbonates

All carbonates give off carbon dioxide when they react with acids. This is another useful test to see if you have an acid!
　The pattern here is:

carbonate + acid → salt + carbon dioxide + water

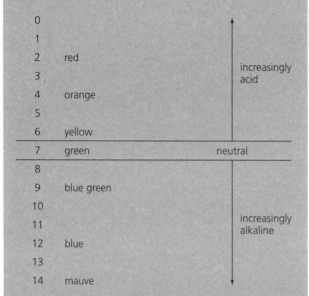
Thermal decomposition

All thermal decomposition reactions have two features in common:

• They need heat to cause the reaction.
• The products are simpler than the starting substance, ... hence the name thermal (using heat) decomposition (split up).

Unlike a neutralisation reaction it is *not possible* to write a general word equation for all the different thermal decomposition reactions.

You are probably familiar with several examples of this type of reaction. For example:

copper carbonate(s) → copper oxide(s) + carbon dioxide(g)

$$CuCO_3(s) \rightarrow CuO(s) + CO_2(g)$$

one starting substance   two products formed by decomposition

Fermentation

This reaction involves the production of ethanol and carbon dioxide from glucose by the action of an enzyme (zymase) in the micro-organism called yeast.

glucose (aq) → ethanol (aq) + carbon dioxide(g)

$$C_6H_{12}O_6 \rightarrow 2C_2H_5OH(aq) + 2CO_2(g)$$

This reaction is very important to the brewing and baking industries. The brewing industry makes use of the ethanol product of this reaction and the baking industry makes use of the other product – the carbon dioxide – to produce the light texture of bread.

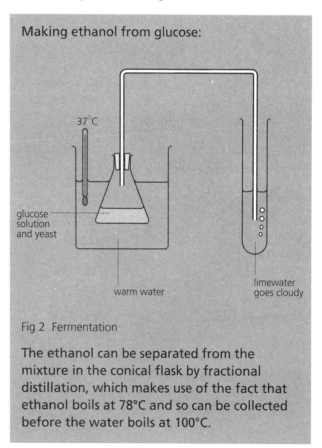

Making ethanol from glucose:

37°C

glucose solution and yeast

warm water

limewater goes cloudy

Fig 2   Fermentation

The ethanol can be separated from the mixture in the conical flask by fractional distillation, which makes use of the fact that ethanol boils at 78°C and so can be collected before the water boils at 100°C.

Details of separating techniques are on p 140–141.

Oxidation and reduction

Oxidation and reduction reactions are grouped together. If one of these types of reaction occurs the other will usually occur. Depending on which reactant you are considering you can call the reaction oxidation or reduction. These reactions are sometimes called redox (reduction – oxidation reactions).

> Oxidation can be:
> - adding oxygen
> - removing hydrogen
> - losing electrons
>
> Reduction can be:
> - removing oxygen
> - adding hydrogen
> - gaining electrons

Oxidation as adding oxygen

Reactions where oxygen is added to a reactant are called oxidation reactions.

There are three common reactions which fall into this pattern:

- respiration
  glucose (aq) + oxygen (g) → water(l) + carbon dioxide (g)
  $C_6H_{12}O_6$ (aq) + $6O_2$(g) → $6H_2O$(l) + $6CO_2$(g)

Glucose reacts with oxygen to form water and carbon dioxide, and energy is released.

- combustion: When a fuel burns it combines with oxygen and forms water and carbon dioxide, and energy is released.
  methane(g) +   →   water(l) + oxygen(g)   carbon dioxide(g)
  CH_4(g) + $2O_2$(g) $2H_2O$(l) + CO_2(g)

- rusting: When iron reacts with oxygen in the presence of water it forms rust (hydrated iron oxide). It is only correct to talk about iron (and steel) rusting, but *all corrosion reactions* where different metals form oxides are examples of *oxidation* reactions.
  magnesium (s) + oxygen (g) → magnesium oxide (s)
  $2Mg$(s) O_2 (g)   → $2MgO$(s)

Oxidation as removing hydrogen

Oxidation can also be used to describe reactions in which hydrogen is removed from a substance.
Hydrogen   + chlorine (g) → sulphur(s) + hydrogen sulphide (g)   chloride(g)
H_2S(g) + Cl_2(g)   → S(s) + $2HCl$(g)

There is no oxygen involved in this reaction, but it is still an oxidation reaction. In this case, hydrogen is removed from the hydrogen sulphide to leave the element sulphur.

Oxidation as the loss of electrons

The reaction:
magnesium(s) + oxygen (g) → magnesium oxide(s)
can be written in terms of what happens to the electrons:
Mg   → Mg^{2+} + $2e^-$
                       (the electrons)

The magnesium atom loses two electrons to form the magnesium ion. (These two electrons are given to the oxygen atom to form the oxide ion.) In this example the magnesium has been oxidised as it has lost some electrons.

This type of reaction also occurs at the anode in electrolysis.

Reduction as the removal of oxygen

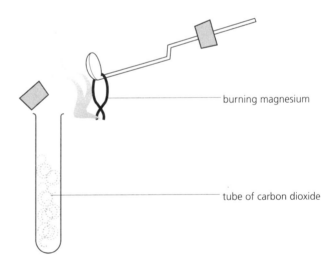

Fig 3 Adding magnesium to carbon dioxide

If burning magnesium is plunged into a tube of carbon dioxide, you see white fumes and large black smudges on the sides of the tube. This is a reduction reaction. The magnesium has reduced the carbon dioxide to carbon (the black smudges) by removing the oxygen from it and in the process formed magnesium oxide.
Magnesium(s) + carbon   → magnesium + carbon(s)
                 dioxide(g)   oxide(s)
$2Mg$(s) + CO_2(g)   → $2MgO$(s) + C(s)

Carbon dioxide has been reduced.
Magnesium is the reducing agent.

Magnesium has been oxidised.
Carbon dioxide is the oxidising agent.

Redox reactions of this type are very important in obtaining metals from their ores (see p 222).

Reduction as adding hydrogen

Ammonia is made when nitrogen reacts with hydrogen. In this case the nitrogen is reduced as the hydrogen 'adds on' to it.

nitrogen(g) + hydrogen(g) $\rightarrow$ ammonia(g)
$$N_2(g) + 3H_2(g) \rightarrow 2NH_3(g)$$

Nitrogen has been reduced.
Hydrogen is the reducing agent.

Reduction as gaining electrons

Electrolysis is used to obtain pure aluminium from its ore, bauxite (see p 198). The reaction which occurs at the cathode is a reduction reaction.
$$Al^{3+} + 3e^- \rightarrow Al$$
(the electrons)

The aluminium ion gains electrons and is reduced to the aluminium atom. (The electrons come from the cathode.)

> There is a phrase which will help you to remember about oxidation and reduction in terms of electrons:
>
> OIL RIG
>
> oxidation is loss, reduction is gain ... of electrons
>
> The term REDOX is used for reduction-oxidation reactions.

Are all chemical reactions useful?

Unfortunately, not all of them are. Some are very costly to the country. Some of these are:

Problems related to the oxidation of food

Oxidation is an important reaction in the food industry. It can be a reaction that is a real nuisance! For example, apples 'going brown' as you peel them is due to an oxidation reaction. Crisps taste 'off' if the fats used to cook them become rancid due to oxidation.
Additives, called anti-oxidants, are added to many foods to prevent their flavour being spoilt by oxidation.

Problems related to the oxidation of fuels

1 Carbon monoxide
When fossil fuels like coal and oil burn, they produce carbon dioxide and water. If there is insufficient oxygen for this combustion process, incomplete combustion occurs and soot and carbon monoxide are formed as well. This happens in a car engine.

petrol + oxygen gives carbon (soot) + carbon dioxide + carbon monoxide + water

Carbon monoxide is poisonous and stops haemoglobin in the blood from transporting oxygen to the cells of the body.

2 Sulphur dioxide and nitrogen oxides
Both power stations and vehicles add nitrogen oxides to the air during the combustion of fuel. Power stations are also a major source of sulphur dioxide, produced as a result of burning fossil fuels. These gases react with water in the atmosphere to form sulphuric acid and nitric acid which contribute to acid rain (see p 127–128). Nitrogen dioxide (NO_2) is involved in the formation of photochemical smog. Some molecules are involved in the formation of PAN (peroxyacetyl nitrate). Sunlight causes other nitrogen dioxide molecules to split up:

$$NO_2(g) \rightarrow NO(g) + O(g)$$

The oxygen atoms that are formed are very reactive. They react with hydrocarbons present in car exhaust fumes to form aldehydes and some ozone. The resulting smog, which is a mixture of PAN, aldehydes and ozone as well as the gases from exhaust fumes, irritates the eyes and lungs. It is particularly hazardous to people who suffer from asthma.

Lead in petrol
Lead is added to some types of petrol, as a compound called tetraethyllead(IV). This is called an anti-knock additive as it helps the car to run smoothly. It reacts with another compound in petrol (added to stop the lead building up in the engine) and is present in exhaust fumes as lead bromide. Lead is a poison that builds up in the body over a period of years. It is thought to damage the nervous system. All new cars now run on 'lead free' petrol to cut down on this form of air pollution.

Problems related to the oxidation of iron (Rusting)

Millions of pounds are lost each year because iron rusts. There are several ways to prevent rusting. They involve stopping the oxygen in the air reaching the iron:

- Galvanising – coating with a layer of zinc (e.g. dustbins).
- Tin plating – coating with a layer of tin (e.g. cans for food).
- Chromium plating – coating with a layer of chromium (e.g. taps in the bathroom).
- Painting.
- Greasing.
- Bitumen coating (e.g. underbody of a car).
- Plastic coating (e.g. a wire fence).
- Enamelling (e.g. fridge).

In many cases there is also the option of using a substitute material (e.g. plastic guttering instead of iron for a house).

QUESTION

Which of the following is a chemical reaction?

A Boiling water
B Cooking a cake
C Melting ice
D Tearing paper
(1 mark)   [SEG]

ANSWER

B

QUESTION

When limestone is heated strongly it changes. The change is:

A catalytic conversion
B electrolytic decomposition
C salt formation
D thermal decomposition
(1 mark)

[SEG]

ANSWER

D

QUESTION

Look at the reactions of iron and sulphur with oxygen.

$$4Fe + 3O_2 \rightarrow 2Fe_2O_3$$
iron oxygen   iron oxide

$$S + O_2 \rightarrow SO_2$$
sulphur oxygen   sulphur dioxide

A What process do both of these reactions represent?
....(1 mark)

B Dilute hydrochloric acid reacts with iron oxide but it does not react with sulphur dioxide. Explain why.

....
....
....
....(3 marks)
[SEG 1994]

ANSWER

A Oxidation.

B Iron oxide is a metal oxide and acids react with metal oxides to form a salt and water. Sulphur dioxide is a non-metal oxide, it is acidic and does not react with the hydrochloric acid.

Metal and non-metal oxides are discussed on p 137.

QUESTION

Sodium hydroxide is an alkali. It will neutralise dilute sulphuric acid to form a salt and water.

a What is the name of the salt formed?
....(1 mark)
b Sodium hydroxide solution is slowly added to dilute sulphuric acid until it is in excess. Describe the changes in the pH value which take place.

....
....(2 marks)

c The neutralisation of dilute sulphuric acid by sodium hydroxide can be represented by the equation:

$$H^+(aq) + OH^-(aq) \rightarrow H_2O(l)$$

Which ion is always present in an aqueous solution of an acid?

....(1 mark)

[MEG]

ANSWER

a Sodium sulphate.

b Sulphuric acid solution has a low pH. The pH quickly increases to 7 (neutral) and then goes on above 7 when the solution is in excess.

c $H^+(aq)$.

Energy transfers and chemical reactions

Exothermic reactions

Most chemical reactions give out energy in the form of 'heat'. These are called exothermic reactions. All combustion reactions in which a fuel reacts with oxygen (called 'burning') are exothermic reactions. The fuel could be coal or it could be glucose in the cells of your body.

In any chemical reaction bonds must be broken between the particles in the reactants. Energy is required for this process. It takes energy to break a bond.

Breaking a bond is like snapping a ruler – both need energy. Making a bond gives out energy – just as clapping your hands together gives out sound energy.

When a bond is formed energy is given out.
A reaction gives out energy (that is, it is exothermic) when on balance the bonds that are made are stronger than those that were broken.

For example:

ethanol + oxygen $\rightarrow$ carbon dioxide + water

$$C_2H_5OH(aq) + 3O_2(g) \rightarrow 2CO_2(g) + 3H_2O(g)$$
$$\Delta H = -1367 \text{kJmol}^{-1}$$

ΔH is always *negative* for an exothermic reaction. Remember the energy is being 'given away' or *lost*.

Endothermic reactions

Some chemical reactions take in heat. The reading on a thermometer set up to monitor the reaction would go down. In this case the bonds that are formed are less strong than those that were broken.

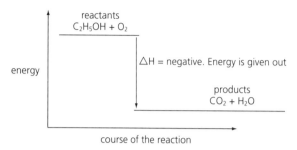

Fig 4 Energy level diagram for an exothermic reaction

A reaction takes in energy (that is, it is endothermic) when on balance the bonds in the reactants are stronger than those in the products.

For example: $6CO_2 + 6H_2O \rightarrow C_6H_{12}O_6 + 6H_2O$

This is the equation for photosynthesis, where energy is 'taken in' from the sun.

ΔH is always *positive* for an endothermic reaction. Remember the energy is being 'taken in' or *added*.

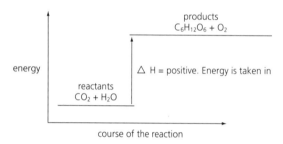

Fig 5 Energy level diagram for an endothermic reaction

Calculations involving bond energies

Bonds between atoms must be broken if the reactant is to take part in a chemical reaction. The amount of energy needed to break one mole of the bond is called the bond energy. The same amount of energy is released when one mole of the bond is made. By using these figures it is possible to calculate the energy change for the reaction and decide if it is an exothermic or endothermic reaction.

See p 174 for more details on the mole.

For example:

Using the bond energies given, calculate the expected energy change for the reaction:

$$CH_4(g) + 2O_2(g) \rightarrow 2H_2O(g) + CO_2(g)$$

(Bond energies (in kJ/mol): C–H: 435, O=O: 497, O–H: 464, C=O: 803)

It is best to write this in such a way that the structure of each substance can be seen:

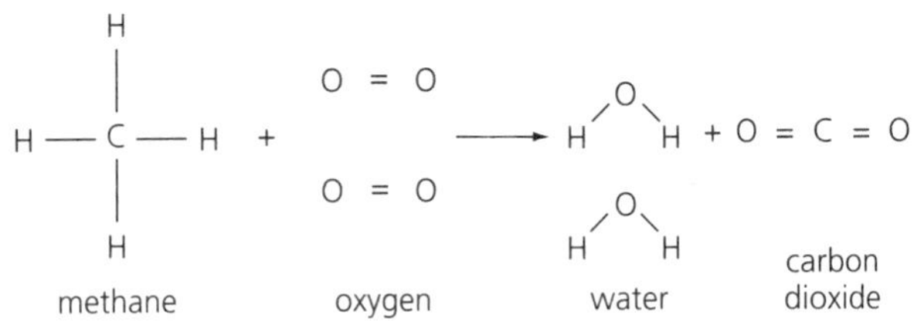

methane   oxygen   water   carbon dioxide

Fig 6

Bond breaking		Bond making	
Bonds broken	Energy needed (kJ/mol)	Bonds made	Energy released (kJ/mol)
4mol C–H	4×435	4 mol O–H	4×464
2mol O=O	2×497	2mol C=O	2×803
	$\overline{2734}$		$\overline{3462}$

Change in energy during the reaction:
$2734 - 3462 = -728\,kJ$
This is an exothermic reaction, as 728kJ of energy are given out.

QUESTION

Magnecal plc is a company which uses limestone (calcium carbonate) to manufacture quicklime (calcium oxide).
The equation for the reaction is:

calcium carbonate → calcium oxide + carbon dioxide
$CaCO_3$ → CaO + CO_2

Explain, in terms of the making and breaking of chemical bonds, why this reaction is endothermic.

....
....
....
....(3 marks)

[MEG]

ANSWER

Energy is needed to break the bonds in the calcium carbonate. Energy is released when bonds are formed in the calcium oxide and carbon dioxide. The reaction is endothermic because more energy is needed to break the bonds than is given out when the bonds are made.

QUESTION

The main part of a match is made of wood which contains carbohydrates. When a match is lit, the head starts burning and this then sets light to the rest of the match.

a When wood burns the bonds in the carbohydrate molecule are broken. What is needed to break these bonds?

....
....(1 mark)

b Wood burning is an exothermic process. Explain where the energy comes from.

....
....
....
....
....(2 marks)

c Explain, in scientific terms, why matches need to have heads.

....
....
....
....(2 marks)

[MEG]

ANSWER

a Energy must be transferred to break the bonds.

b As wood burning is an exothermic reaction, more energy must be released when the bonds are formed in the products than is needed to break the bonds in the carbohydrate molecules of the wood. *The total of the bond energies in the products is greater than the total of the bond energies in the reactants.*

c The match head starts to burn at a lower temperature than the wood, so it burns more easily and as it does so there is enough energy to start the wood burning.

QUESTION

Hydrogen reacts with bromine according to the equation below:

$H_2(g) + Br_2(g) \rightarrow 2HBr(g)$

The table below gives the bond energies of the molecules involved.

Molecule	Bond energy (kJ/mol)
H-H	436
Br-Br	193
H-Br	366

Calculate the energy change for this reaction.

....
....
....(4 marks)
[ULEAC]

ANSWER

Bonds broken	Energy needed (kJ/mol)	Bonds made	Energy released (kJ/mol)
1 mol H–H	436	2mol H–Br	2×366
1 mol Br–Br	193		
	– – – – –		– – – – –
	629		732

Change in energy during the reaction:
$629 - 732 = -103$ kJ
This is an exothermic reaction as 103 kJ of energy are given out.

What is the difference between a chemical reaction and a physical change?

To decide if a change is a physical change rather than a chemical reaction you need to look for:

- No new substances being made (if there are new substances then it is a chemical reaction).
- Whether it is easy to get the starting substance back again – this is a property of a physical change.
- A change of state from being a solid, liquid or gas into one of the other states. This is an example of a physical change.

Note that the total mass before the physical change is the same as the total mass after the physical change. Even if you can't see one of the substances because it is a gas, it still has mass.

Can the kinetic theory be used to explain changes?

The kinetic theory is also helpful in understanding a number of important ideas such as melting, freezing, evaporation, condensation, dissolving and diffusion.

Changes of state

This triangle can be used to describe the changes that happen when you heat a solid and a liquid, and when you cool a gas and a liquid.

Useful terms to know about physical changes:
Boiling point – the temperature at which a liquid boils. Although heat is still being added the temperature remains constant as the liquid is turned into gas.
Change of state – for example, solid to liquid, liquid to gas, gas to liquid, liquid to solid.
Condensation – gas turning to liquid.
Evaporation – when particles escape from the surface of a liquid and turn into the gaseous state.
Melting point – the temperature at which a solid melts. Although heat is still being added the temperature remains constant as the solid is turned into liquid.
Kinetic theory – this says that all matter is made up of moving particles and their movement depends on their mass and energy.
Matter – the term used to describe all the chemical substances in the universe.
States of matter – the three states of solid, liquid and gas.

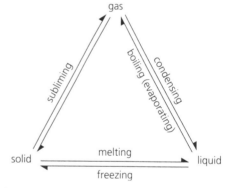

Fig 7 The changes of state triangle

Melting and freezing

When the liquid freezes, energy is released and the temperature stays constant.

Boiling and condensing

When the gas condenses, energy is released and the temperature stays constant.

QUESTION

1 a What words are used to describe:
  i turning a solid to a liquid? (1 mark)
  ii turning a gas to a liquid? (1 mark)
  b i Complete the chart overleaf saying whether each substance is a solid, liquid or gas at room temperature (20°C). (4 marks)

Substance	Melting point (°C)	Boiling point (°C)	Solid, liquid or gas
A	283	732	
B	−86	−62	
C	−23	77	
D	17	118	

ii Which substance in the chart is a solid at 200°C?

....(1 mark)

iii Which substance is a liquid over the smallest
temperature range?

....(1 mark)

ANSWER

1 a i Melting.
    ii Condensing.
  b i A: Solid.
      B: Gas.

Fig 8 Melting a solid

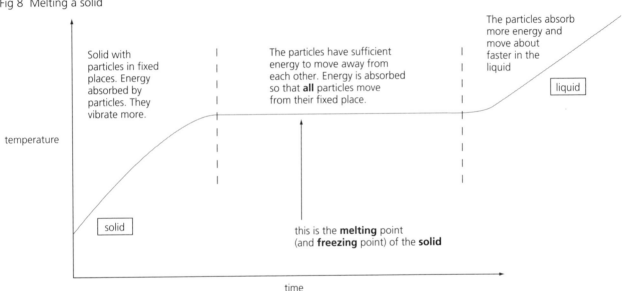

The particles absorb more energy and move about faster in the liquid

Solid with particles in fixed places. Energy absorbed by particles. They vibrate more.

The particles have sufficient energy to move away from each other. Energy is absorbed so that **all** particles move from their fixed place.

liquid

temperature

solid

this is the **melting** point (and **freezing** point) of the **solid**

time

Fig 9 Boiling a liquid

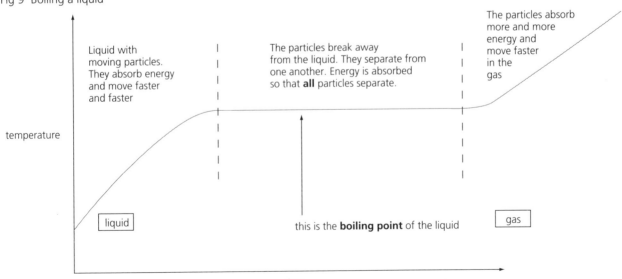

The particles absorb more and more energy and move faster in the gas

Liquid with moving particles. They absorb energy and move faster and faster

The particles break away from the liquid. They separate from one another. Energy is absorbed so that **all** particles separate.

temperature

liquid

gas

this is the **boiling point** of the liquid

time

C: Liquid.
D: Liquid.
ii A
iii B

How can the volume and pressure of a gas be changed?

The volume of a solid or a liquid can be measured fairly easily if you have the correct equipment. The volume of a gas is not so easy to measure. It is complicated because the volume of a gas can be changed easily, just by altering the temperature or the pressure.

Boyle's law

If you increase the pressure of a gas you decrease its volume.

This is easy to remember if you have ever pushed in the plunger of a syringe of air with your finger over the outlet.

It is helpful to work out what is happening by thinking in terms of particles.

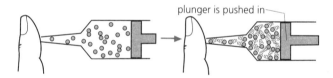

Fig 10 Pushing in the plunger on a syringe of gas

Boyle's law states that:
For a fixed mass of gas at a fixed temperature, increasing the pressure decreases the volume in proportion:
or volume α 1/pressure
$V = $ constant/p
$pV = $ constant

Charles' law

If you increase the temperature of a gas, the volume also increases, assuming that you do not change the pressure. You can remember this easily if you have seen the experiment in Fig 11.

Charles' law states that:
For a fixed mass of gas, the volume increases in proportion to the temperature if the pressure of the gas is kept constant.
$V \alpha T$
or $V = $ constant $\times T$
or $V/T = $ constant

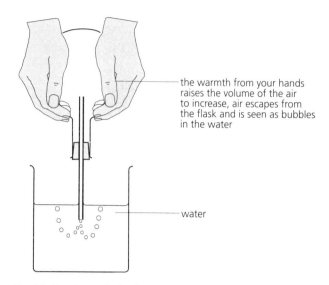

the warmth from your hands raises the volume of the air to increase, air escapes from the flask and is seen as bubbles in the water

water

Fig 11 Heating a flask of air

The Kelvin scale of temperature
If a graph is drawn of results for an experiment where the temperature of the gas is varied and the volume measured, it is noticed that the volume of the gas would be zero at –273°C. This is called absolute zero or zero kelvin. This is the temperature at which the particles of a substance would stop moving.

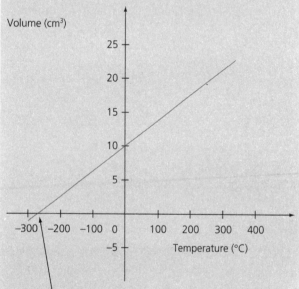

The volume would be zero at -273°C (called zero kelvin)
Fig 12 Graph showing how the temperature of a gas affects the volume

In any calculations involving the temperature, volume and pressure of a gas, the Kelvin temperature scale should be used. To turn °Celsius into kelvins you just add 273, so room temperature that is about 20°C would be 293K.

The ideal gas equation

Boyle's Law and Charles' Law can be combined. This equation is useful to convert one set of conditions relating to a gas to another set.

$$p_1V_1/T_1 = p_2V_2/T_2$$

where p_1, V_1 and T_1 are the pressure, volume and temperature of a gas at one time and p_2, V_2 and T_2 are the pressure, volume and temperature of a gas at a later time.

QUESTION

a Many chemical reactions produce gases. Gases are affected by changes in temperature and pressure. For a fixed mass of gas, what would happen to the volume if:

   i the pressure were increased and the temperature kept constant;

   ....(1 mark)

   ii the temperature were increased and the pressure kept constant?

   ....(1 mark)

b A fixed mass of hydrogen, of volume 10dm³, at a constant pressure had its temperature increased from 100K to 200K. Calculate the new volume.

   ....
   ....
   ....(1 mark)
   [WJEC]

ANSWER

a   i The volume would decrease.
    ii The volume would increase.
b 20 dm³ *(don't forget the units)*.

QUESTION

Mountaineers who climb high mountains have problems cooking food. Water does not always boil at 100°C.

a What is the relationship between height above sea level and the boiling point of water?

   ....
   ....(1 mark)

b Use the information to explain why an egg heated in boiling water for three minutes will be cooked at sea level, but a similar egg heated in boiling water for three minutes on the top of Mount Everest will be almost raw.

   ....

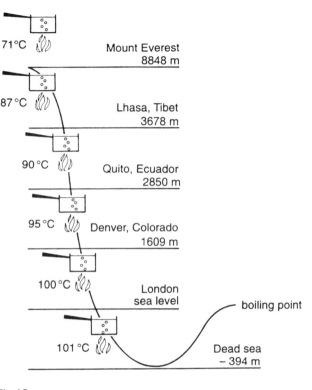

Fig 13

   ....
   ....
   ....(2 marks)

c Some mountaineers carry cylinders of oxygen. It gets colder as they climb higher.

   i How will the fall in the temperature affect the pressure of the oxygen in the cylinders?

   ....
   ....(1 mark)

   ii A mountaineer's cylinder contains 1m³ of oxygen at 180 atmospheres pressure at a temperature of 300K. His friend has an identical cylinder which is completely empty. The mountaineers connect the cylinders to share the oxygen.
   What is the new oxygen pressure in the joined cylinders?

   ....(2 marks)

   iii State the formula linking pressure, volume and temperature for a fixed mass of gas under different conditions.

   ....
   ....(1 mark)
   [MEG]

ANSWER

a As the height above sea level increases the temperature at which water boils decreases.

b On Mount Everest water boils at 71°C, which is nearly 30°C lower than at sea level. The reactions involved in cooking the egg will take longer at this lower temperature, so after three minutes the egg is still almost raw.

c i The fall in temperature will decrease the pressure of the oxygen.

ii The new pressure will be 90 atmospheres pressure – half what it was.

The new volume is $2m^3$ (as the volume of *each* cylinder is $1m^3$)

Using: $V_1p_1 = V_2p_2$

$$1 \times 180 = 2 \times p_2$$
$$1 \times 180/2 = p_2$$
$$90 = p_2$$

iii $p_1V_1/T_1 = p_2V_2/T_2$

Revision sheet

Some important chemical ideas

1 Describe diffusion in terms of particles.
2 A pure substance:
   a has a sharp melting and .... point.
   b can be an element or a ....
3 Metals form oxides which turn damp pH paper ...., whereas non-metal oxides turn damp pH paper ....
4 a An aqueous solution is formed when a solid .... in ....
   b The solid is called the solute and the liquid that it is dissolved in is called the ....
   c If a solid is formed when two solutions are mixed, the solid is called a ....
5 a To get a dissolved solid from a solution I would ....
   b To get an insoluble substance from a mixture with water I would ....
   c To separate two liquids, which mix, I would ....
   d To separate two colours, for example in ink, I would use ....

Chemical reactions and physical processes

1 To see if there is a chemical reaction we look for:
   a ....substance being made.
   b a change of ....

2 An exothermic reaction remove gives off ...., the sum of the bond energies of the products is .... than the reactants.
3 An endothermic reaction .... energy, the sum of the bond energies of the products is .... than the reactants.
4 What do each of these symbols mean if you see them in a chemical reaction:
   (s)............... (g)............... (aq)............... (l)............... .
5 In a neutralisation reaction we can write a general equation like this:
   acid + ... → salt +............... .
6 A solution which has H^+ ions is an .... and a solution which has OH^- ions is an ....
7 A thermal decomposition reaction occurs when a subtance is split up into simpler substances using ....
8 An oxidation reaction can be where:
   a .... is one of the reactants.
   b .... is removed from a reactant.
   c .... are lost from a reactant.
9 Finish these sentences:
   a Turning a gas into a liquid is called ....
   b Turning a liquid into a solid is called ....
   c If room temperature is 20°C, and a substance melts at −23°C and boils at 77°C, at room temperature it is a ....
10 The equation which tells you how pressure, temperature and volume are linked for a fixed mass of gas under different conditions is ....

Revision sheet answers

Some important chemical ideas

1 Particles spread out from a substance, they move from an area of high concentration to one of low concentration.
2 a Boiling.
   b Compound.
3 Metal oxides: purple/blue (alkaline), non-metal oxides: red/orange (acidic).
4 a Dissolves, water.
   b Solvent.
   c Precipitate.
5 a Evaporate or crystallise it.
   b Filter it.
   c Distil them.
   d Chromatography.

Chemical reactions and physical processes

1 a New.
 b Energy.
2 Energy (often as heat), more.
3 Takes in, less.
4 (s) – solid; (g) – gas; (aq) – aqueous; (l) – liquid
5 Acid + alkali → salt + water
6 Acid; alkali.
7 Heat.
8 a Oxygen.
 b Hydrogen.
 c Electrons.
9 a Condensing.
 b Freezing.
 c Liquid.
10 $p_1V_1/T_1 = p_2V_2/T_2$

Student Answer with Comments

The approximate bond energies in kilojoules per mole (kJ/mol) are given for some bonds.

Bond	Bond energy in kJ/mol
C–H	435
O=O	498
O–H	464
C=O	805

i Calculate how much energy is used in breaking the four C–H bonds in one mole of methane (CH_4). (1 mark)
 $4 \times 435 = 1740$ ✓ ①
                              Answer = 1740 kJ

ii Calculate how much energy is released in making the two C=O bonds in one mole of carbon dioxide (CO_2). (1 mark)
 energy needed   *watch this carefully!* ✓ ①
 $= 805 \times 2 = 1610$ Answer = 1610 kJ

iii Calculate how much energy is released by the combustion of one mole of methane.
 $CH_4 + 2O_2 \rightarrow 2H_2O + CO_2$
 Show clearly how you obtain your answer.
                              (3 marks)
 $4 \times 435 + 2 \times 498 \rightarrow 2 \times 464 + 2 \times 805$
 $2736 \rightarrow 2538$
 $2736 - 2538$ ② ✗
 $= 198$ Answer = 198 kJ

There are 4 O–H bonds, not 2!
Even though the answer is not correct, you've shown your working: worth 2 marks.

iv A mixture of methane and oxygen needs to be heated before it starts to burn. Use the idea of breaking and making bonds to explain why. (3 marks)
 The oxygen bonds need 498 kJ/mol to break.
 The methane bonds need 1610 kJ/mol to break.
 No reaction can take place until there is 1610
 KJ of energy per mol of CH_4. Heating the
 mixture is one way of obtaining the energy
 needed.   ③

 $7/8$ Part question [SEG 1994]

An exam question for you to try

QUESTION

Ammonia gas and hydrogen bromide gas react together to give ammonium bromide in the form of a white smoke.
In an experiment, solutions of each gas were put onto separate pieces of cotton wool. These were placed at either end of a 1 metre glass tube. The gases started to move along the tube and after about 3–4 minutes a ring of white smoke appeared as shown below.

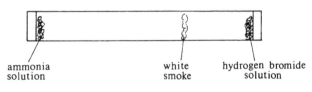

ammonia   white   hydrogen bromide
solution   smoke   solution

Fig 1

a i What is the name given to the movement of the gases?
 ....(1 mark)

ii Explain why it took the gas particles so long (3–4 minutes) to travel such a short distance (less than 1m).
 ....
 ....(2 marks)

iii Suggest why the smoke formed nearer one end of the tube rather than in the middle.
 ....(1 mark)

iv Write a word equation for the formation of the white smoke.
 ....(2 marks)

b The experiment was repeated at a higher temperature. The white smoke formed within 2 minutes but in the same position in the tube as in the first experiment. Explain these observations.

....
....
....
....(4 marks)

c Hydrogen bromide solution is an acid.

i Describe a simple test that you could do to show this.

Test.................................Result......................
....
....(2 marks)

ii Name another solution which would behave in a similar way to hydrogen bromide in the above test.

....(1 mark)

[ULEAC]

Answer

a i Diffusion.

ii The particles bump into particles of air that are in the tube. It takes them several minutes to diffuse between the air particles.

iii The particles of one substance (ammonia) diffused more quickly than the particles of the other (hydrogen bromide). The ammonia particles are lighter and move more quickly at the same temperature.

iv ammonia + hydrogen bromide = ammonium bromide.

b At higher temperatures the particles move more quickly so diffuse more quickly. However as both types of particles diffuse more quickly the white substance is formed at the same place.

c i Test: Dip a piece of UI paper in the hydrogen bromide solution.
Result: It goes red.

ii Any acid! e.g. Hydrogen chloride solution.

Inside atoms

8

Inside atoms	Midland (MEG)				Northern (NEAB)		London (ULEAC)				Southern (SEG)		Welsh (WJEC)
	Own	Nuffield	Salters	Suffolk	Co-ordinated	Modular	Modular GASP	Combined	Co-ordinated	Modular	Double	Modular	Co-ordinated
ATOMIC STRUCTURE													
Electrons, protons and neutrons	✓	✓	✓	✓	✓	✓	✓	✓	✓	✓	✓	✓	✓
Electronic structure and the periodic table	✓	✓	✓	✓	✓	✓	✓	✓	✓	✓	✓	✓	✓
Isotopes	✓	✓	✓	H	✓	✓	✓	✓	✓	✓	✓	✓	✓
Formation of ions	✓	✓	✓	✓	✓	✓	✓	✓	✓	✓	✓	✓	✓
RADIOACTIVITY													
Types of radiations	✓	✓	H	✓	✓	✓	✓	✓	✓	✓	✓	✓	✓
Half-life	✓	H	H	H	H	H	H	H	H	H	✓	H	H
Uses of radioactivity	✓	✓	✓	✓	✓	✓	✓	✓	✓	✓	✓	✓	✓

Atomic structure

What do we mean when we use the word 'particles'?

It is often helpful to think of matter as being made up of particles. It is important to know about three sorts of particles. These are:

- atoms.
- ions.
- molecules.

Important facts about atoms

- Each element consists of atoms of one kind.
- Atoms are very small; their radius is about 10^{-10} metres (2 million atoms would fit into the thickness of a page of this book).
- Atoms cannot be created or destroyed (atoms around today were formed when the Earth was formed).
- Atoms contain smaller particles called sub-atomic particles (these are called electrons, protons and neutrons).
- Most of an atom is empty space. There is a tiny nucleus in the centre and this is surrounded by the electrons which form a cloud and extend a long way from it.

Electrons

These are very important as they are the outer particles of an atom and take part in chemical reactions. They can be thought of as being arranged in shells, rather like the layers in an onion. Electrons are very light (about 1,840 of them weigh the same as a hydrogen atom) and they have a negative charge.

Protons

These are found in the nucleus of the atom, which is at its centre. Each one weighs about the same as a hydrogen atom (called 1amu or atomic mass unit). A proton has a positive charge.
Note that in an atom there are as many protons as there are electrons. This is what makes the atom have a neutral electrical charge.

Neutrons

These are also found in the nucleus, with the protons. Each neutron also has a mass of 1amu. Neutrons do not have a charge.

name of particle	where it is found in the atom	charge	mass (in amu)
electron	moving outside the nucleus	−1	1/1840
proton	in the nucleus	+1	1
neutron	in the nucleus	0	1

Note: the unit a.m.u. stands for atomic mass unit. Atomic mass units are defined by reference to an atom of carbon.

$$^{12}_{6}C$$

This has a mass of exactly 12.0 units.

Finding out information about electrons, protons and neutrons

You will often see information about an element written like this. Take oxygen for example:

mass number → | 16 |
| O | ← the symbol for
atomic number → | 8 | oxygen

From this information you can tell that:

- Oxygen has 8 protons (the number of protons is the same as the number of electrons in an atom).
- Oxygen has 8 electrons (the atomic number – given the symbol Z – tells you this.)
- Oxygen has a total of 16 nucleons (protons plus neutrons) in the nucleus (the mass number – given the symbol A – tells you this).
- Oxygen has 8 neutrons (if it has 16 protons and neutrons combined then it must have 8 neutrons as it has 8 protons).

More about the electrons

Bohr proposed an 'electron shell' idea which helps us to understand more about electrons in an atom. The main points of this are:

- Electrons are arranged in layers (usually called shells) around the nucleus.
- The shell nearest the nucleus (called the first shell) can only contain up to 2 electrons.
- The second shell can contain up to 8 electrons.
- The third shell can contain up to 18 electrons. (But for small atoms with less than 20 electrons in all, this third shell only contains up to 8 electrons.)
- The shell nearest the nucleus fills with electrons first.
- The electrons furthest from the nucleus can be removed more easily. It gets harder and harder to remove electrons the nearer to the nucleus they are.

Oxygen can be written as 2,6 to show how the electrons are arranged in shells. This may be drawn as:

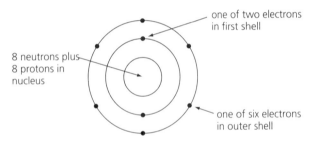

8 neutrons plus 8 protons in nucleus

one of two electrons in first shell

one of six electrons in outer shell

Fig 1 The atomic structure of oxygen

What are isotopes?

If you look at a periodic table you will see that the relative atomic mass for chlorine is 35.5 This is because chlorine, like many other elements, has a number of isotopes. Chlorine has two stable isotopes, $^{35}_{17}$Cl and $^{37}_{17}$Cl.

The atomic number of each of the isotopes is 17, which means they each have 17 electrons and 17 protons, but Chlorine –35 has 18 neutrons and Chlorine –37 has 20 neutrons.
Isotopes of an element have the same atomic number (Z) but different mass numbers (A).

How do you work out the mass number when the element has isotopes?

In the example above, the relative atomic mass is given as 35.5.

This is the average mass of the two different isotopes, and takes account of the proportion of each isotope in the element.
For example:
75% of chlorine is made up of Chlorine–35 and 25% is made up of Chlorine–37. To work out the average suppose that you have 100 atoms, 75 of ^{35}Cl and 25 of ^{37}Cl.
The average of this is: $(75 \times 35) + (25 \times 37) / 100$ = 35.5.
This is the relative atomic mass of chlorine that is seen on the periodic table.

QUESTION

The two carbon atoms represented below are isotopes.

ISOTOPE 1		ISOTOPE 2
14	← mass number →	12
C		C
6	← proton number →	6

a Describe two ways in which the isotopes are similar.

....
....(2 marks)

b Describe as fully as you can one way in which they are different.

....
....
....(2 marks)

[NEAB]

ANSWER

a The isotopes each have six electrons and six protons.

b Isotope 1 has two more neutrons (8) than isotope 2, which only has 6 neutrons.

QUESTION

An atom has the atomic (proton) number 17 and the mass (nucleon) number 35. Another atom has the atomic (proton) number 17 and the mass (nucleon) number 37.

i These atoms are called *isotopes*. Explain why.

....
....(2 marks)

ii These are isotopes of chlorine. How can you tell?

....(1 mark)

iii There are 17 electrons in every chlorine atom. What is the number of electrons in each energy level (shell) of the chlorine atom? Write your answers inside the boxes. (3 marks)

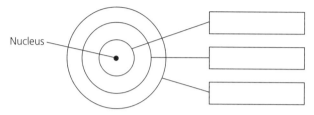

Fig 2

Part question [SEG 1994]

ANSWER

i Isotopes contain the same number of protons and electrons but contain different numbers of neutrons. *Notice there are two marks so you must try and include two points here.*

ii The atomic number of both isotopes is 17, this is the atomic number of chlorine.

iii First box 2; Second box: 8; Third box: 7

QUESTION

Boron is a non-metallic element.

a The table shows information about two types of boron atom.

atom	symbol	protons	electrons	neutrons
boron-10	10 B 5			
boron-11	11 B 5			

i Complete the table. (3 marks)

ii What term is used for different atoms of the same element?

....(1 mark)

iii The relative atomic mass of boron measured precisely is 10.82. What does this tell you about the relative amounts of the two different boron atoms in a sample of boron? (No calculation required).

....
....(1 mark)

iv What is the electron arrangement in a boron atom?

....(1 mark)

[MEG]

ANSWER

i

atom	symbol	protons	electrons	neutrons
boron-10	10 B 5	5	5	5
boron-11	11 B 5	5	5	6

ii Isotopes.

iii There are more boron-11 atoms in boron than there are boron-10 atoms.
(This is because 10.82 is nearer to 11 than to 10.)

iv Electron arrangement in boron: 2,3

Important facts about ions

- An ion has a charge.
- The symbol of the atom is used for the ion (but it must always be followed by the charge).
- Metals form positive ions (called cations).
- Non-metals form negative ions (called anions).
- A positive ion is formed when an atom loses an electron or electrons.
- A negative ion is formed when an atom gains an electron or electrons.
- Elements at the left and right of the periodic table are more likely to form ions than elements in the middle.

How ions are formed

Forming Positive ions

The 11 electrons in sodium can be written to show how they are arranged around the nucleus as: 2,8,1. The sodium atom also has 11 protons so it has no charge; it is electrically neutral.

The outer electron can be removed fairly easily in a chemical reaction to leave only 10 electrons. As a negative electron has been removed, what is left has one extra positive charge compared to the atom. It cannot be called an atom. It is called a positive sodium ion.

Na	$\rightarrow$	Na^+	+	e^-
sodium atom with no charge	loses an electron	sodium ion with a positive charge		electron

Forming negative ions

The 17 electrons in chlorine can be written to show their arrangement around the nucleus as: 2,8,7.
The chlorine atom also has 17 protons so it has no charge; it is electrically neutral.
The 7 outer electrons can fairly easily gain another so that the outer shell has 8 electrons. A negative electron has been gained and so the resulting particle has one more negative charge than the nucleus. This is now called a negative chloride ion.

Cl	+ e^-	→ Cl^-
chlorine atom with no charge	gains an electron	chloride ion with a negative charge

How can the periodic table tell us about the structure of atoms?

If you look at the periodic table (for example Fig 3) you will see that it is made up of a number of columns and rows containing elements.

Basic facts about the periodic table

- The elements are listed in order of their atomic number (Z).
- The elements are listed in rows.
- A new row starts after each noble gas.
- There are seven horizontal rows – these are called periods.
- There are eight main columns – these are called groups.

Using the periodic table to give information about the elements

- The number of the group tells you how many electrons are in the outer shell of the atom; e.g. sodium is in group 1 and so has one electron in the outer shell.
- As all the elements in a group have the same number of electrons in their outer shell they react in a similar way.
- The number of the period tells you how many shells of electrons the atom has, eg. sodium can be written as 2,8,1 … there are three shells of electrons.
- As you move down a group there are more shells of electrons. Therefore, the atoms in any one group get bigger as you move down the group.
- Moving from left to right across a period, for example period 2, the number of electrons increases. The number of electrons in the outer

Group Period	I Alkali metals	II Alkaline earth metals											III	IV	V	VI	VII Halogens	0 Noble gases
1				1 H Hydrogen 1.0														2 He Helium 4.0
2	3 Li Lithium 6.9	4 Be Beryllium 9.0											5 B Boron 10.8	6 C Carbon 12.0	7 N Nitrogen 14.0	8 O Oxygen 16.0	9 F Fluorine 19.0	10 Ne Neon 20.2
3	11 Na Sodium 23.0	12 Mg Magnesium 24.3											13 Al Aluminium 27.0	14 Si Silicon 28.1	15 P Phosphorus 31.0	16 S Sulphur 32.1	17 Cl Chlorine 35.5	18 Ar Argon 39.9
4	19 K Potassium 39.1	20 Ca Calcium 40.1	21 Sc Scandium 45.0	22 Ti Titanium 47.9	23 V Vanadium 50.9	24 Cr Chromium 52.0	25 Mn Manganese 54.9	26 Fe Iron 55.9	27 Co Cobalt 58.9	28 Ni Nickel 58.7	29 Cu Copper 63.5	30 Zn Zinc 65.4	31 Ga Gallium 69.7	32 Ge Germanium 72.6	33 As Arsenic 74.9	34 Se Selenium 79.0	35 Br Bromine 79.9	36 Kr Krypton 83.8
5	37 Rb Rubidium 85.5	38 Sr Strontium 87.6	39 Y Yttrium 88.9	40 Zr Zirconium 91.2	41 Nb Niobium 92.9	42 Mo Molybdenum 95.9	43 Tc Technetium (99)	44 Ru Ruthenium 101.1	45 Rh Rhodium 102.9	46 Pd Palladium 106.4	47 Ag Silver 107.9	48 Cd Cadmium 112.4	49 In Indium 114.8	50 Sn Tin 118.7	51 Sb Antimony 121.8	52 Te Tellurium 127.6	53 I Iodine 126.9	54 Xe Xenon 131.3
6	55 Cs Caesium 132.9	56 Ba Barium 137.3	57 ▸ La Lanthanum 138.9	72 Hf Hafnium 178.5	73 Ta Tantalum 181.0	74 W Tungsten 183.9	75 Re Rhenium 186.2	76 Os Osmium 190.2	77 Ir Iridium 192.2	78 Pt Platinum 195.1	79 Au Gold 197.0	80 Hg Mercury 200.6	81 Ti Thallium 204.4	82 Pb Lead 207.2	83 Bi Bismuth 209.0	84 Po Polonium (210)	85 At Astatine (210)	86 Rn Radon (222)
7	87 Fr Francium (223)	88 Ra Radium (226)	87 ▸▸ Ac Actinium (227)	104 Unq Unnil-quadium (261)	105 Unp Unnil-pentium (262)	106 Unh Unnil-hexium (263)												
▸ Lanthanide elements					58 Ce Cerium 140.2	59 Pr Praseo-dymium 140.9	60 Nd Neody-mimum 144.2	61 Pm Promethium (147)	62 Sm Samarium 150.4	63 Eu Europium 152.0	64 Gd Gadolinium 157.3	65 Tb Terbium 158.9	66 Dy Dysprosium 162.5	67 Ho Holmium 164.9	68 Er Erbium 167.3	69 Tm Thulium 168.9	70 Yb Ytterbium 173.0	71 Lu Lutetium 175.0
▸▸ Actinide elements					90 Th Thorium 232.0	91 Pa Protactinium (231)	92 U Uranium 238.1	93 Np Neptunium (237)	94 Pu Plutonium (242)	95 Am Amercium (243)	96 Cm Curium (247)	97 Bk Berkelium (245)	98 Cr Californium (251)	99 Es Einsteinium (254)	100 Fm Fermium (253)	101 Md Mendelevium (256)	102 No Nobelium (254)	103 Lr Lawrencium (257)

Fig 3 The periodic table

shell determines the chemical properties of the element. As a general rule, on the left hand side of a period the elements have the properties of metals, and on the right hand side of a period the elements have more non-metallic properties.

(Section 10 gives you more information about the periodic table and how the reactions of the elements depend on the arrangement of electrons in their atoms.)

QUESTION

Magnecal plc manufactures magnesium oxide (MgO), which has a very high melting point and is used for lining iron and steel furnaces.

   i Write down the formula for a magnesium ion, showing its charge.

     ....(1 mark)

  ii Refer to the Periodic Table to explain why the ion has this charge.

     ....

     ....(2 marks)

 iii Describe the change which takes place when this ion is formed from a magnesium atom.

     ....

     ....

     ....(2 marks)

 iv Why does magnesium oxide have a high melting point?

     ....

     ....

     ....(2 marks)

                                    [MEG]

ANSWER

   i Mg^{2+}.

  ii Magnesium is in group two. It has two outer electrons; when it loses these it forms the Mg^{2+} ion.

 iii When the magnesium ion is formed from the magnesium atom the two electrons are lost.

 iv Magnesium oxide has ionic bonding. The magnesium atom loses two electrons which are taken up by the oxygen atom. Compounds with ionic bonds have high melting points. (See p 184 for more details of this.)

QUESTION

a The reactivity series places metals in order of their ability to lose electrons to form ions.

The table below shows metals in order of decreasing reactivity and their Groups.

Metal	Group	Reactivity
potassium	1	most reactive
sodium	1	
strontium	2	
calcium	2	
magnesium	2	
aluminium	3	
zinc	–	
iron	–	
copper	–	
silver	–	least reactive

   i How is the reactivity of a metal related to its Group in the periodic table?

     ....

     ....(1 mark)

  ii Explain your answer to part (i).

     ....

     ....

     ....

     ....(3 marks)

b The table below lists some metals in Groups 1, 2 and 3. The metals within each Group are arranged in order of increasing proton number.

Group 1	Group 2	Group 3
sodium	magnesium	aluminium
potassium	calcium	gallium
rubidium	strontium	indium
caesium	barium	thallium

   i What is the pattern of reactivity within each Group?

     ....(1 mark)

  ii Explain your answer to part (i)

     ....

     ....

     ....

     ....(3 marks)

 iii Between which two metals in the reactivity series in part (a) would you place gallium?

     ....and............................(1 mark)

                                 [ULEAC]

ANSWER

a   i The reactivity of the metals decreases as the Group number increases.

ii *There are three marks here. Your answer should include the following points:*
As the Group number increases there are more electrons in the outer shell of the atom. More energy is needed to remove these electrons (it takes more energy to remove three electrons, for example, than one electron). Atoms with only one electron in their outer shell are therefore more reactive as less energy is needed to remove the single electron.

b i The reactivity increases as you move down each group.

ii *There are three marks here. Your answer should include the following points:*
Moving down a Group there are more shells of electrons. At the bottom of each Group, the outer electrons are further away from the nucleus than at the top of each Group. Less energy is required to remove these electrons and so the elements at the bottom of each Group are more reactive.

iii Between magnesium and aluminium.
(Gallium is more reactive than aluminium, and the least reactive element in group 2 is magnesium, so it should be placed between them.)
Page 208 on the periodic table may help you if you had difficulty with this question

Important facts about molecules

- Molecules are formed when atoms share electrons.
- The sharing of electrons in a molecule is called a covalent bond.
- Molecules are formed when two non-metals react.

QUESTION

Chlorine will combine with the non-metal element, carbon, to form this molecular compound.
a What is the type of bond in this molecule?
....(1 mark)

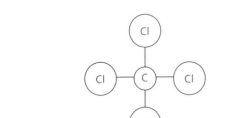

Fig 4

b Explain how these bonds are formed. (You may use a diagram.)

....
....
....
....(2 marks)
[NEAB]

ANSWER

a Covalent.
b In each covalent bond the carbon and the chlorine share a pair of electrons.
You could draw a dot and cross diagram as on p 184 to show this.
(You will find more information on molecules on p 184–185.)

Radioactivity

What is radioactivity?

This was the word first used to describe the invisible rays given out spontaneously by some substances. A radioactive substance is a substance that gives out high energy rays – called radiations. There are some radiations around us all the time. Together they are called background radiation. This type of radiation comes mainly from rocks, soil and cosmic rays from outer space.

Why are some substances radioactive?

Radiations are formed when the nucleus of an atom breaks apart. Very heavy nuclei with many neutrons and protons are sometimes unstable, and for smaller nuclei it is the balance between the number of neutrons and protons that determines whether a particular nucleus is stable. When a nucleus breaks up (or decays) the nucleus that forms is more stable than the original.

unstable nucleus → more stable nucleus + radiation

What are the types of radiation?

There are three main types of radiation. One common feature is that they can all cause atoms that they hit to form positive ions by losing electrons. Their ability to cause this ionisation varies, and is described along with their other characteristics in the following table.

The three main types of radiation

type	description	how stopped	example and notes
alpha (α) particles	made up of 2 protons and 2 neutrons, actually a helium nucleus; positive charge (He^{2+})	thin piece of paper	e.g.: $$^{226}_{88}Ra \rightarrow {}^{222}_{86}Rn + {}^{4}_{2}He \text{ (alpha particle)}$$ particles which attract electrons from other atoms; can only travel a few centimetres in air, highly ionising
beta (β) particles	electrons; formed when a neutron in a nucleus turns into a proton and electron, the electron is ejected from the nucleus; negative charge; travels close to the speed of light	thin sheet of aluminium	e.g.: $$^{90}_{38}Sr \rightarrow {}^{90}_{39}Y + e^- \text{ (beta particle)}$$ travel further than alpha particles, but not so ionising
gamma (γ) rays	electromagnetic radiations given out when a nucleus loses an alpha or beta particle; high energy rays with a very short wavelength	several metres of concrete	the mass number and atomic number of the substance do not change; cause little ionisation but are very penetrating

Alpha, beta and gamma radiation from uranium.

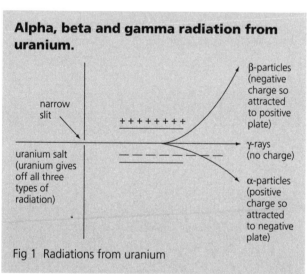

Fig 1 Radiations from uranium

Detecting radiation
The different ways of detecting radiation make use of the fact that the rays cause atoms to form ions:
- Cloud chamber: tracks are seen as water condenses on the ions formed, due to the movement of an alpha particle.
- Geiger-Muller tubes: ions in a gas are formed. These are detected by an electrical pulse meter – you may hear these as 'clicks'.

QUESTION

Radioisotopes decay to become more stable. Carbon-14 emits a beta particle when it decays. It decays according to the equation:

$$^{14}_{6}C \rightarrow {}^{14}_{7}N + {}^{0}_{-1}e$$

i What is a beta particle?

....(1 mark)

ii What change occurs in the nucleus of the carbon-14 when it decays?

....

....

....(3 marks)

iii How can beta particles be detected?

....(1 mark)

iv In the diagram below, a beam of beta particles is passing through an electric field. Complete the diagram to show what happens to the beam in the field.

(1 mark)

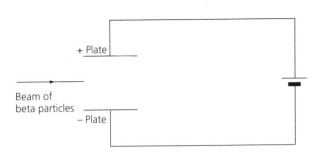

Fig 2

[ULEAC]

ANSWER

i A beta particle is an electron.

ii In the nucleus a neutron turns into a proton and an electron. The electron is ejected from the nucleus. This results in the neutron number decreasing by one (from 8 to 7) and the proton number increasing by one (from 6 to 7).

iii Beta particles can be detected by a Geiger-Muller tube. *(You could also give: cloud chamber, photographic film.)*

iv *As the beta particles are negative they move towards the positive top plate. Therefore, you should draw a curve from the entry of the beam towards the top plate.*

What is half-life?

When the nucleus of an unstable atom decays it gives out radiation. In a radioactive isotope (see p 160) it is not possible to predict when any one nucleus will decay, but it is possible to measure what fraction of the atoms will decay in a given time. The half-life is the time taken for half the atoms in a radioactive isotope to decay.

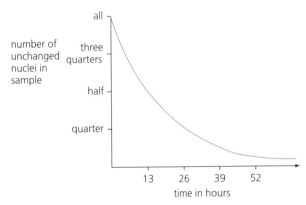

Fig 3 The half life of iodine-123 is about 13 hours

Iodine-123 is a radioactive tracer that may be used to check the activity of a patient's thyroid gland. A Geiger-Muller tube connected to a ratemeter may be used to determine the count rate, that is the amount of radiation given out per second from an isotope.

A radioactive tracer is an isotope which is used to follow any biological (or physical) process or chemical reaction.

Each isotope has its own half life. For example, the half life of uranium-238 is 5×10^9 years but for lawrencium-140 it is just 14 seconds.

QUESTION

i On the axes provided plot a half-life graph (decay curve) for carbon-14. (Remember that carbon-14 has a half life of 5,600 years.) The first point has been plotted for you.

(3 marks)

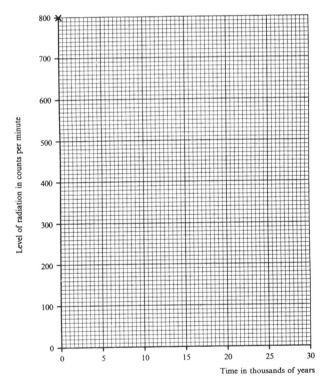

Fig 4

ii Use your graph to estimate how long it would take for the radiation due to carbon-14 to fall to 20 per cent, that is one fifth of its original value.

....(1 mark)

Part question [SEG 1994]

ANSWER

i   You should draw a smooth curve, starting at the point given. The level of radiation should be 400 counts per minute to correspond with 5.6 (the x axis is in 'thousands of years'), then 200 counts per minute should correspond to 11.2 etc. *The more points that you can plot the smoother the curve that you can draw.*

ii From the graph you should be able to read this as between 12,000 and 13,000 years *(don't forget the units).*

How does radioactivity affect living organisms?

The effect of radiations on the body is due to a combination of two of their features:

* How easily they cause atoms to form ions – that is how ionising they are.
* How easily they pass through materials – that is how penetrating they are.

alpha particles

* Highly ionising.
* Stopped by a thin layer of paper.
  BUT if they enter the body they are very dangerous.

beta particles

* Less ionising than alpha particles.
* More penetrating than alpha particles, but cannot penetrate as far as the internal organs.

gamma rays

* Little ionisation.
* Highly penetrating, gamma rays will pass through the body affecting the internal organs.

Radiation is most dangerous if it reaches the DNA in cells and causes changes to occur in the genes. The cells may divide in an uncontrolled way and form a tumour. This may be malignant if cells break off and travel round the body in blood or lymph to other parts, where tumours can be established. This results in cancer. If gametes (the sperm and ova) are affected this can cause defects in babies (see p 100).

QUESTION

Alpha and gamma radiation can affect humans in different ways. A source of alpha radiation has little effect unless it is absorbed into the body, where it can be very damaging. Gamma sources can cause most damage from outside the body.
Explain how the properties of alpha and gamma radiation cause these differences.

....

....

....

....(4 marks)

[MEG]

ANSWER

Alpha radiation can be stopped by a thin layer of paper so it is not likely to enter the body unless the source is actually absorbed into the body. The particles attract electrons from other atoms, so they are highly ionising. Therefore if they get into the body they are likely to cause damage in the cells. Gamma radiation, unlike alpha radiation, is much more penetrating and is only stopped by many metres of concrete. It is therefore more likely than alpha radiation to penetrate the body. Once in the body however it causes little ionisation – unlike alpha radiation.
(Do remember to talk about both sorts of radiation in you answer.)

QUESTION

In an experiment to study a radioisotope a teacher used a special detector to measure the radioactivity. The detector produced an electrical pulse when a radioactive particle entered it. The pulses were counted by an electrical counter.

a Name a suitable radioactivity detector.

....(1 mark)

b The teacher first used the detector to measure the background radiation level. This was done by switching it on for one minute. The background count was found to be 24 counts/minute.
Suggest two sources of background radioactivity.

1 ....

....

2 ....

....(2 marks)

c The teacher then placed the radioisotope close to the detector as shown in the diagram below. The radiation reaching the detector in one minute was measured.

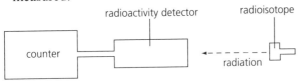

radioactivity detector   radioisotope

counter   radiation

Fig 5

Then different materials were placed between the radioisotope and the detector. The radiation which reached the detector was measured each time. During the experiments the teacher took great care not to bring the radioisotope near the hands or to point it at anyone. The results of the experiment are shown in the table.

RADIATION DETECTED (counts/minute)				
No material	Paper	Thin metal	Thick lead	Background count
895	460	24	24	24

  i What type or types of radiation did this radioisotope emit?

....(1 mark)

  ii Explain the reasons for your answer.

....

....

....

....

....(3 marks)

d Explain, as fully as you can, how the radioisotope could cause damage to your hand if you put your hand near it.

....

....

....

....

....

....

....(4 marks)

[NEAB]

ANSWER

a Geiger-Muller tube.

b *Many suitable answers here*, any two from: cosmic rays from outer space, rocks and soil, medical uses (e.g. X-rays), radon inside houses.

c i Alpha and beta.

  ii There is a big reduction when thin paper is used – indicates presence of alpha radiation. Further reduction with thin metal – indicates presence of beta radiation.
The count for thick lead is the same as for the background – indicates no gamma radiation.

d Alpha and beta particles are ionising (although beta particles are less ionising than alpha particles).
Should these radiations penetrate the body then they cause atoms in the cells to ionise.
This may cause damage to the cells and may lead to mutations in the DNA, causing the cells to divide in an uncontrolled way. A tumour may form.

Radon

Radon-222 is a radioactive gas that is formed when uranium decays. As radon is formed in rocks in the ground it rises and collects in buildings. Radon is thought to be a bigger risk to health than any other form of environmental pollution. It can cause lung cancer.

Being a gas, radon can be breathed in. As it is a radioactive substance it decays and forms polonium-218 and other isotopes. During decay alpha particles are emitted and may stay in the lungs where they attack cells.

Houses which are at risk can be radon-proofed. This involves:

- installing a fan below the floor and a ventilation system.
- Placing a plastic sheet over wooden floors.

Both these measures help to ensure that the radon does not rise into the house.

QUESTION

Radon is a naturally occurring radioactive gas. It is made during the radioactive decay of uranium, which occurs in rocks and soils. As it is a gas, radon can seep into enclosed spaces, such as under the floor of houses; it can then build up to a high concentration and seep up through the house floor. It is a problem in certain parts of Britain. Fig 6 shows how radon concentration inside a British house varies during one day in Summer.

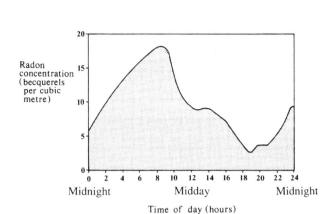

Fig 6

a Suggest reasons for the general pattern shown in
Fig 6.

....
....
....
....(3 marks)

b Suggest a way to reduce the concentration of
radon inside a house.

....
....
....(2 marks)

c Radon gives out an ionising radiation, which can
greatly increase the risk of developing lung cancer.
   i Explain what is meant by 'ionising radiation'.

....
....(1 mark)

   ii Explain how radon may cause lung cancer.

....
....(1 mark)
[ULEAC]

ANSWER

a The radon builds up during the night. It is trapped
in the house because the doors are shut. During the
day the doors (and probably the windows as it is
summer) are likely to be open and radon, being a
gas, can escape.

b *Notice that the question asks for 'a way' so you
need only to suggest one, but you need to explain
how it would work.*
For example:
Placing a plastic sheet over the floors or the floor
space to trap the radon below the house.
Installing a ventilation system, involving a fan,
below the floor so that the radon is removed and
does not enter the house.

c   i Ionising radiation means that atoms are
converted into ions.
   ii The radon gas may be breathed in. It travels
down to the lungs. Here it may cause atoms in
the cells of the lungs to be ionised and thus
could lead to lung cancer.

What are the uses of radioactivity?

There are many uses of radioactivity. One of the
important uses is in the production of electricity
using nuclear fission (see p 320).

Some other uses of radioactivity are shown in the
table below.

Task	Type of radiation	Possible isotope	Reason for choice
dating archaeological remains	beta	carbon-14	The amount of this isotope decreases from the date of the death of an organism. By estimating the fraction that remains, it is possible to estimate how long ago the organism died.
preserving foodstuffs	gamma	cobalt-60	destroys micro-organisms
sterilising medical equipment	gamma	cobalt-60	destroys micro-organisms
detecting cracks in aircraft	gamma	indium-192	radiation is not stopped by the thickness of the metal body of the plane
investigating kidney function	gamma	iodine-123	half life of 13 hours
treating cancer	gamma	cobalt-60	destroys diseased cells

QUESTION

The table below shows the half-life of some radioactive isotopes.

Radioactive Isotope	Half-Life
Nitrogen-16	7 seconds
Sodium-24	15 hours
Sulphur-35	88 days
Carbon-14	5,600 years
Chlorine-36	300,000 years
Potassium-40	1,300,000,000 years

Suggest with a reason which one of the isotopes in the table could be part of a compound which is used as a tracer in medicine.

....
....
....
....(2 marks)

Part question [SEG 1994]

ANSWER

Sodium-24. Nitrogen-16 would have too short a half-life to allow the system or process to be investigated, and all the other isotopes have a half-life which is too long.

Revision sheet

Atomic structure

1 Name three sorts of 'particles' that make up chemical substances.
2 Draw an atom and indicate:
   a The three types of sub-atomic particles that are found;
   b Where they are found in the atom;
   c Their charge.
3 Which sub-atomic particles are involved in bonding?
4 What are isotopes?
5 What information can you get from this information about calcium: Atomic number 20, relative atomic mass 40.1?
6 Draw an equation to show how iodine (Group 7) forms an ion.
7 What happens to the number of electrons in an atom:
   a Moving from left to right across a period in the periodic table;
   b Moving down a group in the periodic table?
8 Give two differences between an ionic bond and a covalent bond.

Radioactivity

1 What is a radioactive substance?
2 What is meant by the terms:
   a Background radioactivity;
   b Ionising radiation;
   c Half-life;
   d Radioactive tracer?
3 a Name the three main types of radiation.
   b State how each may be stopped.
4 Describe each of the main types of radiation.
5 What two properties of radiations determine how harmful they are to the human body?

Revision sheet answers

Atomic structure

1 Atoms, ions, molecules.
2 Structure of an atom.

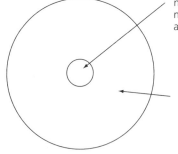

nucleus contains neutrons (no charge) and protons (positive charge)

electrons (negative charge) in a cloud, thought of as in shells (2 electrons nearest nucleus, 8 possible electrons in next shell etc)

3 Electrons involved in bonding.
4 Atoms of the same element, same number of protons and electrons but different numbers of neutrons. (Same atomic number – Z, but different mass numbers – A.)
5 Calcium has:
   20 electrons
   20 protons
   It contains isotopes (relative atomic mass not a whole number).
   20 neutrons in most of the atoms (R.A.M. nearly 40).
   Electrons arranged as (starting at the nucleus):
   2,8,8,2

2 electrons in the outer shell
Calcium is in group 2

6 I   +   e⁻   →   I⁻
   iodine atom   gains an electron   iodide ion with a
   no charge   negative charge

7 a Moving across a period the number of electrons
    in the outer shell increases (by one for each
    group).
  b Moving down a group the number of shells of
    electrons increases (by one for each period).

8 In an ionic bond: electrons are lost by one atom
  and gained by another, ions are formed.
  In a covalent bond: a pair of electrons is shared
  between the atoms. The bond can be drawn as
  Cl-Cl; a molecule is formed (see section 9 for
  more on bonding).

Radioactivity

1 A substance where the nucleus of the atom is
  unstable and therefore decays, emitting radiation.

2 a Background radioactivity: the radioactivity that
    is around us naturally, for example from cosmic
    rays from space, rocks etc.
  b Ionising radiation: the radiations cause atoms
    that they hit to form ions.
  c Half-life: the time taken for half the atoms in a
    radioactive isotope to decay.
  d Radioactive tracer: an isotope that is used to
    follow a biological, chemical or physical
    process.

3 a Alpha particles, beta particles and gamma rays.
  b Alpha particles stopped by a thin sheet of paper,
    beta particles stopped by a thin sheet of metal,
    gamma rays stopped by several metres of
    concrete.

4 An alpha particle is a helium nucleus, with 2
  protons and 2 neutrons. It has a charge of 2+.
  A beta particle is an electron, it has a charge of 1−.
  A gamma ray is a high energy ray with a short
  wavelength.

5 Damage to the body depends on:
  – How penetrating the radiation is.
  – How ionising the radiation is.

Student Answers with Comments

a Complete the table below by putting in the missing
  numbers.

Element symbol	Proton number	Mass number	Number of protons	Number of neutrons	Electron arrangements
He	2	4 ✔	2	2	2
Na	11	23	11	12 ✔	2,8,1
P	15	31	15	16 ✔	2,8,5
Ca	20	40	20	20	2,8,8,2 ✔
Cl	17	37	17	20	2,8,7 ✔

⑤

b Some atomic nuclei are unstable and give out
  radiation. The radiation could be alpha, beta or
  gamma radiation.
  i Radiation from a source may be *increased*,
    unchanged or *decreased* in intensity after
    passing through 1cm of air or 1cm of
    aluminium.
    Choose a description from the words in italics
    above to complete the following table.

(2 marks)

Radiation	Air	Aluminium
alpha	decreased	decreased ✔
beta	unchanged ✔	decreased

 ii What happens to the nucleus of an atom when
    alpha radiation is emitted?

(1 mark)

It changes to form a new element as neutrons
have been released. ✗

*It does form a new element but 2 protons and
2 neutrons have been released. It is a new
element because of the loss of protons.*

iii Why is it necessary to monitor the levels of
    radiation to which people are exposed?

(1 mark)

Because radiation can be dangerous and
harmful above certain levels. ⓪

Too vague – mention cell damage/cancer

iv Give one beneficial use of high doses of
   radiation. (1 mark)

To help combat cancer. ⓪

*Be more specific. Radiation damages cells that
are dividing rapidly (cancer) so can be used to
treat tumours.*

7/10   [WJEC]

An exam question for you to try

This question is about sodium chloride (common salt) which is an important chemical.
Sodium chloride can be made by burning sodium in chlorine gas.

a   Balance the symbol equation for the reaction of sodium with chlorine.

$Na(s) + Cl_2(g) \rightarrow NaCl(s)$ (1 mark)

b   i   Complete the diagrams below to show the electronic structure of a sodium and a chlorine atom. (Atomic number of sodium = 11 and chlorine = 17) (3 marks)

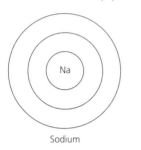
Sodium

Chlorine

Fig 1

ii When sodium reacts with chlorine the sodium atoms are changed into sodium ions (Na^+) and the chlorine atoms are changed into chloride ions (Cl^-). Explain how:

1 A sodium atom changes into a sodium ion;

....
....(2 marks)

2 A chlorine atom changes into a chloride ion.

....
....(2 marks)

c   The element potassium is in the same group of the Periodic Table as sodium. Potassium reacts with chlorine to make potassium chloride which is sometimes used instead of common salt in cooking.

i   Predict the formula of potassium chloride.

....(1 mark)

By reference to the electronic structures of potassium and sodium explain:

ii Why the reaction of potassium with chlorine is similar to the reaction of sodium with chlorine.

....
....(1 mark)

iii Why the reaction of potassium with chlorine is more violent than the reaction of sodium with chlorine.

....
....
....
....
....
....(3 marks)

[NEAB]

Answer

a $2Na(s) + Cl_2(g) \rightarrow 2NaCl(g)$

b   i

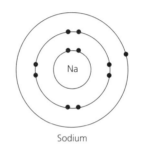
Sodium

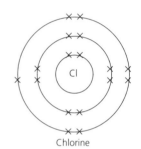
Chlorine

Fig 2

ii 1. Sodium atom changing to a sodium ion: the sodium atom loses one electron.

2. Chlorine atom changing to a chloride ion: the chlorine atom gains an electron.

c   i   KCl (as potassium is in the same group as sodium).

ii Both potassium and sodium have the same number (one) of electrons in the outer shell.

iii Potassium is below sodium in the periodic table. This means that there is one extra shell of electrons compared to sodium.

The outer electron in potassium is further from the nucleus, less energy is needed to remove it and so the electron is more easily lost. This means that potassium is more reactive than sodium.

9

Joining atoms

Joining atoms	Midland (MEG)				Northern (NEAB)		London (ULEAC)				Southern (SEG)		Welsh (WJEC)
	Own	Nuffield	Salters	Suffolk	Co-ordinated	Modular	Modular GASP	Combined	Co-ordinated	Modular	Double	Modular	Co-ordinated
FORMULAE, EQUATIONS AND AMOUNTS													
Formulae	✓	✓	✓	✓	✓	✓	✓	✓	✓	✓	✓	✓	✓
Importance of 'the mole'	✓	✓	✓	✓	✓	✓	✓	✓	✓	✓	✓	✓	✓
Word equations	✓	✓	✓	✓	✓	✓	✓	✓	✓	✓	✓	✓	✓
Balanced symbolic equations	✓	✓	✓	H	✓	✓	✓	✓	✓	✓	✓	✓	✓
Calculations involving equations	H	H	✓	H	H	H	H	H	H	H	✓	H	H
Calculations involving gases	H	H			H	H	H		H	H	✓	H	H
BONDING AND THE PROPERTIES OF MATERIALS													
Types of bonding	✓	✓	✓	H	✓	✓	✓	✓	✓	✓	✓	✓	✓
Properties of materials	✓	✓	✓	✓	✓	✓	✓	✓	✓	✓	✓	✓	✓
Relating properties of materials to their structure	H	H	✓	H	H	H	H	✓	H	H	✓	H	H

Formulae, equations and amounts

If a substance is written just as a symbol, e.g. H or He, this tells you that it is an element (see p 137). You need to look carefully to see how many capital letters there are. For example, Co is the element cobalt but CO is the compound carbon monoxide. By using the periodic table on p 162 you can compare the mass of each atom of any element to that of carbon – which is taken as 12.

| 6 |
| C |
| CARBON |
| 12.0 |

The bigger number of the two numbers is called the relative atomic mass.

What is a mole?

If you weighed out 12g of carbon, 59g of cobalt and 23g of sodium you would have the same number of atoms in each of your samples! There would be 6.02×10^{23} atoms; this is called the Avogadro constant. The amount of the substance that contains this number of atoms is called a mole. You can have a mole of any type of particle – atom, molecule, ion or electron, but you always have 6.02×10^{23} particles in your sample.

Note that the mass of a mole of hydrogen atoms (H) is one gram, but the mass of a mole of hydrogen molecules (H_2) is 2 grams.

Relative atomic masses:

calcium	40
carbon	12
chlorine	35.5
copper	64
hydrogen	1
iron	56
lead	207
magnesium	24
nitrogen	14
oxygen	16
potassium	39
sodium	23
sulphur	32

QUESTION

What is the mass of:
1 1 mol of potassium atoms?
2 3 mol of nitrogen atoms?
3 0.5 mol of calcium atoms? (3 marks)

ANSWER

1 39g.
2 42g (3×14).
3 20g (0.5×40).

QUESTION

How many moles of atoms are there in:
1 4g of calcium?
2 1.4g of nitrogen?
3 78g of potassium? (3 marks)

ANSWER

1 $4/40 = 0.1$ mol.
2 $1.4/14 = 0.1$ mol.
3 $78/39 = 2$ mol.

Formulae

When elements combine during a chemical reaction to form a compound, the composition of the compound can be described in a type of shorthand, called a formula. Every compound has a fixed formula. For example, H_2O is water, but H_2O_2 is hydrogen peroxide – a type of hair bleach!
Note: The composition of a compound, and thus the formula, can be checked by an experiment in which the actual masses of the reactants which combine to form the compound are measured.

What information can formulae give?

The formula of a compound tells you:

• The elements that are present in the compound.
• The proportions in which the elements are combined.

It also allows you to calculate the mass of one mole of the substance. Formulae are used in equations to describe the reaction accurately and allow you to calculate the quantities involved.

Information from formulae

1 Water: H_2O, there are 2 atoms of hydrogen and one atom of oxygen.
2 Hydrogen peroxide: H_2O_2, there are 2 atoms of hydrogen and 2 atoms of oxygen.
3 Sodium carbonate: Na_2CO_3, there are 2 atoms of sodium, one atom of carbon and 3 atoms of oxygen.
4 Magnesium nitrate: $Mg(NO_3)_2$, there is one atom of magnesium, 2 atoms of nitrogen and 6 atoms of oxygen. Notice how $(NO_3)_2$ means 2 of everything inside the bracket.

Note: If a formula has a number in front of it (for example in an equation), this means that the number refers to all of the formula.

For example:
$2H_2SO_4$ means two molecules (or 2 moles) of sulphuric acid. Therefore, altogether there are: 4 atoms of hydrogen, 2 atoms of sulphur and 8 atoms of oxygen.

How to write formulae

Many compounds are in fact made up of ions and not atoms (see p 183). You will find it helpful to know the names, formulae and charges of some common ions.

Positively charged ions (Cations)

aluminium ion	Al^{3+}
ammonium ion	NH_4^+
calcium ion	Ca^{2+}
copper(II) ion	Cu^{2+}
hydrogen ion	H^+
iron(II) ion	Fe^{2+}
iron(III) ion	Fe^{3+}
lead ion	Pb^{2+}
lithium ion	Li^+
magnesium ion	Mg^{2+}
potassium ion	K^+
sodium ion	Na^+
zinc ion	Zn^{2+}

Negatively charged ions (Anions)

bromide ion	Br^-
carbonate ion	CO_3^{2-}
chloride ion	Cl^-
hydroxide ion	OH^-
iodide ion	I^-
nitrate ion	NO_3^-
oxide ion	O^{2-}
phosphate ion	PO_4^{3-}
sulphate ion	SO_4^{2-}

To work out the formula of an ionic compound you need to use the charges on these ions.

For example, what is the formula of magnesium oxide?

It is helpful to draw a table like this:

Name of substance	magnesium	oxide
Ions in the compound (and their charges)	Mg^{2+}	O^{2-}

In this case the charges balance ($^{2+}$) and ($^{2-}$)
So, *the formula is MgO.*

For example, what is the formula of zinc nitrate?

It is helpful to draw a table like this:

Name of substance	zinc	nitrate
Ions in the compound (and their charges)	Zn^{2+}	NO_3^-
In this case, 2 nitrate ions are needed to balance the 2+ on the zinc ion	Zn^{2+}	NO_3^- NO_3^-

So, formula of zinc nitrate is: $Zn(NO_3)_2$.

Note the brackets around (NO_3) to show that there are two nitrate ions in zinc nitrate. You use brackets where you need more than one ion which contains more than one element – in this case the nitrate ion.

QUESTION

What is the formula of:

1 sodium sulphate?
2 aluminium oxide?
3 sodium hydroxide? ....(3 marks)

ANSWER

1 Sodium sulphate: Na_2SO_4

Name of substance	sodium	sulphate
Ions in the compound (and their charges)	Na^+	SO_4^{2-}
In this case, 2 sodium ions are needed to balance the 2– on the sulphate ion	Na^+ Na^+	SO_4^{2-}

So, formula of sodium sulphate is: Na_2SO_4.

2 Aluminium oxide: Al_2O_3

Name of substance	*aluminium oxide*

Ions in the compound
(and their charges) Al^{3+} O^{2-}
In this case, 2 aluminium
ions are needed and 3 oxide
ions to balance the charges

Al^{3+} O^{2-}
Al^{3+} O^{2-}
                O^{2-}

So, formula of aluminium oxide is: Al_2O_3

3 Sodium hydroxide: NaOH

Name of substance	*sodium hydroxide*

Ions in the compound
(and their charges) Na^+ OH^-
In this case, the charges on the ions balance
So, formula of sodium hydroxide is: NaOH.

Calculating the mass of a mole of substance

Once you know the formula of a compound you can work out the mass of one mole:

For example,

CO: This molecule of carbon monoxide contains one atom of carbon and one atom of oxygen.
The mass of one mole is $12 + 16 = 28g$.

CO_2: This molecule of carbon dioxide contains one atom of carbon and two atoms of oxygen.
The mass of one mole is $12 + (2 \times 16) = 44g$.

$CuSO_4$: This compound, copper sulphate, contains one ion of copper (Cu^{2+}) and one sulphate ion (SO_4^{2-}).
The mass of one mole is $64 + 32 + (4 \times 16) = 160g$.

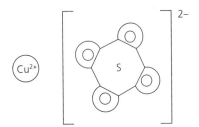

Fig 1 The ions in copper sulphate

Note: If you have something like O_4 in the formula then you must multiply the relative atomic mass of that element by 4.

$Pb(NO_3)_2$: This compound, lead nitrate, contains one ion of lead, and two nitrate ions.

Note $(NO_3)_2$ means that when you do the calculation you will need '2 of all of NO_3' and in the NO_3 you need '3 of O' so:
The mass of one mole is $207 + (2 \times (14 + (3 \times 16)) = 207 + (2 \times 62) = 207 + 124 = 331g$.

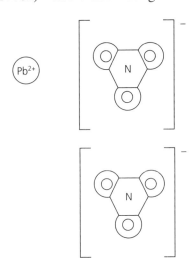

Fig 2 The ions in lead nitrate

QUESTION

What is the mass of:

1 1 mole of HC1 molecules?
2 0.5 mol of ethanol molecules (C_2H_5OH)?
3 0.1 mol of water molecules (H_2O)? (3 marks)

ANSWER

1 36.5g
    Mass of one mole: HC1
                    1 + 35.5
                    = 36.5 g

2 23g
    Mass of one mole: C_2H_5OH
                    $(2 \times 12) + (5 \times 1) + 16 + 1$
                    24 + 5 + 17
                    46g
    Question asks for mass of 0.5 mol
                    = 0.5 × 46
                    = 23g

3 1.8g
    Mass of one mole: H_2O
                    $(2 \times 1) + 16$
                    2 + 16
                    18g
    Question asks for mass of 0.1 mol
    = 0.1 × 18
    = 1.8g

Calculating the number of moles in a sample of given mass

You can also work out how many moles of a substance you have if you are given the mass of the sample.

For example:
How many moles are there in 80g of calcium?
Calcium is an element, symbol Ca: the relative atomic mass is 40.
So, the number of moles in the sample is:
80/40 = 2 moles.
How many moles of molecules are there in 9g of water?
Water is a compound, H_2O: the relative molecular mass is: $(2 \times 1) + 16 = 18$g.
So, the number of moles in the sample is:
9/18 = 0.5 of a mole.

QUESTION

How many moles are there in:

1 44g of carbon dioxide, CO_2?
2 80g of sodium hydroxide, NaOH?
3 0.68g of hydrogen peroxide, H_2O_2? (3 marks)

ANSWER

1 1 mole
   Mass of 1 mole of CO_2:
$$12 + (2 \times 16)$$
$$12 + 32$$
$$44g$$
   So, number of moles in sample is:
   44/44 = 1 mole.
2 2 moles
   Mass of one mole of NaOH
$$23 + 16 + 1$$
$$40g$$
   So, number of moles in 80g of sample is:
   80/40 = 2 moles.
3 0.02 moles
   Mass of one mole of H_2O_2:
$$(2 \times 1) + (2 \times 16)$$
$$2 + 32$$
$$34g$$
   So, number of moles in 0.68g sample is:
   0.68/34 = 0.02 moles.

Finding the formula of a compound given the mass of substances involved

3.6g of magnesium react with oxygen to form 6.0g of magnesium oxide. What is the formula of magnesium oxide?
First, find out how much oxygen combines with the magnesium to form magnesium oxide.
If you have 6.0g of magnesium oxide and you started with 3.6g of magnesium, then the magnesium reacted with $(6.0 - 3.6) = 2.4$g of oxygen
Then it is helpful to draw a table like this:

	magnesium	oxygen
mass involved	3.6g	2.4g
Mass of 1 mole of each element (you can look this up on the periodic table)	24g	16g
number of moles involved	3.6/24 = 0.15	2.4/16 0.15
Turn this into simple whole numbers, in this case divide by 0.15, *you must do the same thing to both amounts!*	0.15/0.15 = 1	0.15/0.15 = 1

So, 1 mole of magnesium combines with one mole of oxygen.
This means that the formula of magnesium oxide is Mg_1O_1 which is written as MgO.
If you work through calculations of this type using this table you should always get the right formula!

QUESTION

A sample of an oxide of lead with a mass of 239g contains 32g of oxygen. What is the formula of this oxide? (Relative atomic masses O 16; Pb 207)
(1 mark)

A PbO
B Pb_2O
C PbO_2
D Pb_3O_4

[SEG 1994]

ANSWER

C
239g of the sample contains 32g of oxygen so the mass of lead in the sample is:
239 − 32g = 207g

	lead	oxygen
mass involved	*207g*	*32g*
Mass of 1 mole of each element	*207g*	*16g*

(you can look this up on the periodic table)
number of moles involved

	207/207	*32/16*
	= 1	*2*

1 mole of lead combines with 2 moles of oxygen, so the formula is PbO₂. Therefore answer C is correct.

Calculating the percentage by mass of each element in a compound

To do this you need to know:

- The formula of the compound.
- The relative atomic mass of each element in the compound.

For example: What is the percentage by mass of each element in copper(II) sulphate, $CuSO_4$? ($Cu = 64$, $S = 32$, $O = 16$)
First, calculate the mass of one mole of copper(II) sulphate.

$CuSO_4$
$64 + 32 + (4 \times 16)$
$= 64 + 32 + 64$
$= 160g$

Then take each element in turn.
Of the 160 units of mass, 64 are of copper, so the percentage by mass of copper is:
$(64/160) \times 100$
$= 40\%$

It is a good idea to write it out like this:
copper   Percentage mass $(64/160) \times 100$ = 40%
sulphur   Percentage mass $(32/160) \times 100$ = 20%
oxygen   Percentage mass $(64/160) \times 100$ = 40%

Note:
1   You use '64' for oxygen and not '16' because there are 4 atoms of oxygen in the compound.
2   You could work out the percentage mass of oxygen by doing a subtraction:
    $100\% - (\% \text{ copper} + \% \text{ sulphur})$
    $100\% - (40 + 20)$
    $= 40\%$
    This is a useful check if you have to work out the % of each element in a compound.

QUESTION

Which of these two fertilisers contains the highest percentage by mass of nitrogen: ammonium nitrate (NH_4NO_3) or sodium nitrate ($NaNO_3$)? Show your working. (3 marks)
($H = 1$, $N = 14$, $O = 16$, $Na = 23$)

ANSWER

Ammonium nitrate
For ammonium nitrate (NH₄NO₃)
Mass of 1 mole:
  NH₄NO₃
14 + (4 × 1) + 14 + (3 × 16)
14 + 4 + 14 + 48
80

nitrogen   Percentage mass (28/80) × 100 = 35%
(note there are 2 atoms of nitrogen so you must use '28' and not '14')

For sodium nitrate (NaNO₃)
Mass of one mole:
  NaNO₃
23 + 14 + (3 × 16)
23 + 14 + 48
85

nitrogen   Percentage mass (14/85) × 100 = 16.47%
Therefore ammonium nitrate contains a higher percentage of nitrogen by mass than sodium nitrate.

Calculations involving solutions

Many reactions take place in solution. Usually water is the solvent and so the solution is called an aqueous solution.

Some important terms for solutions

- Concentration: The concentration of a substance in solution tells you how much of a substance has been dissolved in a given volume of solution. This is often shown as mol dm⁻³ (moles of substance per cubic decimetre of solution).
- Molar solution: The solution contains the molar mass of the substance made up to a decimetre cubed (or litre) with water.
  You may see this written like this, on bottles:
  1M NaCl. (This is often called a 1 molar solution or, more correctly, to have a concentration of 1 mol dm⁻³.)

Finding the concentration of a solution in moles per cubic decimetre.

You need to know

- The formula of the compound.
- The molar mass.

Example:
What is the concentration in moles of sodium hydroxide (NaOH) per cubic decimetre of a solution containing 60g of sodium hydroxide in one litre of solution? (H = 1, O = 16, Na = 23)

1 litre is just another way of saying 'one cubic decimetre'.

The molar mass of NaOH:
   23 + 16 + 1
= 40
So a solution containing 40g sodium hydroxide per litre has a concentration of 1 mol dm^{-3} (1 molar).

60g of sodium hydroxide are contained in one litre, therefore the concentration of the solution is:
60/40
= *1.5 mol dm^{-3}*

How to make a solution of a given concentration

You need to know:

- The formula of the compound.
- The molar mass of the compound.
- The concentration of the solution needed.
- The volume of the solution needed.

Example:
How would you make 100cm^3 of 0.5 mol dm^{-3} sodium chloride, NaCl? (Na = 23, Cl = 35.5)

The molar mass of sodium chloride:
NaCl
23 + 35.5
= 58.5g

To make a solution of concentration 1 mol dm^{-3}, 58.5g must be dissolved and made up to a litre.
So to make a solution of concentration 0.5 mol dm^{-3}, $58.5 \times 0.5 = 29.25$g must be dissolved and made up to a litre.
But only 100cm^3 of solution is needed, not a litre (1000cm^3).

Therefore, 29.25/10 = 2.925g are needed.
Answer: 2.925g of sodium chloride are needed in 100cm^3 of solution, to make a solution of concentration 0.5 mol dm^{-3}.

These equations might be useful:
Mass of a substance (g) = number of moles ×
                          mass of one mole (g)

Amount of solute = volume of the
in a sample of   solution (dm^3) ×
solution (mol)   concentration (mol/dm^3)

QUESTION

What is the concentration of a solution in which 41.5g of potassium iodide (KI) are dissolved and made up to 200cm^3? (K = 39, I = 127) (1 mark)

ANSWER

1.25 mol dm^{-3}.

The molar mass of potassium iodide, KI:
= 39 + 127
=166g
Amount of potassium iodide used = 41.5g/166g mol^{-1}
*   = 0.25 mol*
Volume of the solution = 200/1000dm^3
*   = 0.2dm^3*
Concentration = 0.25mol/0.2dm^3
*   = 1.25 mol dm^{-3}*

QUESTION

How much solute is there in 25cm^3 of 0.1 mol dm^{-3} HCl? (H = 1, Cl = 35.5) (1 mark)

ANSWER

0.09125g.

The volume of the solution is 25/1000 dm^{-3}
*   = 0.025 dm^{-3}*
Concentration of the solution is 0.1 mol dm^{-3}
Number of moles in the solution = 0.025 × 0.1
*   = 0.0025*
The molar mass of HCl = 1 + 35.5
*   = 36.5*
So mass of solute present = 0.0025 × 36.5
*   = 0.09125g*

Equations

When a chemical reaction takes place, it can be summarised by an equation, using words and then symbols.

What information can equations give?

- The reactants involved (the left hand side of the equation).
- The products formed (the right hand side of the equation).
- The direction of the equation, usually left to right and shown by an arrow '$\rightarrow$'. Occasionally the reaction is reversible and shown by '$\rightleftharpoons$'.
- The state of the substances involved in the reaction.

Once a balanced symbolic equation has been written, the amounts of all the substances involved can be calculated.

When a chemical reaction takes place the total mass stays the same. A gas may escape into the air, but remember that it still has mass.

How to write a balanced symbolic equation

For example: Hydrogen peroxide decomposes to form water and oxygen. It is helpful to write this out as a table:

1 A word equation	hydrogen peroxide $\rightarrow$	water + oxygen
2 Replace the names with the formulae	$H_2O_2 \rightarrow$	$H_2O + O_2$

Once you have checked that the formulae are correct you can only balance the equation by adding numbers in front of the substances, you cannot alter their formulae.

3 Count the atoms on each side of the equation	Left hand side	Right hand side
	H : 2 atoms	H : 2 atoms
	O : 2 atoms	O : 3 atoms

It looks as if an oxygen atom has been 'made'. This has not happened.

4 Balance the equation by changing the numbers in front of the formulae. Do this by trial and error in pencil until you have the same number of atoms on each side of the equation. $2H_2O_2 \rightarrow 2H_2O + O_2$

5 Count the atoms on each side of the equation, as a check	Left hand side	Right hand side
	H : 4 atoms	H : 4 atoms
	O : 4 atoms	O : 4 atoms

So, the balanced equation is: $2H_2O_2 \rightarrow 2H_2O + O_2$

6 If possible, add the state symbols:
$$2H_2O_2(aq) \rightarrow 2H_2O(l) + O_2(g)$$

See pp 196–197 for half equations.

QUESTIONS

Write balanced symbolic equations for the following reactions:

a If calcium carbonate ($CaCO_3$) is heated strongly enough it decomposes to form calcium oxide (CaO) and the gas carbon dioxide (CO_2). (2 marks)

b In the Haber process, hydrogen gas (H_2) reacts with nitrogen gas (N_2) to form ammonia (NH_3). (2 marks)

ANSWER

a $CaCO_3(s) \rightarrow CaO(s) + CO_2(g)$
b $N_2(g) + 3H_2(g) \rightarrow 2NH_3(g)$

Don't forget the state symbols when you balance equations.

QUESTION

One molecule of decane can be cracked to produce one molecule of ethene and one molecule of octane. Balance the equation:
Decane $\rightarrow$ ethane + octane (1 mark)
$C_{10}H_{22} \rightarrow C_2H_4 + \ldots\ldots\ldots$

[ULEAC]

ANSWER

$C_{10}H_{22} \rightarrow C_2H_4 + C_8H_{18}$

QUESTION

Write a balanced symbolic equation for the complete combustion of petrol (octane C_8H_{18}). (1 mark)

Part question [SEG 1994]

ANSWER

$2C_8H_{18}(l) + 25O_2(g) \rightarrow 16CO_2(g) + 18H_2O(g)$
(Don't be worried by the big numbers. Work it out as before. The trick is to leave the 'O₂' until last. This is an element and any number that you put in front of it will only affect the number of oxygen atoms and no other element.) (See p 147 for more details on complete combustion.)

QUESTION

Balance the symbol equation for the reaction of sodium with chlorine.

$Na(s) + Cl_2(g) \rightarrow NaCl(s)$ (1 mark)

[NEAB]

ANSWER

$2Na(s) + Cl_2(g) \rightarrow 2NaCl(s)$

QUESTION

When chalcopyrite, an ore of copper, is heated in excess air it forms copper(II) oxide, iron(III) oxide and sulphur dioxide.

$4CuFeS_2 + \ldots O_2 \rightarrow \ldots CuO + \ldots Fe_2O_3 + \ldots SO_2$

Balance the equation by putting the correct numbers in the spaces provided. (2 marks)

[WJEC]

ANSWER

$4CuFeS_2 + 13 O_2 \rightarrow 4CuO + 2Fe_2O_3 + 8SO_2$

Calculations involving equations

A word equation tells you what the reactants and products are in the reaction. A balanced symbol equation tells you how much of each reactant and product is involved in the reaction.

Example:
Copper can be obtained from copper(II) sulphate solution by adding waste iron to the solution. If 112g of iron is added, how much copper can be obtained? It is helpful to draw a table like this:

Word equation   iron + copper sulphate →
                              iron sulphate + copper
Symbol equation $Fe + CuSO_4 \rightarrow FeSO_4 + Cu$

(In this case it is balanced, so you do not need to do anything else.)
Work through both of these methods and see which one works best for you.

Method One

Mass of mole of substances involved   Fe   Cu $56g \rightarrow 64g$
(Only write down the ones that are involved *NOT* all of them.)
Actual masses involved $112g \rightarrow ?g$
(You are trying to find out how much copper you will get!)

Compare the masses. At this stage it is often helpful to write it in words:
If 56g of iron give 64g of copper, then,
1g of iron will give 64/56g of copper and
112g of iron will give $64/56 \times 112g$ of copper
Answer: *112g of iron will give 128g of copper.*

Method Two

56g of iron is one mole
112g of iron is two moles
From the equation, if 2 moles of iron are used 2 moles of copper are formed.
2 moles of copper = $2 \times 64 = 128g$.

QUESTION

Iron is made in a blast furnace when the ore haematite, Fe_2O_3, is reduced to iron by carbon monoxide. How much iron can be produced from 1,600 tonnes of haematite? Show your working. (Fe = 56, O = 16)
(3 marks)

ANSWER

1,120 tonnes

Using Method One above

Word equation
Iron oxide + carbon monoxide → iron + carbon dioxide
symbol equation:
$Fe_2O_3(s) + 3CO_2(g) \rightarrow 2Fe(l) + 3CO(g)$
Mass of mole of substances
involved   160g   →   112g
(Only write down the   of iron(III) oxide   of iron
ones that are involved   (the haematite)
NOT all of them.)
Notice that there is a '2' in front of the Fe, so 2 moles of iron are formed.
If 160g of iron oxide give 112g of iron, then,

*1g of iron oxide will give 112/160g of iron
and
1,600 tonnes of iron oxide will give (112/160) × 1600
tonnes of iron = 1,120 tonnes of iron.*

Using Method Two above

1 mole of iron oxide gives	*2 moles of iron*
160g of iron oxide give	*112g of iron*
160 tonnes of iron oxide give	*112 tonnes of iron*
1,600 tonnes of iron oxide give	*1,120 tonnes of iron*

QUESTION

Magnecalc plc is a company which uses limestone
(calcium carbonate) to manufacture quicklime
(calcium oxide).
The equation for the reaction is:

calcium carbonate $\rightarrow$ calcium oxide + carbon dioxide
$CaCO_3$ CaO + CO_2

Magnecalc sell 224 tonnes of quicklime a week.
Calculate the mass of limestone which has to be
quarried to provide 224 tonnes of quicklime. Assume
the limestone is pure. (4 marks)
(relative atomic mass for C = 12, Ca = 40, O = 16)

[MEG]

ANSWER

400 tonnes
Formula mass of limestone: $CaCO_3$
$$40 + 12 + (3 \times 16)$$
$$40 + 12 + 48$$
100g
Formula mass of quicklime: CaO
$$40 + 16$$
56g
$CaCO_3 \rightarrow CaO + CO_2$
100g of $CaCO_3 \rightarrow 56g\ CaO$
or 100 tonnes of $CaCO_3 \rightarrow 56$ tonnes of CaO
(as the question is dealing in tonnes)
*(100/56) × 224 tonnes of $CaCO_3$ will give 224 tonnes
of CaO.*
400 tonnes of $CaCO_3$ will give 224 tonnes of CaO.
*Therefore, 400 tonnes of limestone will need to be
quarried to provide 224 tonnes of quicklime.*

QUESTION

Either quicklime or limestone can be used to
neutralise acidity in lake water. The neutralisation

reactions which take place can be represented by the
equations:

$$CaO + 2H^+ \rightarrow Ca^{2+} + H_2O$$
$$CaCO_3 + 2H^+ \rightarrow Ca^{2+} + H_2O + CO_2$$

(relative atomic mass for H = 1, C = 12, Ca = 40, O = 16)
Sometimes helicopters are used to spread the material
over the lakes. Helicopter transport is expensive.
Use this information to explain the advantage of
using quicklime rather than limestone. (3 marks)

[MEG]

ANSWER

*Use the formula mass of quicklime and limestone:
For quicklime (CaO) this is 56g
and for limestone ($CaCO_3$) this is 100g.
In each case 1 mole of substance will neutralise 2
moles of H^+ ions.*
As 1 mole of quicklime only weighs 56g, more moles
could be carried on each journey than if limestone
was used.

Calculations involving gases in the reaction

Many reactions, for example the Haber process,
involve gases. It is easier to measure the volume of a
gas than its mass.

Important points to remember about gases.

- The volume of gas depends on the number of
  particles in the gas (not on what sort of particles
  they are).
- If the pressure and volume of *different* gases are the
  same then the gases contain equal numbers of moles.
- The volume of a mole of gas is 24,000cm^3 (24dm^3)
  at room temperature and normal pressure (written
  as RTP).
- If the volume of a gas is measured then the
  number of moles of the gas can be calculated.

QUESTION

a What is the volume of 2 moles of oxygen
   molecules at room temperature and pressure (RTP)?
b How many moles of gas are there in 0.12 dm^3 of
   argon? (at RTP) (2 marks)

ANSWER

a 1 mole of gas occupies 24dm^3 under these conditions,
   so 2 moles of gas will have a volume of 48dm^3.

b 1 mole of gas occupies 24dm³ at RTP,
so 1/24 mole of gas occupies 1dm³ at RTP
so, (1/24) × 0.12 moles of gas occupies 0.12 dm³
so 0.005 moles of argon has a volume of 0.12dm³.

QUESTION

Natural gas (methane) burns in oxygen to form water and carbon dioxide. How much carbon dioxide is formed from 100cm³ of methane? Show your working. (2 marks)

ANSWER

Methane + oxygen → water + carbon dioxide
$CH_4(g)$ $+2O_2(g)$ → $2H_2O(1) + CO_2(g)$
1 mole   2 moles   2 moles   1 mole
So 1 mole of methane will form 1 mole of carbon dioxide
100cm³ of methane will form 100cm³ of carbon dioxide
Note: Once you know the ratio of the moles then you can work out volumes as the ratio is the same.

QUESTION

The equation for the reaction of magnesium with hydrochloric acid is:

$Mg(s) + 2HCl(aq) \rightarrow MgCl_2(aq) + H_2(g)$
(H = 1, Mg = 24, C1 = 35.5)

Calculate the relative formula masses (Mr) of:
   i $MgCl_2$...(1 mark)
   ii H_2...(1 mark)
   iii Calculate the volume of hydrogen (at 1 atmosphere and 25°C) which would be obtained from 1g of magnesium reacting with excess hydrochloric acid.
      (The relative formula mass of hydrogen measured in grams occupies a volume of 24 litres (24dm³) at the above conditions.)
      ....
      ....
      ....(2 marks)
                                          [WJEC]

ANSWER

   i $MgCl_2$: relative formula mass = 24 + (2 × 35.5) = 95g.
   ii H_2: relative formula mass = 2 × 1 = 2g.
   iii $Mg(s) + 2HCl(aq) \rightarrow MgCl_2(aq) + H_2(g)$
      1 mol of Mg gives   1 mol of hydrogen gas

24g of Mg gives   1 mol of hydrogen gas
                            (24 litres)
But 1g of magnesium is used, so volume of hydrogen formed is 24/24 = 1 litre.

Bonding and the properties of materials

Do all compounds have similar characteristics?

The periodic table contains all the known elements. Each element is made up of atoms with the same number of protons (see p 159). These atoms are different from the atoms of other elements. A compound is formed when two or more elements combine during a chemical reaction. The compound has its own distinct properties. There are two important types of compounds, whose properties depend on the types of particles in the compound and how they are bonded together. They are:

• ionic compounds.
• molecular compounds.

What happens to the atoms in elements when a compound is formed?

The outer particles in an atom are electrons (see p 159) and it is these that are most likely to be involved in a chemical reaction. When two atoms come together one of three things may occur. What happens depends on the electron structure of the atoms involved.

1 *The atoms remain as they are and no bond is formed*
   Atoms that belong to group 0 (the noble gases) contain a full shell of outer electrons. For example argon is Ar: 2,8,8. The outer electron shell is 'full' and the atom is stable. The element is unreactive. Atoms with a 'full' shell of outer electrons are unlikely to form bonds.

2 *One atom 'gives' electrons to another atom and an ionic bond is formed.*
   This type of bond is likely to be formed between a metal and a non-metal. A metal atom such as sodium (Na: 2,8,1) has one outer electron. A non-metal such as chlorine (C1: 2,8,7) has 7 outer electrons, one short of the full set of 8 that enables

atoms to be stable. If the sodium atom 'gives' its outer electron to the chlorine atom then both will have a full set of 8 in their outer shells. When this occurs the sodium and chlorine atoms form ions.

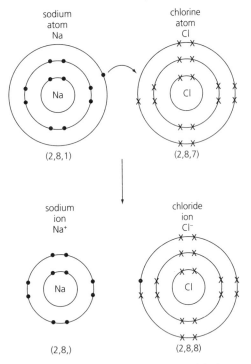

Fig 1 An ionic bond formed by sodium and chlorine

This is often called a dot and cross diagram.

As the sodium has 'given away' a negative electron it has formed a positive ion (Na^+). The chlorine has formed a negative ion (Cl^-) as it has gained an electron (see p 161–162 for more information on ions). These ions have opposite charges so they are strongly attracted to each other. The bond between them is called an ionic bond.

You must never talk about sodium chloride molecules, the particles in the compound are ions.

3 *One atom 'shares' electrons with another atom to form a covalent bond.*
   This type of bond is likely to be formed between two non-metals. Chlorine has the electron structure Cl 2,8,7; the outer shell is one short of the full set of eight electrons. If this atom shares one of the outer electrons with another atom of chlorine then both of them will have the full set of eight in the outer shell.

The chlorine atoms are sharing a pair of electrons. The bond between them is called a covalent bond. This is written as Cl-Cl. The formula for this is Cl_2 and the particle is called a molecule.

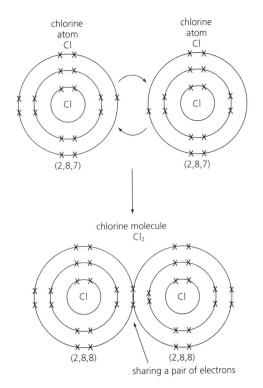

Fig 2 A covalent bond formed by two chlorine atoms

How do ionic and molecular compounds differ?

Type	Example	Properties
Ionic	sodium chloride, magnesium oxide, most 'salts'	high melting point high boiling point high density (most are solids at RT) hard but brittle often soluble in water conduct electricity when molten conduct electricity in aqueous solution reactions happen quickly
Molecular	chlorine, hydrogen, water, carbon dioxide, ammonia	low melting point low boiling point usually gas or liquid at RT if solid, soft and melts easily do not conduct electricity when molten do not conduct electricity in aqueous solution reactions happen slowly

The bonding in the molecules of covalent substances is strong – it is difficult to break the molecule into the separate atoms. However, the attraction between the atoms in different molecules is weak. It is fairly easy to separate the molecules from each other.

What are giant covalent structures?

Covalent substances are often made up of small molecules, for example carbon dioxide and water. These have the properties shown on p 184. However, some substances, such as diamond and silicon dioxide, are covalent but different. For example, diamond melts at 3550°C.

They are said to have a giant covalent or giant molecular structure. The atoms are linked to form large three dimensional structures.

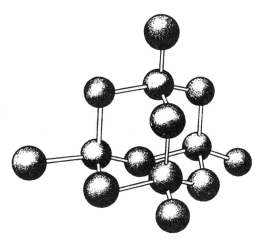

Fig 3 The structure of diamond

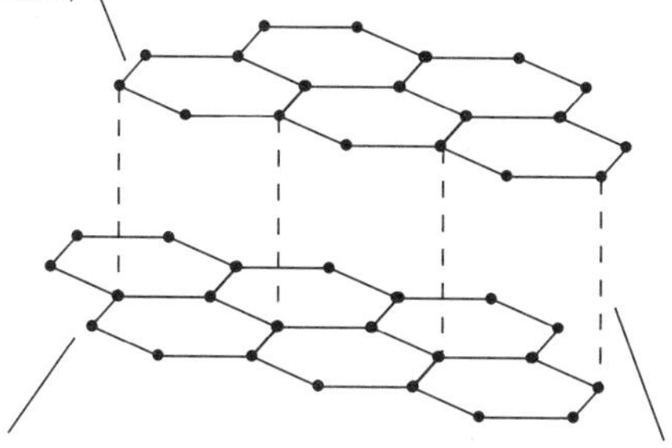

A layer of atoms held together tightly by covalent bonding (3 covalent bonds from each atom to others)

Electrons move easily in the layers, conduct electricity

Weak forces hold the layers together, layers can slide on each other, graphite is a lubricant

Fig 4 The structure of graphite

Graphite fibres are strong if all the layers are lined up.

Properties of giant covalent structures

High melting point
High boiling point
Difficult to melt
Hard but brittle
Insoluble
Do not conduct electricity, except graphite

What is metallic bonding?
The atoms of metals are arranged in an ordered way in a giant structure. The outer electrons of each atom are shared equally between all the atoms in the structure and act as a sort of 'electron glue'. The electrons can move through the structure and this is what happens when metals conduct electricity. Metals have high melting points due to the strength of the 'electron glue'.

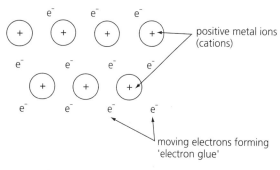

positive metal ions (cations)

moving electrons forming 'electron glue'

Fig 5 Metallic bonding

QUESTION

Sand is silicon(IV) oxide. It has a structure similar to that of diamond. Part of its structure is shown in the diagram below.

a i What does X represent?

....(1 mark)

  ii What is particle Y?

....(2 marks)

  iii What type of structure is shown by the diagram? Tick the box beside the correct answer. (1 mark)

Giant ionic solid ☐

Giant molecular solid ☐

Simple ionic solid ☐

Simple molecular solid ☐

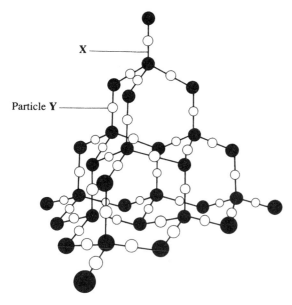

Fig 6

b Predict one physical property of silicon(IV) oxide
and explain how the property you have predicted
is due to its structure. (2 marks)
Predicted property...
Explanation..
....

Part question [SEG 1994]

ANSWER

a   i Covalent bond/pair of electrons.
    ii An atom of oxygen (*make sure you put oxygen
       and not oxide*).
    iii Giant molecular solid.
b *The explanation that you give must explain the
  property. There are several possibilities:*
  Forms crystals – the atoms are arranged in a
  regular way.
  Hard – there are strong covalent bonds between
  the atoms.
  High M.Pt or B.Pt – there are strong covalent
  bonds between the atoms.
  Does not conduct electricity – there are no free
  electrons that can move in the structure.

QUESTION

              H
              |
a Methane, H – C – H, contains covalent bonds.
              |
              H

   Describe, in terms of electrons, how atoms joined
   by a covalent bond are held together.

   ....
   ....(2 marks)

b Simple covalent compounds are usually gases or
  liquids with relatively low boiling points. Explain
  the reason for this.
  ....
  ....(1 mark)
c In a metal the atoms are held together in giant
  structures.
    i State, in terms of electrons, how the atoms are
      bonded together in giant structures.
      ....
      ....(1 mark)
    ii State and explain below two properties of metals
       which result from this bonding. (4 marks)

	Property	Explanation
I		
II		

[WJEC]

ANSWER

a A covalent bond is formed when atoms share two
  (a pair) of electrons.
b The bonds in the molecules of the gas or liquid are
  strong but the bonds *between* the molecules are
  weak. It is fairly easy to separate the molecules
  from each other.
c   i In a metallic structure some of the electrons are
      shared between the metal ions (cations). The
      electrons form a sort of 'electron glue'. *Do
      read the first part of this question, it says
      'metal atoms' and so you must answer about
      metal atoms and not about all giant structures.*
    ii *The table should help you to get all the marks
       here.*
       I Property: Conduct electricity.
       Explanation: Electrons can move through the
       structure.
       II Property: Conduct heat.
       Explanation: Some of the 'heat energy' goes
       into electron movement. As electrons can move
       more freely through the structure they disperse
       this energy.
*You can give other answers such as: malleable/ductile
(the layers of atoms can slide over each other); high*

melting points (the atoms are packed closely together and the bonds holding them together are strong); but you must be able to give an explanation in terms of the bonding in metals.

QUESTION

Fig 7 on p 188 shows the properties of five substances.

Each substance can be used once, more than once or not at all to answer the following.

Choose from A to E a substance which is:

a a metal; ....(1 mark)
b a non-metallic element; ....(1 mark)
c a molecular covalent compound; ....(1 mark)
d an ionic compound; ....(1 mark)
e a giant covalent structure ....(1 mark)

[ULEAC]

ANSWER

a B (*good electrical conductor, high M.Pt. and B.Pt*).
b D (*poor electrical conductor, low M.Pt. and B.Pt., only forms an acidic gas when it burns. Note C forms carbon dioxide and water so cannot be an element*).
c C (*poor electrical conductor, low M.Pt. and B.Pt.*).
d A (*good electrical conductor when liquid, high M.Pt. and B.Pt.*).
e E (*poor electrical conductor, high M.Pt. and B.Pt.*).

Properties of materials

The properties of materials depend on:

• The particles in the material – atoms, molecules and ions.
• The bonding in the material – ionic, covalent or metallic.

The table on p 188 gives a summary of some important types of materials, relating these to their properties.

QUESTION

All composite materials are

A brittle
B corrugated
C mixtures
D tough (1 mark)

[SEG 1994]

ANSWER

C

QUESTION

The table shows the properties of four strong, composite materials. Which material is best for making a car tyre?

	Flexibility	Density	Wear resistance	Easily moulded
A	low	medium	high	no
B	medium	medium	high	yes
C	low	high	medium	no
D	medium	high	low	yes

[SEG 1994]

ANSWER

B

QUESTION

Copper is a dense, ductile (that is, can be drawn out into a wire) metal with a high resistance to corrosion. Aluminium bronze is an alloy of copper and aluminium. This alloy has the same resistance to corrosion as copper but has twice the strength. The greatest strength is obtained when the alloy contains 10 per cent of aluminium by mass.

a Sketch on the axes provided in Fig 9, a graph to show how the strength of aluminium bronze changes with composition. (1 mark)
b Fig 10 shows the arrangement of atoms in pure copper metal.

Substance	Melting point (°C)	Boiling point (°C)	Electrical conductivity when		Effect of heating in air
			solid	liquid	
A	800	1470	poor	good	no reaction
B	650	1110	good	good	burns to form a white solid
C	19	287	poor	poor	burns to form carbon dioxide and water
D	114	444	poor	poor	burns to form an acidic gas only
E	1700	2200	poor	poor	no reaction

Fig 7

Type of material	Important properties	Notes
Metals	strong can be rolled or hammered into shape can be cast or combined with another metal to form an alloy can be welded good thermal conductors good electrical conductors strong in compression and tension shiny hard react with acids	properties are due to metallic bonding
Glass	hard but brittle strong in compression, but weak in tension not affected by many chemical substances high melting point transparent may crack if there is a sudden change of temperature electrical insulator	unusual giant structure of silicon and oxygen covalently bonded. Particles not arranged in a regular way.
Ceramics	hard but brittle strong in compression, weak in tension not affected by chemical substances high melting point electrical insulator	mostly made from clay, oxygen atoms covalently bonded to silicon. High proportion of oxygen makes ceramics resistant to attack by chemical substances
Plastic polymers	strong (for their mass) flexible easily melted and moulded, but thermosets can only be moulded once thermal and electrical insulators not very elastic may burn when heated	(see p 228 for more details of polymers)

Some important terms connected with materials

Alloy: This is a mixture of metals. A small amount of another metal (or carbon) is added to the main one. In nearly all cases the alloy is harder than either of the two metals it contains. The small amounts of other atoms that are added have the effect of preventing the atoms of the main metal sliding over each other so easily.

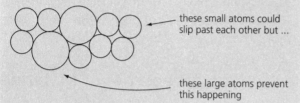

these small atoms could slip past each other but ...

these large atoms prevent this happening

Fig 8 The structure of an alloy

Composites: A mixture of two or more different materials. For example:

Glass reinforced plastic: Plastic polymer containing strands of glass fibre. Light (due to the plastic polymer) but strong (due to the glass).

Reinforced concrete: Steel rods add strength to the concrete which otherwise has poor tensile properties and is likely to crack when bent or stretched.

Bone: The protein collagen adds flexibility to the mineral hydroxyapatite part of bone, which gives bone its hardness.

Fibres: These may be natural or synthetic. They are likely to be polymers which are strong when stretched along their length. The molecules are arranged in long chains.

Plastics: Materials which can be moulded. Be careful not to confuse these with with polymers (a long chain molecule which may be made from thousands of atoms). Not all polymers are plastic (see p 306 for more details).

Thermosoftening plastics: Weak forces between the chains mean that the material can be melted and moulded many times, e.g. polythene.

Thermosetting plastic: Strong bonds are formed as cross-links between the chains of the polymer, so that the material can only be moulded once.

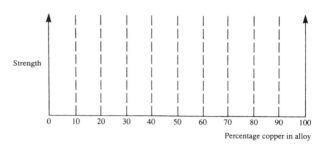

Fig 9

Use Fig 10 to help you to explain why copper metal:

   i is dense

....

....

....

....(2 marks)

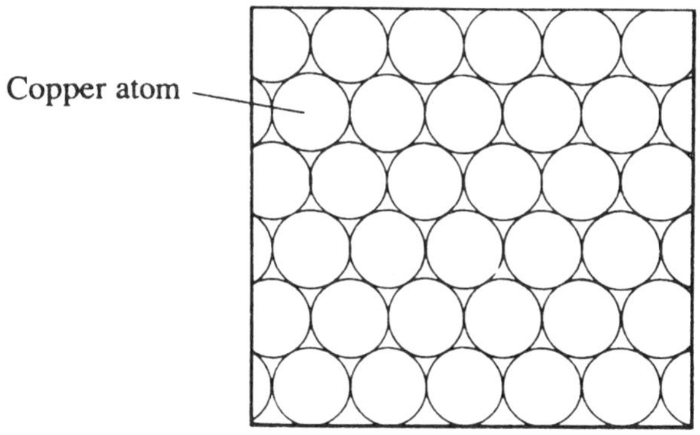

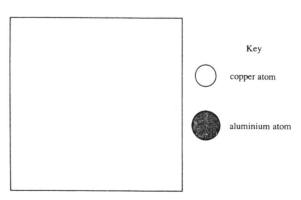

Copper atom

Fig 10

   ii is ductile

....

....

....

....(2 marks)

c i In the space provided below draw a labelled diagram to show the arrangement of atoms in aluminium bronze.
     (2 marks)

Key

◯ copper atom

⬤ aluminium atom

Fig 11

ii Use your completed diagram to help you to explain why aluminium bronze is much stronger than pure copper.

....
....
....
....(2 marks)

iii Suggest one use of aluminium bronze. State the reason why aluminium bronze is used for the purpose you have suggested.

....
....(1 mark)

[SEG]

ANSWER

a *The maximum of the graph should be at 90% copper on the x-axis. Look at the axis carefully and don't make the maximum at 10% as this would be 10% copper. If you read the question carefully you will see that the alloy has twice the strength of 100% copper.*

b i The copper atoms are closely packed *and so* there are a lot of copper atoms per unit volume.

ii The copper atoms are arranged in layers *and so* these can be pulled over one another. *Notice that the question requires you to 'explain' and gives you 2 marks for each part.*

c i *You should draw a diagram based on the previous one, but replacing some of the copper atoms by the larger aluminium ones. You must also remember to label both types of atoms.*

ii The aluminium atoms prevent the copper atoms sliding over each other so easily.

iii There are several suitable answers here. For example: for pistons in light aircraft engines. *You should stress that the purpose you have given makes use of the strength of the alloy.*

Revision sheet

Formulae, equations and amounts

1 Which of the following are elements and which are compounds:
Ag, Br, Fe, Mg, NO, PbO, Zn?

2 How do you work out the mass of 1 mol of:
a chlorine atoms?
b chlorine molecules?

3 How many atoms of each element are there in $Ca(NO_3)_2$?

4 Given that the calcium ion is Ca^{2+} and the phosphate ion is PO_4^{3-}, what is the formula of calcium phosphate?

5 What fraction of a mole is 4g of sulphur? (Relative atomic mass: S = 32)

6 How would you make a molar solution of potassium iodide?

7 Balance this equation:
Magnesium + oxygen $\rightarrow$ magnesium oxide

8 If the volume of a mole of gas is $24dm^3$, how many moles of nitrogen are there in $2.4dm^3$ of the gas?

Bonding and Properties of Materials

1 Finish these sentences:
a Ionic bonding is formed when atoms .... electrons.
b Covalent bonding is formed when atoms .... electrons.
c In metallic bonding the outer electrons of the atoms are ....

2 Which type of bond is likely to be formed:
a Between a metal and a non-metal;
b between two non-metals?

3 a What type of structure is found in graphite and diamond?
b How are the atoms linked in these structures?

4 a Draw a sketch to show the structure of an alloy.
b How does this make the metal 'hard'?

5 What is a composite?

6 Describe the difference in structure between thermosetting and thermosoftening plastics.

Revision sheet answers

Formulae, equations and amounts

1 Elements: Ag, Br, Fe, Mg, Zn only one capital letter in each case.
Compounds: NO, PbO.

2 a Look up the relative atomic mass – this is the mass of a mole of chlorine atoms.
b Double the relative atomic mass; there are two atoms of chlorine in each molecule.

3 $Ca(NO_3)_2$: Ca-calcium: one atom; N-nitrogen: 2 atoms, O-oxygen: 6 atoms.

4 Ca^{2+}, PO_4^{3-}, formula: $Ca_3(PO_4)_2$.

5 4/32 mol = 0.125 mol.

6 Find the relative atomic masses of potassium (39)
and iodine (127).
Write the formula for potassium iodide: KI.
Work out the formula mass: 39 + 127 = 166.
Dissolve 166g of potassium iodide in distilled
water and make up (accurately) to a cubic
decimetre (litre) in a volumetric flask.
7 $2Mg + O_2 \rightarrow 2MgO$.
8 $2.4/24dm^3 = 0.1$
There are 0.1 mol of nitrogen gas in $2.4dm^3$.

Bonding and Properties of Materials

1 a Ionic bonding: when atoms give away and
   receive electrons.
 b Covalent bonding: when atoms share electrons.
 c Metals – the outer electrons are shared between
   the atoms.
2 Metal and non-metal: likely to be ionic.
 Two non-metals: likely to be covalent.
3 a Graphite and diamond: giant covalent
   structures.
 b Atoms linked to form a large 3-D structure (by
   covalent bonds).
4 a

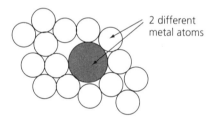

Fig 1

 b The larger atoms prevent the smaller ones
   slipping.
5 A composite is a mixture of two or more different
 materials.
6 Thermosetting: strong bonds are formed as cross
 links between the chains of the polymer.
 Thermosoftening: weak forces exist between the
 chains of the polymer.

Student Answer with Comments

a The following diagrams represent four different
 solid structures.
 Which diagram represents;
  i diamond;

B   ✓ ①

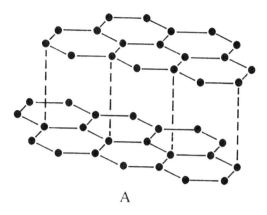

A

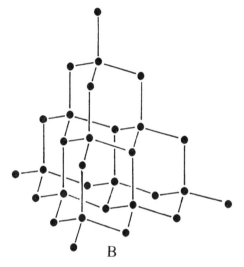

B

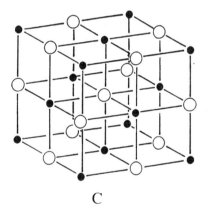

C

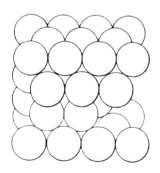

D

Fig 2

ii copper?

D .... ✓ ①

b In the box below, draw a diagram to show the structure of sodium chloride after it has melted.

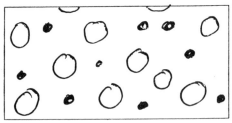

⓪

This is a liquid so I would like to see ions closer together.

c Explain why sodium chloride has a relatively high melting point.

Sodium Chloride has a high melting point because of its bonds. It has ionic bonds which are very strong and require a lot of energy to break. This energy comes from heat thus requiring a lot to melt (high melting point). ②

⁴/₅   (Total 5 marks)
[ULEAC]

An exam question for you to try

Soluble Aspirin tablets contain sodium acetylsalicylate. This is made from insoluble acetylsalicylic acid by neutralising it with sodium hydroxide solution.

The equation for the reaction is:

acetylsalicylic acid + sodium hydroxide → sodium acetylsalicylate + water

$C_9H_8O_4$ +NaOH →$C_9H_7O_4Na$ + H_2O

(relative atomic mass: H = 1, C = 12, O = 16, Na = 23)

a Which ions have combined together to form a molecule in the reaction?

....

....(1 mark)

b i A drug company has a supply of sodium hydroxide solution which contains 200 grams of sodium hydroxide per litre of solution (200g/litre). Calculate the concentration of this solution in moles per litre.

....

....

....

....

....(2 marks)

ii The drug company carries out the conversion reaction in 1,000 litre tanks. How many moles of sodium hydroxide are there in 1,000 litres of this solution?

....(1 mark)

iii How many moles of acetylsalicylic acid will this amount of sodium hydroxide react with?

....(1 mark)

iv Calculate the maximum mass of sodium acetylsalicylate that could be made from 1,000 litres of the sodium hydroxide solution?

....

....(2 marks)
[MEG]

Answer

a H⁺ (or H_3O^+) and OH⁻; *the sodium acetylsalicyclic is a salt (ionic) and not a molecule.*

b i 5 (answer gives units as moles/litre)
Formula of sodium hydroxide: NaOH
Formula mass = 23 + 16 + 1
*   = 40*
The solution contains 200g of NaOH per litre, this is 200/40 = 5 moles/litre.

ii 5,000 moles
There are 5 mol in every litre so in 1,000 litres there are 5,000 mol NaOH.

iii 5,000 moles of acetylsalicyclic acid
From the equation 1 mole of acetylsalicyclic acid reacts with 1 mole of sodium hydroxide, so if there are 5,000 moles of sodium hydroxide this will react with 5,000 mol of acetylsalicyclic acid.

iv 1,010,000g (*don't forget the units*).
1 mol of sodium acetylsalicylate ($C_9H_7O_4Na$) =
$(9 \times 12) + (7 \times 1) + (4 \times 16) + 23$
= 108 + 7 + 64 + 23
= 202 g
5,000 mol of acetylsalicyclic acid will give 5,000 mol of sodium acetylsalicylate. So maximum mass that could be made from 1,000 litres of sodium hydroxide is:
$5,000 \times 202g$
= 1,010,000g.

10 Patterns of reactions

Patterns of reactions	Midland (MEG)				Northern (NEAB)		London (ULEAC)				Southern (SEG)		Welsh (WJEC)
	Own	Nuffield	Salters	Suffolk	Co-ordinated	Modular	Modular GASP	Combined	Co-ordinated	Modular	Double	Modular	Co-ordinated
ELECTROLYSIS													
What happens in electrolysis	✓	✓	✓	✓	✓	✓	✓	✓	✓	✓	✓	✓	✓
Reactions at the electrodes in terms of electrons	✓	H	✓	H	✓	✓	✓	✓	✓	✓	✓	✓	✓
Calculations involving electrolysis	H	H	✓	H	H	H	H	H	H	H	✓	H	H
Uses of electrolysis	✓	✓	✓	✓	✓	✓	✓	✓	✓	✓	✓	✓	✓
RATES OF REACTION													
Particles in reactions	✓	✓	✓	✓	✓	✓	✓	✓	✓	✓	✓	✓	✓
Measuring a rate of reaction	✓	✓	✓	✓	✓	✓	✓	✓	✓	✓	✓	✓	✓
Changing the rate of a reaction	✓	✓	✓	✓	✓	✓	✓	✓	✓	✓	✓	✓	✓
Enzymes	✓	✓	✓		✓	✓	✓	✓	✓	✓	✓	✓	✓
Reversible reactions and equilibria	H	✓	✓	✓	H	H	H	✓	H	H	✓	H	H
The Haber process	H	✓	✓		H	H	✓	✓	H	H	✓	H	H
PATTERNS IN THE PERIODIC TABLE													
Importance of the periodic table	✓	✓	✓	✓	✓	✓	✓	✓	✓	✓	✓	✓	✓
Key features of the periodic table	✓	✓	✓	✓	✓	✓	✓	✓	✓	✓	✓	✓	✓
Noble gases	✓	✓	✓	✓	✓	✓	✓	✓	✓	✓	✓	✓	✓
Groups 1 and 2	✓	✓	✓	✓	✓	✓	✓	✓	✓	✓	✓	✓	✓
Group 7	✓	✓	✓	✓	✓	✓	✓	✓	✓	✓	✓	✓	✓
Trends in a period	✓	✓	✓	H	✓	✓	✓	✓	✓	✓	✓	✓	✓
Transition metals							✓						
Hydrogen in the periodic table	✓	✓	✓	✓	H	H	✓	✓	H	✓	✓	✓	H

Electrolysis

What is electrolysis?

Electrolysis is a chemical reaction that occurs when electricity splits up a substance (called an electrolyte) into new substances.
You need to know:

- Why some substances can be decomposed by electricity.
- What happens at each of the electrodes in the circuit.

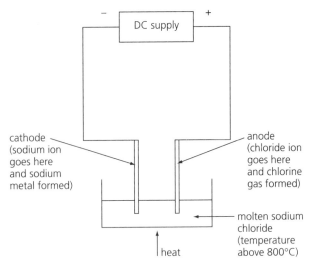

Fig 1 Electrolysis of molten sodium chloride
When sodium chloride is actually electrolysed you have to stop the sodium reaching either the air or the chlorine.

How can some substances be decomposed by electricity?

If a substance is to be an electrolyte and decomposed by electricity, then it must be a compound. Metals conduct electricity but they are not electrolytes. They cannot be decomposed by the current. Most metals are elements and so they cannot be decomposed. Ionic compounds (see p 184) can conduct electricity when they are molten or when they are dissolved in water (an aqueous solution). When they are solids the ions are not free to move so they cannot conduct electricity.

Electrolysis can occur in ionic compounds when they are molten or dissolved in water.

Electrolysis of an ionic compound in aqueous solution

Here, in addition to the ions of the compound, hydrogen ions and hydroxide ions from the water are present.

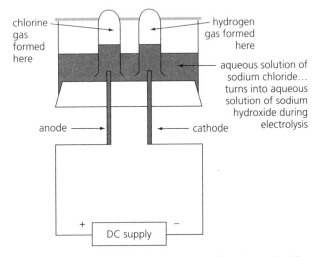

Fig 2 Electrolysis of an aqueous solution of sodium chloride

What happens at each of the electrodes in the circuit?

This depends on whether the ionic compound is molten or whether it is dissolved in water.

Electrolysis of a simple molten ionic compound

This is the simplest to think about because there will only be two ions present:

- A positive ion or cation which is attracted to the cathode.
- A negative ion or anion which is attracted to the anode.

See p 175 for a list of some common ions.

There are some rules to help you work out what happens at each electrode for an aqueous solution:

cathode
- Metals and hydrogen appear at the cathode.
- If metals and hydrogen are present, hydrogen appears in preference to the metals, unless the metal is below hydrogen in the reactivity series e.g. copper or nickel. In this case the metal appears at the cathode.

anode
- Non-metals appear at the anode.
- Chlorine, bromine and iodine appear in preference to oxygen if both are present.

From this you can work out which ions (there will be a negative and a positive one) are left in the solution.

What happens at the electrodes in terms of electrons?

If we think about the electrolysis of aqueous sodium chloride, then:

At the cathode

Hydrogen appears.
The positive hydrogen ion attracts an electron from the negative cathode. Neutral atoms of hydrogen are formed and these join together to form molecules of hydrogen gas.

hydrogen ion   gains an electron   to form a hydrogen
                                          atom
$$H^+ \quad + \quad e^- \rightarrow \quad\quad H(g)$$
2 hydrogen atoms form a hydrogen molecule
$$2H(g) \quad\quad\quad \rightarrow \quad\quad H_2(g)$$

At the anode

Chlorine appears
The anode attracts the electron from the negative chloride ion, leaving a neutral chlorine atom. This combines with another chlorine atom to form a molecule, which appears as chlorine gas.

chloride ion   loses an electron   to form a chlorine
                                          atom
$$Cl^- \quad\quad -e^- \rightarrow \quad\quad Cl(g)$$
2 chlorine atoms form a chlorine molecule
$$2Cl(g) \quad\quad\quad \rightarrow \quad\quad Cl_2(g)$$

QUESTION

The diagram below shows the electrolysis of sodium chloride solution in the laboratory.

a Which gas forms at the negative electrode?

....(1 mark)

b Explain why chlorine gas forms at the positive electrode.

....

....

....(2 marks)

c State one use of chlorine gas.

....(1 mark)

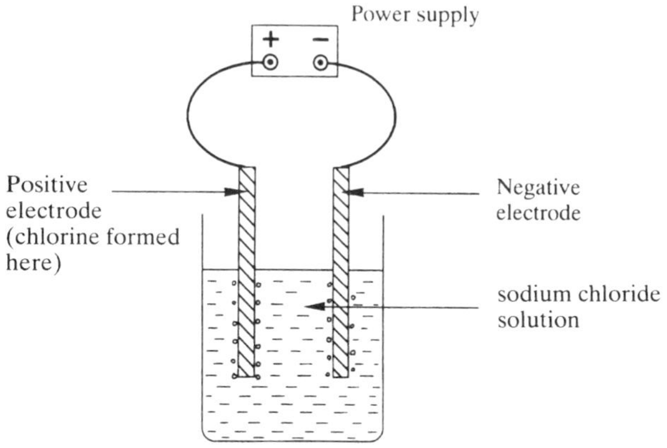

Power supply

Positive electrode (chlorine formed here)

Negative electrode

sodium chloride solution

Fig 3

[NEAB]

ANSWER

a Hydrogen.

b The positive electrode attracts the electron from the negative chloride ion. This leaves a neutral chlorine atom which combines with another to form a molecule of chlorine. This appears as the gas.

c *There are many uses of chlorine, any one from:*
  Bleaching (or making sodium chlorate(I) which is then used in bleaching).
  Textiles, paper manufacture.
  Making solvents e.g. for dry cleaning.
  Making PVC e.g. for window frames, pipes, packaging etc.

QUESTION

Scientists in America are now investigating a new method of cleaning up the sites of old tips, such as those at copper mines.

Two electrodes are driven into the ground, and electricity is passed between them, as shown in the diagram below. Water-soluble pollutants which collect around the electrodes are then pumped to the surface.

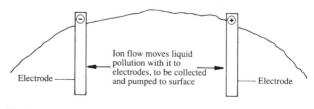

Electrode

Ion flow moves liquid pollution with it to electrodes, to be collected and pumped to surface

Electrode

Fig 4

i Malachite, $Cu_2CO_3(OH)_2$, behaves in a similar way to a mixture of copper(II) carbonate and copper(II) hydroxide.
Write a balanced equation for the reaction between copper(II) hydroxide and sulphuric acid.
....(2 marks)

ii Most of the soluble copper ions will be removed by pumping out the solution surrounding one of the electrodes.
Name, and give the charge of this electrode.
....(1 mark)

iii Explain whether or not it would be possible to remove more reactive metals, such as zinc, from tips by this method.

....
....
....
....
....(2 marks)

[ULEAC]

ANSWER

i $Cu(OH)_2 + H_2SO_4 \rightarrow CuSO_4 + 2H_2O$
(Do read the question carefully, it does not ask you to write an equation for malachite!)

ii Cathode, which has a negative charge.

iii Yes, it would be possible.
Zinc is a metal and so would move towards the cathode.
Zinc is more reactive so it will not be deposited at the cathode, but as the solution is pumped to the surface from around each electrode then it is likely that zinc could be removed in this way.

Calculations involving electrolysis

If you look at the balanced equations which occur at the electrodes during electrolysis you can see how many moles of ions and electrons are involved.
For example:
At the anode when electrolysis occurs in aqueous sodium chloride,

Cl^- $-$ e^- $Cl(g)$
1 mole   1 mole   1 mole

A mole of electrons is called a Faraday. A Faraday is a certain amount of electricity. 1 Faraday is 96,500 coulombs.
The number of coulombs can be calculated for the electrolysis circuit in use from this equation:

Charge passing (coulombs) = current (amps) × time (seconds)

See p 257–259 for more discussion about charge.

Three factors are important in electrolysis experiments:

• The amount of electricity used (in coulombs).
• The amount of the element formed at the electrodes.
• The charge on the ions.

If you know any two of these you can calculate the third one!

Example
A current of 5 amps is passed through a solution of copper(II) sulphate for 20 minutes. How much copper is formed at the cathode? (relative atomic mass of copper 64g, 1 Faraday is 96,500 coulombs)
First of all write the equation for the cathode:

Cu^{2+} $+$ $2e^-$ $\rightarrow$ $Cu(s)$
2 moles   2 moles   1 mole

1 mole of copper is formed when 2 Faradays of electricity pass.
or 0.5 mole of copper is formed when 1 Faraday of electricity passes.

Actual amount of electricity passed is:
5 × 20 × 60 coulombs
= 6000 coulombs

So, number of Faradays used = 6000/96,500 = 0.062

If 1 Faraday deposits 0.5 mole of copper
then 0.062 Faradays deposits 0.062 × 0.5 moles of copper = 0.031 moles of copper.

1 mole of copper is 64g, so 0.031 moles of copper is
64 × 0.031
= 1.984 g of copper.

QUESTION

High purity copper is needed because it is used in electrical wires. You get high purity copper by electrolysis using a thin, pure copper cathode and a solution of copper sulphate.
(The Faraday constant (F) is 96,000 coulombs per mole (C/mole). The relative atomic mass of copper is 64. A current of 200 Amperes (A) is used for 12 hours.
What mass of copper is formed at the cathode?

Show clearly how you obtain your answer

....

....

....

....

....

....(5 marks)

Part question [SEG 1994]

ANSWER

2,880g of copper is formed at the cathode.

The equation at the cathode is:

Cu^{2+} + $2e^-$ → $Cu(s)$
2 moles   *2 moles*   *1 mole*

1 mole of copper is formed when 2 Faradays of electricity pass, or 0.5 mole of copper is formed when 1 Faraday of electricity passes.

Using:
Charge passing (coulombs) = current (amps) × time
(seconds)

Charge passing = 200 × (12 × 60 × 60)
= 8,640,000 coulombs

Number of Faradays used = 8,640,000/96,000
= 90

If 1 Faraday deposits 0.5 mole of copper then 90 Faradays deposit 90 × 0.5 mole = 45 moles of copper

1 mole of copper = 64 g, so 45 moles of copper = 45 × 64 g = 2880 g or 2.880 Kg.

QUESTION

The following data is needed for this question: RAM carbon = 12, oxygen = 16. The volume of 1 mole of gas at room temperature and normal pressure is 24dm³. In the manufacture of aluminium by electrolysis of molten aluminium oxide, the electrode changes are:

at the negative electrode $Al^{3+} + 3e^- → Al$
at the positive electrode $2O^{2-} - 4e^- → O_2$

a By rewriting the above equations,
$4Al^{3+} + 12e^- → 4Al$
$6O^{2-} - 12e^- → 3O_2$

or otherwise, calculate how many grams of oxygen would be produced for every 27g of aluminium formed.

....

....

....(3 marks)

b For every 8g of oxygen produced:
   i calculate the volume in litres (dm³) that the oxygen would occupy at ordinary (room) temperature and pressure;

....

....

....(1 mark)

   ii calculate the mass of the positive carbon electrode that will burn away to carbon dioxide. (Assume that all the oxygen produced reacts with the carbon electrode)

....

....

....(1 mark)
[WJEC]

ANSWER

a 24 g of oxygen.
   4 moles of aluminium are formed as 3 moles of oxygen molecules are formed.
   1 mole of aluminium forms as 3/4 mole of oxygen molecules is formed.
   27g of aluminium (1 mole) forms 3 × 32/4 g of oxygen molecules = 24 g of oxygen.
b   i 6 dm³.
       1 mole of gas occupies 24dm³ at RTP.
       1 mole of oxygen molecules = 32g
       32g occupies 24dm³,
       8g occupies 24 × 8 / 32
       = 6dm³.
    ii 3 g of carbon.
       $C + O_2 → CO_2$
       1 mole of carbon reacts with 1 mole of oxygen molecules
       12g of carbon would react with 32g of oxygen molecules
       If only 8 g of oxygen molecules are produced then:
       12 × 8/32 g of carbon are used up
       = 3 g carbon
       If you've struggled on the last two parts of this question, look back to section 9.

Some uses of electrolysis

Electroplating

Electroplating is a special kind of electrolysis. One metal is used to form a thin coat (or plate) on another.

The article that is to be electroplated is put at the cathode in the circuit, and a solution of the plating metal is needed as the electrolyte. The metal only coats the article when it faces the anode, so it needs to be turned during the process so that all sides of it get coated. The article that is to be plated must be very clean – if there is grease on it, for example from your fingers, the plating metal will not stick very well.

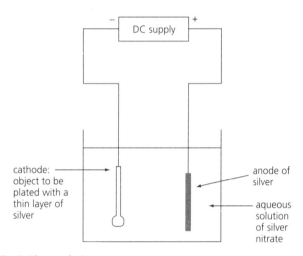

Fig 5 Electroplating

If you look at some 'silver'-looking spoons you may see EPNS, which stands for electroplated nickel silver (a thin layer of silver on top of the nickel).

Purifying metals

If impure copper is put at the anode in an electrolysis cell and the cathode is a thin sheet of the pure metal, then copper will move from the anode to the cathode. Copper sulphate solution can be used as the electrolyte. In this way copper that is 99.9% pure can be formed. It can be used in electrical equipment where very pure metal is required.

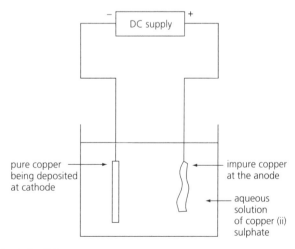

Fig 6 Purifying copper

Extracting metals

Although aluminium is one of the most abundant metals in the Earth's crust, it is not found in a pure form but usually as aluminium oxide (or bauxite). Aluminium is a reactive metal which is difficult to extract from bauxite. It is extracted using electricity.

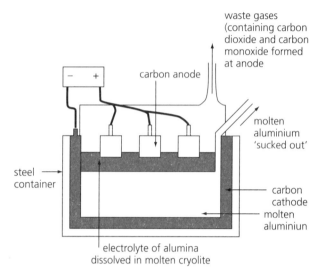

Fig 7 Extracting aluminium

The most reactive metals are obtained from their ores by electrolysis (see p 222).

QUESTION

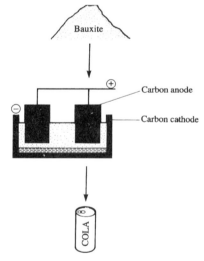

Fig 8

Aluminium oxide is obtained from the mineral bauxite. There is enough bauxite to provide the aluminium needed for about 30 years.

Aluminium is produced by electrolysis from molten aluminium oxide. The process needs a lot of energy.

Many cans for drinks are made from alumium.

a Apart from cost, give two properties of aluminium that make it useful for making cans.

Property 1 ....

Property 2 ....(2 marks) b For the electrolysis of molten aluminium oxide (Al_2O_3):

  i complete and balance the symbolic equation for the reaction at the cathode (negative) electrode; (1 mark)

  $$Al^{3+} + \qquad \rightarrow Al$$

  ii name the element at the anode (positive) electrode

  ....(1 mark)

c Explain how both oxidation and reduction take place during the electrolysis of aluminium oxide (Al_2O_3)

  ....

  ....

  ....(2 marks)

  Part question [SEG 1994]

ANSWER

a *There are several answers you could give here, such as:*
It does not corrode easily, it is easy to shape, it is 'light' (or better still has a low density).

b i $Al^{3+} + 3e^- \rightarrow Al$
  ii Oxygen

c At the cathode, the aluminium ions gain electrons – this is *reduction*. At the anode the oxygen ions lose electrons – this is *oxidation*.
(Look back to p 146–147 if you need more help on oxidation and reduction.)

Rates of Reaction

How does a chemical reaction occur?

Particles in substances are moving all the time. In liquids and gases the particles are free to move their position and the particles collide all the time. A chemical reaction occurs when the particles of the reactants collide with sufficient energy to break the bonds between them. The amount of energy needed for this to happen is called the activation energy. The activation energy differs for different reactions. If the activation energy for a reaction is low there are lots of collisions with sufficient energy to 'react' and the reaction takes place quickly. For example, when silver nitrate solution is added to sodium chloride solution a white precipitate is seen immediately. If

the activation energy is high there are fewer successful collisions and the reaction is slower; for example, when iron rusts.

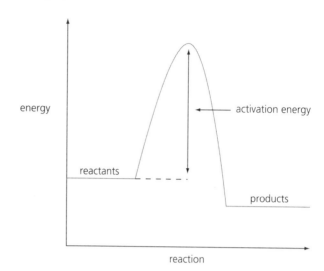

Fig 1 Activation energy for a reaction

How can we measure the rate of reaction?

The rate of reaction is another way of saying how fast the reaction occurs. In any reaction the reactants are used up as products are formed. To find out the rate you need to measure, at suitable intervals of, say, every 30 seconds:

• How much of the reactants is being used.
or
• How much product is being formed.

If there is more than one product then you can measure just one. It will still give you an indication of how fast the reaction is occurring.
Once you have some results you can draw a graph. In the reaction of calcium carbonate with hydrochloric acid, carbon dioxide gas is formed as one of the products. By noting how much mass is lost you can follow the rate of reaction.
Calcium + hydrochloric → calcium + water + carbon
carbonate   acid   chloride   dioxide
$CaCO_3(s) + 2HCl(aq) \rightarrow CaCl_2(aq) + H_2O(l) +$
$$CO_2(g)$$

In Fig 2 (overleaf)
• Up to point A the reaction happens quickly. 1g of gas has been lost in 100s. The slope of the graph is steep.
• From A to B the reaction is beginning to slow down. The slope of the graph is not so steep.

- From B to C the reaction slows even further. The slope of the graph is very gentle.
- At C the graph is horizontal. (The slope is zero). No gas is being given off. The reaction has stopped.

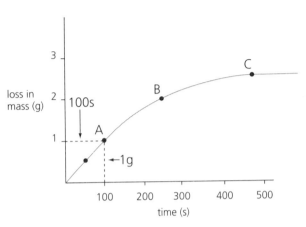

Fig 2 Graph showing the rate of reaction of calcium carbonate and hydrochloric acid

You will notice that the rate is quickest when the reactants first mix and slows down towards the end of the reaction.

Eventually, no more carbon dioxide is produced as either all the calcium carbonate or all the hydrochloric acid has reacted.

Changing the rate of reaction

There are several ways of changing the rate of reaction. You must be able to explain how each works in terms of what happens to the particles, and, in the case of a catalyst or enzyme, in terms of the activation energy.

The word 'particles' is used here – in your answers you should try and be more specific. Depending on which reaction you are describing, you should use the term ion or molecule instead of particle (see section 8 for help in where to use which term).

1 Changing the temperature

Changing the temperature has a big effect on the rate of a reaction. Increasing the temperature increases the energy of the particles. They are likely to have some more collisions but many more of these are likely to be successful in terms of breaking the bonds in the

reactants. A useful rule of thumb is that the rate of many reactions is doubled when the temperature is increased by 10°C.

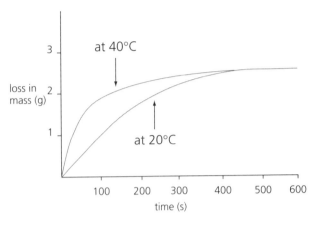

What is happening to the particles

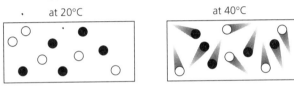

Fig 3 Changing the temperature

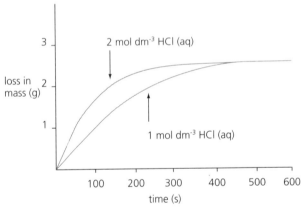

What is happening to the particles

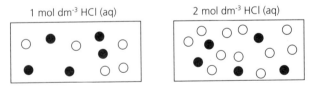

Fig 4 Changing the concentration

2 Changing the concentration

Increasing the concentration increases the rate of reaction. By using more particles of a reactant in a given volume there are more present to collide. The chance of a reaction happening increases so the rate of reaction increases.

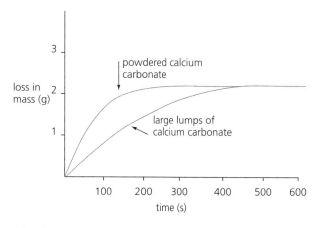

Changing the concentration of a gas
To change the concentration of a gas you need to change the pressure. By increasing the pressure you increase the number of particles in the available space. This has the same effect as increasing the concentration of a solution.

gases at low pressure

increasing the pressure

the gases are at a higher pressure, they are now more concentrated

Fig 5 How increasing the pressure increases the concentration of a gas

What is happening to the particles.

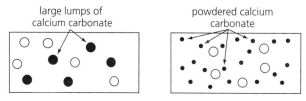

Fig 6 Changing the surface area

3 Changing the surface area

Increasing the surface area of a solid reactant, for example by using smaller pieces, increases the rate of the reaction. You must remember to use the same mass of the reactant and not just swap a big piece of solid for a smaller one! In the example with calcium carbonate the reaction takes place when particles of the acid hit the surface of the calcium carbonate. If there are lots of smaller particles, they have a bigger surface area than a few large lumps. Therefore, there is a greater chance of collisions and the rate of reaction increases.

4 Using a catalyst

The rate of many reactions can be changed (usually increased) by using a catalyst. This takes part in the reaction but at the end is unchanged. You do not include it in the equation as either a reactant or a product, but it may be helpful to write the name of the catalyst on the arrow.

A catalyst is a chemical substance, often a transition metal. Heat is NOT a catalyst.

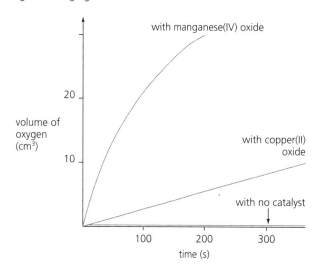

What is happening to the activation energy.

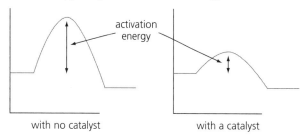

Fig 7 Using a catalyst in the decomposition of hydrogen peroxide

Catalysts lower the activation energy for the reaction so it happens more easily. Different reactions need different catalysts. Catalysts are very important in industry. By increasing the rate of a reaction the process can be more economical.

QUESTION

10g of calcium carbonate was added to 20cm³ of 1mol dm⁻³ hydrochloric acid. The experiment was carried out three times, at 10°C, at 15°C and at 20°C. Which of the following graphs shows the correct results? (1 mark)

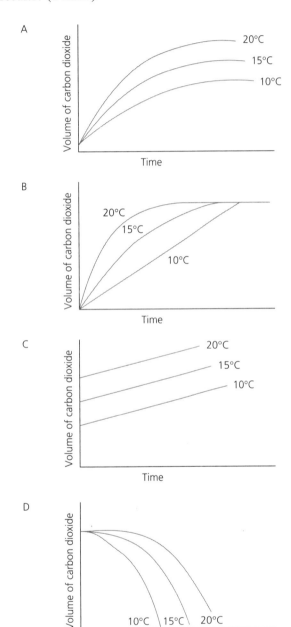

Fig 8 Rate of reaction graphs

ANSWER

B

(The same amount of carbon dioxide is formed in the reaction, however long it takes to form. You can discount C and D, as no carbon dioxide is formed before the reaction starts.)

QUESTION

Equal volumes of hydrochloric acid are added to equal masses of marble chips. Which set of conditions will give the fastest reaction?

sets of conditions		
size of marble chips	concentration of acid	temperature
A large	low	low
B medium	low	high
C small	high	high
D small	high	low

[SEG 1994]

ANSWER

C

QUESTION

Nickel catalyses the reaction between oils and hydrogen to form fats. Which of these statements correctly describe the complete reaction?

1 More fats are formed when more catalyst is used.
2 The catalyst increases the rate of the reaction between hydrogen and the oils.
3 When the reaction is complete, the nickel catalyst has not lost any mass.
   A 1 and 2
   B 1 and 3
   C 2 and 3
   D 1, 2 and 3

[SEG 1994]

ANSWER

C

QUESTION

The table on page 203 gives the results from the reaction of excess marble chips (calcium carbonate) with (A) 20cm³ of dilute hydrochloric acid, (B) 10cm³ of the dilute hydrochloric acid + 10cm³ of water.

a Plot the two curves on the grid on page 203. Label the first curve (A) and the second curve (B). (2 marks)

b *Sketch, on the same grid*, the curve you would have expected for the reaction (A) if it had been

	total mass of carbon dioxide produced in grams	
Time in minutes	(A) 20cm³ dilute HCl	(B) 10cm³ of dilute HCl + 10cm³ H₂O
0	0.00	0.00
1	0.54	0.27
2	0.71	0.35
3	0.78	0.38
4	0.80	0.40
5	0.80	0.40

carried out at a higher temperature. Label this curve (C). (1 mark)

c *Sketch, on the same grid*, the curve you would have expected for the reaction (B) if the marble chips had been ground to a powder. Label this curve (D). (1 mark)

d Explain your answer to part (c)

....

....(1 mark)

[WJEC]

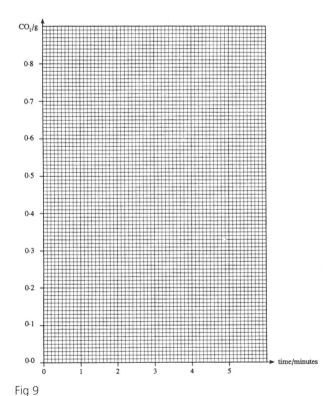

Fig 9

ANSWER

a See the graph – *make sure that you label each curve clearly*.

b See the graph. *The rate will be faster so the curve will go up more steeply. Therefore you need to draw it to the left of the original line – make sure that the volume of gas after 5 minutes is the same as for (A).*

c See the graph. *With a powder the rate will again be increased, so you need to draw the curve to the left of the one for (B), but the total volume of gas must be the same as in (B).*

d The smaller pieces of calcium carbonate (in the powder) have a larger surface area than the marble chips.

(This would be sufficient for the one mark here, but often you need to give more detail for more

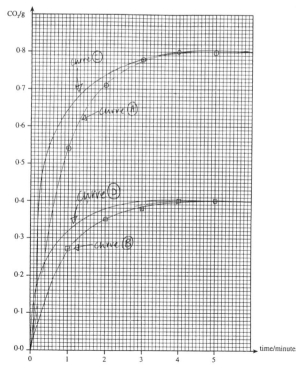

Fig 10

marks. If this is the case you need to expand your explanation like this:
This means that there will be more collisions between the ions in the calcium carbonate and the ions in the acid. It would help to draw a diagram such as in Fig 6.

Enzymes

Enzymes are biological catalysts. They are thought to work in the same way as catalysts by lowering the activation energy for a reaction. Most reactions that take place in the body are controlled by enzymes, which are proteins. They can be visualised as working by a lock and key mechanism (see p 11). Note that as enzymes are proteins they are denatured under certain conditions; for example, temperatures much above 40–45°C and extremes of pH.

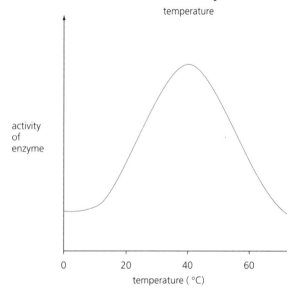

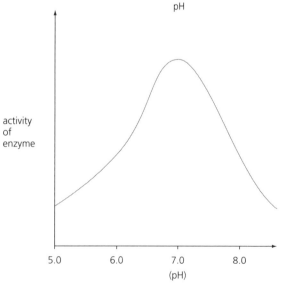

Fig 11 How temperature and pH affect an enzyme

Enzymes in industries

Baking and brewing industry

Zymase is an important enzyme to the baking and brewing industries. It catalyses the breakdown of glucose to ethanol and carbon dioxide (see p 145).

Dairy industry

Some enzymes and their uses in the dairy industry.

type of enzyme	use
fat degrading enzymes	to break up scum on the effluent from dairy ice-cream manufacture
lactase	yoghurt manufacture
proteases	cheese making
lactase in *Kluyveromyces* species of yeast	turns whey (a waste product from cheese manufacture) into ethanol (for consumption or fuel) or biomass (for animal feedstuffs)

Washing powder industry

Biological washing powders contain enzymes, called proteases, which speed up the removal of protein-based stains like blood. These powders need to work at temperatures near to 40°C.

What is a reversible reaction?

When you add hydrochloric acid to calcium carbonate, carbon dioxide gas is given off until either the hydrochloric acid or calcium carbonate is used up.

$$CaCO_3(s) + 2HCl(aq) \rightarrow CaCl_2(aq) + H_2O(l) + CO_2(g)$$

If you bubble some carbon dioxide through the mixture nothing will happen. You will not get the calcium carbonate and hydrochloric acid back again. The reaction only goes in one direction – it is not a reversible reaction.
Many reactions are not like this.
The reaction between nitrogen and hydrogen to produce ammonia is an example of a reversible reaction.

$$N_2(g) + 3H_2(g) \rightleftharpoons 2NH_3(g) \quad \Delta H = -92\,kJmol^{-1}$$

Points to remember about reversible reactions:

- The ⇌ shows that the reaction is reversible.
- The reactants turn into products but the products are also turning into reactants.
- If the products turn back to reactants at the same rate at which they are formed, nothing appears to be happening. We say the reaction has reached equilibrium.
- Changing the conditions of the reaction affects the equilibrium position. The general principle is that: If the conditions are changed the reaction moves to counteract that change.

How does the yield of a reversible reaction depend on the conditions?

The reaction of nitrogen and hydrogen to produce ammonia is important in the industrial production of ammonia by the Haber process.

$$N_2(g) + 3H_2(g) \rightleftharpoons 2NH_3(g) \qquad \Delta H = -92kJmol^{-1}$$

| 1 mole | 3 moles | 2 moles |

(4 moles of reactants
all together)

Changing the pressure

By increasing the pressure, the reaction would move to make the pressure less. This would occur by turning 4 moles of gas into 2 moles of gas. Therefore, the equilibrium would move towards the product and more ammonia would be made.

Changing the temperature

The reaction of nitrogen with hydrogen is exothermic. Heat is given out. By decreasing the temperature the reaction would move to increase the temperature. Therefore, the equilibrium would move towards the product and more ammonia would be made.

Making ammonia as economically as possible

In practice the process of making ammonia is a compromise between:

- Yield (how much ammonia is produced).
- Rate (the speed at which it is produced).

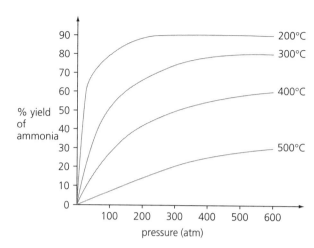

Fig 12 The yield of ammonia at different temperatures and pressures

The actual conditions used are:

Pressure: 200 atmospheres
Temperature: 380–450°C.
Catalyst: Iron (with added 'promoters' to stop it being poisoned by the ammonia).
This gives a yield of about 15% (by volume) of ammonia.

QUESTION

In the Haber Process, ammonia (NH$_3$) is produced by reacting nitrogen (N$_2$) and hydrogen (H$_2$).

   i Write a balanced symbol equation for this reaction.

     ....(1 mark)

  ii The reaction is reversible. What would happen to the equilibrium concentration of ammonia if the pressure of the equilibrium mixture was increased. Explain your answer.

     ....

     ....

     ....

     ....(2 marks)

              Part question [SEG 1994]

ANSWER

   i $N_2(g) + 3H_2(g) \rightleftharpoons 2NH_3(g)$
      Don't forget the state symbols or the arrow showing that the reaction is reversible.
  ii If the pressure of the reaction was increased the equilibrium would move to the right and more ammonia would be made. This is because 4 moles of reactant form only 2 moles of product and the equilibrium moves to reduce the pressure.

QUESTION

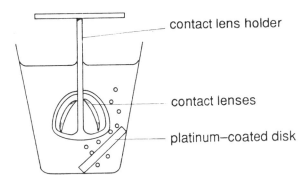

Fig 13

A way of making sure that all the hydrogen peroxide is removed (from the sterilising solution) is to place the contact lenses in water and then to add a plastic disc coated with platinum.

Platinum is a catalyst for the decomposition of hydrogen peroxide to water and oxygen.

$$2H_2O_2 \rightarrow 2H_2O + O_2$$

The table below shows the change in the concentration of a solution of hydrogen peroxide with a platinum catalyst.

a i Plot a graph to show the results of this experiment (3 marks).

ii For most people a solution of hydrogen peroxide of concentration 60 parts per million will not irritate the eyes.
Use the graph to estimate the time taken for the concentration of this solution to fall to 60 parts per million. (1 mark)

(i) Plot a graph to show the results of this experiment.

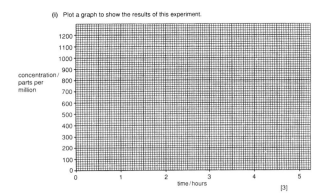

Fig 14

b Why can it be economical to use very expensive metals such as platinum as catalysts?
....(1 mark)

c Another way of removing the hydrogen peroxide is to use a solution containing an enzyme called catalase.

i Explain why you would expect a catalyst to be more effective in a solution than as a solid.
....
....(1 mark)

ii Explain the effect that this would have on the rate of reaction
....
....
....(2 marks)
[MEG]

ANSWER

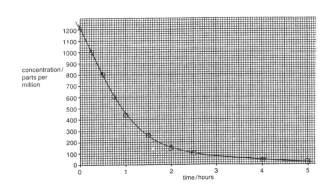

Fig 15

a i See the graph – *remember to plot the points accurately and to draw a smooth line which goes through all your points.*

ii 3.4 hours.

b *There are a few suitable answers here. Your answer must show that you know that a catalyst is not used up in a reaction.* Suitable answers are: catalysts are not used up in the reaction, the catalysts can be used lots of times, only a small amount of a catalyst is needed for a reaction.

c i In solution the rate is not limited by the surface area of the catalyst.

time/hours	0	0.25	0.50	0.75	1.00	1.50	2.00	2.50	4.00	5.00
concentration of hydrogen peroxide/ parts per million	1200	1000	800	600	440	260	150	100	40	25

ii There would be more collisions that lead to a reaction *and so* the rate of reaction would increase.
    (*A common mistake here is to miss the second part of the explanation. Always try and include the section after the* and so *if you are asked to explain.*)

Patterns in the periodic table

Why is the periodic table so important?

The periodic table is a way of making it easier to know about the 106 or so elements that exist. Elements can be grouped (or classified) in several different ways:

- Solids, liquids and gases … but this has problems if you change the temperature!
- Metals or non-metals … but certain elements, like silicon, have some non-metallic and some metallic properties!

The periodic table is a way of classifying all the elements. You can make predictions about a particular element if you know something about the physical and chemical properties of nearby elements.

Remember physical properties are things like boiling point and density. Chemical properties involve chemical reactions such as: Does it form an oxide or hydroxide which dissolves in water to form an acid or alkali?

The periodic table lists all the elements in order of their atomic number, starting with the smallest and ending with the largest. If the elements are listed in this order then it has been found that certain properties of the elements occur regularly – this is where the name periodic comes from. The table is constructed so that these similar elements are situated near each other.

For any element, two numbers are given with the symbol in the periodic table. For example, for sodium:

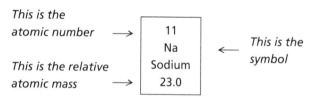

This is the atomic number ⟶ | 11 Na Sodium 23.0 | ⟵ This is the symbol
This is the relative atomic mass ⟶

Important features of the periodic table

- The elements are listed in order of their atomic number.
- The elements are listed in rows, a new row is started after each noble gas.

Group	I Alkali metals	II Alkaline earth metals											III	IV	V	VI	VII Halogens	0 Noble gases
Period																		
1			1 H Hydrogen 1.0															2 He Helium 4.0
2	3 Li Lithium 6.9	4 Be Beryllium 9.0											5 B Boron 10.8	6 C Carbon 12.0	7 N Nitrogen 14.0	8 O Oxygen 16.0	9 F Fluorine 19.0	10 Ne Neon 20.2
3	11 Na Sodium 23.0	12 Mg Magnesium 24.3											13 Al Aluminium 27.0	14 Si Silicon 28.1	15 P Phosphorus 31.0	16 S Sulphur 32.1	17 Cl Chlorine 35.5	18 Ar Argon 39.9
4	19 K Potassium 39.1	20 Ca Calcium 40.1	21 Sc Scandium 45.0	22 Ti Titanium 47.9	23 V Vanadium 50.9	24 Cr Chromium 52.0	25 Mn Manganese 54.9	26 Fe Iron 55.9	27 Co Cobalt 58.9	28 Ni Nickel 58.7	29 Cu Copper 63.5	30 Zn Zinc 65.4	31 Ga Gallium 69.7	32 Ge Germanium 72.6	33 As Arsenic 74.9	34 Se Selenium 79.0	35 Br Bromine 79.9	36 Kr Krypton 83.8
5	37 Rb Rubidium 85.5	38 Sr Strontium 87.6	39 Y Yttrium 88.9	40 Zr Zirconium 91.2	41 Nb Niobium 92.9	42 Mo Molybdenum 95.9	43 Tc Technetium (99)	44 Ru Ruthenium 101.1	45 Rh Rhodium 102.9	46 Pd Palladium 106.4	47 Ag Silver 107.9	48 Cd Cadmium 112.4	49 In Indium 114.8	50 Sn Tin 118.7	51 Sb Antimony 121.8	52 Te Tellurium 127.6	53 I Iodine 126.9	54 Xe Xenon 131.3
6	55 Cs Caesium 132.9	56 Ba Barium 137.3	57 ▶ La Lanthanum 138.9	72 Hf Hafnium 178.5	73 Ta Tantalum 181.0	74 W Tungsten 183.9	75 Re Rhenium 186.2	76 Os Osmium 190.2	77 Ir Iridium 192.2	78 Pt Platinum 195.1	79 Au Gold 197.0	80 Hg Mercury 200.6	81 Tl Thallium 204.4	82 Pb Lead 207.2	83 Bi Bismuth 209.0	84 Po Polonium (210)	85 At Astatine (210)	86 Rn Radon (222)
7	87 Fr Francium (223)	88 Ra Radium (226)	87 ▶▶ Ac Actinium (227)	104 Unq Unnil-quadium (261)	105 Unp Unnil-pentium (262)	106 Unh Unnil-hexium (263)												

	58 Ce Cerium 140.2	59 Pr Praseo-dymium 140.9	60 Nd Neody-mimum 144.2	61 Pm Promethium (147)	62 Sm Samarium 150.4	63 Eu Europium 152.0	64 Gd Gadolinium 157.3	65 Tb Terbium 158.9	66 Dy Dysprosium 162.5	67 Ho Holmium 164.9	68 Er Erbium 167.3	69 Tm Thulium 168.9	70 Yb Ytterbium 173.0	71 Lu Lutetium 175.0
▶ Lanthanide elements														
▶▶ Actinide elements	90 Th Thorium 232.0	91 Pa Protactinium (231)	92 U Uranium 238.1	93 Np Neptunium (237)	94 Pu Plutonium (242)	95 Am Americium (243)	96 Cm Curium (247)	97 Bk Berkelium (245)	98 Cf Californium (251)	99 Es Einsteinium (254)	100 Fm Fermium (253)	101 Md Mendelevium (256)	102 No Nobelium (254)	103 Lr Lawrencium (257)

Fig 1 The periodic table

- Each row going across (horizontal) is called a period.
- Each period has a number; this tells you how many shells of electrons the element has.
- Each vertical column is called a group.
- Each group has a number; for the first twenty elements this tells you how many electrons there are in the outer shell.

Important features of a period

The atomic number increases as you move from left to right across a period. This means that the number of outer electrons increases by one each time. This affects the properties of the element as the outer electrons determine the type of element and the way it reacts. For example, elements on the left have metallic properties and those on the right have non-metallic properties (see p 137).

Na	Mg	Al	Si	P	S	Cl	Ar
number of electrons in outer shell			number of electrons in outer shell				
1	2	3	4	5	6	7	8
metallic			non-metallic				
oxides are basic			oxides are acidic				
chlorides are solids, high melting points, ionic structures			chlorides have low, melting points, not ionic structures				
form positive ions in most compounds			form negative ions in compounds with metals				

argon does not have any chemical properties

Fig 2 Metallic and non-metallic trends in period 3, sodium to argon

Important features of a group

In a group, all the elements have the same number of outer electrons. They all react in a similar way and so have similar properties. However, as you descend the group the atoms of the elements get bigger. This is because the number of shells of electrons increases. This results in a change in the properties of the elements as the group is descended.

Group 0 : The noble gases

0
Noble
gases

2 He Helium 4.0
10 Ne Neon 20.2
18 Ar Argon 39.9
36 Kr Krypton 83.8
54 Xe Xenon 131.3
86 Rn Radon (222)

Fig 3 Group 0, the noble gases

This group contains six elements that all have a full set of electrons in their outer shell. Helium has two outer electrons and all the others have eight. If you know that they are called the noble gases this will help you to remember an important property – they are too noble to react!

Inert means unreactive.

The elements in this group are similar in one respect. They are chemically inert – they do not take part in chemical reactions. It is the 'full' outer shell that makes the atoms unwilling either to give away or share the electrons with other atoms, so they remain unreactive.

It is now possible to form compounds with some of the elements at the bottom of the group; for example xenon fluoride, but this reaction is difficult to achieve!

Group I : The alkali metals

This group contains six elements that all have one electron in their outer shell. If you know that they are called the alkali metals this will help you to remember two of their important properties:

- They are metals.
- Their oxides form alkaline solutions in water.

The single outer electron of the elements is removed fairly easily in a chemical reaction, to leave a positive ion with a 'full' shell of electrons. It is this that makes

I
Alkali
metals

3 Li Lithium 6.9
11 Na Sodium 23.0
19 K Potassium 39.1
37 Rb Rubidium 85.5
55 Cs Caesium 132.9
87 Fr Francium (223)

Fig 4 Group I, the alkali metals

the elements of this group reactive. The outer electron of the elements is further from the nucleus as the group is descended. Therefore, the elements in the group become more reactive as you go down the group.

1 The elements are metals with low melting points but fairly high boiling points.
2 The elements react vigorously with water to form hydrogen and an alkaline solution.

You have probably seen sodium added to water, when it whizzes about the surface (less dense than water) and hisses (as the hydrogen is released). The solution turns universal indicator paper blue (alkaline).

sodium + water → sodium hydroxide + hydrogen

$2Na(s) + 2H_2O(l) \rightarrow 2NaOH(aq) + H_2(g)$

3 The elements react very vigorously with acids. Below lithium the reaction may be explosive.
Lithium + hydrochloric acid → lithium chloride + hydrogen

$2Li(s) + 2HCl(aq) \rightarrow 2LiCl(aq) + H_2(g)$

4 The elements react with the oxygen in the air. They are kept under oil to reduce this reaction.
lithium + oxygen → lithium oxide

$4Li(s) + O_2(g) \rightarrow 2Li_2O(s)$

A common mistake is to think that these elements are stored in a bottle of water. This can't be correct (see this page)!

5 The oxides and hydroxides are basic and react with acids to form a salt and water.
sodium   + hydrochloric → sodium + water
hydroxide   acid   chloride

$NaOH(aq) + HCl(aq) \rightarrow NaCl(aq) + H_2O(l)$

6 The elements react with chlorine in an exothermic reaction to form a solid chloride. This is an ionic solid with a high melting and boiling point.
sodium + chlorine → sodium chloride

$2Na(s) + Cl2(g) \rightarrow 2NaCl(s)$

7 Compounds of the elements :
   • Contain an ion with a positive charge, eg Na^+.
   • Have ionic structures with high melting and boiling points.
   • Are colourless unless the negative ion is coloured.
   • Are nearly all soluble in water.
   • Conduct electricity in aqueous solution.
   • Conduct electricity when they are molten.

QUESTION

Sodium reacts violently with cold water.

a Complete the word equation for the reaction.
   sodium + water → sodium hydroxide + ...
                                                    (1 mark)
b Describe in detail what you see when a small piece of sodium is placed in a dish of cold water.
   ....
   ....
   ....
   ....(4 marks)
c At the end of the reaction, the liquid in the dish is sodium hydroxide solution. If universal indicator is added to this solution it turns purple.
   i What colour is the universal indicator in water?
   ....(1 mark)
   ii Explain why the indicator goes purple in sodium hydroxide solution.
   ....(2 marks)
   iii Suggest a likely pH value for sodium hydroxide solution.
   ....(1 mark)
d Name a metal which reacts:
   i more violently than sodium with water;
   ....(1 mark)
   ii less violently than sodium with water.
   ....(1 mark)
                                                    [ULEAC]

ANSWER

a Hydrogen.

b i The sodium moves on the surface, the sodium melts into a ball, the piece of sodium disappears, the sodium gives off a gas, the water bubbles or fizzes as the sodium moves rapidly over the surface.

You need to describe this in sufficient detail for 4 marks. Be careful that you describe what you can actually see – for example saying that 'hydrogen is formed' is correct but the question clearly asks you to describe what you see.

c i Green (or greeny yellow).

ii Sodium hydroxide is a strong alkali.

iii 11 (or a number between 11 and 14).

d i Potassium, rubidium, caesium, francium *(the metals below sodium in the periodic table).*

ii Lithium *(the metal above sodium in the periodic table).*

Group II: The alkaline earth metals

The name given to this group, the alkaline earths, comes from the fact that they are found in the earth as mineral compounds in rocks. For example, limestone and marble are forms of calcium carbonate. This gives an indication of an important property – the carbonates of this group are insoluble in water.

The elements in this group:

• Are similar to each other in their chemical reactions – due to the fact that they all have 2 electrons in their outer shell.

• Form ions with a charge of 2+.

• React in a similar way to the elements in group I. But they are less reactive than the elements of group I – they have two electrons in their outer shell, whereas there is only one electron in the outer shell of the elements of group I.

• As in group I the elements become more reactive as the group is descended.

• Have higher melting and boiling points – this indicates that the metallic bonding (see p 185) is stronger in this group than in group 1.

Group VII : The halogens

VII
Halogens

| 9
F
Fluorine
19.0 |
| 17
Cl
Chlorine
35.5 |
| 35
Br
Bromine
79.9 |
| 53
I
Iodine
126.9 |
| 85
At
Astatine
(210) |

Fig 5 Group VII, the halogens

This group contains five elements that all have seven electrons in their outer shell. The name halogen means 'salt former' and gives you an important clue to their properties. They are very reactive and are not found as the elements in nature, but in compounds – as salts, such as sodium chloride.

The seven outer electrons of the atoms gain an additional electron fairly easily in a chemical reaction. It is this that makes the elements of this group reactive.

The outer electrons of the atoms are further from the nucleus as the group is descended. The elements in the group become less reactive as you go down the group.

It is important that you know the similarities and differences between the elements of this group.

Similarities between the elements.

1 The elements are made up of molecules (with covalent bonding) containing two atoms: for example, Cl_2. This explains why:

• They have low melting and boiling points.

• They are soluble in solvents which have covalent bonding, such as tetrachloromethane, CCl_4.

2 The elements dissolve in water, but when pH paper is dipped in the resulting solution:

• It is quickly bleached with chlorine.

- It is slowly bleached with bromine.
- Nothing appears to happen with iodine (the iodine colours the paper).

3 The elements react with metals such as sodium to form compounds with ionic bonding.

sodium + chlorine → sodium chloride

$$2Na(s) + Cl_2(g) \rightarrow 2NaCl(s)$$

In ionic compounds formed with metals, the halogen atom forms an ion with a charge of 1^-.

4 The elements react with hydrogen to form compounds with covalent bonding.

hydrogen + chlorine → hydrogen chloride

$$H_2(g) + Cl_2(g) \rightarrow HCl(g)$$

These compounds are very soluble in water. They dissolve to form solutions that are acids, in this case hydrochloric acid.

Differences between the elements

1 Appearance
- Fluorine is a pale yellow gas.
- Chlorine is a green gas.
- Bromine is a dark red liquid.
- Iodine is a grey/black solid with a slight shine.
- Astatine is a solid (it is also radioactive).

2 Reaction with iron

The reaction is most vigorous with chlorine and least vigorous with iodine. This is evidence that the reactivity of the halogens decreases as the group is descended.

3 Displacement reactions

A halogen higher up the group (that is a more reactive one) will displace (push out of solution) a halide ion of a less reactive halogen in solution. For example, chlorine will displace bromine from a solution of a compound containing a bromide. This will be seen as an orange colour as bromine is formed.

chlorine + potassium bromide → potassium chloride + bromine

$$Cl_2(aq) + 2KBr(aq) \rightarrow 2KCl(aq) + Br_2(aq)$$

In a similar way bromine will displace iodine from a solution of a compound containing an iodide. This will be seen as a deep red colour of iodine is formed.

bromine + potassium iodide → potassium bromide + iodine

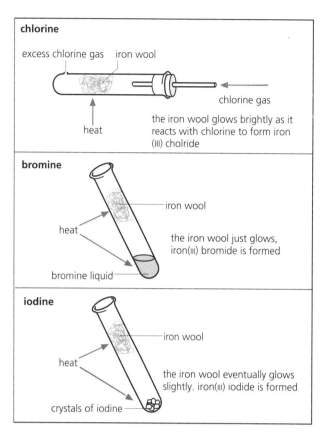

Fig 6 Reacting halogens with iron

$$Br_2(aq) + 2KI(aq) \rightarrow 2KBr(aq) + I_2(aq)$$

This is further evidence that the reactivity of the halogens decreases as the group is descended.

QUESTION

a Chlorine, bromine and iodine all belong to Group VII of the Periodic Table (the halogens). Describe one chemical property of the elements or their compounds which shows the similarity within the Group.

....

....

....(2 marks)

b What is the difference between an atom and an ion?

....

....(1 mark)

c The elements of Group I form ions with a single positive charge e.g. Na$^+$.
The elements from Group II form ions with a double positive charge e.g. Ca^{2+}.
Explain this in terms of their electronic structure.

....

....

....

....

....
....(2 marks)

[MEG]

ANSWER

a *Make sure that you:*
  * *Give a chemical and not a physical property (see p 151 if you are not sure of the difference).*
  * *Give the result of the chemical reaction such as:* React with the alkali metals, e.g. sodium, to form a white compound (e.g. sodium chloride).
    React with hydrogen to form compounds with covalent bonding, e.g. HCl.
    These dissolve in water and the resulting solution bleaches universal indicator paper.
    Compounds can be decomposed by electricity when molten or aqueous. The halogen is formed at the anode.

b An atom forms an ion when it gains or loses an electron or electrons.

c The elements in Group I have one outer electron. When they lose this to form an ion, eg Na^+, all the electron shells in this ion are full. The elements in Group II have two outer electrons. When they lose these they form an ion, eg Ca^{2+}. This ion also has full shells.

11	12	13	14	15	16	17	18
Na	Mg	Al	Si	P	S	Cl	Ar
Sodium	Magnesium	Aluminium	Silicon	Phosphorus	Sulphur	Chlorine	Argon
23.0	24.3	27.0	28.1	31.0	32.1	35.5	39.9

Fig 7 The elements of period 3

Period 3 : From Na to Ar

By knowing which group each element in this period belongs to, it is possible to make some predictions about trends or patterns across the period. The main trend is that elements on the left are metals and those on the right are non-metals. Many of the other properties can be worked out from this.

In Fig 8 you will see that the dividing line between metal on the left of the period and non-metal on the right goes somewhere in the region of aluminium and silicon. In fact, these two elements both show some properties which are characteristic of metals and some properties which are characteristic of non-metals.

For example:
* The oxide of aluminium is both basic and acidic. (The name given to an oxide of this type is amphoteric.)

* The oxide of silicon is a solid, but it has a covalent structure rather than ionic.

1. The elements	Na	Mg	Al	Si	P	S	Cl	Ar
atomic number	11	12	13	14	15	16	17	18
number of electrons in outer shell	1	2	3	4	5	6	7	8
state	← solid →						← gas →	
does it conduct electricity?	← yes ⊣⊢		no				→	
reaction with acids	← forms salt → and water		← no → reaction					
reactions with other elements	only reacts with ← non-metals		reacts with ← metals and → non-metals					
2. The oxides								
state	← solid →		← mostly → gases					
structure	← ionic →		← molecular →					
pH	← alkaline →		← acidic →					
3. The chlorides								
state	← solids →		← liquids or → gases					
structure	← ionic →		← molecular →					

argon does not have any chemical properties

Fig 8 A summary of the trends across period 3

QUESTION

Calcium oxide forms an alkaline solution in water and carbon dioxide forms an acidic solution.

a What type of elements usually have:
  i alkaline oxides..(1 mark)
  ii acidic oxides...(1 mark)

b Use the periodic table (*this was given in the exam paper*) to suggest another example of an element which forms:
  i Alkaline oxides..(1 mark)
  ii Acidic oxides...(1 mark)

c Here is a list of compounds

   calcium fluoride   carbon dioxide
   sulphur dioxide   potassium chloride
   sodium oxide   nitrogen dioxide

   Choose from the list above:
   i one compound which has a molecular structure, ...(1 mark)

ii one compound which has an ionic structure.
....(1 mark)

d Chlorine, bromine and iodine all belong to group VII of the periodic table (the halogens). Describe one chemical property of the elements or their compounds which shows the similarity within this group.

....
....
....(2 marks)

[MEG]

ANSWER

a i Alkali metal or metal or alkaline earth metal.
   ii Non-metals.
      Note that it says type of element so you must not name a specific element.

b i Any metal oxide.
   ii Any non-metal, *but do not put oxygen, hydrogen (as it forms a neutral oxide) or any noble gas (as these do not form oxides.)*

c i Carbon dioxide or sulphur dioxide or nitrogen dioxide.
   ii Calcium fluoride or potassium chloride or sodium oxide.

d *You must describe a chemical reaction which shows the similarities of the halogens. Remember to describe the reaction and say what the result is. For example, reacts with sodium to form salts, or reacts with iron to form a coloured salt. Or, reacts with alkenes to de-colourise the halogen, or forms a compound with hydrogen which dissolves to form an acidic solution.*

QUESTION

The table below shows some of the properties of the elements in Period 3 of the periodic table.

NOTE:

Atomic radius is the radius of a neutral atom and is measured in nanometres (nm).

Ionic radius is the radius of an ion and is measured in nanometres (nm).

An amphoteric oxide reacts with both acids and alkalis.

a Using the information in the table, discuss the reactions of the oxides with acids and alkalis.

....
....
....
....
....
....(4 marks)

b i How does the ionic radius of aluminium compare with its atomic radius?
....(1 mark)

   ii How does the ionic radius of sulphur compare with its atomic radius?
....(1 mark)

   iii Explain the reasons for your answers to parts i and ii.

....
....
....(2 marks)

   iv Use the atomic and ionic radii of silicon to predict what the charge on its ion would be.
....(2 marks)

c Magnesium chloride has the formula $MgCl_2$ and sulphur(I) chloride has the formula S_2Cl_2. Complete the table to predict the properties of these compounds.

Property/Element	Sodium	Magnesium	Aluminium	Silicon	Phosphorus	Sulphur	Chlorine
Appearance	silver metal	silver metal	silver metal	black solid	yellow solid	yellow solid	green gas
Proton Number (Atomic Number)	11	12	13	14	15	16	17
Charge on ion	1+	2+	3+	—	3–	2–	1–
Atomic radius	0.186	0.160	0.143	0.117	0.110	0.104	0.099
Ionic radius	0.098	0.065	0.054	0.041	0.212	0.184	0.181
Formula of oxide	Na_2O	MgO	Al_2O_3	SiO_2	P_2O_5	SO_2	Cl_2O
Type of oxide	basic	basic	amphoteric	acidic	acidic	acidic	acidic

Fig 9

Property	Magnesium chloride	Sulphur(I) chloride
Melting point	High	low
Solubility in water		
Type of bonding		

[ULEAC]

ANSWER

a Metal oxides, for example those of sodium and magnesium, are basic and react with acids to form a salt and water.
   Non-metal oxides, for example that of sulphur, are acidic and react with bases to form a salt and water.
   Amphoteric oxides, for example that of aluminium, react with acids *and* bases.

b i The ionic radius of aluminium is less than the atomic radius.
   ii The ionic radius of sulphur is more than the ionic radius.
   iii When aluminium forms its ion it loses three electrons. This results in the reduction in the radius.
        When sulphur forms its ion, it gains two electrons. This results in the increase in the radius.
   iv 4+ *(Notice that the ionic radius is less than the atomic radius so you need to follow the pattern from the left of the table).*

c solubility: soluble   insoluble
   bonding :   ionic   covalent

The transition elements

Sc	Ti	V	Cr	Mn	Fe	Co	Ni	Cu	Zn
Y	Zr	Nb	Mo	Tc	Ru	Rh	Pd	Ag	Cd
La	Hf	Ta	W	Re	Os	Ir	Pt	Au	Hg

Fig 10 The transition elements

The transition elements are a block of 30 elements in the middle block of the periodic table.

They are different from the other elements in that the shell of electrons inside the outer shell is not full. This accounts for many of their properties.

These elements are similar to each other in several ways:

• They have the properties of metals (see p 137).

The top row of the transition elements contains well known metals, such as iron and copper.

• They are dense elements.
• They have high melting and boiling points.
• The atoms form more than one type of positive ion, for example Cu^+, Cu^{2+}, Fe^{2+}, Fe^{3+}, so many different compounds are formed.

You may have noticed compounds labelled as:
copper(I) oxide.
copper(II) oxide.
This is to show which ion is involved in the formation of the compound.

• The metals are in the bottom and middle of the reactivity series.
• They react slowly or not at all with acids.
• The hydroxides are not soluble.
• The ions are coloured in aqueous solutions. For example, solutions of copper compounds are blue/green in colour.
• The element and compounds of the element are often used as catalysts in chemical reactions.

Where does hydrogen fit in the periodic table?

Hydrogen is difficult to classify. It is the smallest atom. It may be placed in group I as it has one outer electron, or it may be placed in group VII as it is one electron 'short' of the full number of two for the inner shell of electrons. More often it is placed on its own – as in the periodic table in this section.

Hydrogen:

• Is a gas.
• Is made up of molecules (with covalent bonding) containing two atoms, H_2.
• Can form positive ions, like a metal. It may be formed at the cathode during electrolysis.
• Reacts with non-metals to form compounds which contain covalent bonds, for example hydrogen chloride, HCl.

QUESTION

In the Periodic Table (*this was given in a data book but use fig 1 page 207*), hydrogen is placed somewhere between Group 1 and Group 7, whereas in other versions of the Periodic Table it is placed at the top of Group 1 and at the top of Group 7. Justify the placement of hydrogen at the top of:

i Group 1;

....

....(2 marks)

ii Group 7.

....

....(2 marks)

[WJEC]

ANSWER

i It can lose an electron to form a positive ion, in the same way that elements in group I do.

ii It is a non-metal which usually occurs as a diatomic molecule (like the halogens).

In a question like this you need to try to say how hydrogen is similar to group I and group VII.

Revision sheet

Electrolysis

1 Explain these terms:
   a Electrolysis.
   b Electrode.
   c Electrolyte.
   d Electroplating.
2 In electrolysis of an aqueous solution what is formed at:
   a anode?
   b cathode?
3 What is formed at the anode when a current is passed through:
   a aqueous potassium iodide?
   b molten potassium iodide?
4 Are reactive or non-reactive metals likely to be extracted from their ores by electrolysis?
5 Finish this equation, and add the units:
   Charge (.........) = current (.........) × ....(.........)
6 Electrolysis can be used to purify metals – at which electrode will the pure metal form?
7 Finish this half-equation for an anode during electrolysis:
   Cl^- – .... → ....
8 What is the term given to 'a mole of electrons'?

Rates of reaction

1 What must happen to the particles in the reactants before a chemical reaction can occur?
2 Sketch a graph to explain activation energy for a reaction.

3 Give four ways of increasing the rate of a reaction.
4 To increase the concentration of a gas, what would you need to do to the pressure?
5 a How does an enzyme work like a metal catalyst?
   b How does an enzyme differ from a metal catalyst in its behaviour?
6 Describe two important features of a reversible reaction.
7 In the Haber process for making ammonia the important reaction is:
   $$N_2(g) + 3H_2(g) \rightleftharpoons 2NH_3(g) \quad \Delta H = -92kJ$$

How could you increase the amount of ammonia formed by:
a changing the temperature?
b changing the pressure?

Patterns in the Periodic Table

1 Which property of an element is used to arrange the elements in the periodic table?
2 Describe the position of each of these in the periodic table:
   a Group.
   b Period.
   c Alkali metals.
   d Transition metals.
   e Halogens.
   f Noble gases.
3 Finish these sentences:
   a As a group is descended the number of shells of electrons ....
   b As a period is crossed from left to right, the number of electrons ....
   c As a period is crossed from left to right, the properties of the elements change from .... to ....
   d All the elements in a group have similar properties because ....
4 What is the group and period number for element number 14?
5 Why are the noble gases unreactive?

Revision sheet answers

Electrolysis

1 Explain these terms:
   a Electrolysis – a chemical reaction where electricity decomposes a substance.

b Electrode – carries the current to the substance.

c Electrolyte – the substance that is decomposed during electrolysis.

d Electroplating – a type of electrolysis where a thin coat of metal is placed on another (situated at the cathode).

2 a At the anode – non-metals (chlorine, bromine or iodine in preference to oxygen, if both are present).

b At the cathode – metals and hydrogen. If the metal is above hydrogen in the reactivity series then hydrogen is formed.

3 a Aqueous potassium iodide gives iodine at the anode.

b Molten potassium iodide gives iodine at the anode.

4 Reactive metals are likely to be extracted from their ores by electrolysis.

5 Charge (Coulombs) = current (amps) × time

(seconds)

6 Cathode.

7 $Cl^- - e^- \rightarrow Cl$

8 Faraday.

Rate of Reaction

1 They must collide with sufficient energy to break the bonds between the particles in the reactants.

2

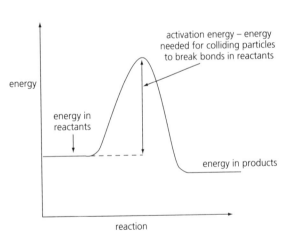

activation energy – energy needed for colliding particles to break bonds in reactants

energy

energy in reactants

energy in products

reaction

Fig 1

3 Increasing the temperature, increasing the concentration, increasing the surface area, using a catalyst.

4 In a gas, increasing the pressure increases the concentration.

5 a A catalyst and an enzyme both lower the activation energy for the reaction.

b An enzyme is denatured by high temperatures (usually 40°C) and extremes of pH (in most cases).

6 Important features of a reversible reaction:

• The reactants turn into products but the products also turn into reactants.

• Changing the conditions affects the equilibrium.

7 a Decreasing the temperature will increase the amount of ammonia formed.

b Increasing the pressure will increase the amount of ammonia formed.

Patterns in the periodic table

1 The atomic number, that is the number of protons which is the same as the number of electrons.

2 a Group – vertical column.

b Period – horizontal row.

c Alkali metals – first vertical column, on the left.

d Transition metals – middle of the table, starting after group II in period 4.

e Halogen – on the right, group VII, last but one vertical column.

f Noble gases – group O, last vertical column on the right.

3 a As a group is descended the number of shells of electrons increases by one each time.

b As a period is crossed from left to right, the number of electrons increases by one each time.

c As a period is crossed from left to right, the properties of the elements change from metallic to non-metallic.

d All the elements in a group have similar properties because they have the same number of electrons in their outer shell.

4 Si (silicon), electronic structure: 2,8,4. It is in group IV and period 3.

5 The noble gases have a complete 'shell' of outer electrons.

Student Answers with Comments

Aluminium is manufactured by passing electricity through a molten mixture containing aluminium oxide, Al_2O_3. The electrolysis is carried out in cells lined with carbon which forms the negative electrode (cathode). Carbon rods are used as positive electrodes (anodes). Bauxite, the ore of aluminium, is imported into the British Isles. The production of aluminium requires very large amounts of electricity.

a i Write a balanced equation, including electrons, for the reaction producing aluminium at the negative electrode (cathode).

$Al_2O_3 + C \rightarrow 2Al + CO_3$ ✗

This told you electrons were needed, i.e.
$Al^{3+} + 3e^- \rightarrow Al$ needed

(1 mark)

ii One cell produces 500 kg of aluminium per day. Calculate the mass of aluminium oxide used by this cell each day.

Al_2O_3 gives $2Al$.   RAM of $Al = 27$

RAM of $O_2 = 16$.

∴RAM of $Al_2O_3 =$

$2(27) + 3(16)$

$= 102$ ✓

∴$\dfrac{500 \times 102}{54} = 944.444$ ✓

Ans 944.45 kg.   ②

RAM of O is 16– not O_2

(2 marks)

b Suggest and explain **two** economic or environmental points to consider when deciding where to build a new aluminium plant

first point: As the Bauxite is imported the plant would need to be near a port so transport was quick and cheap. ✓ ②

second point: As the process takes up a lot of electricity the plant would need to be near a power station or near the raw materials that would allow it to have its own ✓ ①

(4 marks)

Doesn't have to be near but it does need cheap electricity

c To produce one mole of aluminium metal by electrolysis needs 289,500 coulombs of electric charge. Explain why it only needs 193,000 coulombs to liberate a mole of lead.

1 Farad = 96000 coulombs

$Al = \dfrac{289500}{96500} = 3$ $Pb = \dfrac{193000}{96500} = 2$

$Al = Al^{3+}$ $Pb = Pb^{2+}$

It takes less charge as lead needs less electrons. ✓ ②

(2 marks)

Good – it is the charges on the ions as you have shown $7/9$

[MEG]

An exam question for you to try

QUESTION

a Ammonia is used to manufacture fertilisers. The flow diagram below shows the main steps in the production of ammonia by the Haber Process.

i Why is a catalyst used in the process?

....(1 mark)

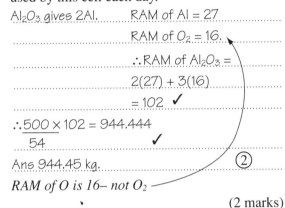

Fig 2 The flow chart

ii Why are the unreacted nitrogen and hydrogen recycled?

....
....(1 mark)

b The graph below shows the effect of pressure and temperature on the percentage conversion of nitrogen and hydrogen into ammonia.

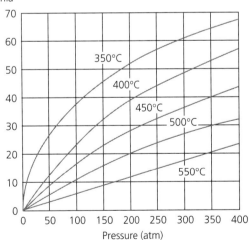

Fig 3

i From the data given on the graph, suggest the most suitable temperature and pressure to produce the maximum yield of ammonia.

Temperature =   Pressure =   (2 marks)

ii Suggest THREE reasons why the reaction is conducted at 450°C and 350 atmospheres.

1 ....

....

2 ....

....

3 ....

....

....(3 marks)

c i The reaction between nitrogen and hydrogen is said to be reversible. The equation for the reaction is given below.

$$N_2(g) + 3H_2(g) \rightleftharpoons 2NH_3(g) \ \Delta H = -92kJ$$

After a time, the reaction comes to equilibrium, i.e. the rates of the forward and backward reactions are equal. In the process it is important to increase the rate of the forward reaction to increase the yield of ammonia.

Suggest and explain ONE way of increasing the rate of the forward reaction.

Suggestion ....

Explanation ....

....

....(2 marks)

ii 7,000 tonnes of ammonia are produced each day in the UK by the Haber process. How much nitrogen is needed to produce this much ammonia?

(Relative atomic masses : N = 14, H = 1: 1 tonne = 1000kg)

....

....

....

....

....

....(4 marks)

[ULEAC]

Answer

a i It increases the rate of the reaction.

ii *Your answer needs to show that you know it is more economic to do this*, such as: it will save money, it will be less wasteful, particularly of methane (not so important for the air!).

b i temperature = 350°C, pressure 400 atm.

ii *Your answer ought to refer to the different conditions of temperature and pressure, but there are several points that you could make.*

Any three points from:
The higher temperature gives a faster rate of formation of ammonia.
It is expensive to produce pressures of 400atm (there are also safety implications) and the yield is not reduced very much by reducing the pressure to 350atm.
In this process it is important to balance the yield and the rate of the reaction. This will affect the final decisions made about the operating conditions. A catalyst is used and the effect of this on the rate must be considered as well.

c i Your explanation needs to fit your suggestion. There are a number of suitable answers. You only need one, such as:
Suggestion: Increase the pressure. *Explanation*: More collisions happen so the rate is increased.
Suggestion: Use more of one of the reactants. *Explanation*: Higher concentration of a reactant will give a faster reaction.
Suggestion: Increase the temperature. *Explanation*: More collisions will reach the activation energy. *(Decreasing the temperature moves the equilibrium to the right but this question asks about increasing the* rate. *Increasing the temperature increases the rate at which equilibrium is reached.)*

ii 5,764.71 tonnes.

$$N_2(g) + 3H_2(g) \rightleftharpoons 2NH_3(g) \ \Delta H = -92kJ$$

1 mole of nitrogen gives 2 moles of ammonia

28g of nitrogen gives $2 \times (14 + 3)$g of ammonia
28g of nitrogen gives 34g of ammonia

28 tonnes of nitrogen would give 34 tonnes of ammonia
$(28/34) \times 7,000$ tonnes of nitrogen would give 7,000 tonnes of ammonia
5,764.71 tonnes of nitrogen would give 7,000 tonnes of ammonia
Look back to section 9 if you need help with the calculation.

11 Extracting materials

Extracting materials	Midland (MEG)				Northern (NEAB)		London (ULEAC)				Southern (SEG)		Welsh (WJEC)
	Own	Nuffield	Salters	Suffolk	Co-ordinated	Modular	Modular GASP	Combined	Co-ordinated	Modular	Double	Modular	Co-ordinated
METALS FROM ORES													
Minerals and ores	✓	✓	✓	✓	✓	✓	✓	✓	✓	✓	✓	✓	✓
Reactivity series	✓	✓	✓	✓	✓	✓	✓	✓	✓	✓	✓	✓	✓
Extraction of metals	✓	✓	✓	✓	✓	✓	✓	✓	✓	✓	✓	✓	✓
Blast furnace	✓		✓				✓	✓					
OIL INDUSTRY													
Formation of oil		✓	✓	✓		✓							
Distillation of oil	✓	✓	✓	✓	✓	✓	✓	✓	✓	✓	✓	✓	✓
Cracking	✓	✓	✓	H	✓	✓	✓	✓	✓	✓	✓	✓	✓
Polymerisation	✓	✓	✓	H	✓	✓	✓	✓	✓	✓	✓	✓	✓
Pollution from burning fuels	✓	✓	✓	✓	✓	✓	✓	✓	✓	✓	✓	✓	✓
Products from oil	✓	✓	✓	✓	✓	✓	✓	✓	✓	✓	✓	✓	✓

Metals from ores

About 75% of all elements are metals. The majority of these are found as compounds, called minerals, in the earth. They are extracted in processes involving a number of chemical reactions. Only a few metals are found as the pure element. These are called native metals. They include gold, silver and copper, which were the first metals that people learnt to use.

What is the difference between a metal, a mineral and an ore?

A metal is an element. Metals have a number of physical and chemical properties in common. For example, metals are good thermal and electrical conductors and form solid oxides which, if soluble, give alkaline solutions (see p 137 for details of more of their properties).

In general use, the term metal is also used for an alloy, a mixture of metals (see p 189).

A mineral has a fixed chemical composition, and a regular structure. Galena is a mineral containing lead. It has the chemical name lead(II) sulphide and the chemical formula PbS.
An ore contains the mineral (and the metal!) but often contains unwanted impurities that have to be removed as the metal is extracted. It is the rock that is mined from the Earth.
The first metals that people used were those found on their own in the earth and not combined with other elements in a compound. Later, about 5,000 years ago, tin and lead were used but it was not until 1825 that aluminium was obtained. Tin and lead were extracted from their ores using heat and charcoal, but to obtain aluminium it was necessary to use electricity. How a metal is extracted from its ore depends on how reactive it is.

The reactivity series

The reactivity series is a list of metals with the most reactive at the top. As well as indicating how a metal is extracted from its ore, it is used to predict what will happen in chemical reactions involving metals.

| K | Potassium | } these two are so reactive they are stored under oil to |
| Na | Sodium | prevent air reaching them |

Ca Calcium – sometimes stored under oil
Mg Magnesium
Al Aluminium
    ← C (Carbon) would go here
Zn Zinc
Fe Iron
Sn Tin
Pb Lead
    ← H (Hydrogen) would go here
Cu Copper
Ag Silver
Au Gold

You should be given enough information to answer any reactivity question, but it is probably worth learning the series. The following mnemonic may help you to remember all but the last two metals. It uses the first letter of the symbol of each element.

Kittens Not Cats Make a Colourful Zoo For Some Poor Hungry Children

Evidence for the reactivity series

1 The reaction of metals with water

- Potassium: a fast reaction, the potassium catches fire, hydrogen is given off and a strongly alkaline solution is formed.
- Sodium: a fast reaction, sodium occasionally catches fire, hydrogen is given off and a strongly alkaline solution is formed.
- Calcium: a moderate reaction, hydrogen is given off and an alkaline solution is formed.
- Magnesium: a very slow reaction, hydrogen is given off and a slightly alkaline solution is formed. Metals below magnesium do not react with water at room temperature.

Iron does react with water to form rust but this is a very slow chemical reaction and needs both oxygen and water for the reaction to take place.

2 The reaction of metals with acids

- Metals above hydrogen in the reactivity series react with acids to form hydrogen and the salt. For example, sodium, magnesium and zinc.

magnesium + hydrochloric acid → magnesium chloride + hydrogen

$Mg(s) + 2HCl(aq) \rightarrow MgCl_2(aq) + H_2(g)$
- Metals below hydrogen in the reactivity series do not react with acids to form hydrogen and the salt. For example, copper and gold.

3 Displacement reactions

In a displacement reaction a metal is added to a salt solution containing a different metal. If there is a chemical reaction then the added metal is the most reactive. We can tell if a reaction takes place by observing carefully and looking for different substances being formed.
For example, if magnesium metal is added to blue copper(II) sulphate solution, the blue colour of the copper(II) sulphate fades as colourless magnesium sulphate solution is formed and orange/brown copper metal sinks to the bottom of the test tube. The magnesium is more reactive than the copper and so displaces it from solution.

magnesium + copper(II) sulphate $\rightarrow$ magnesium
$$\text{sulphate} + \text{copper}$$
$Mg(s) + CuSO_4(aq) \rightarrow MgSO_4(aq) + Cu(s)$

The following table gives some results of a number of displacement reactions. A tick (✔) indicates a reaction and a cross (×) indicates that there is no reaction.
NA means the reaction is not appropriate; for example, reacting magnesium with magnesium chloride!

	magnesium	lead	iron	zinc	copper
magnesium chloride	NA	×	×	×	×
lead nitrate	✔	NA	✔	✔	×
iron(II) sulphate	✔	×	NA	✔	×
zinc sulphate	✔	×	×	NA	×
copper(II) sulphate	✔	✔	✔	✔	NA
silver nitrate	✔	✔	✔	✔	✔
total number of ticks	5	2	3	4	1

From this the following reactivity order can be deduced:
Magnesium
Zinc
Iron
Lead
Copper

QUESTION

When plates of magnesium are bolted to the steel hull of some ships to reduce rusting the:

A Magnesium corrodes instead of the steel?
B Oxygen cannot reach the steel hull?
C Sea-water reacts rapidly with the steel?
D Steel forms a rust-proof layer on the hull's surface?
[SEG 1994]

ANSWER

A – *The magnesium acts as a sacrificial metal as it is more reactive. It corrodes in place of the iron.*

QUESTION

Metal X reacts with cold water. Metals Y and Z do not react with cold water. Metal Y is displaced if metal Z is placed in a solution of the chloride of Y. Which line shows the order of reactivity of the metals?

	Most reactive	$\rightarrow$	Least reactive
A	X	Y	Z
B	X	Z	Y
C	Y	X	Z
D	Z	X	Y

[SEG 1994]

ANSWER

B

QUESTION

a Describe how the elements magnesium and iron react with dilute sulphuric acid.
   Magnesium: ....
   Iron: ....(2 marks)
b Predict how readily, if at all, calcium would react with dilute sulphuric acid.
   (You would have a data book to help here)
   ....(1 mark)

c i What changes would you expect to see if a piece of zinc were left in some blue copper(II) sulphate solution?

....
....
....(1 mark)

ii Name the substsances formed in the reaction.
....(1 mark)

[WJEC]

ANSWER

a Magnesium: forms magnesium sulphate and hydrogen. Fast reaction.
Iron: forms iron sulphate and hydrogen. Slow reaction.

b Calcium reacts with sulphuric acid to form calcium sulphate and hydrogen. The reaction is faster than the reaction of magnesium and sulphuric acid. *(Calcium is above magnesium in the reactivity series.)*

c i The zinc would get coated with brownish-coloured copper and the colour of the blue copper(II) sulphate solution would fade. *(Don't forget this second point – it is often overlooked.)*

ii Copper, zinc sulphate.

What is the connection between the position of the metal in the reactivity series and how it is extracted?

Potassium
Sodium
Calcium
Magnesium
} These are extracted by electrolysis of the molten chloride (see p 194 on electrolysis).

Aluminium This is extracted by electrolysis of aluminium oxide in molten cryolite (see p 198 for details).

Zinc
Iron
Lead
Copper
} These can be extracted by heating the ore with carbon.

Notice that carbon is between aluminium and zinc in the reactivity series.

Carbon is not reactive enough to reduce magnesium oxide to magnesium.

Obtaining less reactive metals from their ores using carbon (and sometimes carbon monoxide) is an example of a reduction reaction (see p 146–147). The carbon acts as a reducing agent.

For example:
lead(II) oxide + carbon → lead + carbon dioxide
$2PbO(s) + C(s) \rightarrow 2Pb(s) + CO_2(g)$

Lead is reduced.
Carbon is oxidised.
Carbon is the reducing agent (as it removes oxygen from lead).

Oxidation is the opposite of reduction.

Extracting iron from its ore using a blast furnace

The main ores of iron are:
Haematite: Fe_2O_3
Magnetite: Fe_3O_4
Siderite: $FeCO_3$

Before entering the blast furnace

Whichever ore is used, it is roasted in air to form iron(III) oxide: Fe_2O_3.

In the blast furnace

Two processes take place:
• Iron(III) oxide is separated from its impurities.
• Iron(III) oxide is reduced to iron.

Substances are added to the top and bottom of the blast furnace:
• *At the top*
Iron(III) oxide, coke (to give the carbon) and limestone (to give calcium oxide and help remove the impurities).
• *At the bottom*
Hot air is blown into the furnace all round the bottom.
Oxygen in air reacts with carbon to (form carbon monoxide, which reduces the iron(III) oxide to iron).

See Fig 1 on following page. To work out exactly what is happening in the blast furnace it is best to start from the bottom and work upwards:

1 The temperature is the highest here. The oxygen reacts with the coke to form carbon monoxide – an exothermic reaction. Heat released in the reaction helps to maintain the correct temperature.
carbon + oxygen → carbon monoxide
$2C(s) + O_2(g) \rightarrow 2CO(g)$

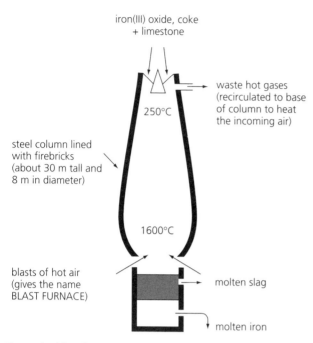

iron(III) oxide, coke + limestone

250°C

waste hot gases (recirculated to base of column to heat the incoming air)

steel column lined with firebricks (about 30 m tall and 8 m in diameter)

1600°C

blasts of hot air (gives the name BLAST FURNACE)

molten slag

molten iron

Fig 1 The blast furnace

2 Carbon monoxide passes up the furnace. At about 1000°C it meets the iron(III) oxide and reduces it to iron.

iron(III) oxide + carbon monoxide → iron + carbon dioxide

$Fe_2O_3(s) + 3CO(g) \rightarrow 2Fe(l) + 3CO_2(g)$

The carbon dioxide passes out in the waste hot gases at the top. Molten iron runs down the furnace and collects at the bottom, where it is run off.

3 At the same time, limestone is split up by the heat (a thermal decomposition reaction) into calcium oxide and carbon dioxide.

calcium carbonate → calcium oxide + carbon dioxide

$CaCO_3(s) \rightarrow CaO(s) + CO_2(g)$

The carbon dioxide moves up and out of the blast furnace.

4 The calcium oxide reacts with silica (silicon oxide), the main impurity in the iron ore, to form calcium silicate.

calcium oxide + silicon oxide → calcium silicate

$CaO(S) + SiO_2 \rightarrow CaSiO_3(l)$

The calcium silicate (called slag) is molten and runs down the furnace. It is less dense than the iron and therefore floats on the surface of the molten iron. It is run out of the furnace after the iron has been tapped off.

The layer of slag on the top of the iron prevents the iron from reacting with the oxygen in the air.

Products of the blast furnace:

- Iron – this is called pig iron or *cast iron*. It is impure and very brittle, and contains about 4% carbon. It can be purified by heating with more iron(III) oxide to form *wrought iron*, which is less brittle. It can also be hammered into shape and welded. *Steel* can be made from pig iron by blowing air or pure oxygen through it. Small percentages of carbon or metals can be added to make alloys with special properties; for example, chromium can be added to make *stainless steel*.
- Slag – this is used in road-building and in producing materials for the thermal insulation of buildings.

QUESTION

Between about 1750 and 1900, large veins of copper ore were taken from a copper mine in Staffordshire called Ecton Hill. A large vertical vein of copper ore was extracted from the surrounding rock.
The main ore present in the mine was Malachite. Malachite has the formula $Cu_2CO_3(OH)_2$ and is converted into copper oxide on heating. The copper oxide is then converted into copper in a furnace.
  i Give the name of the chemical process which takes place when copper oxide is converted into copper.
  ....(1 mark)
 ii Suggest the name of a substance which might be used in the furnace to convert the copper oxide into copper.
  ....(1 mark)
iii Limestone is also put into the furnace when copper oxide is converted into copper. Suggest a reason for this.
  ....(1 mark)
  [ULEAC]

ANSWER

 i Reduction.
 ii Coke – or any source of carbon such as coal, charcoal, or carbon itself.
iii It removes the impurities from the Malachite ore.

QUESTION

a Slag is a by-product of the blast furnace. Unused slag has been piled up forming unsightly slag heaps but it could be used for road-building. The cost of bringing slag from outside an area is estimated to be £8.00 per tonne, whilst the cost of materials such as sand and gravel is estimated to be £1.50 per tonne. Sand and gravel are often extracted from areas of natural beauty.

Discuss the economic and environmental implications of using slag for road-building.

....
....
....
....
....
....
....
....(3 marks)

b There are abundant world reserves of iron ore so price is not forced up by short supply.
State three different factors which determine the price of iron.

....
....
....
....
....
....(3 marks)
[MEG]

ANSWER

a It is more economic, in the short term to use sand and gravel for road-building than to bring the slag from out of the area.
Slag is formed as a waste product in the production of iron. There are large amounts of this that are not being used and are probably quite an eyesore around the area where the blast furnace is situated. Using slag in road-building could improve the appearance of these industrial areas. Also, extracting sand and gravel causes disruption to the area; for example, in terms of increased noise and traffic from the gravel pits. Using less sand and gravel for road-building would help to preserve these areas of natural beauty – which are often close to rivers.
It would be sensible to use the slag to build the roads if the difference in the cost could be resolved.

You need to try and give a balanced discussion, but do mention economic and environmental implications.

b The cost of limestone – used to remove the slag.
The cost of the coke – used to reduce the iron oxide.
The cost of transporting the iron ore to the blast furnace.
The cost of transporting the iron to the customer.
The cost of heating the air before it is blown into the blast furnace.
Try to name specific factors that are involved, rather than giving too general an answer.

The oil industry

Why is oil called a fossil fuel?

There has been life on Earth for millions of years. Living organisms contain a lot of carbon. When organisms died many years ago, their remains rotted to form a layer containing much carbon. Over a long period of time these layers were covered by other layers and subjected to changes of temperature and pressure, which altered the decaying material still further. Without oxygen present, carbon compounds in the living organisms were turned into hydrocarbons. These are compounds of carbon and hydrogen which we use today as fuels. Coal was formed from the decay of land plants, and oil and gas were formed from marine plankton (microscopic plants and animals) that lived in tropical oceans. The term fossil fuel refers to the fact that when they burn they release the energy that was absorbed from the sun by the plants during photosynthesis millions of years ago. During combustion carbon dioxide and water are formed as products.

The simplest hydrocarbons are methane, CH_4 and ethane, C_2H_6.

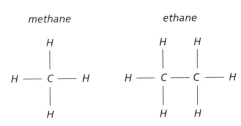

Fig 1

Where oil and gas are found

Oil and gas are often found together in the ground.

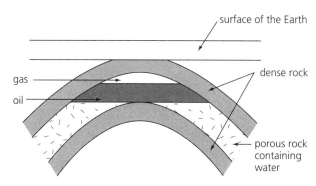

Fig 2 Where oil and gas are found

Oil and gas are found absorbed in a layer of porous rock. They are less dense than the water in the porous rock and so float to the top. The porous rock is itself trapped between layers of denser rock, which stop the oil and gas seeping away. As the rocks were subjected to pressure changes over the years, the oil and gas were compressed and are now at high pressure in the ground. This actually helps us to extract them – as an oil well is drilled the oil may come out under its own pressure. Oil obtained in this way is called crude oil or petroleum oil and is a mixture containing hydrocarbons.

> **Renewable and non-renewable energy sources:**
>
> *Renewable energy sources* are those that replenish themselves, that is they are not used up. Most of these rely on either the sun directly (solar energy) or indirectly on the weather (wind power, wave power, hydroelectric power). Alcohol fuels (produced by fermenting plants which trapped the sun's energy during photosynthesis), wood and geothermal energy (using energy trapped inside the Earth) also fit into this category. *Non-renewable energy sources* are those that have taken millions of years to form and cannot be replenished as they are used. Coal, oil and natural gas fall into this category. (See p 320–321 for more details of renewable and non-renewable energy sources.)

What happens at an oil refinery?

Three important processes at an oil refinery turn the crude oil into useful products:

- Fractional distillation – separates the mixture into different fractions.

- Cracking – converts the large molecules in the fractions into smaller molecules.
- Reforming – combines small molecules and restructures molecules to give the products which are needed.

Fractional distillation

Crude oil does not have a fixed boiling point because it is a mixture. When it is heated each fraction boils and turns into a gas at a different temperature. As a general rule, the first fractions to boil have the smallest molecules, and those with between one and four carbon atoms in their molecules are gases at room temperature.

No chemical reactions occur here – fractional distillation is a physical process.

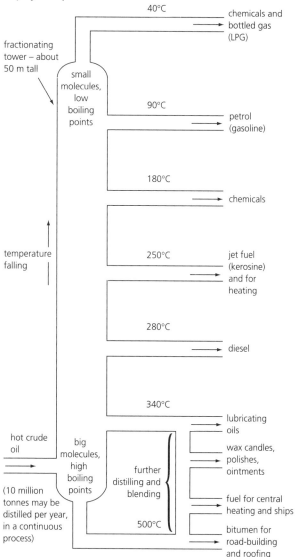

Notice how further distilling and blending provides the required products.

Fig 3 Fractional distillation of crude oil

QUESTION

Deposits of crude oil are found trapped in some rock structures. Crude oil is a mixture of many different hydrocarbons.

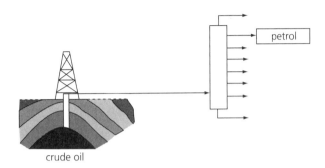

crude oil

Fig 4

Describe how petrol is obtained from crude oil.

....
....
....(2 marks)

Part question [SEG 1994]

ANSWER

The crude oil is heated and the different fractions, of which petrol is one, separate because they have different boiling points. This is called fractional distillation.

Note: It asks you to describe how petrol is obtained, so just saying 'fractional distillation' is unlikely to get you 2 marks.

> **Burning the fractions**
> Hydrocarbon fuels form carbon dioxide and water when they burn. For example, butane is used in gas lighters and independent hair curlers:
>
> butane + oxygen → water + carbon dioxide
> $2C_4H_{10}(g) + 13O_2(g) \rightarrow 10H_2O(g) + 8CO_2(g)$

Fig 3 shows some uses of the different fractions of crude oil. These depend on their different properties, particularly how they burn. Many fractions are used as fuels. The larger the molecule the higher the boiling point and the less flammable the hydrocarbon. This means that larger molecules are not so useful as fuels.

This table summarises the properties of some important fractions.

Fraction	Property	Uses
LPG (liquid petroleum gas)	colourless, highly flammable, burns with a clean flame	fuel for portable heaters
petrol	liquid which evaporates easily, highly flammable, some smoke on burning	car fuel
paraffin	liquid which lights quite easily, smoky flame with some smell	jet fuel, fuel for portable heaters
lubricating oil	viscous liquid, difficult to light, very smoky flame which smells	lubricating machinery
bitumen	solid which melts when heated, difficult to light, a very smoky smelly flame	road-building and roofing

Pollution and burning fuels

The table on p 227 summarises some major air pollutants associated with burning fuels.

QUESTION

Many electric power stations use fossil fuels. Coal and crude oil are fossil fuels.

A few power stations are experimenting with an alternative fossil fuel. It uses a tar-like material found in South America. This tar-like material is called 'Orimulsion'.

Orimulsion is a black liquid made up of 70% natural tar and 30% water. Orimulsion is about half the price of coal.

a Give the names of two fossil fuels that can be made from crude oil. (2 marks)

1 ....

2 ....

b Orimulsion is a mixture of hydrocarbons. Hydrocarbons are compounds containing only carbon and hydrogen. Orimulsion also has a large sulphur content. When Orimulsion is burnt at a power station several substances are formed. Carbon dioxide is one of these substances.

i Give the names of two other substances formed when Orimulsion is burnt at a power station. (2 marks)

1..

2..

ii The burning of Orimulsion is an example of oxidation. Explain what is meant by oxidation.

....(1 mark)

iii Scientists are concerned about the use of Orimulsion as a fuel. They believe it will damage the environment.

Pollutant	Effect	Remedy
carbon dioxide (CO_2)	contributes to greenhouse effect	burn less fossil fuel
carbon monoxide (CO)	prevents blood carrying oxygen, can be fatal	ensure that fuels burn completely with sufficient oxygen
hydrocarbons	contribute to photochemical smog	develop engines to run on a different ratio of fuel to air, fit catalytic converters to cars
smoke	stunts plant growth by reducing photosynthesis, causes lung problems particularly to asthmatics	use smokeless fuels, ensure that the fuels burn completely with sufficient oxygen
lead compounds	damage nervous tissue	use unleaded petrol
nitrogen oxides (NO, N_2O, NO_2)	contribute to acid rain and photochemical smog	develop engines to run on a different ratio of fuel to air, fit catalytic converters to cars
sulphur dioxide	contributes to acid rain	remove sulphur where possible from fuels before use, remove sulphur from waste gases at power stations

Why are the scientists worried about the environmental effects of using Orimulsion as a fuel in power stations?

....

....

....(2 marks)

iv Suggest a reason why power stations may switch from using coal as a fuel to using Orimulsion.

....(1 mark)

[MEG]

ANSWER

a Any two from: propane, butane, petrol, paraffin, diesel, heating oil for central heating, fuel oil.

b i Water, carbon monoxide, carbon (or soot), sulphur dioxide.

ii A reaction involving the addition of oxygen (*or the removal of hydrogen or the loss of electrons*).

iii The sulphur dioxide produced will contribute to acid rain. *You could give an effect of acid rain, such as the damage to leaves of trees.* Orimulsion contains 70% tar, so burns with a very smoky flame. This gives off dust which is difficult to remove from the waste gases. It produces carbon dioxide which contributes to the greenhouse effect. The carbon dioxide will contribute to global warming. *You could also give an example of the greenhouse effect such as the sea level rising.*

iv Orimulsion is cheaper than coal, or reserves of coal are being used up.

Do not fall into the trap of discussing CFCs and the destruction of the ozone layer if you are asked a question about pollution associated with fuels.

Cracking

In cracking, large molecules (called the feedstock) are broken down into smaller molecules by a chemical reaction.

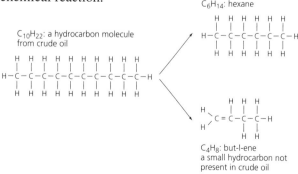

Fig 5 Cracking a hydrocarbon molecule

Many different substances can be used as feedstock but naphtha and gas oil are commonly used. In industry, the feedstock is heated with steam to about 800°C. The steam breaks the carbon–carbon bonds in the feedstock.

Alternatively, a mixture of powdered silica and alumina may be used as a catalyst, so that the reaction can take place at a lower temperature (around 500°C).

You may have carried out the following cracking in the laboratory.

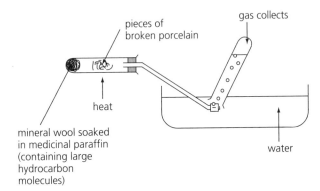

Fig 6 Cracking

The gas which is collected:

- Burns with a yellow flame.
- Removes the orange colour from bromine water when shaken with it.

The medicinal paraffin used as the feedstock does neither of these.

Medicinal paraffin contains large molecules (alkanes), and the gas formed contains a mixture of small molecules (alkenes and alkanes).

The product is a gas and the feedstock is a viscous liquid. This provides more evidence that large molecules are cracked into smaller ones by the reaction.

QUESTION

Petrol (octane) can be made into ethene.

$$C_8H_{18} \rightarrow 4C_2H_4 + H_2$$
octane   ethene   hydrogen

i State what happens to the octane in this reaction.

....

....(2 marks)

ii Give two conditions needed for this reaction.
   (2 marks)
   Condition 1...
   Condition 2...

Part question [SEG 1994]

ANSWER

i It is cracked or decomposed into smaller molecules.
ii A high temperature or a catalyst of silica and alumina.

Reforming

Once small molecules are obtained from the 'cracker' (the name given to the industrial plant where cracking takes place), these can be further changed, or the molecules can be reacted together to form larger molecules again. These processes are called reforming. Reforming may be necessary to provide customers with the products they need.

Crude oil from different regions of the world contains different percentages of the different fractions. By the processes of distillation, cracking and reforming the refinery can match its products to the demand for the different fractions.

What is polymerisation?

A polymer is a long chain molecule made up of lots (often thousands) of smaller molecules called monomers. A necklace is a simple model of a polymer.

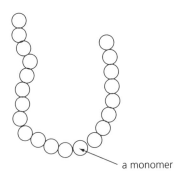

Fig 7 A necklace as a model of a polymer

Polymers are not only synthetic compounds. Many natural substances are polymers; for example, starch and proteins. The reaction involved in combining monomer molecules to make a long chain is called polymerisation.

QUESTION

Crude oil produces many simple molecules, some of which are monomers. A glue can be made, using a monomer which polymerises as the glue sets.

a Explain what a polymer is.

....

....(1 mark)

b The polymerisation must not happen while the glue monomer is stored in a tube. Suggest TWO ways in which the polymerisation reaction can be started when the glue is used.

1 ....

....

2 ....

....(2 marks)

c Solvent glues have a solid dissolved in a solvent. The solvent evaporates easily but leaves tiny gaps in the solid.
Explain which type of glue – a polymerisation glue or a solvent glue – you consider to be better.

....

....

....(2 marks)

[ULEAC]

ANSWER

a It is a long chain molecule made of many monomer units.

b The reaction may start when air reaches the monomers.
There may be a second tube, the contents of which need to be mixed with the monomer in the first tube. This second tube may contain a catalyst.
You may have seen the second tube called an initiator or hardener in glues that work this way.

c The disadvantage of the solvent glue is that the solvent that evaporates as the glue sets may be toxic or harmful.
Don't get into the habit of saying 'dangerous' in an answer such as this – it is too vague!
The polymerisation glue is likely to have stronger bonds between the monomers and so be a stronger glue.

Addition polymerisation

The simplest type of polymerisation is where the monomer molecules are identical and join end to end, see Fig 8. Ethene, one of the small molecules formed in the cracking reaction, is ideal for this. It contains a double bond which makes it quite reactive. Under the right conditions (200°C and 29MPa, using a catalyst) the double bond breaks, allowing the molecule to join

on to others. When this happens the long chain molecule is called poly(e)thene, which today we call polythene.

The double bond in ethene allows it to react with bromine water to decolourise it. It is called an unsaturated molecule because of the double bond.

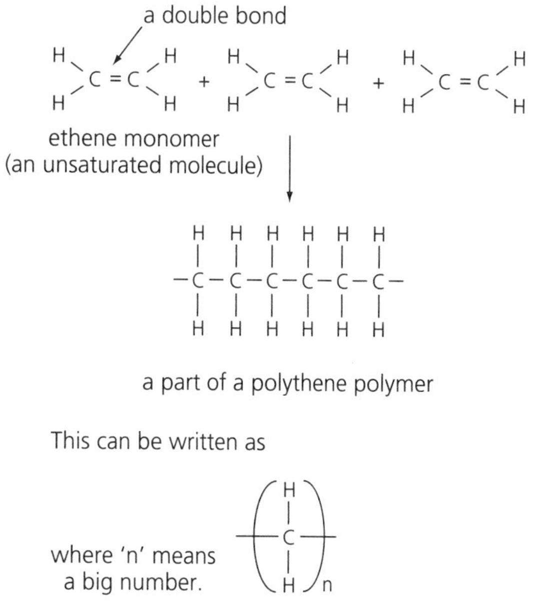

Fig 8 Ethene forming polythene

Condensation polymerisation

In this type of polymerisation two different monomers are involved and a small molecule is formed as well as the main product. Often this small molecule is water – which will help you to remember that the reaction is called condensation polymerisation. However, the small molecule could be hydrogen chloride. Nylon is formed by condensation polymerisation.

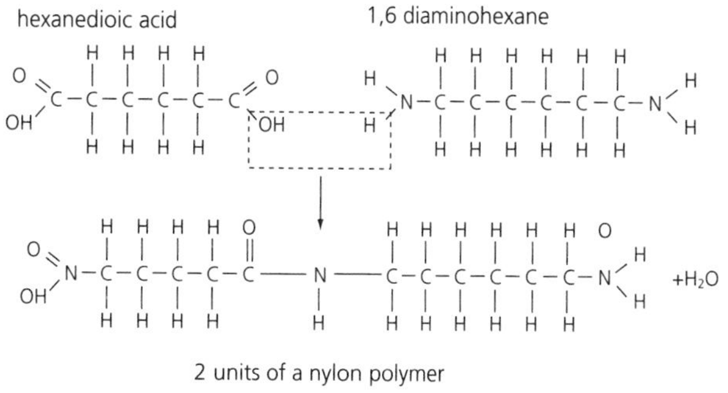

Fig 9 Nylon formed in a condensation reaction

This looks more complicated than it is. All you need to do is look at the ends of the molecule and see if you can find either H_2O or HCl to remove. Then join up the remaining structures to form a section of polymer.

QUESTION

This represents the structure of polyvinylchloride.

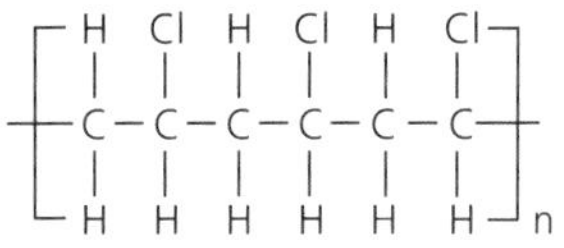

$$\left[\begin{array}{cccccc} H & Cl & H & Cl & H & Cl \\ | & | & | & | & | & | \\ -C & -C & -C & -C & -C & -C- \\ | & | & | & | & | & | \\ H & H & H & H & H & H \end{array}\right]_n$$

Fig 10

The formula of the monomer used in its manufacture is:

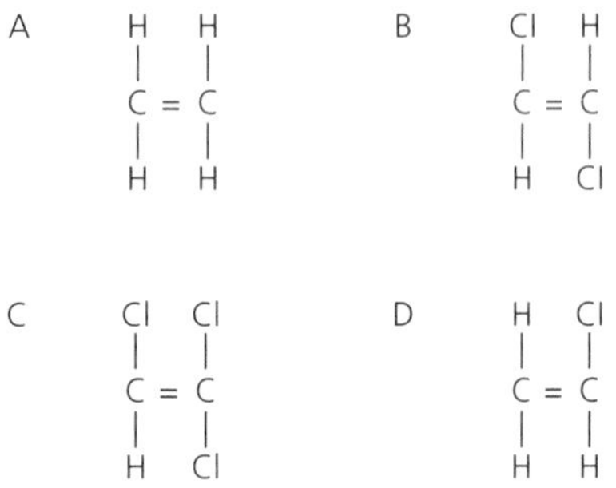

A
$$\begin{array}{cc} H & H \\ | & | \\ C & = C \\ | & | \\ H & H \end{array}$$

B
$$\begin{array}{cc} Cl & H \\ | & | \\ C & = C \\ | & | \\ H & Cl \end{array}$$

C
$$\begin{array}{cc} Cl & Cl \\ | & | \\ C & = C \\ | & | \\ H & Cl \end{array}$$

D
$$\begin{array}{cc} H & Cl \\ | & | \\ C & = C \\ | & | \\ H & H \end{array}$$

Fig 11

[SEG]

ANSWER

D

QUESTION

The equation below shows the cracking of a hydrocarbon compound into two different compounds, A and B.

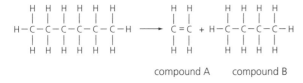

compound A   compound B

Fig 12

a State the differences between the structure of compounds A and B.

....
....
....
....(2 marks)

b Why is compound A useful in industry?

....
....(1 mark)

[NEAB]

ANSWER

a Compound A has a double bond and compound B does not (or compound A is unsaturated and compound B is saturated).
Compound A has fewer carbon atoms than compound B.

b Compound A is a reactive molecule (or compound A can take part in polymerisation reactions to form polymers).

What are polymers from crude oil used for?

Note: (A) indicates addition polymerisation and (C) indicates condensation polymerisation.

Name of polymer	Uses
Acrylics (A)	jumpers and other clothing, buttons
Nylon (C)	clothing, rope, plastic hinges, curtain rail fittings
Polychloroethene (PVC) (A)	drink bottles, casing for electrical wiring, records
Polyesters (C)	clothes
Polyphenylethene (polystyrene) (A)	disposable cups, yoghurt containers
Polypropene (A)	rope, carpets, crisp packets – the transparent sort
Polytetrafluorethene (PTFE or Teflon) (A)	non-stick coating to cooking pans
Polythene (A)	bin liners, carrier bags
Polyurethanes (C)	paints

QUESTION

a Ethene is used in the manufacture of the plastic poly(ethene). Ethene is heated under high pressure in the presence of a catalyst. Many ethene molecules join together to form a giant molecule of poly(ethene). The diagram below shows what happens in the reaction:

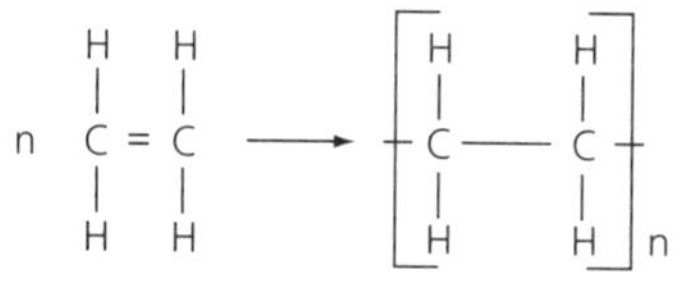

Fig 13

  i What is the name given to this type of reaction?

....(1 mark)

  ii Describe how the ethene molecules join to form poly(ethene).

....
....
....
....(3 marks)

  iii The poly(ethene) was heated and moulded into the shape of a bucket. The design of the bucket was changed. All the buckets were heated and remoulded.

How type of plastic is poly(ethene)? Explain your answer.

....
....(2 marks)

[ULEAC]

ANSWER

  i Polymerisation *(addition polymerisation is more accurate).*

  ii The double bonds in the monomers break. This needs a fairly high temperature (about 200°C), a pressure of about 20MPa, and a catalyst. Bonds form between the monomers to form the polymer poly(ethene).

  iii It is a thermoplastic, because it can be melted and remoulded into another shape.
(See p 189 if you need reminding about thermoplastics and thermosets.)

Revision sheet

Metals from ores

1 Give the difference between:
  a Metal.
  b Mineral.
  c Ore.

2 Metals are arranged in a reactivity series. Where in this list would you find metals which:
  a Occur in their native form?

  b Are extracted from their ores using electricity?
  c Are extracted from their ores by a reduction reaction involving carbon or carbon monoxide?
  d Are stored under oil?
  e Have lots of compounds?

3 In a displacement reaction:

$X + YSO_4 \rightarrow XSO_4 + Y$

(where X and Y are two metals)
  a Which is the most reactive metal?
  b How might you observe that this reaction had taken place?

4 In the blast furnace, what is the function of:
  a Carbon monoxide?
  b Calcium oxide?

5 Name two products of the blast furnace and give a use for each.

Oil

1 Finish these sentences:
  a Oil is called a fossil fuel because....
  b Many substances in oil are hydrocarbons, which contain the elements ... and....
  c When hydrocarbons are burnt they produce ... and ....
  d Oil is found underground in ... rock.
  e Oil cannot be replenished as it is used, we call this a ... energy source.

2 a Name three processes which occur at an oil refinery to turn oil into a useful product.
  b Which one of these does not involve a chemical reaction?
  c Ethene is a useful molecule produced from oil. What makes it so useful?

3 a What is polymerisation?
  b What are two types of polymerisation?
  c How do they differ as chemical reactions?
  d Give an example of each of these types of polymer.

Revision sheet answers

Metals from ores

1 a Metal – an element, but alloys are often called metals. These are mixtures of metals or metals and carbon.

  b Mineral – a compound such as a galena PbS, which occurs naturally and has a definite chemical formula.

c Ore – a rock containing a mineral and impurities.

2 a Occur in their native form – bottom, very unreactive.

b Are extracted from their ores using electricity – top.

c Are extracted from their ores by a reduction reaction involving carbon or carbon monoxide – middle, above the unreactive ones and below aluminium.

d Are stored under oil – top, very reactive.

e Have lots of compounds – top (and middle).

3 a X as it displaces Y.

b Solution gets warmer (energy is given out), metallic colour of Y as it is formed, change in colour of the solution.

4 a Carbon monoxide – reduces iron(III) oxide to iron.

b Calcium oxide – reacts with silicon oxide (the main impurity) to form slag.

5 Iron (pig or cast iron) – used to make steel and anything containing iron! Slag – building roads or manufacture of thermal insulation for buildings.

Oil

1 a Oil is called a fossil fuel because the energy released on burning was absorbed from the sun millions of years ago during photosynthesis in plants.

b Many substances in oil are hydrocarbons, which contain the elements carbon and hydrogen.

c When hydrocarbons are burnt they produce water and carbon dioxide.

d Oil is found underground in porous rock.

e Oil cannot be replenished as it is used; we call this a non-renewable energy source.

2 a Fractional distillation, cracking, reforming.

b Fractional distillation.

c Ethene is a small molecule containing a double bond which makes it reactive.

3 a Polymerisation is a chemical reaction in which small monomer molecules form a long chain called a polymer.

b Two types of polymerisation are addition and condensation.

c Addition polymerisation: identical monomers are joined end to end. Condensation polymerisation: formed from two different monomers. Also, a small molecule (often water) is formed as another product.

d Addition polymers: acrylic, polychloroethene (PVC), polyphenylethene (polystyrene), polypropene, polytetrafluroethene (PTFE or Teflon), polythene. Condensation polymers: nylon, polyesters, polyurethanes.

Student Answer with Comments

The following diagrams represent saturated hydrocarbons.

$$H-\overset{\overset{\displaystyle H}{|}}{\underset{\underset{\displaystyle H}{|}}{C}}-\overset{\overset{\displaystyle H}{|}}{\underset{\underset{\displaystyle H}{|}}{C}}-\overset{\overset{\displaystyle H}{|}}{\underset{\underset{\displaystyle H}{|}}{C}}-H$$

A

$$H-\overset{\overset{\displaystyle H}{|}}{\underset{\underset{\displaystyle H}{|}}{C}}-\overset{\overset{\displaystyle H}{|}}{\underset{\underset{\displaystyle H}{|}}{C}}-\overset{\overset{\displaystyle H}{|}}{\underset{\underset{\displaystyle H}{|}}{C}}-\overset{\overset{\displaystyle H}{|}}{\underset{\underset{\displaystyle H}{|}}{C}}-\overset{\overset{\displaystyle H}{|}}{\underset{\underset{\displaystyle H}{|}}{C}}-H$$

B

a. What is meant by the term hydrocarbon? (1 mark)

A hydrocarbon is a chemical made up of hydrogen and carbon atoms in a chain. ✓ ①

They don't have to be in a chain!

b Which is more volatile, A or B? (1 mark)

A ✓ ①

c Draw a diagram below of another hydrocarbon which is less flammable than B. (1 mark)

$$H-\overset{\overset{\displaystyle H}{|}}{\underset{\underset{\displaystyle H}{|}}{C}}-\overset{\overset{\displaystyle H}{|}}{\underset{\underset{\displaystyle H}{|}}{C}}-\overset{\overset{\displaystyle H}{|}}{\underset{\underset{\displaystyle H}{|}}{C}}-\overset{\overset{\displaystyle H}{|}}{\underset{\underset{\displaystyle H}{|}}{C}}-\overset{\overset{\displaystyle H}{|}}{\underset{\underset{\displaystyle H}{|}}{C}}-\overset{\overset{\displaystyle H}{|}}{\underset{\underset{\displaystyle H}{|}}{C}}-\overset{\overset{\displaystyle H}{|}}{\underset{\underset{\displaystyle H}{|}}{C}}-H$$ ①

d Give the name of the process for obtaining the unsaturated hydrocarbon,

from B. (1 mark)

cracking ✓ ①

e i Under suitable conditions many

$$\overset{H}{\underset{H}{\diagdown}}C=C\overset{\diagup H}{\underset{\diagdown H}{}}$$

units combine to form a long chain molecule. Give the name of the process for the formation of these long chains. (1 mark)

addition polymerisation. ✓ ①

good

ii Complete the following equation for the previous process. (1 mark)

$$n \begin{pmatrix} H & & H \\ & \diagdown & \diagup & \\ & C = C & \\ & \diagup & \diagdown & \\ H & & H \end{pmatrix} \rightarrow -\overset{\overset{\displaystyle H}{|}}{\underset{\underset{\displaystyle H}{|}}{C}} - \overset{\overset{\displaystyle H}{|}}{\underset{\underset{\displaystyle H}{|}}{C}} - \overset{\overset{\displaystyle H}{|}}{\underset{\underset{\displaystyle H}{|}}{C}} - \overset{\overset{\displaystyle H}{|}}{\underset{\underset{\displaystyle H}{|}}{C}} - \overset{\overset{\displaystyle H}{|}}{\underset{\underset{\displaystyle H}{|}}{C}} - \quad \checkmark ①$$

You can write this

$$\begin{pmatrix} \overset{\displaystyle H}{|} \\ -C- \\ \underset{\displaystyle H}{|} \end{pmatrix}_n$$

$^6/_6$ [WJEC]

An exam question for you to try

The list shows some metals in the reactivity series.

magnesium   (Mg) most reactive
aluminium   (Al)
zinc   (Zn)
iron   (Fe)
lead   (Pb)
copper   (Cu) least reactive

a Pieces of iron and magnesium of the same size are placed in dilute hydrochloric acid.

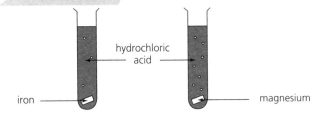

Fig 1

i What happens to show that the reaction with magnesium is exothermic?

....
....(1 mark)

ii Give two differences you would observe between these reactions. (2 marks)

Difference 1...

....

Difference 2...

....

b A piece of zinc is added to copper sulphate (CuSO$_4$) solution.

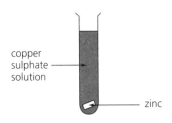

Fig 2

What would you observe? Explain your observations.

....
....
....
....(3 marks)

c Window frames made from iron corrode faster than those made from aluminium. This observation does not follow the order of the reactivity series. Explain the reasons for this.

....
....
....
....
....
....(3 marks)

d The diagram shows how railway lines are welded together. The reaction of aluminium and iron oxide (Fe$_2$O$_3$) forms molten iron which is run between the lengths of railway line.

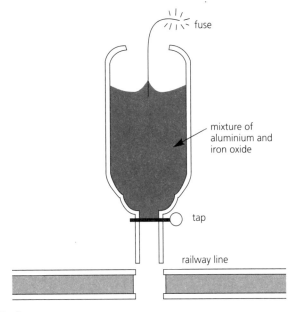

Fig 3

i Explain how aluminium reacts with iron oxide to form iron.

....

....

....(2 marks)

ii Why does this reaction form molten iron?

....

....

....(2 marks)

iii Give a balanced symbol equation for the reaction.

....(1 mark)

[SEG 1994]

Answer

a i The temperature of the tube rises or the tube feels warmer.

ii Magnesium would react faster than iron, after a short time there would be no magnesium left. The hydrogen gas would be produced faster with the magnesium than with the iron. The tube containing the magnesium would get hotter than the tube containing the iron.
Don't forget in a question like this where you are asked to give differences, you need to mention both metals so that your answer is very clear.

b *Observations*
The zinc would react with the copper sulphate solution.

A brown colour would coat the zinc as copper was deposited.
The solution would lose its blue colour as copper sulphate was used up.
Explanation
Zinc is more reactive than copper so displaces copper from the copper sulphate solution.
Three marks are given and the question asks for observations and an explanation. You may also like to include the word or balanced symbolic equation.
zinc + copper sulphate → zinc sulphate + copper
$Zn(s) + CuSo_4(aq) \rightarrow ZnSO_4(aq) + Cu(s)$

c Aluminium and iron react with oxygen in the air to form the metal oxide.
(The question tells you that they both react.)
The aluminium oxide layer formed on aluminium creates a protective barrier so that the aluminium metal below is protected from further corrosion. This is not the case with iron oxide. It does not form a continuous layer and the iron below continues to corrode.

d i Aluminium is more reactive than iron and in the reaction aluminium oxide and iron are formed.

ii This reaction is very exothermic; sufficient energy is released to melt the iron.

iii $2Al(s) + Fe_2O_3(s) \rightarrow Al_2O_3(s) + 2Fe(1)$
(The question gives you the formula of iron oxide.)

The earth and its resources

The Earth and its resources	Midland (MEG)				Northern (NEAB)		London (ULEAC)				Southern (SEG)		Welsh (WJEC)
	Own	Nuffield	Salters	Suffolk	Co-ordinated	Modular	Modular GASP	Combined	Co-ordinated	Modular	Double	Modular	Co-ordinated
ROCKS													
Types of rocks	✓	✓	✓	✓	✓	✓	✓	✓	✓	✓	✓	✓	✓
Rock cycle	✓	✓	✓	✓	✓	✓	✓	✓	✓	✓	✓	✓	✓
Weathering	✓	✓	✓	✓	✓	✓	✓	✓	✓	✓	✓	✓	✓
Transportation, erosion and deposition	✓	✓	✓	✓	✓	✓	✓	✓	✓	✓	✓	✓	✓
Faulting and folding	✓	✓	✓	✓	✓	✓	✓	✓	✓	✓	✓	✓	✓
Plate tectonics	H	H	✓	✓	H	H	H	H	H	H	✓	H	H
Earthquakes	✓	✓	✓	✓	H	H	H	H	H	✓	✓	✓	H
AIR, ATMOSPHERE AND WEATHER													
Air as a raw material	✓	✓	✓	✓	✓	✓	✓	✓	✓	✓	✓	✓	✓
How the atmosphere formed	✓		✓	H	✓	✓	✓	✓	✓	✓	✓	✓	✓
How the oceans formed	✓		✓	H	✓	✓	✓	✓	✓	✓	✓	✓	✓
Weather	✓	✓	✓	✓	✓	✓	✓	✓	✓	✓	✓	✓	✓
Water cycle	✓	✓	✓	✓	✓	✓	✓	✓	✓	✓	✓	✓	✓

Rocks

What are the main sorts of rocks?

Rocks in the Earth's crust are mixtures. They can be divided into three types: igneous, sedimentary and metamorphic. Each of these terms refers to the way in which the rock was formed. There are differences between these types of rocks in the minerals they contain and their texture. It is possible to identify many rocks by looking at their texture.

Igneous rocks

Just below the Earth's surface, between 50 km and 250 km, about 5% of the rock is molten (called magma). Igneous rocks are formed as this cools, and they can usually be recognised because they are crystalline. If the rock cools before it reaches the Earth's surface, the crystals are likely to be large as it will have cooled slowly. Example: granite. If the rock cools more quickly on the surface of the Earth the crystals will be smaller. Examples: basalt and rhyolite.

Sedimentary rocks

When rocks are worn away they form sediments. These are moved by water, wind and ice. Over many, many years they become compacted and eventually the grains may fuse to form a solid rock. Rocks formed from layers of sediment are called sedimentary rocks. Examples: sandstone, mudstone,

shale and conglomerate. If the layers of sediment are buried deeply the greater pressure causes harder rocks to be formed. Example: limestone.

Sedimentary rocks cover 75% of the continents.

Metamorphic rocks

High temperatures and pressures may cause the structure of solid rocks to change. Rocks formed in this way are called metamorphic rocks. The type of rock formed depends on the starting rock, the type of change and the length of time taken. Examples: mudstone can be turned into slate or schist, limestone may be changed into marble. The temperature and pressure may be so high deep inside a mountain that the rocks actually melt to form magma again.
The way in which the types of rocks are connected can be shown by a rock cycle diagram.

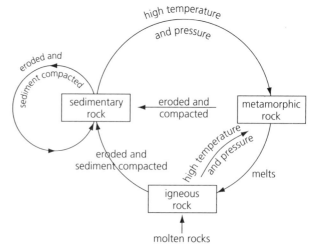

Fig 1 The rock cycle

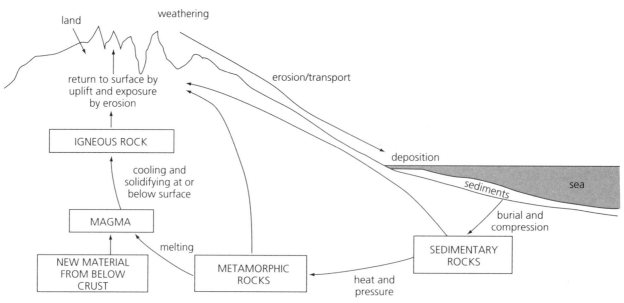

Fig 2

QUESTION

Classify the following as igneous, metamorphic or sedimentary rocks: basalt, granite, marble, mudstone, rhyolite, sandstone, shale, slate.

ANSWER

Basalt – igneous; granite – igneous; marble – metamorphic; mudstone – sedimentary; rhyolite – igneous; sandstone – sedimentary; shale – sedimentary; slate – metamorphic

QUESTION

a   The diagram (Fig 2) shows the rock cycle
  i   Limestone is a sedimentary rock. Explain how limestone is formed.

  ....
  ....
  ....(2 marks)
  ii   What happens to limestone to form marble?

  ....
  ....
  ....(2 marks)
                                    Part question [SEG 1994]

ANSWER

  i   Limestone is formed when the shells of sea creatures are compressed.
     Or:
     In hot countries limestone is deposited as sea water evaporates.
  ii   Limestone is changed by intense heat and/or pressure. The structure of the rock is changed.

Useful materials from rocks
Many rocks are used as construction materials – in some towns most of the buildings may be of sandstone. Limestone is another important building material. Marble is more expensive and may be used just to 'face' a building that is made of another less attractive stone. Diamonds, rubies and other precious stones are found as minerals in rock.

Some other tips for identifying rocks are:

- If the grains rub off … likely to be sedimentary.
- May have fossils … likely to be sedimentary, could possibly be limestone.
- Fizzes with hydrochloric acid, … a 'carbonate' rock – either limestone or marble.
- Can be split along cleavage planes … probably metamorphic, for example slate.

Cleavage planes are parallel planes.

QUESTION

Choose words from this list to answer the questions below:

granite   limestone   slate   sandstone   marble

Which of these rocks is:
a   Metamorphic?
b   Made up of large crystals?
c   Affected by acid rain?

ANSWER

a   Slate, marble.
b   Granite.
c   Limestone, marble.

QUESTION

Rocks are continually being changed.
a   How can sedimentary rocks be turned into metamorphic rocks?
b   How can metamorphic rocks be turned into sedimentary rocks?

ANSWER

a   By the action of high temperature and/or pressure.
b   The rocks are eroded and the sediment formed is then compacted to form sedimentary rock.

What is weathering?

Once rocks have formed they do not stay like that, they are changed by the Earth's atmosphere. This is called weathering. This process can be divided into two main types – chemical weathering and physical weathering.

Chemical weathering

Chemical reactions change the substances in the rocks. As chemical reactions are involved, chemical weathering takes place most rapidly in hot conditions, but there must be sufficient dampness to provide the necessary water.

For example, acid rain reacts with limestone – evidence for this reaction can be seen on limestone gravestones where the letters have become difficult to read.

The action of acid rain on limestone is the same reaction that you may have carried out in the laboratory when you added an acid to a carbonate to make a salt.

acid + carbonate → salt + water + carbon dioxide (See p 144 for more information on making salts.)

Physical weathering

This occurs when fragments of rock are broken away from the parent rock but no chemical reaction is involved. It can happen when water gets into a crack and freezes. As it does so, it expands and forces the parent rock to split. Rocks are frequently made up of a number of different substances. These expand and contract at different rates and can cause the outer layers of rock to break away. This occurs particularly in parts of the world where there is a big temperature difference between day and night.

Roots of plants can get into cracks between different layers and loosen the fragments of rock still further.

The following gives an idea of the order of weathering of some common rocks:

limestone .... weathers most easily
sandstone
granite
quartzite
quartz .... resistant to weathering: river beds and beaches have a high percentage of this mineral.

How are transportation, erosion and deposition connected?

Transportation

This is the movement of fragments of rock from the parent rock. It sorts the fragments into different sizes and also makes the fragments more rounded.

Erosion

This is the wearing away of rocks as fragments of other rocks are transported over them. It can happen in a number of ways:

Cause of erosion	What happens	Evidence
Gravity	fragments fall down	rocks found in gullies on mountains
Wind	small fragments blown away	sand dunes
Water	rivers, rain and ice move fragments	in a river bed stones may be seen moving

Valleys are formed by erosion.

Deposition

This occurs when the fragments which have been weathered, transported and eroded come to rest as sediment. Deltas are formed in this way.

QUESTION

Rocks can be changed by weathering and erosion. For each of the examples below indicate if the change is due to erosion (E) or weathering (W).

a The cracking of a rock on a high mountain due to a severe winter.
b Pebbles being thrown down a waterfall onto rock.
c Rock debris being thrown by wind against boulders on a Yorkshire moor.
d The dissolving of carbonate-containing rocks by acid rain.

ANSWERS

a W
b E
c E
d W

QUESTION

Look at this diagram of a coastal region (Fig 3).

a Explain how weathering of rock could have occurred in this area.
b Label with a T two places where rock fragments are being transported.
c Describe what is happening at E causing the erosion of the cliff.

Fig 3 A coastal region

ANSWERS

a Roots of trees breaking up the cliff, or acid rain on the chalk cliff.
b In the sea; in the river, from sand dune, 'bits' of the cliff falling down.
c The sea is throwing pebbles onto the cliff face therefore eroding the cliff. *(Or the action of fine particles in the sea erodes the cliff.)*

How does faulting and folding of rocks happen?

The rocks which make up the Earth change if they are put under enough stress.

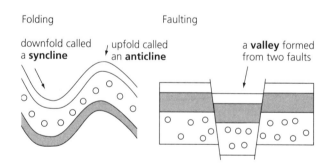

Fig 4 Folding and faulting

Whether a fold or a fault occurs depends on:

* The type of force – a push (compression) or a pull (tension).
* The direction of the force.
* The type of rock. Hard, crystalline, igneous rocks like granite are brittle and may form a fault, but softer sedimentary rocks are more likely to form a fold.

If a rock (or other material) is subjected to stress it may change in one of three ways:

* *Brittle deformation:* breaks or fractures.
* *Plastic deformation:* changes shape and stays in the new shape.
* *Elastic deformation:* changes shape but will return to the original shape if the stress is removed.

Folding

This can be caused by plastic deformation. If rocks in the Earth's crust are compressed they become folded. All the large mountain ranges, such as the Alps, have been formed by folding.

Faulting

Rocks that are subjected to folding are often brittle and they break or fracture. The rocks on either side of the fracture move at different rates and a fault is seen. They may move in a vertical or horizontal direction. The San Andreas fault in America is one example of an area where large blocks of the Earth's crust have moved relative to one another.

What evidence about the Earth's movements can we get from the rock record?

By looking at sections through the Earth's crust much information can be obtained.

If one of the layers is clay this indicates that the area has been flooded in the past.

EXAMPLE

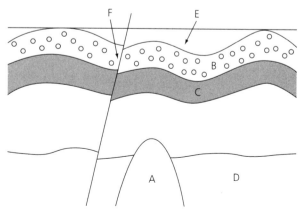

Fig 5 Section through the Earth's crust

Position	Feature	Evidence
A	large crystals of granite	igneous rock – cooled slowly, newer rock than D which it intrudes (pushes into)
B	small crystals	igneous rock – cooled quickly
C	rock fizzes with hydrochloric acid, contains fossils	sedimentary rock, limestone
D	i) layers seen in the rock	sedimentary
	ii) may be some changed rock next to A	metamorphic rock
E	fossils seen and layers noticed in rock	sedimentary, younger rock than B
F	fault in the rock and folds on both sides of the fault are displaced	fault occurred after the folding

QUESTION

Fig 6 shows a section through the rocks of southern England.

a The rock layers of southern England provide evidence of changes that have taken place since the rocks were formed.
Describe these changes. (5 marks)

....
....
....
....
....
....

b What evidence would be needed to confirm that the chalk of the South Downs, North Downs and Chiltern Hills was all laid down at the same time?

....
....
....(2 marks)
[ULEAC]

ANSWER

a Folding of the rocks has occurred and there is evidence of an anticline and a syncline.
The top part of the anticline has been weathered and eroded.
Faulting has occurred and the layers of rock have moved relative to one another at these faults.
Faulting occurred after the folding.
The presence of clay indicates that this area has been flooded in the past.

b Chalk is a sedimentary rock. It is likely to contain fossils. You could look at the fossils found in these three areas. If the same fossils were found in these rocks this would be evidence that the rocks were all laid down at the same time. (If the fossils were found in the same positions relative to one another this would provide additional evidence.)
You could also explain how radioactive dating could be used.

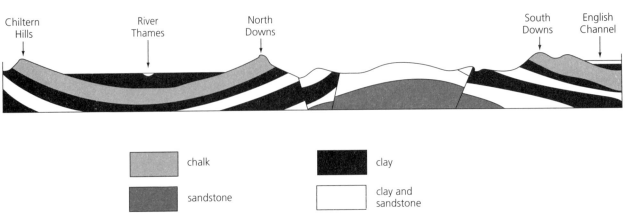

Fig 6

What do we mean by plate tectonics?

The theory of plate tectonics was suggested in the 1960s to explain how the major features of the Earth's surface were formed. This theory is based on the following observations.

Ocean ridges

It has been found that each ocean has a ridge system on the sea bed. At the ridges new rock is formed by volcanic activity. There is also a lot of earthquake activity in this ridge area. These two phenomena (the volcanoes and earthquakes) have been used to explain why the Earth is not getting bigger.

The Atlantic Ocean is spreading at a rate of 2 to 5 cm/year.

Magnetic evidence

The Earth behaves rather like a magnet. The magnetic north pole is at an angle of about 11°C to the Earth's axis. Data on the Earth's magnetic field shows that the magnetic north pole appears to be moving. This data, together with other data on where minerals are found, has provided scientists with evidence about the relative positions of the continents in the past.

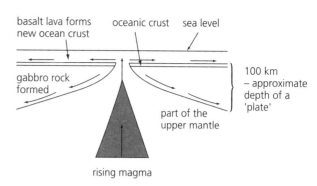

Fig 7 How an ocean ridge is formed

By considering evidence from the formation of ocean ridges and how continents appear to have moved, the theory of **plate tectonics** was developed. The main points of this theory are:

- The Earth's crust is made up of a number of rigid plates.
- The plates are moving relative to one another.

There appear to be three types of join between the plates (called plate margins):

- *Constructive:* new crust is being formed – as at the oceanic ridges, where plates are moving away from one another.

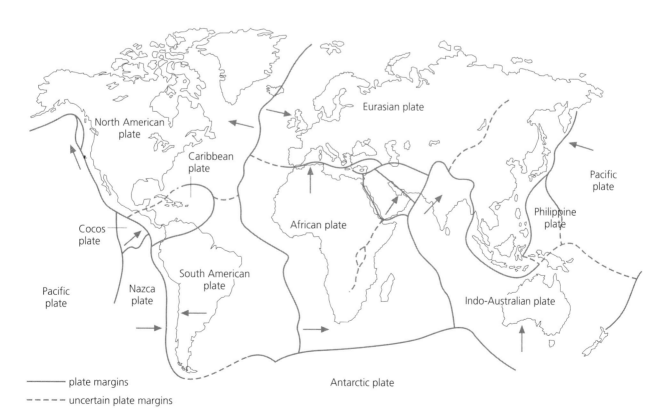

Fig 8 The main tectonic plates

- *Destructive:* new crust is being destroyed or modified – as at an oceanic trench, where one plate is moving over another.
- *Conservative:* plates are sliding past each other.

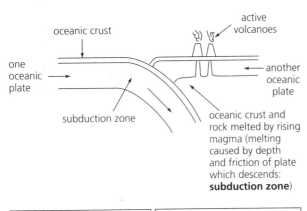

If an **oceanic plate** meets a **continental plate**, the denser oceanic plate is subducted – in this case there are lots of volcanoes and **fold mountains** are formed. e.g. Andes in South America

If **two continental plates** meet, fold mountains form as the two continents collide e.g. the Himalayan Mountains; Mount Everest is getting about 1cm higher each year

Fig 9 Activity when two ocean plates meet, e.g. Japan

Plate tectonic theory provides evidence for the rock cycle.

- Magma (for example in volcanic action) may rise into rocks where it cools and crystallises – **igneous** rocks are formed.
- Rocks may be weathered, eroded and transported so that fragments settle and form **sedimentary** rocks.
- Rocks may be buried, subjected to high temperatures and pressures, and form **metamorphic** rocks.
- Rocks may be buried deeply, in a subduction zone. Here they become so hot that they melt and form magma.

Earthquakes
An earthquake occurs when stresses build up inside the Earth. (Note: the earthquake does not cause the stresses!) Most earthquakes occur along faults. As the rock breaks, energy is released which causes the Earth to 'shake'. The faults are substantial at plate margins and many of the world's earthquakes happen at these "earthquake zones".

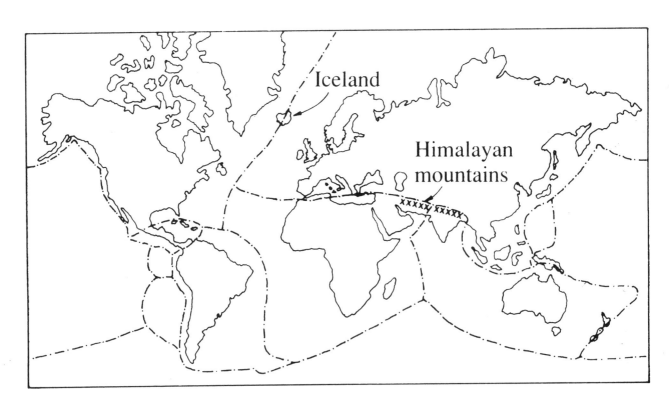

— · — · — · — boundary of plate

Fig 10

QUESTION

The map (Fig 10) shows the boundaries of the Earth's plates.

Use the map to answer the following questions.

i Explain why the island of Iceland consists almost entirely of igneous rock.

....

....

....

....

....

....(3 marks)

ii Describe how the Himalayan mountains were formed.

....

....

....

....(2 marks)

[ULEAC]

ANSWER

i Iceland is situated on the boundary of a plate. The North American plate is moving away from the Eurasian plate (a constructive plate margin). Rising magma is forming new crust in this region. This means that the rock is molten and forms igneous rock as it cools. This type of rock makes up the island of Iceland.

ii The Himalayan mountains are an example of a mountain chain formed by folding, when two plates collide. The rocks in this region are plastic. They have been compressed and remain in their new folded shape.

Air, atmosphere and weather

What is the link between air and the atmosphere?

The blanket of gases which surrounds the Earth is called the **atmosphere**. It is about 800 km (500 miles) thick. However, beyond about 80 km (50 miles) from the Earth the atmosphere becomes much thinner. The atmosphere can be thought of as being made up of a number of different layers.

The layer nearest to the Earth is the troposphere. It includes the air as we know it. Air is a mixture of gases and so its composition is never completely constant. The percentage of the different gases can be calculated, assuming that an average sample of clean, dry air is taken.

Differences between mixtures and compounds are discussed on p 136.

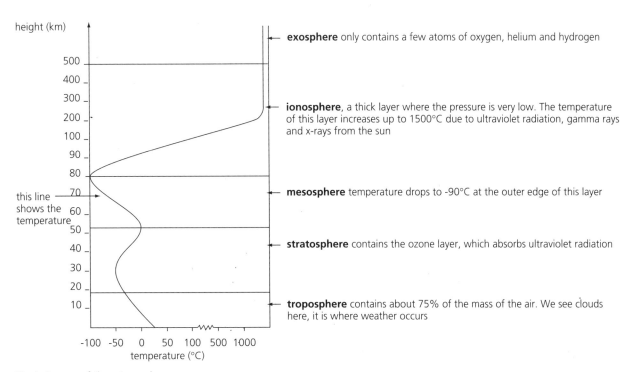

Fig 1 Layers of the atmosphere

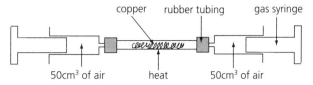

Fig 2 Percentage composition of a sample of clean dry air (by volume). Volume of air not used up by the copper is 79%, the 21% that is used up in the reaction with copper is oxygen.

Average composition of clean, dry air (% by volume)

Nitrogen   78
Oxygen   21
Argon   0.9

The remaining 0.1% is made up of:

Carbon dioxide 0.03.
Very small amounts of other gases.

Air as a raw material

The air around the Earth is an important mixture which contains many useful substances. It also has another important feature as a raw material – there is a lot of it and it will not run out soon.

Oxygen

Oxygen is one element that is obtained from the air. It is used, for example, in making steel. In this and other industrial processes, as well as in hospitals, pure oxygen is needed. It is obtained from the air by fractional distillation.

Distillation is used to separate mixtures and makes use of the fact that the pure substances in mixtures boil at different temperatures.

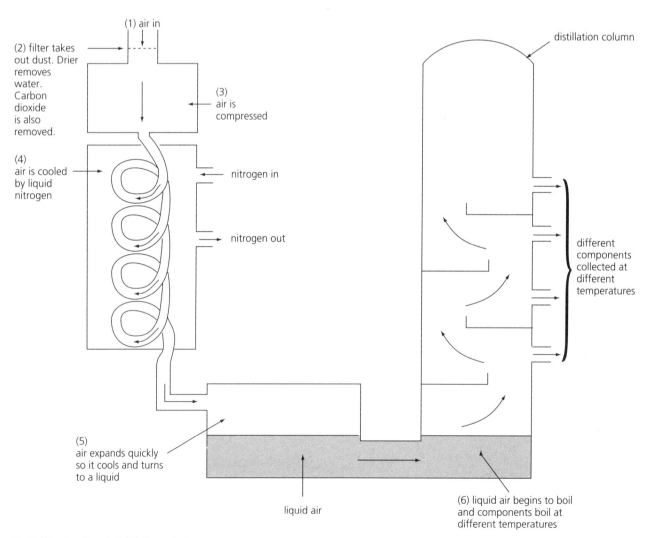

Fig 3 The fractional distillation of air

Nitrogen

78% of the air (by volume) is made up of nitrogen. Nitrogen is a vital element for living organisms. Both plants and animals need it to make proteins. Unfortunately, few plants can absorb nitrogen directly from the air for this purpose. Fertilisers containing nitrogen are used by arable farmers to increase the growth of crops such as wheat. Nitrogen from the air is used in the manufacture of fertilisers by the Haber process (see p 205 for more details).

Legumes (plants with pods, like peas, beans and clover) are able to absorb nitrogen from the air. They contain bacteria which carry out this function in nodules in their roots.

How did the atmosphere form?

After the formation of the planets

It is thought that when the planets were formed (about 4500 million years ago) the Earth had a thick layer of hydrogen and helium surrounding it. (This idea is supported by the fact that Jupiter and Saturn have such an atmosphere now.)

Gases from the Earth's volcanoes

As the molten Earth cooled it formed a thin crust on the outside. Volcanoes erupted through this crust. The volcanoes gave out ammonia, carbon monoxide, methane, nitrogen and probably some carbon dioxide.

Further cooling of the Earth

As the Earth cooled to less than 100°C, the water vapour condensed – rain formed. It is thought this is how the first oceans appeared. Ultraviolet light from the Sun penetrated the oceans and rivers. It is thought that conditions were right for the chemical reactions which led to the first life appearing about 10 metres below the surface of the oceans. Here, most UV light would have been filtered out by the water, but there would have been sufficient for these reactions. Scientists think this led to the first bacteria and primitive plants (probably algae) appearing about 3000 million years ago.

The first oceans appeared about 3800 million years ago.

Oxygen is formed in the atmosphere

As plants absorbed light from the Sun, they carried out photosynthesis and oxygen was released. Ultraviolet light from the Sun broke down some of the oxygen molecules into atoms.

$$O_2 \quad\quad \text{ultraviolet radiation} \quad\quad O + O$$
oxygen molecules $\quad\quad \rightarrow \quad\quad$ free oxygen atoms

These combined with oxygen molecules to form ozone.

$$O + O_2 \quad\quad\quad \rightarrow \quad\quad\quad O_3$$
ozone molecules

Ozone is unstable and is itself decomposed by ultraviolet light to form oxygen atoms and oxygen molecules.

$$O_3 \quad\quad \text{ultraviolet radiation} \quad\quad O + O_2$$
ozone molecules $\quad\quad \rightarrow \quad\quad$ free oxygen atom and oxygen molecule

This meant that the composition of the upper atmosphere was in balance. Ozone was an important gas in the atmosphere as it formed a layer which protected the Earth from the harmful effects of ultra violet radiation.

The appearance of simple animals

Beneath the layer of ozone, the atmosphere was rich in oxygen. Simple animals developed which did not rely on sunlight for their energy, as the first plants had done. The animals combined oxygen with carbon from their food and this released the energy they needed (as in human respiration!). The first land animals, a type of fish with lungs, moved from the oceans to the land about 350 million years ago.

The other gases stabilised

- Methane and ammonia
  These gases from the primary atmosphere reacted with the oxygen. **Nitrogen** was formed during the reaction of ammonia with oxygen and was also formed by the action of denitrifying bacteria.

- Carbon dioxide
  Much of the carbon dioxide of the early atmosphere became locked up during the formation of sedimentary rock, in the form of carbonates and fossil fuels.

Maintaining the composition of the atmosphere

The composition of the air has been more or less the same for 200 million yeras, and is quite constant up to a height of about 16 km (10 miles). The atmosphere is kept in place by gravity. A number of factors operate to maintain the composition of the atmosphere.

- Volcanoes.
- Chemical reactions (in particular photosynthesis and respiration).
- Radioactive decay.

However, there is evidence that the balance is being altered by human activity. (Details of the so-called 'hole in the ozone layer' are on p 123.)

QUESTION

a The main gases in the Earth's atmosphere are nitrogen, oxygen, water vapour and carbon dioxide. When the atmosphere was first formed it was mainly composed of carbon dioxide, nitrogen, methane and water vapour. The table below shows how the percentages of some gases in the atmosphere have changed over time.

  i How has the percentage of carbon dioxide in the atmosphere changed?

....
....(1 mark)

  ii Suggest TWO reasons for this change.
  Reason 1 ....
....

Reason 2 ....
....(2 marks)

b Explain how the gradual evolution of different life forms is related to changes in the atmosphere.

....
....
....
....
....
....
....
....
....
....
....
....(5 marks)

[ULEAC]

ANSWER

a i It has decreased.
    You ought to be able to add 'from 90% to less than 1%'.
  ii There are several things you could discuss here.
    Carbon dioxide was:
    – Combined in sedimentary rocks.
    – Combined and 'locked up' as fossil fuels were formed.
    – Dissolved in the oceans.
    – Used in photosynthesis.

b *This asks you to explain, and gives you lots of scope to present your ideas clearly. There are 5 marks, are there five things you could discuss?*

Millions of years ago	Percentage composition			Main Events
	Carbon dioxide	Nitrogen	Oxygen	
4500	90	10	0	Earth formed
4000	40	30	0	oceans formed
3500	21	40	trace	
3000	15	55	1	first sea plants
2500	10	60	5	
2000	7	70	10	
1500	5	75	18	
1000	2	77	20	first sea animals
500	1	77	21	first land plants and animals
0	less than 1	78	21	

Fig 4

- Carbon dioxide was used by the first plants in photosynthesis.
- Cooling of the Earth resulted in the formation of oceans. Suitable conditions were created, protected from the damaging effects of UV light, for the formation of simple animals.
- Oxygen, produced by land plants, was used by the animals in respiration.
- Ozone acted as a shielding layer, enabling organisms on the Earth to be protected from ultraviolet radiation. *(If you discuss this you could write some equations to show how oxygen (given off by plants) is involved in the formation of ozone.)*

- Denitrying bacteria increased the amount of nitrogen in the air *(they decrease the amount of nitrogen in the soil).*

Weather

Our weather depends on two main factors:

1 Where the air in the wind started from.
2 Its path before reaching us.

Weather instruments

We can describe the weather in a particular place using measurements of temperature, rainfall, wind speed and wind direction.

Maximum and minimum thermometer
- records highest and lowest temperature, as the iron pin stays where it is pushed by the mercury (can be reset by using a magnet to move the iron pin)

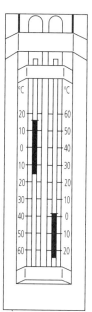

Rain gauge
- records the number of millimetres of rain which fall in a certain time

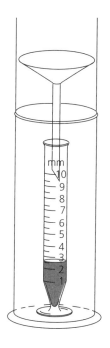

Anemometer
- measures the speed of the wind; the cups rotate as the wind blows

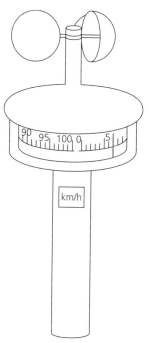

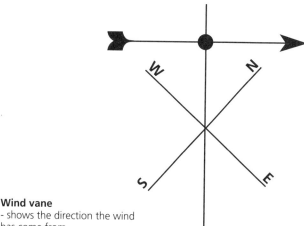

Wind vane
- shows the direction the wind has come from

Fig 5 Weather instruments

Why is the water cycle so important to our weather?

Just over 70% of the surface of the Earth is covered by water. The seas make up 97% of the Earth's water. It is the water in the atmosphere, oceans and ice caps, and the way it moves around, that is responsible for much of our climate.

Less than 3% of the total is fresh water and three quarters of this is frozen at the poles.

The water cycle (see Fig 6) is the name given to the way in which water moves around in the Earth's atmosphere.

The sun heats the air which expands. As it does so it becomes less dense and rises. Cooler air then moves in to take its place. We call this a convection current. The sun also heats the water in the sea. Air above the oceans rises but contains a lot of moisture. As it gets higher and higher it cools, and the water vapour in it condenses to form water droplets (a cloud). If the air cools below 0°C, then the water in it turns into ice crystals, and falls as snow or hail rather than rain.

Origin of the oceans
There are two main theories:
- As the Earth solidified, water formed in volcanoes.
- The oceans were formed as the granite continental crust crystallised.

QUESTION

Rain which falls in areas like the Lake District came originally from the sea. The diagram shows how water from the sea falls as rain on the land.

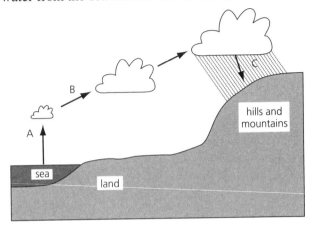

Fig 7

Complete the following sentences to explain what happens at A, B and C in the diagram.

i Evaporation at A is caused by

....
....(1 mark)

ii Condensation takes place at B because

....
....(1 mark)

iii Precipitation of rain takes place at C because

....
....(1 mark)
[MEG]

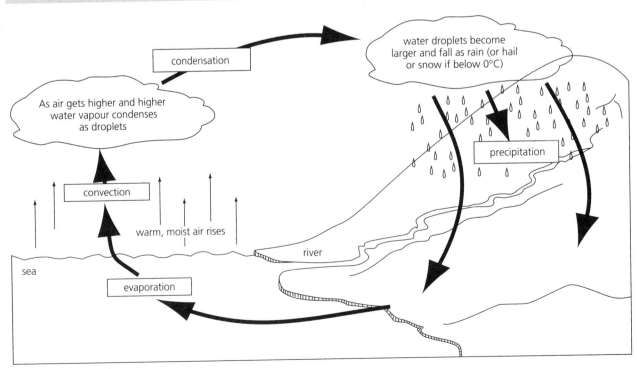

Fig 6 The water cycle

ANSWER

   i Energy from the Sun.
   ii As the air rises it cools.
   iii The droplets of water in the cloud become heavier.

How are airstreams important to our weather?

The climate in different parts of the world is affected by the movement of large masses of air. These are called **airstreams**. There are four general types of wind which affect the weather of the British isles. They come from the following directions:

north/north-west   south-east
north-east   south-west

The winds from the north-east and north/north-west are called polar winds and those from the south and south-west are known as tropical winds. If the wind has come over the sea it is known as a maritime wind. If it has come over land it is known as a continental wind. The airstreams associated with these winds are:

- Polar maritime (north-west wind)
  This comes from the cold northern regions but then travels over a warmer sea. It can give shower clouds on the west coast.
- Polar continental (north-east wind)
  This is a dry wind which is warm in summer and cold in winter. It can also give rise to fog on the east coast, due to the moisture it has picked up over the North Sea.
- Tropical continental (south-east wind)
  This is a hot summer wind from north Africa. It can bring thunderstorms.
- Tropical maritime (south-west wind)
  This wind, probably the most common, brings warm, wet weather. It produces low cloud and fog over the hills in the south-west.

What causes the air to move?

Our weather is due to energy from the Sun reaching the Earth. More of this energy is absorbed in the tropics (near the equator) than at the poles. In very simple terms, the atmosphere moves to try and even out these differences in energy distribution. There are patterns in the way the atmosphere circulates, and understanding these enables us to forecast the weather with some accuracy.

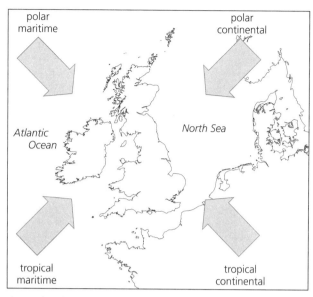

Fig 8 The airstreams which affect Britain

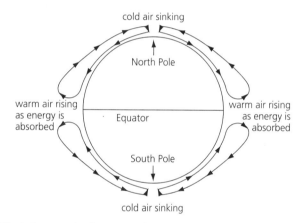

Fig 9 Patterns in the atmosphere

Areas where air is rising are called Low Pressure areas or lows. These tend to produce clouds and precipitation (rain, sleet or snow). Where large masses of cooled air sink back towards the surface there are High Pressure areas, or highs, with little cloud and fine weather. The weather is more settled and the air gets warmer as it is compressed (squeezed) near the warm ground.

The weather in Great Britain comes mostly from the west, and results from the movement of depressions over the country. Looking at weather maps on consecutive days provides evidence for this. The depressions usually have **fronts** associated with them. A front is the boundary separating different regions of air at different temperatures. A warm front separates cold air from warm air that is moving up behind it. (On a weather map the symbol for this is a line of bowler hats!) A cold front separates warm air from cold air that is coming up behind it. (On a weather map the symbol for this is a row of witches hats!)

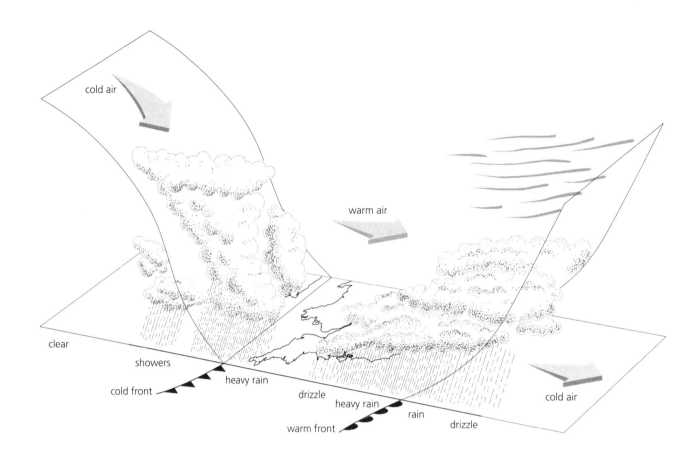

Fig 10a Cross section of a front

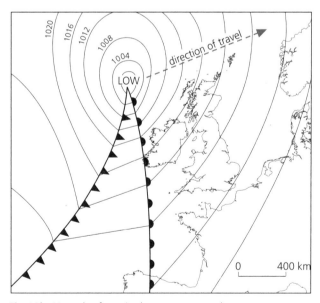

Fig 10b How the front is shown on a weather map

What do the thin lines on weather maps tell us?

The thin lines on a weather map are called **isobars**. They link together places with the same atmospheric

pressure. Notice the *low* (low pressure). A high would represent a high pressure area called an **anticyclone**. When isobars are close together, the pressure changes a lot over a short distance. This means that it is windy. The wind moves rapidly from an area of high pressure to an area of low pressure. On the weather map (Fig 10b) the arrow shows you the general wind direction. It is worth remembering that the wind blows **clockwise** around high pressure areas and **anti-clockwise** around low pressure areas in the northern hemisphere, where Great Britain is situated. This is because of the rotation of the Earth.

QUESTION

The diagram below shows the main airstreams which affect the British Isles.

a Which air stream is likely to give very hot dry weather in Britain?

....(1 mark)

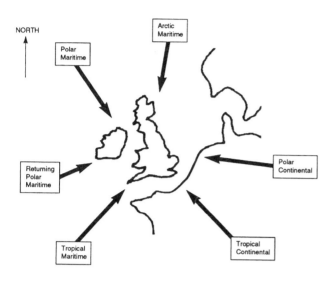

Fig 11

b Give two reasons for your answer to (a)

1 ....
....
....
2 ....
....
....(2 marks)

c The weather map below was taken from a newspaper.

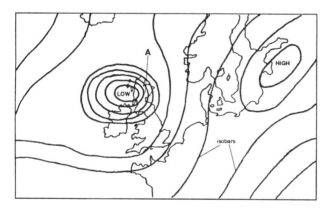

Fig 12

i On the map, what are joined by the lines labelled 'isobars'?

....
....(2 marks)

ii What would you expect the strength of the wind to be at point A?

....

How do you know?

....
....(2 marks)

iii Mark the direction of the wind, at point A, as an arrow on the weather map.
How do you know?

....
....(2 marks)
[NEAB]

ANSWER

a Tropical continental.

b The air mass has come from over land so it will be dry.
The air mass has come from the continent, that is from a hot region, so it will bring hot weather.

c
   i Places of equal pressure.
  ii Strong winds.
     The isobars are very close together at A.
 iii The arrow should point in a north (or north-west direction), indicating south or south-easterly winds.
     The winds move counterclockwise around a low pressure area in the northern hemisphere.

Revision sheet

Rocks

1 a Are the rocks in the Earth's crust elements, compounds or mixtures?
  b Name the three major types of rock in the Earth's crust.
  c How is each type of rock formed?
  d Give an example of each type of rock.
2 Describe each of these terms:
  a Physical weathering
  b Chemical weathering.
  c Transportation.
  d Erosion.
  e Deposition.
3 What is the difference between faulting and folding of rocks?
4 a What are the main points of the theory of plate tectonics?
  b What are the features of the three types of plate boundary?
5 How do earthquakes occur?

Air, atmosphere and weather

1 a What percentage of the air (by volume) is: oxygen, nitrogen?

   b How are nitrogen and oxygen obtained from the air?

   c Give a use for nitrogen and oxygen.

   d Name some other gases found in (clean) air.

2 Briefly, how did the following evolve to their present form:

   a The atmosphere.

   b The oceans.

3 a What is the water cycle?

   b What is the importance of the sun in the water cycle?

   c Describe what happens in the following processes in the water cycle: evaporation, condensation, precipitation.

4 a Name the 4 main airstreams which bring 'weather' to the British Isles.

   b Describe the type of weather that each brings.

5 What information do each of these features on a weather map give you about the weather:

   a Isobar.

   b 'Low'.

   c 'High'.

   d Cold front.

   e Warm front.

Revision sheet answers

Rocks

1 a Mixtures.

   b Igneous, sedimentary, metamorphic.

   c Igneous – formed from cooling molten magma. Sedimentary – formed when rocks are worn away to form sediments, which are then compacted. Metamorphic – formed when high temperature and/or pressure changes the structure of rocks.

   d Igneous – granite, basalt, rhyolite. Sedimentary – sandstone, mudstone, shale, conglomerate, limestone. Metamorphic – slate or schist (from mudstone), marble from limestone.

2 a Physical weathering – fragments of rock are broken off, for example due to temperature changes – no chemical reactions involved.

   b Chemical weathering – chemical reactions, for example due to acid rain, cause fragments of rock to break off.

   c Transportation – the movement of fragments of rock away from the parent rock.

   d Erosion – the wearing away of rocks by fragments of other rocks passing over them.

   e Deposition – the build up of fragments of rock formed by weathering or erosion.

3 Folding – occurs when rocks change shape due to forces acting on them, and the rocks remain in the new shape.
Faulting – occurs when forces act on brittle rocks which then break or fracture.

4 a Main points of plate tectonic theory:
   – The Earth's crust is made up of a number of rigid plates.
   – The plates move relative to one another.

   b Constructive plate margins – plates move away from one another and new crust is formed. Destructive plate margins – plates move over one another, the crust is modified or destroyed. Conservative plate margins – plates slide past one another.

5 Earthquakes occur when stresses build up within the Earth and the rocks break, releasing energy. The earth 'shakes'.

Air, atmosphere and weather

1 a Oxygen – 21%, nitrogen – 78%.

   b Fractional distillation.

   c Nitrogen – used to make fertilisers; oxygen – used to make steel, in hospitals.

   d Other gases in air: carbon dioxide, water vapour, argon, neon, helium, krypton.

2 a Formation of the atmosphere – As the Earth cooled, gases (e.g. ammonia, carbon dioxide, nitrogen) formed from the volcanoes. Further cooling of the Earth, water vapour condensed. Plants formed in the oceans, carried out photosynthesis, oxygen released.

   b Formation of the oceans – cooling of the Earth, the water vapour condensed, water formed as granite in the continental crust crystallised.

3 a Water cycle – the way that water moves around the atmosphere.

   b Sun provides the energy for the evaporation of water.

   c Evaporation – water changes from the liquid to the vapour (gaseous) state.

Condensation – water vapour changes into liquid water.

Precipitation – water falls as rain (or hail or sleet or snow) as the water droplets become larger when the cloud cools.

4 a Main air masses affecting the British Isles:
   Polar maritime.
   Polar continental.
   Tropical maritime.
   Tropical continental.

 b Weather associated with each:
   Polar maritime – rain in the west, can be cold.
   Polar continental – dry, can be cold.
   Tropical maritime – warm, damp.
   Tropical continental – warm, dry.

5 a Isobar – lines joining places of equal pressure. The closer together they are the more wind there is.

 b 'Low' – low pressure area, poor weather, cloudy and wet.

 c 'High' – high pressure area, hot in summer, cold in winter but dry, little cloud.

 d Cold front – rain along the front, the air behind will be colder.

 e Warm front – rain along the front, the air behind will be warmer.

Student Answer with Comments

The diagram shows some features of the Earth's crust.

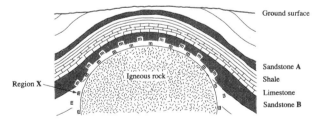

Fig 1

a List the four layers of sedimentary rock named in the diagram, in order of age starting with the oldest. (1 mark)

(oldest)   1 _Sandstone B_
            2 _Limestone_
            3 _Shale_
(youngest)   4 _Sandstone A_ ✓ ①

b i What types of rocks are likely to be formed in region X? (1 mark)
     Metamorphic rocks ✓ ①

ii Name a rock formed from limestone in region X. (1 mark)
     Chalk ✗ _No! Marble_

c Describe how sedimentary rock, such as sandstone, is formed from sediment. (2 marks)
These rocks are usually formed under water. The animals die creating silt and dead matter and sand is mixed in, all this sinks to the bottom, ✓ _layers build up, gradually squashing it together to form rock._ ✓ ②

d The sketch map A shows a region in Scotland. Two granite areas are shaded in.

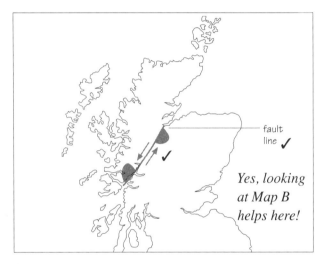

fault line ✓

✓

Yes, looking at Map B helps here!

Fig 2

Map A

It is thought that the granite once formed part of a single area (sketch map B).

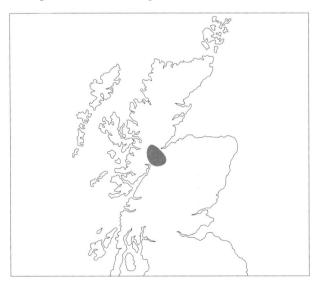

Fig 3

Map B

Separation along a fault line has continued over a period of time.

  i Draw on map A the fault line responsible for the separation. *(Make sure this is very clear)* ① (1 mark)

  ii Add arrows to map A to show the direction of movement on each side of the fault. (1 mark)①

e The granite found in both areas contained crystals which were much smaller than those found in another location. Explain why the crystal size differs. (2 marks) ✓

  This is because the speed at which molten rock cools affects the size of the crystals. If it cools ② *quickly, this causes the crystals to be a lot smaller.* ✓

  8/9 ✓ [SEG]

An exam question for you to try

QUESTION

Fig 4 shows a weather map for a day in January.

a The weather system shown in Fig 1 has travelled to Britain from a south-westerly direction ↗, and gave very windy weather plus a large amount of rain and snow.

  i Explain how this weather system has produced such weather.

  ....
  ....
  ....
  ....
  ....
  ....(3 marks)

  ii Explain why the weather would be different if the weather system had travelled to Britain from the east (←).

  ....
  ....(1 mark)

b Fig 5 shows a vertical section through the depression (between B and A).

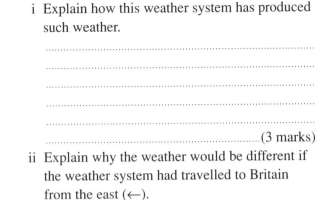

Fig 5

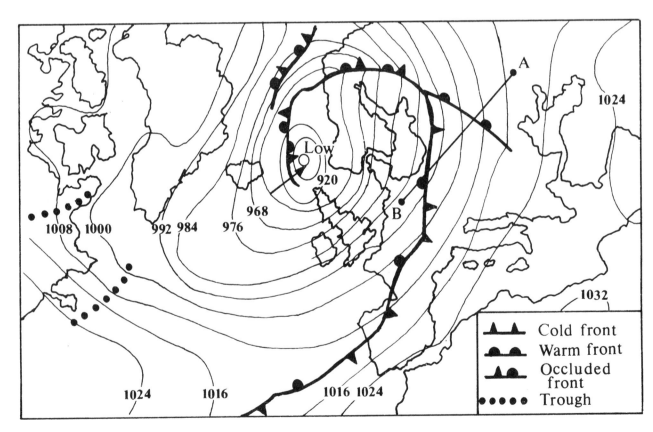

Fig 4

The weather in the four different places (1, 2, 3 and 4) between B and A is shown in the table below.

Position	Weather
1 (nearest to A)	snow
2	dry, warmer temperatures, some sunshine, more humid
3	heavy rain
4 (nearest to B)	some snow showers, colder temperatures

By describing the movement of cold and warm air, explain how these places had such different weather.

....

....

....

....

....(4 marks)

[ULEAC]

Answer

a   i   A low pressure area is influencing the weather in Britain. When weather comes from the south-west it is brought by a tropical maritime airstream. This has travelled over the sea and picked up a lot of water. It is January so precipitation is likely to include snow as well as rain. The isobars are close together so it is windy. *Notice how the question mentions 'south-westerly wind direction', 'windy weather', 'a large amount of rain and snow', these will all help you in your answer.*

     ii   If the weather came from the east, the air mass would have come over land so it would be a lot drier. *(Notice the question asks you to explain so don't just say that it would have come over the land.)*

b   *There are 4 marks available so it would be a good idea to write about each place.*
Place 1: This is at a warm front (warm air behind the line). The warm air rises over the cold air as it is less dense. It then cools and forms clouds. These have given rise to the snow.
Place 2: This is between the two fronts. The air is warmer than at place 1. Although it is not drizzling (which could happen) the air is damp.
Place 3: This is just in front of a cold front. The cold air behind the front is pushing the warm air up. This is cooling and causing heavy rain.
Place 4: This is behind the cold front so the temperature is lower than at Places 2 and 3. There are likely to be some showers. The colder air cannot hold as much water vapour as the warmer air at place 2.

13 Using electricity

Using electricity	Midland (MEG)				Northern (NEAB)		London (ULEAC)				Southern (SEG)		Welsh (WJEC)
	Own	Nuffield	Salters	Suffolk	Co-ordinated	Modular	Modular GASP	Combined	Co-ordinated	Modular	Double	Modular	Co-ordinated
ELECTRICAL CIRCUITS													
Electrical current	✓	✓	✓	✓	✓	✓	✓	✓	✓	✓	✓	✓	✓
Types of cells		✓											
Series and parallel circuits	✓	✓	✓	✓	✓	✓	✓	✓	✓	✓	✓	✓	✓
Resistance	✓	✓	✓	✓	✓	✓	✓	✓	✓	✓	✓	✓	✓
Ohmic and non-ohmic conductors		H			H			H	H				H
Electrostatics			✓		✓	✓	✓	✓	✓	✓	✓	✓	✓
ELECTRICITY IN THE HOME													
Production of electricity	✓	✓	✓	✓	✓	✓	✓	H	✓	H	✓	H	✓
Power stations and power lines	H	✓	✓	✓	✓	✓	H	H	✓	H	✓	H	✓
Transformers	H	H	✓	✓	✓	✓	✓	H	✓	H	✓	H	✓
Electrical safety in the home	✓	✓	✓	✓	✓	✓	✓	✓	✓	✓	✓	✓	✓
Cost of using electricity	✓		✓	✓	✓	✓	✓	✓	✓	✓	✓	✓	✓
Decision-making circuits (electronic components)	✓	✓	✓	✓	✓	✓	✓	✓	✓	✓	✓	✓	✓
ELECTROMAGNETISM													
Magnets	✓	✓	✓	✓	✓	✓	✓	✓	✓	✓	✓	✓	✓
Magnetic effect of electricity	✓	✓	✓	✓	✓	✓	✓	✓	✓	✓	✓	✓	✓
Uses of electromagnets	✓	✓	✓	✓	✓	✓	✓	✓	✓	✓	✓	✓	✓
Electric motor	✓	✓	✓	✓	✓	✓	✓	✓	✓	✓	✓	✓	✓
Loudspeaker and microphone	✓	✓	✓	✓	✓	✓	✓	✓	✓	✓	✓	✓	✓

Electrical circuits

> Important equations used in the chapter are summarised on p 267

What is an electric current?

When working with an electrical circuit you may talk about a current. The electric current in the metal wires of the circuit is a flow of charged particles. These charged particles are negative electrons. We cannot see them moving but we are aware of their effect. For example, a wire carrying a current becomes warm and a bulb in the circuit lights up. The unit of electric current is the ampere, usually shortened to 'amp'.

For an electric currrent to flow:

- There must be energy available to move the charge.
- There must be a complete circuit of conducting material for the charge to flow through.

Which way does current flow round a circuit?

The electrons flow from the negative terminal of the cell to the positive terminal. However, the convention is that an electric current flows from the positive terminal to the negative.

Conventional current flows from positive to negative but electrons move from negative to positive.

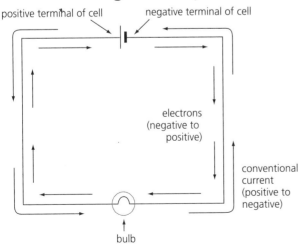

Fig 1 The connection between conventional current and electron flow

What makes the current flow round a circuit?

A cell, such as you put in a torch, pushes electrons around an electrical circuit. A cell can be thought of as an 'electron pump'. The cell is a device that changes chemical energy into electrical energy. In a circuit the chemical reactions in the cell provide energy that allows the circuit to light a bulb or heat a resistor. This energy provides the electromotive force (e.m.f.) of the cell. The e.m.f. is measured in volts (v) and we usually talk about the voltage of a cell. A zinc/carbon dry cell has an e.m.f. of 1.5 volts. Across the lamp there is now a potential difference of 1.5 volts, called the 'voltage'.

The current produced by a cell flows in one direction and is called direct current. A group of cells is called a battery.

If the circuit contains a lamp, we can work out what is happening to the electrons as they move round the circuit.

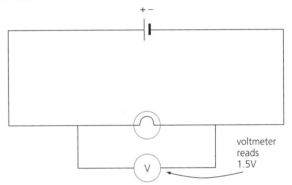

Fig 2 A simple circuit

Energy from the chemicals in the cell causes the cell to push electrons around the circuit. At the lamp the energy is transferred to the thin wire (called a filament) which becomes hot and glows. As it does so it gives out light.

Current and charge

In a circuit, if we mark a point on the wire we can say that:

The amount of charge passing = current × time.

In an equation, charge is given the symbol Q, current is given the symbol I, and time is t.

Therefore, $Q = It$

The unit of charge is the coulomb (C).

One coulomb is the charge passing a point in a circuit when one amp flows past the point on the wire for 1 second.

Put another way: current = charge/time
or I = Q/t
That is:
Current is the rate of flow of charge

Types of cell

1 Simple cell

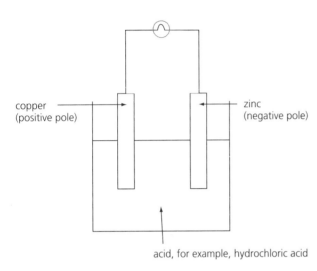

Fig 3 Simple cell

The metal higher in the reactivity series (see p 220) acts as the negative pole.
Here:

$$Zn(s) \rightarrow Zn^{2+}(aq) + 2e^-$$

The electrons flow through the circuit and a reading is detected on the voltmeter.
At the positive pole:

$$2H^+(aq) + 2e^- \rightarrow H_2(g)$$

The acid provides the hydrogen ions.

2 Dry cell

This is a common type of cell used in torches, radios etc. When a connection is made the zinc gives up electrons as in the simple cell.

$$Zn(s) \rightarrow Zn^{2+}(aq) + 2e^-$$

These cells do not last long because the zinc reacts even when the cell is not producing a current. Both the simple cell and the dry cell are called **primary cells** – they are used up as they produce electricity and cannot be recharged. They have to be thrown away.

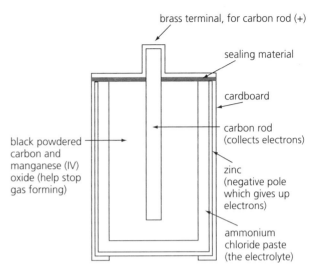

Fig 4 Dry cell. Commonest and cheapest type of cell, liable to leak when old

3 Rechargeable cells

These are called secondary cells because they can be recharged.
• Lead-acid cell.

This is the type of cell used as a car battery.

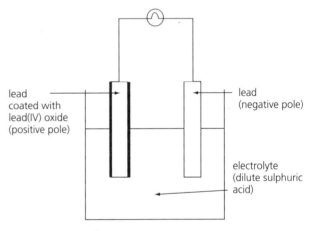

Fig 5 Lead-acid cell

As current is taken from the cell the surfaces of the electrodes form lead sulphate, and the acid gets weaker. When the car is running the process is reversed. The surface of the electrodes is converted back into lead and lead oxide, and the acid gets stronger.

Lead-acid cells can be used for emergency lighting in hospitals and public buildings.

• Rechargeable nickel-cadmium cells.

These are more expensive than dry cells but can be recharged up to 500 times. For this you need a special transformer (see p 270).

4 Fuel cell

This uses energy from the reaction between a fuel and oxygen to produce a voltage. Fuel cells have been used as a source of power in space craft.

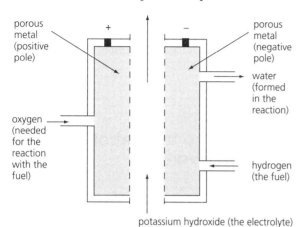

Fig 6 Fuel cell. The electrodes are also catalysts for the reaction (see p 194)

The connection between electric current, charge, energy, voltage and power.
The voltage is the energy that is transferred per coulomb.
Voltage (volts) = energy (joules) / charge (coulombs)
One volt is one joule per coulomb.
Using this equation and also: (from above)
Charge = current × time

We can write:
voltage = energy / (current × time)

This can be re-written as:
Energy converted = current × time × voltage
Energy converted = I × t × V
If the current is measured in amps, the time in seconds and the voltage in volts, the energy will be in joules.
This can also be written as: Energy converted per second = V × I
The energy converted per second is called the power.
So, power (watts) = voltage (volts) × current (amps)
or P = V × I

Voltmeters measure the potential difference across a component. They are always connected in parallel. Ammeters measure the current flowing through a component. They are always connected in series.

Reminder – Symbols

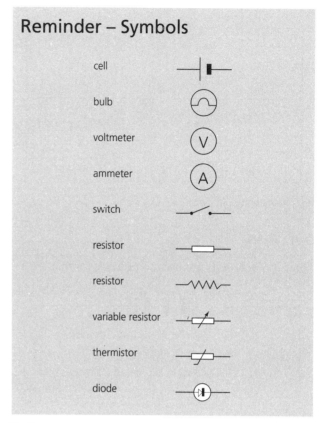

Fig 7

Series and Parallel Circuits

In the first circuit two bulbs are connected in series. This means the current flows through them both, one after the other.

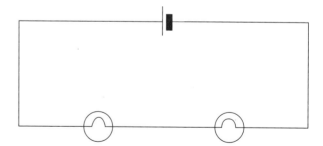

Fig 8 Series circuit

In the next circuit two bulbs are connected in parallel. This means the current is divided, some flowing through one bulb and some through the other. If the bulbs have the same resistance the current will divide equally; the same amount will flow through each bulb.

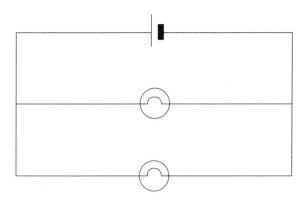

Fig 9 Parallel circuit

QUESTION

Three 1.5 volt cells are used to power a torch.

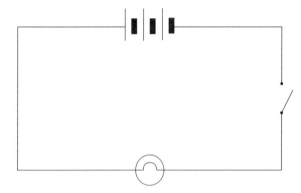

Fig 10

a What is the total e.m.f. provided by the cells?
b How would you connect a voltmeter to measure the potential difference across the bulb?
c What would be the potential difference across the bulb?

d What two forms of energy is the electrical energy converted into by the bulb?

ANSWER

a 4.5 volts.
b In parallel (*as fig 9*).
c 4.5 volts (*see 'internal resistance' later in this chapter*).
d Light and heat.

Resistance and its relationship to Current and Voltage

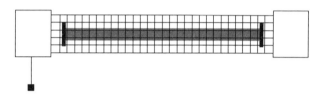

Fig 11 A bathroom heater

If you have ever been near one of these electric heaters you will know that it can give out a lot of heat. As the electrons move round the circuit they knock into atoms in the nichrome wire. These atoms resist the movement of the electrons. Nichrome is said to have a high resistance. You feel heat as the electrons increase the vibration of the atoms in the wire.

Factors affecting resistance of a wire

Factor	How it affects resistance	Explanation	Use
length	Increasing the length increases the resistance	More atoms to bump into	Dimmer switch to darken a room
cross-sectional area	Increasing the cross-sectional area decreases the resistance	More room for electrons to move through	Wires which are designed to get hot have a smaller diameter
type of wire	For example: copper has a low resistance, nichrome has a high resistance	Different types of atoms and strength of bonding	Copper is used for electrical wiring, nichrome is used for heating elements
temperature	increasing the temperature increases the resistance	Atoms vibrate more	In electrical thermometers

A circuit for measuring resistance

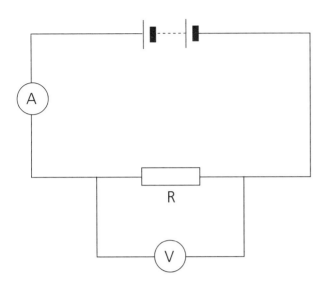

Fig 12 A circuit for measuring resistance

If different devices are connected into the circuit at R, even though the voltage remains constant, the ammeter reading will change. Each component connected into the circuit has a different resistance.

The resistance of a component is given by

$$\text{Resistance (symbol R)} = \frac{\text{p.d. across component}}{\text{current through component}}$$

R = V/I   or   I = V/R   or   V = I×R

Ohm's Law

These formulae are all ways of expressing what is referred to as Ohm's Law. Resistance is measured in a unit called the ohm (Ω). Ohm was a German scientist who investigated resistance in the early 19th century. His law says:

The current through a conductor is proportional to the potential difference across it provided its temperature remains constant.

You can use a diagram like this to help to remember the three equations that represent Ohm's Law. Cover up the symbol you want to find; what you are left with tells you how to do your calculation.

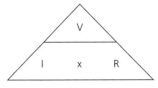

Fig 13 Helping you to use Ohm's Law

Reminder – Units you may meet in work about resistance

kΩ	kilo ohm	1 thousand ohms	1,000Ω
MΩ	mega ohm	1 million ohms	1,000,000Ω
mΩ	milli ohm	1 thousandth of an ohm	1/1,000Ω
μΩ	micro ohm	1 millionth of an ohm	1/1,000,000Ω

QUESTION

a A 6 volt power pack sends a current of 2 amps through a resistor. What is the resistance?

b A resistor of 10Ω has a current of 2 amps flowing through it. What is the potential difference across the resistor?

c A potential difference of 4.5 volts is measured across a resistor of 3Ω. What current is flowing through the resistor?

ANSWER

a R = V/I   R = 6/2   R = 3Ω
b V = I × R   V = 2 × 10   V = 20V
c I = V/R   I = 4.5/3   I = 1.5A

QUESTION

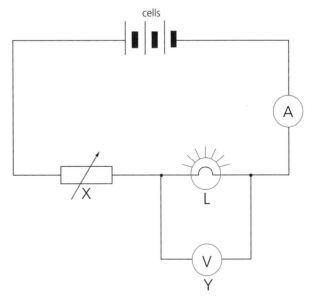

Fig 14

a Name component   X...
                              Y.............................(1 mark)

b What effect would reducing the number of cells have on:

   i the current in the circuit;

   ....(1 mark)

   ii the reading on V?

   ....(1 mark)

c State two changes to the circuit that would increase the brightness of the lamp L.

   i ....

   ii ....(2 marks)

                      [WJEC]

ANSWER

a X – variable resistor.

  Y – voltmeter.

b i Reduce it.

  ii Reduce it.

c Increase the number of cells *(increase the voltage and hence the current)*. Decrease the resistance of the variable resistor.

QUESTION

A student wants to find the electrical resistance of a heating element at room temperature.

Fig 15 shows the heating element

Fig 15

   i On the Figure draw the complete electrical circuit that would be needed for the electrical resistance to be found. Label any meters used in the circuit. (3 marks)

   ii State how the electrical resistance can be found from the readings of the meters.

   ....

   ....

                   (1 mark)

                 [ULEAC]

ANSWER

i

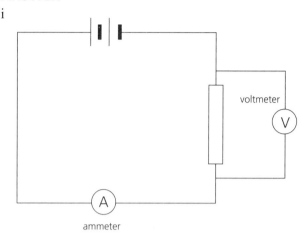

Fig 16

Make sure that you draw a complete circuit. Also, you must draw the ammeter in series with the resistor and the voltmeter in parallel with the resistor.

ii

You would use resistance = reading on voltmeter/reading on ammeter (R = V/I)

Circuits with more than one resistor

Often a circuit has more than one resistor in it. Resistors can be arranged in parallel or series. The total resistance can be calculated by using one of two formulae.

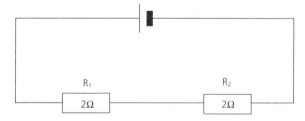

Fig 17 Resistors in series

$R = R_1 + R_2$

$R = 2\Omega + 2\Omega = 4\Omega$

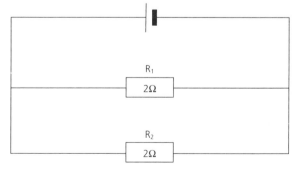

Fig 18 Resistors in parallel

$1/R = 1/R_1 + 1/R_2$

Or $R = R_1 \times R_2 / (R_1 + R_2)$

$R = 2 \times 2 / (2 + 2) = 1\Omega$

(Notice that if 2 equal resistors are in parallel, the total resistance is half the value of one of the resistors on its own.)

Once you have calculated the resistance you can use V = IR to calculate the voltage or the current.

QUESTION

Jane wished to find the resistance of an electric bulb. She set up this circuit.

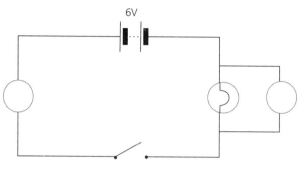

Fig 19

a Label the voltmeter V.
b The voltmeter reading was 6V. The resistance of the bulb was 3Ω. What would be the reading of the ammeter?
c She then added a 5Ω resistor in series.

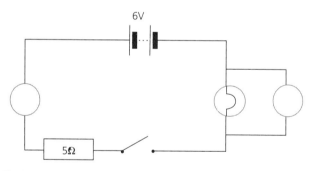

Fig 20

What is the reading of the ammeter now?

ANSWER

a The circle on the right should be labelled V.
b Use V = IR. Rearrange this to give I = V/R; the ammeter would read 2 amps *(don't forget the units)*.
c Use R = R₁ + R₂. Total resistance is 3 + 5 = 8Ω. Then I = V/R; the ammeter would read 0.75 amps.

QUESTION

The diagram below shows how one type of fuel gauge in a car works. A sliding contact makes contact with a resistance wire wound in a coil (a rheostat). It is connected to a float with a pivot P. When the petrol level changes the circuit resistance changes. This causes the pointer in the fuel gauge to move and show how much petrol is in the tank.

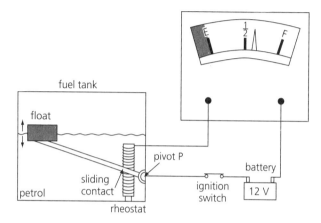

The circuit diagram is shown below

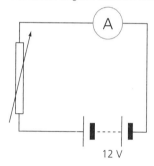

Fig 21

The petrol gauge is an ammeter. Explain why the reading on the ammeter falls as the petrol is used.

....
....
....
....(3 marks)

[NEAB]

ANSWER

As the petrol is used the float (on the surface of the petrol) falls. This causes the contact to move on the rheostat, increasing the length of the wire and hence the resistance. This causes the reading on the ammeter to fall as the current is decreased.

Ohmic and non-ohmic conductors

Ohmic conductors

If pure metals and alloys are kept at a constant temperature, the voltage across them is proportional to the current flowing; ie their resistance remains constant. They are called ohmic conductors because they obey Ohm's Law and their resistance can be calculated using R = V/I. A graph can be drawn for this type of conductor.

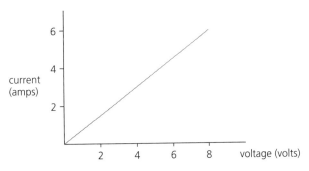

Fig 22 Graph of an Ohmic conductor

It is a straight line graph which goes through the origin. This means that if the voltage doubles, the current also doubles. (For example: if the voltage is 3V and the current is 2 amps, the resistance is 1.5Ω. If the voltage is doubled to 6V, then the current doubles to 4 amps as the resistance is still 1.5Ω.)

Non-ohmic conductors

For many conductors, for example silicon, the voltage is not proportional to the current. Graphs can be drawn for these non-ohmic conductors but the pattern is different in each case. They do not obey Ohm's Law.

QUESTION

The circuit in Fig 24 shows a thermistor. This is used to protect the filament of a TV from a surge of current when it is first switched on.

a Name the component Y.
b What electrical property is measured in Ω?
c Sketch a graph of voltage against resistance for the themistor and explain the shape of this.
d What is the resistance of the thermistor if the potential difference across it is 5V and the current is 0.5A.

Fig 23 Graphs of Non-Ohmic conductors

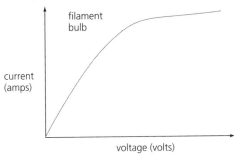

The graph becomes flatter because the resistance increases as the filament in the bulb becomes hotter.

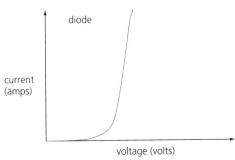

The current flows when the voltage reaches a certain value.

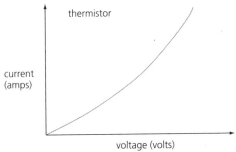

The graph becomes steeper because as the thermistor becomes hotter its resistance decreases.

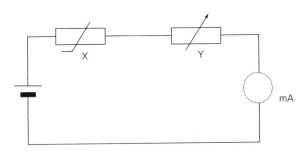

Fig 24

ANSWER

a Variable resistor.
b Resistance.
c Fig 25

The graph is this shape because as a thermistor becomes hotter its resistance decreases.

d Use V = IR. R = V/I, resistance = 5/0.5 = 10Ω

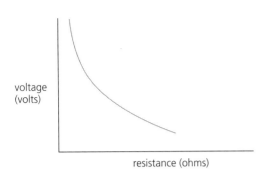

Fig 25

QUESTION

A light-dependent resistor (LDR) can be used in a photographer's light meter. In a circuit one of these devices has a potential difference of 6V across it. When no light is shining on it the resistance is 7kΩ and when light is shining on it the resistance changes to 113Ω. Calculate the current in each case.

ANSWER

Use $V = IR$, so $I = V/R$.
With no light shining on it:
$6/7000 = 0.00086A = 0.86mA$.
With light shining on it: $6/113 = 0.053A = 53mA$.

Internal resistance
In a cell some of the energy is used in pushing electrons through the actual cell. The resistance of the cell itself is called the internal resistance. It means that the energy transferred from the cell is actually less than that available from the chemical reactions which occur.
The voltage supplied from the chemical reactions occurring in the cell = $I(R +r)$...........
(As the two resistors are in series)
This is called the electromotive force (e.m.f.) of the cell.
I = current which flows from the cell
R = resistance of the components in the circuit
r = internal resistance of the cell

Electrostatics

If you rub a piece of polythene on a woollen sleeve you may build up 'static'. You actually transfer electrons to the polythene from the wool.

Investigating static electricity

- The electroscope

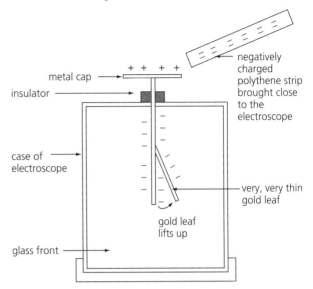

Fig 26 The electroscope

When the negatively charged polythene comes very close to the top of the electroscope, some electrons pass through the metal and cause the gold leaf to lift up. The like charges at the bottom of the electroscope repel each other.

- The Van de Graaf generator

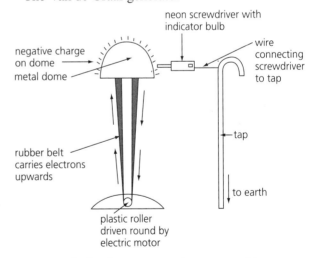

Fig 27 Van de Graaf generator and neon screwdriver

The belt in the Van de Graaf generator transfers electrons from the plastic roller at the base to the dome at the top. When the neon screwdriver is brought near to the dome, electrons are transferred quickly enough to provide current which lights up the neon.
If the voltage becomes high enough on the dome you may see a spark jump across the gap as the screwdriver (which is earthed) is brought near it.

Uses of static electricity

- Paint spraying
  The object to be sprayed is given one charge and the nozzle of the spray gun is given the opposite charge. As the fine particles of paint come out of the nozzle they are all given the same charge as the nozzle.
  - They repel each other (helping to provide an even coating of paint).
  - They are attracted to the object (due to it having an opposite charge). This helps to reduce wastage.
- Photocopying
  A lens projects an image of the original onto a drum in the machine. The drum is coated with a light sensitive material such as selenium. A pattern of the dark areas of the original is held on this material by static electricity. Toner (a fine powder) sticks to the charged areas of the drum. This is transferred to the final sheet of paper (the copy), which is heated briefly to fix the image.
- Dust precipitation

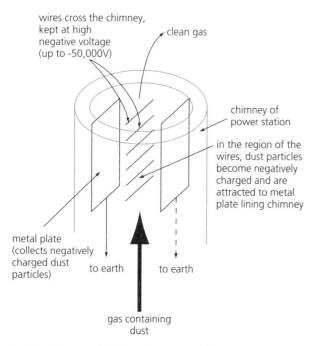

wires cross the chimney, kept at high negative voltage (up to -50,000V)

clean gas

chimney of power station

in the region of the wires, dust particles become negatively charged and are attracted to metal plate lining chimney

metal plate (collects negatively charged dust particles)

to earth

to earth

gas containing dust

Fig 28 A dust precipitator at a power station

The chimneys at power stations are lined by metal plates. These are earthed. Inside the chimneys are also a number of wires. These wires have a high negative voltage (relative to the metal plates lining the chimney). As waste gases come close to these wires they are ionised (the particles are turned into ions). The negatively charged electrons that are released are drawn to the earthed metal lining of the chimney. As the electrons move towards the plates they collide with dust particles and cause them to be negatively charged. In this way the dust hits the side of the chimney. Once it touches the plates it loses its charge and falls down the chimney.

99.5% of the dust going up the chimney may be removed in this way. This is more efficient than filtering the smoke because dust precipitation removes smaller particles.

Some dangers of static electricity

- Lightning conductor
  Lightning usually strikes the highest point of a building, and the current passes to the Earth via the route with the least resistance. If this is through the soot in a chimney it can start a fire.
  A thick copper wire can be fixed to the outside of a wall. This must be higher than the building and end in a spike (or collection of spikes). If there is a thunder storm and a negatively charged cloud passes over, then negative ions give up their electrons to the copper spike which conducts the charge to the Earth.
- Filling a car with petrol
  As petrol flows through the pipe from the pump a charge builds up. This must be earthed to the car body. If this does not happen a spark may jump to the nozzle of the pump – or to the person filling up the car! It is important that there are no sparks near the entrance to the petrol tank, where there is a potentially flammable mixture of petrol vapour and air.

QUESTION

a Rods of glass, plastic and rubber can be charged by rubbing them with materials such as fur or silk. Explain why it is not possible to charge rods of metal in the same way.

....
....
....
....(2 marks)

b Electrostatic charges have many commercial uses. Two important uses are in the spray painting of motor car bodies and in the removal of dust from chimney gases. The use of electrostatic charges in spray painting is shown in the diagram below.

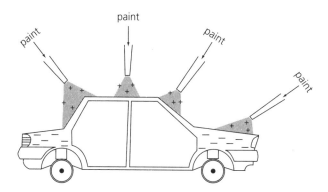

Fig 29

The spray of paint is given a positive charge and the car body a negative charge.
Explain why it is an advantage to give:
  i a charge of the same sign to all the paint droplets in the spray;

....
....
....
....(2 marks)

  ii the car body a charge of the opposite sign to that of the droplets.

....
....
....
....
....
....(3 marks)

Part question [SEG 1994]

ANSWER

a Metals are conductors and any charge is conducted away.

b i Having the same charge means that the paint droplets repel each other. This helps to spread them out evenly.

  ii As the car body and the paint have different charges, the paint is attracted to the car. This helps the paint to coat the whole of the car and saves paint from being wasted.

Important equations that you must be able to use when thinking about electrical circuits:

Amount of charge (coulombs) = current (amps) × time (seconds)
or $Q = It$

Voltage (volts) = energy (joules) / charge (coulombs)

Power (watts) = voltage (volts) × current (amps)
or $P = VI$

voltage (volts) = current (amps) × resistance (ohms)
or $V = IR$

$R = R_1 + R_2$ (*for resistors in series*)

$1/R = 1/R_1 + 1/R_2$ (*for resistors in parallel*)

Energy converted (joules) = current (amps) × time (seconds) × voltage (volts)
or Energy converted = $I \times t \times V$

Electricity in the home

Important equations used in this chapter are summarised on p 279

How is electricity produced?

Think about the electrical appliances you used today. You have probably used an electric light and you might have used an electric kettle or a cassette player. It is electricity that transfers the energy from the power station to the electrical appliance.

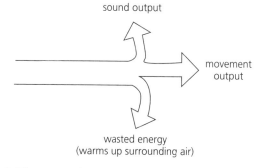

sound output

movement output

wasted energy
(warms up surrounding air)

Fig 1 Diagram to show energy transfer in a cassette player

'Making' electricity using movement and magnetism

If we move a wire in a magnetic field, or move a magnet in and out of a coil of wire, then energy is transferred to the electrons in the wire. The current can be detected by a galvanometer (a sensitive ammeter).

The voltage and the current that are produced in the wire are said to be induced.

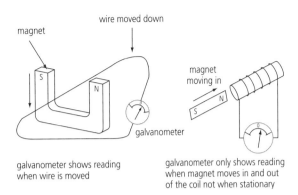

Fig 2 Electromagnetic induction

The galvanometer moves one way when the magnet is moved forward and the other way when the magnet is moved backwards. Reversing the direction of the field also changes the direction of the current.

A dynamo (or direct current generator)

To make current flow all the time, we must make the wire into a loop and rotate it in a magnetic field. The current passes out to other electrical wires through brushes. The current can be detected by a meter or bulb.

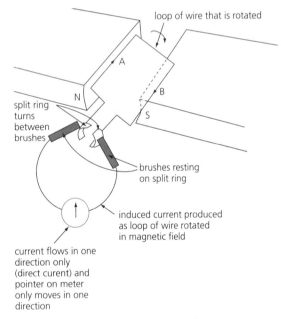

Fig 3 A dynamo (direct current generator)

The left half of the split ring always connects to the wire moving upwards. The right half of the split ring always connects to the wire moving downwards. The final result is that the current flows in one direction; direct current is produced.

An alternator (alternating generator)

If instead of the split rings in the dynamo, the alternator uses two circular slip rings, as the loop of wire is rotated the current first flows in one direction in the circuit, and then in the other direction. We can see how this happens by looking at the meter; the pointer changes direction as the loop is rotated. This type of current is called alternating current (AC for short).

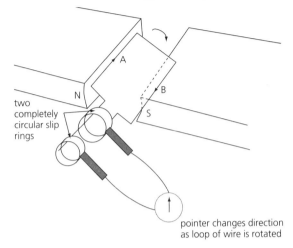

Fig 4 An alternator (alternating generator)

Each wire only touches one ring. As both wires move up and then down the current changes direction. This gives an alternating current.

Both a dynamo and alternator convert kinetic energy into electrical energy.

This is how electricity is 'made' or, more correctly, 'generated' at a power station. To increase the voltage we need to:

• Use more coils of wire.
• Wind the coils onto a soft-iron core to give a stronger magnetic field.
• Turn the coil faster.
• Use a stronger magnet, or an electromagnet to give a stronger magnetic field.

At a power station the alternator is driven by steam, see later for more details.

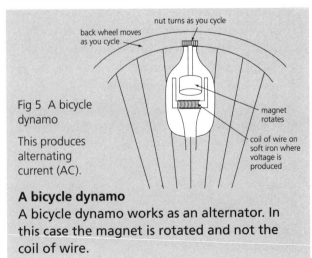

Fig 5 A bicycle dynamo

This produces alternating current (AC).

A bicycle dynamo
A bicycle dynamo works as an alternator. In this case the magnet is rotated and not the coil of wire.

Looking at voltage

We can use an oscilloscope to display voltage. An oscilloscope shows how an electrical signal varies with time.

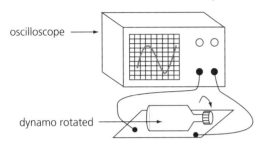

Fig 6 An oscilloscope showing 'alternating current'

One complete turn of the dynamo gives one complete cycle on the screen of the oscilloscope.

The electricity supply (often called 'the mains') which comes into your house is 230 volts, 50 Hertz.

This changed from 240 volts early in 1995.

On an oscilloscope this would look like:

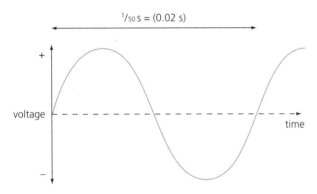

Fig 7 An oscilloscope trace of 'mains' voltage

This tells you:

- There are 50 complete cycles in one second.
- The frequency is 50 Hertz.
- Each cycle takes 1/50 (0.02) seconds.
- The current is constantly changing direction; it is called an alternating current (AC).

When the voltage was 240 volts, the peak voltage was 340V. A mains circuit therefore needed to be insulated to at least 340V. 240 volts was the effective value.

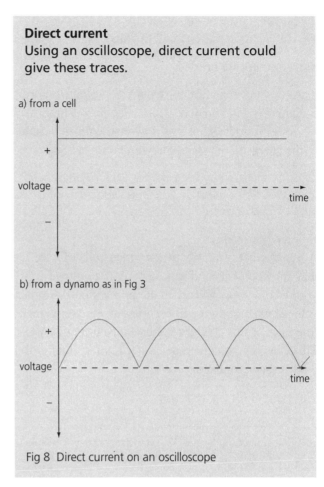

Direct current
Using an oscilloscope, direct current could give these traces.

a) from a cell

b) from a dynamo as in Fig 3

Fig 8 Direct current on an oscilloscope

What are the important features of power lines?

Power lines are the overhead (or underground) cables which conduct electricity from the power station. Many overhead cables are made of aluminium. Aluminium is a good conductor and has a *lower resistance* than a metal such as iron. The resistance is also reduced by using thick cables. This low resistance means the wires do not heat up very much. If the wires carried a high current this would also tend to heat them up. The *current is therefore reduced* to a minimum by transferring the electricity through the power lines at a *high voltage*.

Using : power = voltage × current, you can see that by increasing the voltage and decreasing the current the power of the line can be kept at a high level, with a smaller proportion of it being wasted in heating the cable.

Transformers

To transfer electricity from the power station along the power lines of the National Grid System, a high voltage and a low current is used. The generator at the power station produces electricity at 25,000 volts. We use mains electricity at 230 volts.

Transformers are needed:

- At the power station to step up the voltage before the energy is transferred along the power line.
- At the substation, to step down the voltage before the energy is transferred to your house at 230 volts.

Transformers are also used in door bells, computers, 'mains leads' for portable CD players and many other devices used at home.

Using a transformer.
A transformer is simply two separate coils of wire that are wound around an iron core. If a voltage is produced in one coil (called the primary coil) from an A.C. source, the first coil becomes an electromagnet. The field of this changes because the current is A.C. This causes a voltage to be induced in the other coil (called the secondary coil).

The symbol for a transformer is:

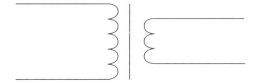

Fig 9 Symbol for a transformer

There is a connection between the voltage and the number of turns of wire in each coil:

output voltage in second coil		number of turns of wire in second coil
input voltage in first coil	=	number of turns of wire in first coil

$$\text{or } V_2/V_1 = N_2/N_1$$

This allows you to calculate an unknown voltage or number of turns of wire if you know the other three values.

Example

A step down transformer is needed to turn 230V A.C. mains voltage to 9 volts for an electronic organiser.

If the primary coil has 920 turns, how many turns are needed in the secondary coil?

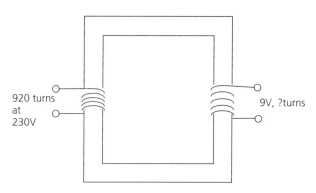

Fig 10 Transformer

Answer

First write the formula;

$$V_2/V_1 = N_2/N_1$$

Then substitute the numbers:
$9/230 = N_2/920$

$(9 \times 920)/230 = N_2$

$N_2 = 36$

36 turns are needed on the second coil.

Two important points about transformers

- They are very efficient – up to 99% of the energy is transferred from the primary to the secondary coil. 1% is lost due to induced currents in the iron core which cause the core to heat up and sometimes make a buzzing sound.
- They only work with A.C. current – there is only a voltage in the second coil if the input (in the primary coil) is changing.

QUESTION

a The following diagram shows a transformer. The input is mains 240V.

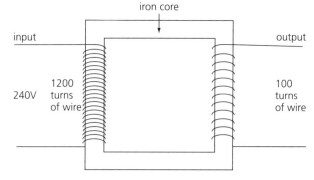

Fig 11

Use the information in the diagram to calculate the output voltage.

....

....

....V.(3 marks)

b The input coil of the transformer has a fuse which melts if the current rises above 1 A.

i Assuming that the transformer is 100% efficient, calculate the maximum current in amps available from the output coil.

....

....

....A. (2 marks)

ii Explain why, in reality, the maximum power available from the output coil will be less than the value you have calculated.

....

....

....

....(3 marks)

[ULEAC]

ANSWER

a 20 volts.

Use $V_2/V_1 = N_2/N_1$

$V_2/240 = 100/1200$

$V_2 = (100/1200) \times 240$

$V_2 = 20V$

b i 12 amps.

Use the formula: power = voltage × current

If the transformer is 100% efficient then:

power input = power output

so: $V_1I_1 = V_2I_2$

$240 \times 1 = 20 \times ?$

$240/20 = 12A$

ii The transformer will be less than 100% efficient (although it might be close to 100%). *There are three marks here so you will need to give reasons why the transformer is not 100% efficient, such as:*
Not all the energy will be transferred to the output coil. Induced currents in the core cause it to heat up and can also cause it to buzz. Not all the magnetism from the primary side is transferred to the secondary side.

The three wires in an electricity cable

- The live (colour brown) is alternately positive and negative (A.C. current), and now has an effective voltage of 230 volts relative to the neutral wire. Switches and fuses are placed on the live side of the supply.

- The neutral (colour blue) is earthed at the electricity substation and has zero potential (voltage). If the switch and fuse were in this neutral side of the supply then an appliance would be live even if it were switched off! If there were a fault in an appliance it would be possible to get a shock even if the fuse had blown.

- The earth (colour green/yellow) is the earth wire. This is a safety measure; the wire only carries a current if there is a fault – see following page.

What happens at a power station
Only about 30% of the energy in the fuel at the power station is transferred into the electrical output! The other 70% is lost:
- Via the cooling towers (which cool steam after it has been used).
- At the transformers (they get warm and hum!).
- Due to friction in the machinery.

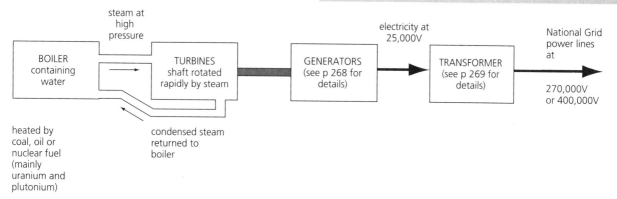

Fig 12 What happens at a power station

Some power stations, eg in the mountains of Scotland, use falling water (not steam) to work the turbines. We say these power stations generate hydroelectricity (see p 321).

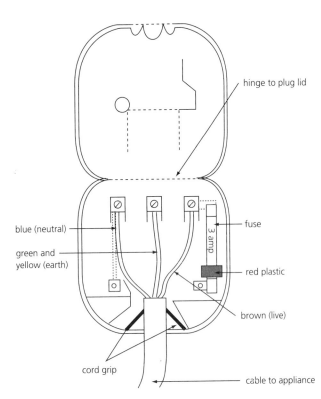

Fig 13 A 3-pin plug

How are we protected when we use electrical equipment?

1 Earthing

The earth wire connects the metal case of an appliance to the ground. If the case becomes 'live' due to a fault then the charge flows into the ground. This prevents any person touching the metal case from getting an electric shock. A surge of current may cause the fuse to blow.

Appliances that are 'double insulated' do not have an earth wire, but they still need to be protected by a fuse or circuit breaker.

2 Fuses

A fuse is the weak link in a circuit. If there is too high a current the fuse melts, there is a break in the circuit and current will not flow. Common sizes for fuses are: 3A, 5A and 13A.
To work out the size of the fuse that you need in a circuit you use:

Power (watts) = voltage (volts) × current (amps)
Power = V × I

You need a fuse just above the current calculated using the equation above.

Example

A hair dryer has this information stamped on the label.

125/240V
1250W

What fuse should be used?

Answer

Use Power = voltage × current
$P = VI$
so, $I = P/V$

1250/240 = current
current = 5.2 amps

A 5 amp fuse would not be sufficient so a 10 amp or 13 amp fuse is needed.
Notice that the voltage is given as 125/240 volts. This means that the hair dryer can be used in the USA, which has a different voltage to the UK. There is a switch on the hair dryer so that the correct voltage for the country can be selected. (The UK worked on 240V until early 1995.)

3 Circuit breakers

In a building such as your house there are several separate ring mains.

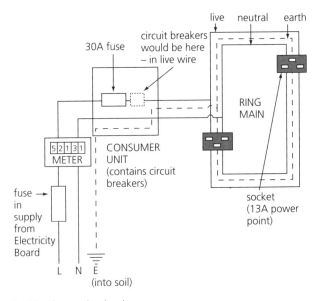

Fig 14 Ring main circuit

Each ring main is likely to have 'miniature circuit breakers' (MCBs) or 'residual circuit devices' (RCDs). If the current in the circuit exceeds a certain value (and this can happen easily, such as when a bulb 'goes') then the device opens automatically and stops the ring main working. Once the fault is corrected the circuit breaker is reset – usually by moving a switch.

QUESTION

A fan heater looks like this inside.

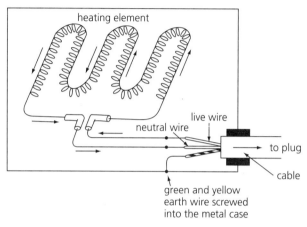

Fig 15

The green and yellow wire is called the earth wire.

a i The blue wire is called the

....(1 mark)

ii The brown wire is called the

....(1 mark)

iii The three cables which go to the plug are all different colours.
Why is this important?

....
....
....(1 mark)

iv The fan heater has an earth wire securely connected. Why is this important?

....
....
....(1 mark)

b Some electrical devices do not need an earth wire. Explain why.

....
....
....(2 marks)
[MEG]

ANSWER

a i Neutral.

ii Live.

iii It is important that the wires are different colours so that you can tell which wire is live,

which is neutral and which is earth, in order to connect them correctly.

iv If there were a fault in the fan heater, such as a live wire touching the case, then the earth wire would stop the person receiving an electric shock. (*Don't write a vague answer such as 'to stop you being killed.'*)

b Devices that do not need an earth wire are 'double insulated'. These devices are likely to have a plastic case, so it is not possible for the case to become live. There is therefore no chance of a user receiving an electric shock.

QUESTION

Three-pin outlet sockets in a house are joined in a 'ring main'. Usually, five outlet sockets are wired in one ring. Each ring main is protected by a 30A fuse. The diagram shows part of the ring main.

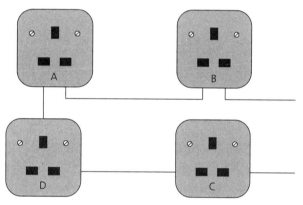

Fig 16

a i These outlet sockets are wired in parallel. State two reasons for this.

....
....
....
....(2 marks)

ii An electric kettle using 12A is plugged into socket A.
A fan heater using 12A is plugged into socket B and an electric fire using 10A into socket C.
[A] What current will flow in the ring main?

....A (1 mark)

[B] What is likely to happen when all three appliances are switched on together?

....
....(1 mark)

A correctly wired outlet socket is shown in the diagram below.

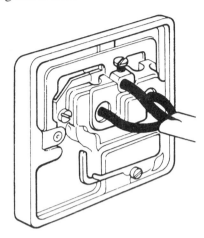

Fig 17

Draw an arrow labelled 'L' to the live wire.
(1 mark)
iv When in use, a plug in socket D becomes very hot. Give two possible causes of the plug getting hot.

....

....

....

....(2 marks)

[SEG 1994]

ANSWER

a i One socket can be used on its own, without the others needing to be used – as would be the case if the sockets were wired in series.
Each socket has the full mains voltage.
ii [A] 34 amps.
[B] The fuse will blow as it is only a 30 amp fuse.
iii Live is the left hand wire on the page (*as this is the back of the socket*).
iv *The plug becoming hot implies that too much current is going through it.* The fuse could be too large.
A short circuit could have developed inside the plug.
Current could be leaking away from an appliance via the earth lead.

Calculating the cost of electrical appliances

We can calculate the power, the rate at which energy is transferred, assuming we know the current and the voltage. From the power, we can work out how much each appliance costs to use.

1 The power of electrical appliances

We use the equation:
Power (watts) = voltage (volts) × current (amps)
$P = V \times I$

EXAMPLE

What is the power of a kettle of 240 volts and using 10 amps of current?

ANSWER

$P = V \times I$
$P = 240 \times 10$
$= 2,400$ watts $= 2.4$ kW

EXAMPLE

What is the current used by an electric heater, that has a power rating of 2kW and works at 240 volts?

ANSWER

$P = V \times I$

Rearranging this formula we get:
$P/V = I$
$2,000/240 = I$
$I = 8.33$A
(Don't forget to change the 2kW into 2,000 watts.)

2 The total amount of energy transferred

This depends on the time that the appliance is switched on. You can work this out once you know the power of the appliance.

Use this equation:
Energy transferred (joules) = power (watts) × time (seconds)

Using symbols:
$E = P \times t$

EXAMPLE

How much energy is transferred when three spotlights, each using 0.5 amp, are left on for 2 hours. (The voltage is 220 volts.)

The power of each spotlight is calculated using:
$P = V \times I$
$P = 220 \times 0.5$
$P = 110$ watts

There are three spotlights so the total power is 3 × 110 = 330 watts.

Calculate the energy transferred from:
E = P × t
(The time must be in seconds.)

E = 330 × 2 × 60 × 60
= 2,376,000 joules
= 2,376kJ
= 2.376MJ

3 The cost of electrical appliances

Once you know the power of the appliance and the duration it is used, you can calculate the cost of using it. You must know the cost of a 'unit of electricity'. A unit of electricity is a kilowatt hour – that is, the energy transferred by a 1kW appliance in one hour. The cost of a unit of electricity is given on the bill from the electrical company. It is about 8p.

1kWh is a unit of energy. It is equivalent to 1000 × 60 × 60 = 3,600,000 Joules

EXAMPLE

What is the cost of using a 1,250 watt hair drier for 10 minutes each day for a week?

The hair dryer is used for 70 minutes in one week. This is 70/60 hours.
The power of the hair dryer is 1250W = 1250/1000kW
The total energy transferred for using the hair dryer = (1250/1000) × (70/60)kWh
The cost of one kWh is 8p,
So, the cost of using the hair drier for a week = (1250/1000) × (70/60) × 8p = 11.67p.

QUESTION

Here is a diagram of a hair dryer.

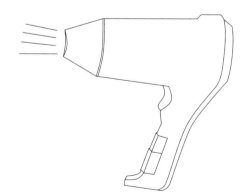

Fig18

It has three settings: cold, warm and hot.
The information about it is shown in the table.

setting	fan power W	heater power W	total power W
cold air fan on heater off	125W	0W	125W
warm air fan on heater low	125W	500W	625W
hot air fan on heater high	125W	1500W	

a Look at the table above. The heater is put on a hot setting.
　i Calculate its total power.
　...(1 mark)
　ii The hair dryer is plugged into a 250V socket. Calculate the current flow when the hair dryer is used on the hot setting.
　..
　...(2 marks)
b On its warm setting, the hair dryer carries 2.5A.
　i Which fuse would allow it to work on this setting?
　(Choose from 1A fuse, 2A fuse or a 3A fuse.)
　...(1 mark)
　ii If you put this fuse in the plug and tried to use the hair dryer on the hot setting, it would not work. Explain why.
　..
　..
　...(2 marks)
　　　　　　　　　　　　　　　　　[MEG]

ANSWER

a　i 1625W *(Don't forget the units.)*
　ii 6.5 amps.
　　Use Power = voltage × current
　　1625 = 250 × I
　　I = 6.5A
　　(Don't forget the units.)
b　i 3A.
　ii On the hot setting 6.5 amps of current flows, this is more than the 3 amps that the fuse would allow without 'blowing'.

QUESTION

Fig 19 shows an advertisement used by a lamp company.

```
┌─────────────────────────────────────────┐
│        ┌──────────────────┐             │
│        │  Save Money!     │             │
│        └──────────────────┘             │
│                                          │
│      ▢            ☒                      │
│     CF lamp      Ordinary                │
│                  Filament lamp           │
│                                          │
│  • Don't buy inefficient filament lamps. │
│                                          │
│  • Buy our Compact Fluorescent (CF)      │
│    lamps now!                            │
│                                          │
│  • One 20W CF lamp will give out the     │
│    same amount of light as one 100W      │
│    filament lamp.                        │
│                                          │
│  • Only £13.20 for one CF lamp.          │
│                                          │
│  • Just plug in like an ordinary lamp.   │
│                                          │
│  • One CF lamp will last 8,000 hours,    │
│    compared with 1,000 hours for a       │
│    filament lamp.                        │
└─────────────────────────────────────────┘
```

Fig 19

a The cost of electricity can be calculated from:
Cost of electricity = kilowatts × hours used × cost of one kilowatt hour

The table below shows a comparison of the costs for the types of lamp.

i Enter the THREE pieces of information missing in the table. You can use the space below for your work.

....
....
....(3 marks)

ii CF lamps can give large savings on the cost of electricity but many people still buy filament lamps instead of CF lamps. Suggest TWO reasons for this.

1...
2..(2 marks)

b Compare and explain the differences in the efficiencies of the two lamps shown in Fig 19.

....
....
....
....(4 marks)
[ULEAC]

ANSWER

a i CF lamp: Electricity costs: $0.02 \times 8000 \times 0.08$ = £12.80.
Total cost = £12.80 + £13.20 = £26.00
Filament lamp: Total cost = £64 + (8×0.50) = £68.

ii *There are many answers you can give here; look at the figures for ideas, such as:*
The CF lamp is much more expensive to buy in the first place.
People may not like the light from a fluorescent lamp.
Filament lamps are more widely available.
People may prefer to buy the sort of lamp they have always bought.
People may not know enough about CF lamps.

b The CF lamp is five times more efficient *(see fig 19 to see that a 20W CF lamp gives the same amount of light as a 100W filament lamp).*
This means that less energy is wasted by the CF lamp. *(A lot of energy in the filament lamp is wasted as 'heat'.)*

Decision-making circuits

Many of the appliances in your home contain decision-making circuits. These have an input (which could be a switch, thermistor or light-dependent resistor) which controls an output (which could be a buzzer, light-emitting diode or motor). Between the input and the output is a processing unit which may contain AND, OR and NOT gates. This makes the decision.

	Power (kW)	Time used (hours)	Cost of 1 kWh (£)	Cost of electricity (£)	Number of lamps needed	Cost of 1 lamp (£)	Total cost (£)
CF lamp	0.02	8000	0.08		1	13.20	
Filament lamp	0.1	8000	0.08	64.00	8	0.50	

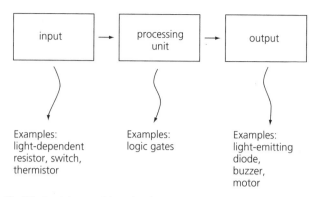

Fig 20 Decision-making circuits

These are only some of the examples – there are many more!

The input and output devices may be called transducers, because they change the way that information is carried. For example, the light-dependent resistor changes light into an electrical signal, and the buzzer changes an electrical signal into sound.

Input devices

- Light-dependent resistor (LDR)
  This detects changes in light intensity.

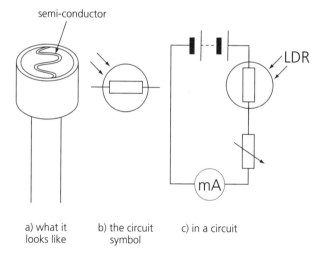

a) what it   b) the circuit   c) in a circuit
looks like   symbol

Fig 21 A light dependent resistor

In the dark the resistance of this might be 10 Mohms. When bright light shines on it, electrons are able to move within the substance (a semi-conductor such as cadmium sulphide) and the resistance can fall to 100 ohms.
It therefore works as a 'light' switch, allowing current to pass when light of a specific intensity falls on it. Circuits containing these devices are used in cameras where the size of the aperture is altered automatically.

- Switch
- Thermistor

In general these input devices work because their resistance can be changed:

- High resistance = OFF
- Low resistance = ON

  (See the chapter on Electrical Circuits for details of these input devices.)

Output devices

- Light-emitting diode (LED)
  This gives out light when a current passes through it. These are often red, but may also be green or yellow. An LED only allows current to pass in one direction, so it must be connected as shown in the figure.

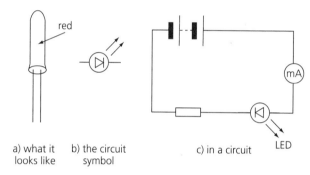

a) what it   b) the circuit   c) in a circuit   LED
looks like   symbol

Fig 22 A light-emitting diode

It works as an indicator lamp. It uses much less current than a filament lamp and lasts for much longer. Many appliances contain an LED which glows to show that the appliance is switched on. LEDs are also used in items such as clocks where the numbers are based on the 7-segment display.

Fig 23 7-segment display used to show numbers

Each LED may be turned ON of OFF to give the required number.

- Buzzer – see p 282
- Motor – see p 284

Processing unit

The processing unit in a decision-making circuit may contain logic gates. These can be used to perform complex switching. They switch outputs on and off depending upon the state of the input. There are several different types of logic gates, but they are all based on just three important types: AND, OR and NOT.

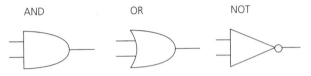

Fig 24 Logic gates

The gates can be combined either in series or in parallel.

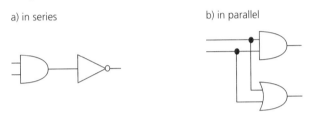

Fig 25 Logic gates in series and parallel

Using truth tables for logic gates

These are used to work out how a logic gate operates in a circuit. There are only two states:

- 0 – electricity is not passing; can be called 'OFF', 'LOW' 'OPEN'
- 1 – electricity is passing; can be called 'ON', 'HIGH', 'CLOSED'

AND truth table

Input A	Input B	Output
0	0	0
0	1	0
1	0	0
1	1	1

For an AND gate there is an output only if there is an input at A *and* B.

OR truth table

Input A	Input B	Output
0	0	0
0	1	1
1	0	1
1	1	1

For an OR gate there is an output if there is an input in A *or* B

NOT truth table

Input	Output
0	1
1	0

For a NOT gate the output is always the opposite of the input.

QUESTION

(You would be able to use a data book to help you with the symbols for this question.)

The diagram below is a block diagram of an electric circuit. The parts of the circuit are labelled X, Y and Z.

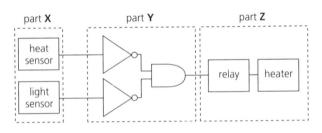

Fig 26

a Name the two types of logic gate used in the circuit above.
  1 ....
  2 ....(2 marks)

b Give an electrical device which could be used as:
  i The heat sensor..
  ii The light sensor..............................(2 marks)

c Which part of the circuit, X, Y or Z is:
  the processor?..
  the input device(s)?.......................................
  the output device(s)? ....
                      (2 marks)

d The heat sensor is ON when it is hot and OFF when it is cold. The light sensor is ON when it is light and OFF when it is dark.
  i Explain what happens in each part of the circuit when it is both cold and dark.

  ....
  ....
  ....
  ....
  ....(3 marks)

ii Describe a practical use for the circuit.

....

....(1 mark)

[NEAB]

ANSWER

a NOT *(on left)* AND *(on right)*.

b i Thermistor.

ii Light-dependent resistor.

c The processor – Part Y.

the Input device(s) – Part X.

the Output device(s) – Part Z.

d i

When it is cold and dark both the sensors are OFF.

The NOT gates change the inputs from 0 to 1. The AND gate has an input of 1, 1 so the output is 1 and the heater would therefore be *on*.

ii *This circuit could be used in a cold place when it is dark*, such as a greenhouse.

Other important components in circuits

Transistor

There are many different kinds of transistor, which is an electronic switch. A transistor can be used to amplify (make larger) small currents. A small current in the base circuit is turned into a large current in the collector circuit.

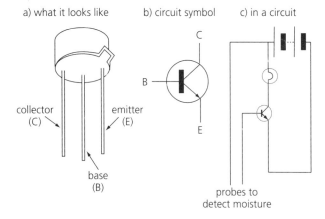

Fig 27 A transistor

When it is moist the circuit is completed and the lamp comes on.

Capacitor

This is used in circuits which need a time delay. It works by storing up electric charge. When the power is on the capacitor is 'charged up'. If it is then connected into another circuit the electricity can be discharged.

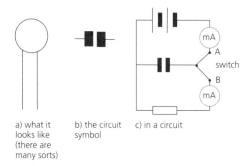

a) what it looks like (there are many sorts) b) the circuit symbol c) in a circuit

Fig 28 One type of capacitor

When the switch is at A, the charge builds up on the capacitor. When the switch is at B, the capacitor discharges – it acts like a battery, sending a current through the resistor and stopping when the voltage reaches zero.

The manual of a small computer says you have 2 minutes to change the batteries when they run out before you lose information. This is because the capacitor in the computer stores enough charge to maintain the memory of the computer for just 2 minutes!

Relay (Reed relay)

A relay can be used as a type of switch. It is made of a glass tube with two iron *reeds* sealed in it. There is a gap between the two iron reeds. If this device is put inside a coil of wire then the iron is magnetised when a current passes through the coil. The two pieces of iron meet, and this can complete a second circuit. A tiny current in the coil can operate the relay, switching on a circuit with a bigger current – the relay acts as a type of amplifier.

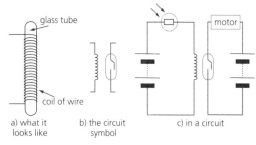

a) what it looks like b) the circuit symbol c) in a circuit

Fig 29 A reed relay

When light shines on the LDR, the electric motor is switched on.

Important equations that you must be able to use when thinking about electricity in the home:

$V_2/V_1 = N_2/N_1$ (for a transformer)

Power (watts) = Voltage (volts) × Current (amps)

$P = V \times I$

Energy transferred (joules) = power (watts) × time (seconds)

Cost of electricity = kilowatts × hours used × cost of one kilowatt hour

Electromagnetism

What do you remember about magnets?

1 Magnets only attract metals that contain iron, cobalt or nickel.
2 If a bar magnet swings freely, one end points to the (magnetic) north pole of the Earth. This is called the north pole of the magnet and the other end is called the south pole.
3 When 2 magnets are brought near one another, one of two things may happen:
Like poles (N-N or S-S) repel each other and unlike poles (N-S) attract each other (see Fig 1).
4 If a magnetic material is brought near a magnet, it becomes a magnet itself. Notice how an object which touches the magnet has the opposite pole induced in it (see Fig 2).
5 If the material is made of iron, such as in a paper clip, then other paper clips can be attracted to the

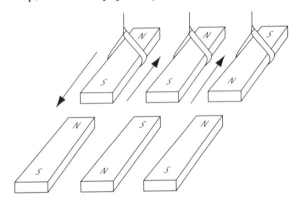

a) attracted   b) repelled   c) repelled

Fig 1 What might happen when two magnets are brought near each other?

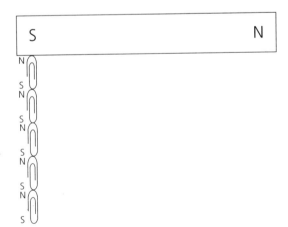

Fig 2 Making another magnet

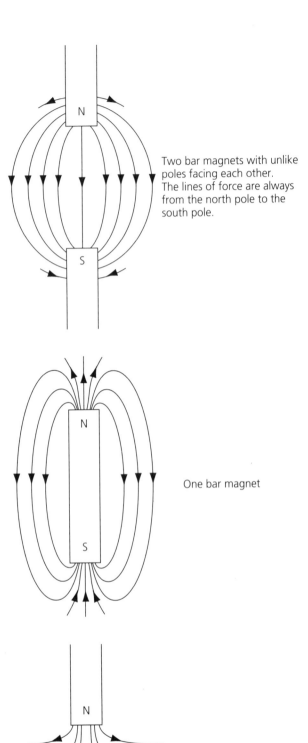

Two bar magnets with unlike poles facing each other. The lines of force are always from the north pole to the south pole.

One bar magnet

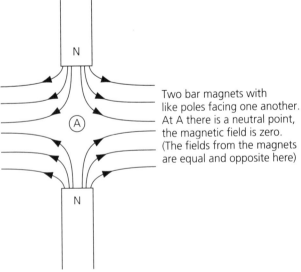

Two bar magnets with like poles facing one another. At A there is a neutral point, the magnetic field is zero. (The fields from the magnets are equal and opposite here)

Fig 3 Magnetic fields around magnets

magnet, as shown. Iron forms a temporary magnet – the paper clips soon lose their magnetism.

6 If steel pins were used instead of iron paper clips, you would notice that the magnet would not support so many of them, but they would keep their magnetism for longer. Steel is used to make permanent magnets.

7 Magnets attract magnetic materials because of the lines of force which make up a magnetic (or force) field, around the magnet.

8 a To magnetise an object
     The best way to do this is to use a coil of wire called a solenoid.

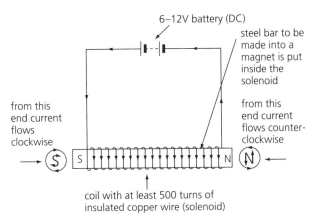

Fig 4 Using a solenoid to make a magnet

Looking at the bar and following the direction of the current allows you to work out which pole is which. See p 282 for more details of the magnetic effect of a current.

b To demagnetise an object
   To do this you need to use a solenoid placed in a west-east direction with an alternating current passing through it.

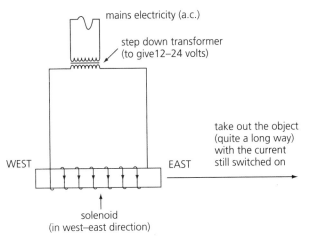

Fig 5 Using a solenoid to demagnetise a magnet

Doing this in a west-east direction reduces the chances of any magnetism remaining due to the Earth's magnetic field. You can also heat the magnet or hit it several times with a hammer.

No experiments should be done at home with mains electricity.

Using the magnetic effect of electricity

You may have seen a demonstration of the experiment in Fig 6. It is simply a wire carrying an electric current. Iron filings or a number of small plotting compasses are placed on a card at right angles to the wire.

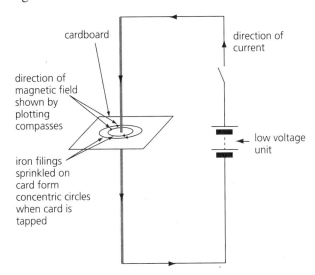

Fig 6 The magnetic field around a wire carrying electricity

This shows that when an electric current passes through a wire, a magnetic field is induced around it. The direction of the magnetic field can be worked out if you know the direction of the current. There is a simple way of working this out using your right hand.

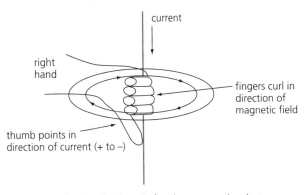

Fig 7 The right-hand grip rule for the connection between direction of the current and the direction of the magnetic field

The electromagnet

If, instead of passing the current through a straight wire the wire is coiled, we call the coil a solenoid. This also has a magnetic field around it. Its magnetic field is similar to that around the bar magnet in Fig 3.

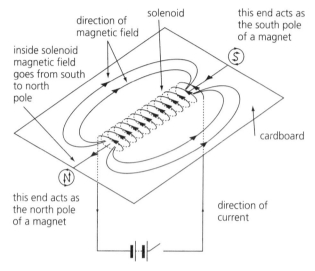

Fig 8 The magnetic field around a solenoid

The solenoid is the basis of the electromagnet – there is a magnetic field around the solenoid when current passes but as soon as the electrical supply is turned off there is no magnetic field.

To increase the strength of an electromagnet:

- Use a soft-iron core inside the solenoid.
- Use more turns of wire in the solenoid.
- Pass a larger current through the solenoid.

You cannot use steel as the core in a solenoid as it would remain magnetised when the current was switched off.

Uses of electromagnets

- Electric bells.
- Relay (see p 279).
- Loudspeaker and microphone (see later).
- Electric motor (see later).

QUESTION

A steel nail may be magnetised by an electric current. Describe, with the aid of a diagram, how you would do this.

....

....

....

....

....

....(3 marks)

[NEAB]

ANSWER

You need a coil of about 500 turns of insulated copper wire. This is connected to a D.C. supply. The nail is placed in it and the current is switched on. *It would be a good idea to draw a diagram such as Fig 4.*

QUESTION

A scrap metal dealer uses a crane with an electromagnet instead of a hook.

Fig 9

a Why does the scrap metal dealer use this type of crane instead of the normal one?

....

....(1 mark)

b Why is this type of crane useful for sorting different types of scrap metal?

....

....

....(2 marks)

c Why does the electromagnet on the crane have a soft iron core rather than a steel core?

....

....(1 mark)

d Suggest two ways, other than changing the core, to make the electromagnet stronger.

1. ....

....

2. ....

....(2 marks)

e i The amount of energy transferred by the electromagnet depends on the amount of charge which flows through the coils and the voltage across the coils.

What is the link between the voltage, energy transfer and charge?

....

....(1 mark)

ii How could you increase the electric current flowing through the coils?

....

....

....(1 mark)

iii What pieces of laboratory equipment would be needed to measure the energy transferred by the magnet in a measured time?

....

....

....(2 marks)

[MEG]

ANSWER

a When the power (to the electromagnet) is turned on a car may be picked up and when the power is turned off the car can be dropped.
(You must write more than 'because it is easier or more convenient'.)

b It only picks up iron and steel.

c The core must be made of iron so that when the electromagnet is switched off the iron (or steel) being carried is dropped. If the core were made of steel then it would still be magnetic when the electromagnet was switched off.

d Use more turns of wire, use a larger current through the electromagnet.

e i Voltage = energy/charge.
      (See p 259 for more details.)

   ii Increase the voltage, decrease the resistance.
      (Use I = V/R for this.)

   iii Ammeter, clock and voltmeter or a joulemeter.
      (You would use:
      Energy converted = current × time × voltage,
      see p 259.)

Using electricity and magnetism to give movement

You may have seen a demonstration of the experiment in Fig 10. When an electric current is passed through the wire it jumps.

If you swap either the poles of the magnet or the direction of the current, the wire will jump in the other direction.

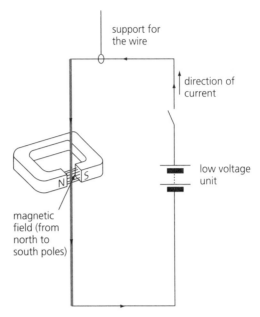

Fig 10 The moving wire

As the current is switched on the wire moves. In this case it moves outwards from the magnet.

You can make the movement larger by:

• Using a longer length of wire in the magnetic field.
• Using a stronger magnet – to give a stronger magnetic field.
• Using a larger current.
• Ensuring that the current and field are at right angles.

The way the wire moves can be worked out using Fleming's Left Hand Rule, as long as you know:

• The direction of the current.
• The direction of the magnetic field.

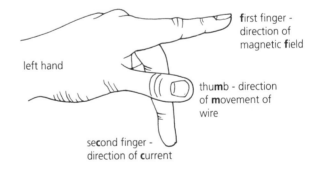

Fig 11 Fleming's left-hand rule

The simple electric motor

If a coil of wire is used between the poles of the magnet instead of a straight wire, then the coil twists to one of the poles. When the current is reversed the coil twists to the other pole.

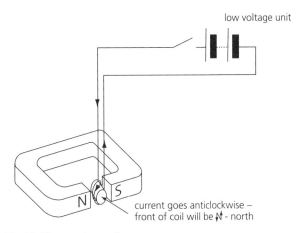

Fig 12 The moving coil

In this case when the current is switched on the front of the coil becomes a north pole. This will be attracted to the south pole of the magnet.

By changing the direction of the current at just the right moment, it is possible to keep the coil of wire spinning round and round. A commutator (which looks like a copper ring split in two) can do this – it reverses the flow of the current every half turn.

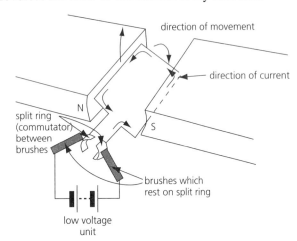

Fig 13 An electric motor

The split ring means that the current on the left of the loop always moves in the same direction. The same applies to the current on the right of the loop. This means that the direction of movement on the left and right of the loop does not change.

An electric motor as a dynamo?
In an electric motor, passing an electric current causes the coil to spin to give movement. The energy transfer is from electrical to movement. If, using a similar set up, the coil is spun round an electric current is produced – this arrangement is called a dynamo. Here the energy transfer is from movement to electrical (see the 'Electricity in the home' chapter for more details of dynamos).

In commercial electric motors:

- An electromagnet rather than a permanent magnet is used (to give a stronger field).
- Many coils of wire are used to make a more powerful motor.
- The coils are wound on a soft-iron core (to make the magnetic field stronger).

Uses of electric motors

- Electic drill.
- Vacuum cleaner.
- Any electrical appliance that involves movement – such as a cassette player!

QUESTION

A remote water pump is planned for a Third World village. The pump consists of a bucket lifted by an electric motor. Since no mains electricity is available the motor must be run from a solar cell and battery.

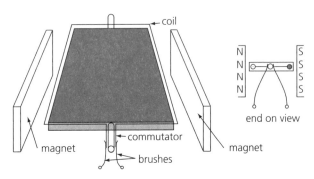

Fig 14

a Explain why the coil starts to rotate when electric current passes through the coil.

....
....
....(3 marks)

b State the function of the commutator.

....
....
....
....(2 marks)

c How could you design a motor which has no permanent magnets?

....
....
....(1 mark)

[MEG]

ANSWER

a The coil is situated between two magnets, so it is in a magnetic field. When a current passes through the coil, a magnetic field is formed around the coil. This is such that one side of the coil is attracted to one of the magnets. *The commutator enables the coil to continue to rotate (see part b).*

b The commutator is a split ring (probably made of copper). Once the coil has rotated one half turn, the commutator reverses the current. The first side of the coil is then attracted to the other magnet. This ensures that the coil continues rotating as the commutator reverses the current each half turn.

c Instead of permanent magnets you could use an electromagnet.

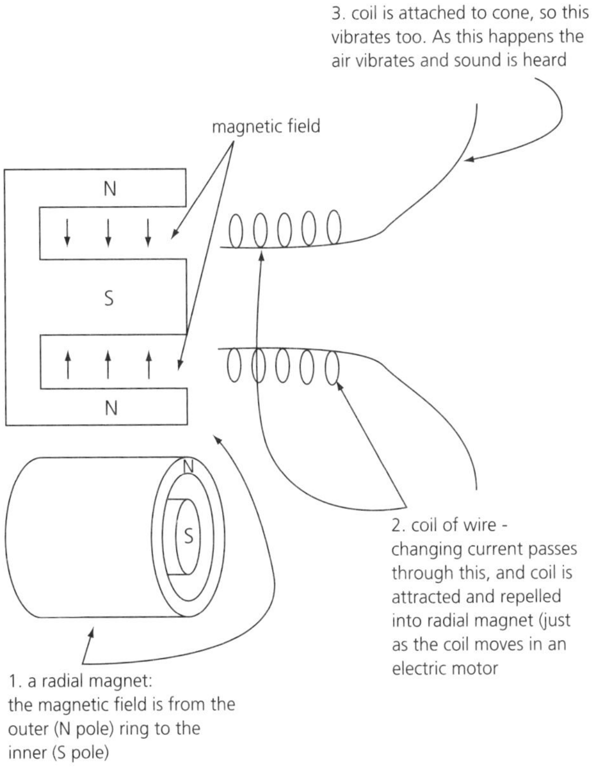

3. coil is attached to cone, so this vibrates too. As this happens the air vibrates and sound is heard

magnetic field

2. coil of wire - changing current passes through this, and coil is attracted and repelled into radial magnet (just as the coil moves in an electric motor

1. a radial magnet: the magnetic field is from the outer (N pole) ring to the inner (S pole)

Fig 15 A loudspeaker

The loudspeaker
A loudspeaker works by making the air vibrate. It is an example of a transducer – it converts electric signals into sound waves.

When an electric current flows, the *coil of wire* becomes an electromagnet, with one end the north pole and one end the south pole. The radial *permanent magnet* in the loudspeaker attracts or repels this

'electromagnetic coil'. When the current is reversed, the coil moves the other way. This happens many times per second and the coil of wire vibrates rapidly. As the coil of wire is attached to a *paper cone*, the cone vibrates and sound waves are transmitted into the air. The frequency and amplitude of the cone vibration are equivalent to the frequency and magnitude of the A.C. signal. Therefore, the sound signal contains the same information as the electric signal.

A moving coil microphone works like a loudspeaker in reverse!

QUESTION

This question is about sending messages.

a Label the parts in this signalling circuit. (3 marks)

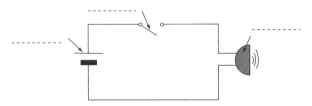

Fig 16

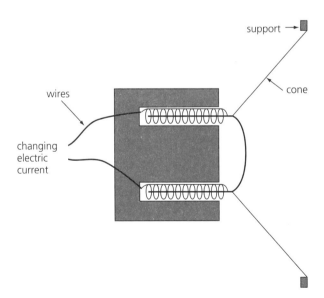

support →

cone

wires

changing electric current

Fig 17

b A telephone handset contains both a microphone and a small loudspeaker. What, in scientific terms, is the purpose of:

   i the microphone?

   ....(1 mark) ii the loudspeaker?

....(1 mark)

c i Label the coil and the magnet in this
      loudspeaker (Fig 17). (2 marks)

   ii How does changing the electric current make
      the coil move?

....
....(1 mark)

[MEG]

ANSWER

a On left: cell (as it is drawn it is a 1.5V cell, but
   'battery' might get you the mark).
   At top: switch.
   On right: any of – buzzer, bell, loudspeaker.

b i The microphone converts sound waves into
      electrical signals.
   ii The loudspeaker converts electrical signals into
      sound waves.

c i Coil – this is the obvious coil, it is within the
      magnet (this is the shaded area surrounding
      the coil).
   ii As the current changes, the coil moves in and
      out of the radial magnet. This allows the cone
      to vibrate the air next to it – by different
      amounts – to make different sounds.

Revision sheet

Electrical circuits

1 a On this circuit how would you draw the
      arrangement for measuring:

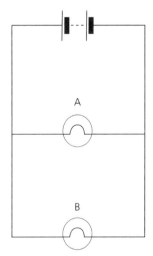

Fig 1

i   Voltage from the battery?
ii Voltage across bulb B?
iii Current through bulb A?

b Draw an arrow to show conventional current flow.

c What particles move around the electric circuit
   when the bulbs light?

2 What components are these the symbols for:

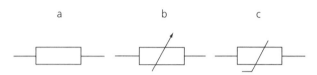

Fig 2

3 a What is the equation linking current, resistance
      and voltage?

   b How do each of the following change the
      resistance of a nichrome wire:
      i   Using a longer wire?
      ii Using a wire of bigger diameter?
      iii Increasing the temperature of the wire?
      iv Changing the wire to a copper wire (of
          identical dimensions)?

   c What are the equations for calculating the
      resistance of resistors in:
      i Series?
      ii Parallel?

   d What is meant by a non-ohmic conductor?

4 Finish these equations:
   a Amount of charge = current × ....
   b Voltage (volts) = .../charge (coulombs)
   c Energy converted (joules) = current (amps) ×
      .... × ....

5 a A polythene rod is rubbed on a jumper. It then
      picks up 'fluff'. We say this is due to static
      electricity. What has built up on the polythene
      rod to attract the dust?

   b Give two uses of static electricity.

Electricity in the home

1 a What is the difference between A.C. and D.C.?
   b Draw the trace from an oscilloscope for:
      i   A.C.
      ii D.C.
   c Mains voltage has a frequency of 50 Hertz.
      Explain what this means.

2 In power lines:
   a What is used to achieve a low resistance?
   b Why is a high voltage used for transferring the
      electricity?

3 a What is a transformer?

b Complete this to show the connection between voltage and the number of turns in a transformer:

$$\frac{\text{output voltage in second coil}}{?} = \frac{?}{?}$$

c What is a step-up transformer?

4 a Finish this:

In a plug the live wire is coloured ...., the neutral is coloured .... and the earth is coloured ....

b When does 'earthing' an appliance protect the user?

c What do we mean by 'double insulated'?

d Which wire is a fuse inserted into?

e Finish these:

  i Power = voltage × ....

  ii Energy transferred (joules) = power (watts) × ....

5 a How does the resistance of an LDR change when it gets dark?

b Give two advantages of using an LED rather than a filament lamp in a circuit?

c Give a function of a transistor in a circuit.

d What is the function of the capacitor in a time delay circuit?

e When might a reed relay be used in a circuit?

6 a Name this gate.

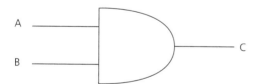

Fig 3

b If there was current present at A but not at B would there be current at C?

c i Complete this truth table which is for a *different* type of gate:

Input		Output
A	B	C
1	1	1
0	0	?
1	0	1
0	1	?

ii What gate is this truth table for?

Electromagnetism

1 Explain the italicised terms in each of these:

a Like poles *repel*.

b Cobalt is a *magnetic* material.

c Iron forms a *temporary* magnet.

2 How can you demagnetise an object using a solenoid?

3 How can you make an electromagnet stronger?

4 For each of the following explain how to use the rule *and* when you would use it:

a Right hand grip rule.

b Fleming's left-hand rule.

5 In an electric motor :

a What is a commutator?

b Why is it important?

Revision sheet answers

Electric circuits

1 a Fig 1

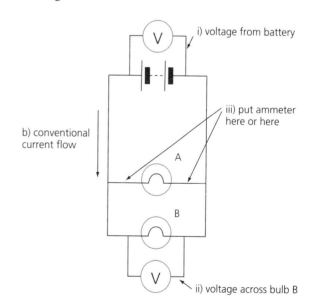

b See arrow on fig 1.

c Electrons.

2 a Resistor.

b Variable resistor.

c Thermistor.

3 a Voltage = current × resistance.

b i Using a longer wire – resistance increases.

ii Using a wire of bigger diameter – resistance decreases.

iii Increasing the temperature of the wire – resistance increases.

iv Changing the wire to a copper wire (of identical dimensions) – resistance decreases.

c i Resistors in series: $R = R_1 + R_2$.
   ii Resistors in parallel: $1/R = 1/R_1 + 1/R_2$.

d The voltage is not proportional to the current. (It does not obey Ohm's law.)

4 a Amount of charge = current × time.

b Voltage (volts) = energy (joules)/charge (coulombs)

c Energy converted (joules) = current (amps) × time(s) × voltage (volts)

5 a Electrons or charge.

b Paint spraying, photocopying, dust precipitation.

Electricity in the home

1 a A.C. is alternating current; the current flows in one direction, then the other. D.C. current flows in one direction only.

b Fig 4

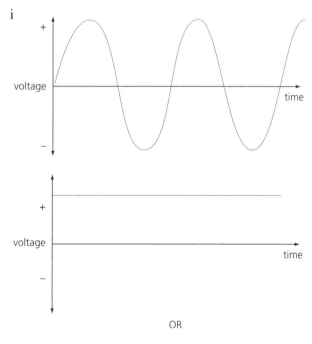

OR

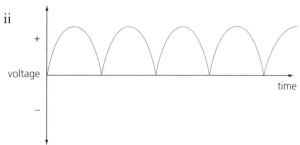

c It has 50 cycles per second.

2 a Thick aluminium cables.

b To reduce the current, so that the power lines do not heat up. This reduces the power loss or voltage drop down the wire.

3 a A device for changing the voltage of A.C. current.

b $$\frac{\text{Output voltage in second coil}}{\text{input voltage in first coil}} = \frac{\text{number of turns in second coil}}{\text{number of turns in first coil}}$$

c Changes the voltage from a low voltage to a higher voltage.

4 a Live – brown, neutral – blue, earth – green and yellow.

b If the case of the container becomes live.

c The case of the container is made of an insulator (usually a plastic), so there is no chance of it becoming live.

d Live.

e i Power = voltage × current
   ii Energy transferred (joules) = power (watts) × time (seconds)

5 a It has a higher resistance in the dark.

b An LED takes less current and lasts longer.

c To amplify the electrical current or as a switch.

d To store up electrical charge.

e When a tiny current is used to switch on a bigger current.

6 a AND gate.

b No.

c i 0,1.
   ii OR.

Electromagnetism

1 a This happens when two like poles of magnets are placed near to each other; they 'push apart'.

b It is possible to turn cobalt into a magnet or it is attracted by a magnet.

c The magnetism does not last (it lasts longer when steel is used). Iron is useful for making the core of an electromagnet.

2 Place the object in a solenoid which is pointing in a west–east direction. Pass A.C. current through the solenoid, slowly take magnet out.

3 Use a soft iron core; use more turns of wire, use a stronger current.

4 a Right hand grip rule: The rule is used to show the connection between the current in a wire and the direction of the magnetic field.

Using the right hand to 'grip' the wire, the thumb shows the direction of the current and the fingers the lines of force.

b Left hand rule: Used to show the connection between the direction of the current in a wire, the movement of the wire and the direction of the magnetic field.
Use the left hand and hold the thumb and first two fingers at right angles, then:
Thumb – direction of movement of wire.
First finger – magnetic field.
Second finger – direction of current.

5 a The commutator is a copper ring that has been cut in half.
b It reverses the current every half turn so that the coil keeps spinning.

Student Answer with Comments

This question is about an automatic washing machine. The diagram below shows an expanded view of the washing machine.

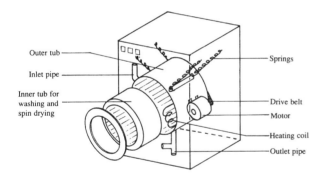

Outer tub
Inlet pipe
Inner tub for washing and spin drying
Springs
Drive belt
Motor
Heating coil
Outlet pipe

Fig 5

a On the wash cycle, the heater and the motor are on at the same time. Each requires a potential difference of 240V to work correctly. In the space below, draw a labelled diagram to show how they should be connected to the supply.

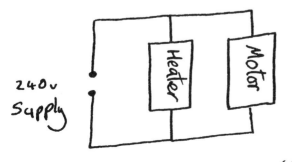

240v
Supply

Heater   Motor

Fig 6   ✓ ②

b i The maximum power rating of the washing machine is 3.0kW at 240V. Calculate the maximum current to the washing machine.

power = voltage × current

∴ current = power   I = 3000
                 volts   240

Ans current = 12.5 amps   ✓ ③

(3 marks)

ii Calculate the effective resistance of the washing machine.

Resistance = volts
                     amps

resistance = 240 = 19.2
                   12.5

Ans = 19.2 Ω (ohms)   ✓ ③

(3 marks)

iii During the heat cycle, 600,000J of energy is transferred to the water. This causes the temperature of the water to increase by 20K. Calculate the mass of water in the washing machine if the specific heat capacity of water is 4200J/(kgK).

Strictly this is not correct as the ÷20 is not shown.

Joules = mass × heat capacity × °kelvin

∴ mass = 600 000 = 142.8574
                 4200

142.85714 = 7.142857
     20

Ans mass = 7.143kg   ✓ ③

(3 marks)

c The outer tub is supported by springs as shown in the diagram.
i It is noticed that, when the inner tub is spinning, the whole of the washing machine vibrates violently because of resonance. Explain what causes this effect.

The clothes in the tub cause the vibrations as they are unbalanced. ✓ As the tub vibrates it reaches the natural frequency of the machine. ✓ The machine then begins to vibrate but harder as the vibrations are magnified.   ✓ ③

(3 marks)

ii To avoid resonance occurring, the inner tub rotates slowly for a few minutes at the start of the spin cycle before switching to a high speed. Explain how this helps.

By spinning slowly the machine tries to even out the unbalanced ✓ state caused by the clothes and therefore stop the tub vibrating. ✓

→ *at the natural frequency of the machine*

$^{16}/_{16}$ (2 marks)

(Total 16 marks)

[ULEAC]

switch 1	switch 2	buzzer ON or OFF
off	off	off
on	off	
off	on	
on	on	

An exam question for you to try

The diagram shows the circuits of two simple alarm systems using push switches.

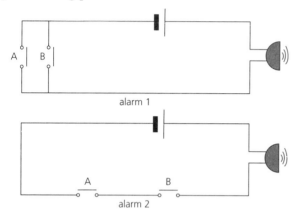

alarm 1

alarm 2

Fig 7

In both circuits, switch A is on if a car door is open, switch B is on when the car engine is started.

a Describe carefully what must happen for each alarm to work.

   i Alarm 1...
   ....(1 mark)
   ii Alarm 2...
   ....(1 mark)

b The switches in these two alarms could be replaced by logic gates. An OR gate can be used in Alarm 1. Which type of logic gate would be used in Alarm 2?
....(1 mark)

c A pupil decided to build a burglar alarm using an OR gate and two push switches. A block diagram of this alarm is shown (Fig. 2):

   i Complete the chart below to show what must happen to make the buzzer sound. The first one has been done for you. (1 mark)

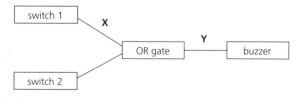

Fig 8

ii The pupil decided to join a wire X to Y. How would this alter the way the alarm works?
....
....(1 mark)

iii Draw a block diagram to show how the alarm could be altered so that the buzzer sounded only when both switches were off. (1 mark)

[MEG]

Answer

a i Alarm 1: Either the car door must be open *(to put switch A on)* or the engine must be started *(to put switch B on)* to sound the alarm.

   ii Alarm 2: Both the car door must be open *(to put switch A on)* and the engine must be started *(to put switch B on)* to sound the alarm.

b AND.

c i

   on – off : ON
   off – on : ON
   on – on : ON ....*(It is an OR gate)*

   ii Once either switch is pressed feedback from Y to X keeps the buzzer on. The circuit acts as a latch. Turning either switch off will not turn the buzzer off.

   iii You need to draw the same circuit as in the figure above, *but* put a NOT gate after the OR gate and before the buzzer. *(You could change the OR gate for a NOR gate.)*

14 Using forces

Using forces	Midland (MEG)				Northern (NEAB)		London (ULEAC)				Southern (SEG)		Welsh (WJEC)
	Own	Nuffield	Salters	Suffolk	Co-ordinated	Modular	Modular GASP	Combined	Co-ordinated	Modular	Double	Modular	Co-ordinated
FORCES AND MOTION													
Importance of forces	✓	✓	✓	✓	✓	✓	✓	✓	✓	✓	✓	✓	✓
Friction	✓	✓	✓	✓	✓	✓	✓	✓	✓	✓	✓	✓	✓
Mass, gravity and weight	✓	✓	✓	✓	✓	✓	✓	H	✓	✓	✓	✓	✓
Balanced and unbalanced forces	✓	✓	✓	✓	✓	✓	✓	✓	✓	✓	✓	✓	✓
Speed, velocity, acceleration and distance calculations	✓	✓	✓	✓	✓	✓	✓	✓	✓	✓	✓	✓	✓
Work, energy and power	✓	✓	✓	✓	✓	✓	✓	✓	✓	✓	✓	✓	✓
Circular motion and projectiles	H	H	H	✓	H	H	H	✓	H	✓	✓	✓	H
MOMENTUM AND COLLISIONS													
Importance of momentum	H	✓	✓	✓	✓	✓	✓	✓	✓	✓	✓	✓	✓
Calculations involving momentum	H	H	✓	H	H	H	H	H	H	H	✓	H	H
Gravity and falling objects	✓	✓	✓	✓	✓	✓	✓	✓	✓	✓	✓	✓	✓
Terminal velocity	✓	✓	✓	✓	✓	✓	✓	✓	✓	✓	✓	✓	✓
Work and energy	✓	✓	✓	✓	✓	✓	✓	✓	✓	✓	✓	✓	✓
Stopping moving objects	✓	✓	✓	✓	✓	✓	✓	✓	✓	✓	✓	✓	✓
FORCES AND MATERIALS													
Hooke's Law	✓	✓	✓	✓	✓	✓	✓	✓	✓	✓	✓	✓	✓
How forces affect materials	✓	✓	✓	✓	✓	✓	✓	✓	✓	✓	✓	✓	✓
Force and pressure	✓	✓	✓	✓	✓	✓	✓	✓	✓	✓	✓	✓	✓
Machines	✓	✓	✓	✓	✓	✓	✓	✓	✓	✓	✓	✓	✓
Efficiency	✓	✓	✓	H	✓	✓	✓	✓	✓	✓	✓	✓	✓
Levers and turning forces	✓	✓	✓	✓	✓	✓	✓	✓	✓	✓	✓	✓	✓
Stable equilibrium	✓	✓	✓	✓	✓	✓	✓	✓	✓	✓	✓	✓	✓

Forces and motion

Important equations used in this chapter are summarised on p 299

Why are forces so important?

A force is a push or a pull. Forces can make objects move or alter their shape. Some forces are easy to recognise – you may pull on a door to open it or push it closed behind you. We constantly use forces to move ourselves around and to move other objects. Some forces, however, are less easy to understand. If you let go of a bag it falls to the floor. The pull of the Earth on an object is called the *force of gravity*. Two magnets attract one another if opposite poles are brought together. *Magnetic forces* are acting here. *Electric forces* can cause attraction between a plastic comb and your hair.

Measuring forces
Forces are measured in newtons after Sir Isaac Newton, who, in about 1665, first realised that gravity was a force. We still use his Laws of Motion (see later) to describe the way that objects move. A 100g apple weighs about 1 newton. A mass of 1kg on Earth weighs almost 10 newtons (see page 301). We often use a spring balance (called a newton meter) to measure the strength of pulling forces.

Forces make things move

If you want to move an object you have to use a force. The way the object moves depends on the size of the force and the direction in which it is applied.

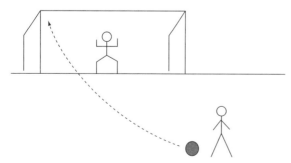

Fig 1 Footballer taking a penalty

The size and direction of the force are very important if the penalty is to be scored.

To describe a force accurately you must therefore give both the size and direction. We use the word vector when both a quantity and a direction are needed. Force is a vector quantity.

Scalar quantities only have a size. Direction is not important. Temperature and volume are examples of scalar quantities.

Using arrows to show forces

- Direction – the way the arrow points shows this.
- Size – the length of the arrow shows this – providing you give the scale that you are using. For example, a 1cm arrow could be used to mean a force of 1 newton. A 5cm arrow would then mean 5 newtons. The direction of the arrow gives the direction of the force.

Adding forces

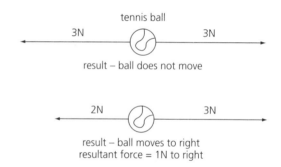

Fig 2 Adding forces

By looking at the direction and the size of the forces you can work out in which direction the ball will move.

Friction
Friction is the name given to forces that try to stop things from moving. These are important when
- A surface moves over another surface.
- An object tries to move through a liquid or gas.
The direction of these forces is always in the opposite direction to that in which the movement occurs.

Examples
1 Dragging a block of stone
This is made easier by placing rollers underneath. The friction between the stone and the ground is reduced.

2 Racing cars

When the road is dry Formula One racing cars use tyres with no tread (called 'slicks'). This increases the area of rubber that is actually touching the road. Friction is increased so that the car can accelerate and corner more quickly without skidding.

3 Human speed

The world record for the 100 metres is much faster for a person moving through air than moving through water. A 100 metre sprint can take less than 10 seconds but to swim 100 metres takes nearly 50 seconds. There is much more friction to be overcome (between water and the surface of the athlete's body) than when the body is moving through air.

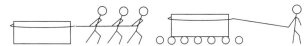

Fig 3 Dragging a stone block

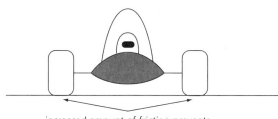

increased amount of friction prevents sideways movement

Fig 4 Racing car

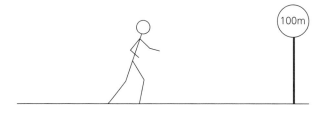

Fig 5 Human speed

How are mass, gravity and weight connected?

- **Mass**: Mass is the amount of matter (see page 134) contained in an object. The unit of mass is the kilogram (kg). For a given object its mass is constant.

- **Gravity**: All objects attract one another, though for nearly all objects this attraction is too small to notice. We call these forces of attraction gravitational forces. However, the mass of the Earth is very large and its gravitational attraction for other objects is significant.

- **Weight**: The gravitational force between the Earth and an object is called its weight. Weight is the downward pull of the Earth on an object and it is measured in newtons, like all other forces.

Example
An astronaut has a mass of 60kg. What will she weigh on

a Earth?
b The moon (gravity is 1/6 of that on Earth)?
c Mars (gravity is 2/5 of that on Earth)?

Answer
a On earth a mass of 1kg has a weight of approximately 10N. The weight of the astronaut is therefore $60 \times 10 = 600$N.
b The moon has a gravitational attraction of about one sixth that of the Earth. On the moon therefore the astronaut will weigh 600/6 = 100N. *However, her mass is still 60kg as the amount of matter making up her body has not changed.*
c On Mars (a small planet) the gravitational attraction is about 2/5 of that on Earth. On Mars the woman astronaut would weigh $600 \times 2/5 = 240$N *even though her mass has still not changed.*

Forces in pairs

We now know that forces are always found in pairs. These may be called action and reaction forces. They are always equal and opposite in direction.

It was Newton who first noted this and described it in his Third Law:
If body A exerts a force on body B, then body B exerts an opposite force of the same size on body A.

The force of gravity on you as you read this book acts downwards onto your chair. It is balanced exactly by the upward force of the chair on you. A rocket engine works by pushing large amounts of hot gas out of the back. The force on the gases moving backwards is the same as the force on the rocket which therefore moves forwards.

How are forces involved in movement?

Only unbalanced forces produce movement. Once an object is moving a force is always needed to change its speed or direction.

- *For a car to accelerate* the engine must apply a force to turn the wheels and push the car along.
- *For a car to slow down* frictional forces are created by applying stationary brake pads to the revolving wheels.
- *For a car to move at constant speed* it needs a force from the engine big enough to overcome friction in the moving parts and the air resistance (another form of friction) that slow the car down. For movement at constant speed the forces are balanced.

Newton's First Law gives the basic principle for this: An object will keep still or carry on moving in a straight line at a steady speed unless a force acts on it.

QUESTION

The diagram shows the direction in which four forces A, F, L and W act on a flying bird. The force arrows are not drawn to scale.

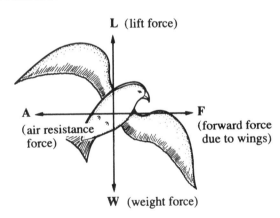

Fig 6

    i Which two forces, from A, F, L and W must be equal if the bird stays at the same height in the sky?
       Force................and force.................... (1 mark)
    ii What causes the weight force acting on the bird?
      ....(1 mark)
                Part question [SEG 1994]

ANSWER

    i L and W.
    ii Gravity.

How do we measure speed?

Speed is the distance travelled by an object in a unit of time. It is measured in metres per second (m/s) or kilometres per hour (km/h). To measure speed we must measure a time and a distance.

Example:
If you walk 800 metres in 10 minutes your speed is $800/10 \times 60 = 8/6 = 1.25$m/s

However this calculation hides the fact that you will not have walked at a constant speed for the whole journey. We have calculated **an average speed**.

Make sure you know this equation:
Average speed = total distance travelled/time taken for journey
$v = s/t$

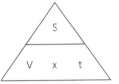

Fig 7

Using a ticker-tape timer to measure speed

The timer puts a dot on a piece of tape 50 times in each second. The time interval between each dot is 1/50s or 0.02s.

Speed and velocity

What is the difference between speed and velocity?

- Speed is the distance travelled by an object in a unit of time.
- Velocity is the term used for speed when its direction is also given. Velocity is a vector quantity (like force). It has a size (speed) **and** a direction.

Distance/time graphs

We can use a graph to show the way something has moved. We can use these graphs to calculate speed (and in some cases velocity).

Example
The graph (Fig 8) shows the journey that a child makes to buy some sweets. He runs to the sweet shop. It takes one minute to get there but two minutes to choose and pay for the packet of sweets. The journey home while eating the sweets takes longer,

four minutes in all. We can use the graph to find the speed at which the child ran to the shop and the speed at which he walked home.

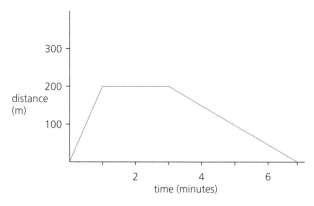

Fig 8 A journey to buy some sweets

a How quickly did the child run to the shop?
Answer:
He ran 200 metres in 1 minute. One minute is 60 seconds so the speed was

200/60 = 3.33m/s.

b How quickly did he walk home?
Answer
He walked the 200 metres in 4 minutes. 4 minutes is 240 seconds so the speed was

200/240 = 0.83m/s.

The slope (gradient) of a distance/time graph gives the speed of travel. We can call this velocity provided we know the direction of each movement.

Using a ticker-tape timer to measure velocity

If you cut the tape into 5 dot lengths (remember the dots are printed every 0.02s), you can see how far the object moved in each tenth of a second (5 × 0.02 = 0.1s). When you stick the strips of tape onto a chart you can see what is happening more easily.
The length of each strip is a measure of the speed of the object in a given direction.

Velocity/Time Graphs

• Describing motion
The length of the pieces of ticker tape shows the velocity at which the object was travelling. We can use measurements like these to draw velocity/time graphs.

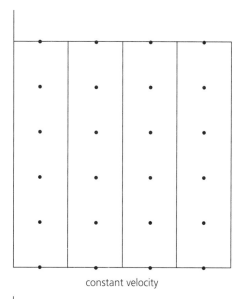

constant velocity

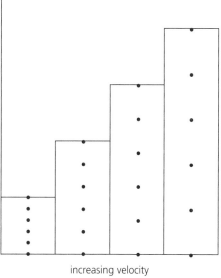

increasing velocity

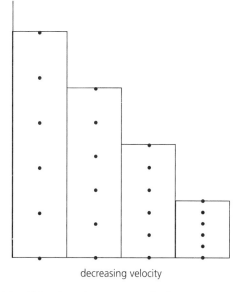

decreasing velocity

Fig 9 Using ticker tape to measure velocity

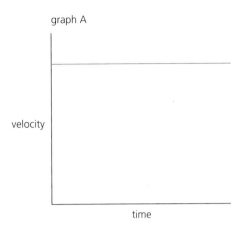

Graph A: An object travelling at the same velocity throughout the measured time.

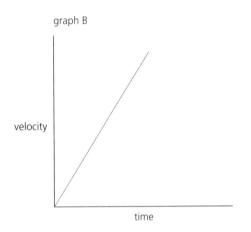

Graph B: An object that is increasing its velocity steadily. It is **accelerating**. If the velocity/time graph is a straight line, we call this **uniform acceleration.**

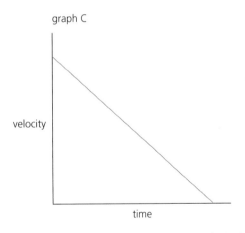

Graph C: An object that is slowing down; its velocity is decreasing. Negative acceleration is called **deceleration**. If the graph is a straight line we call this **uniform deceleration.**

Fig 10 Velocity time graphs

Example

The graph shows a short car journey. Describe what is happening during each of the three labelled parts.

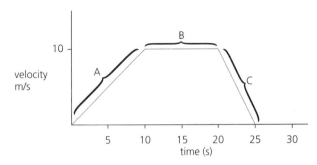

Fig 11 Graph of journey of a car

Answer

During A: The car is accelerating uniformly.
During B: The car is travelling at constant velocity.
During C: The car is decelerating uniformly.

- Calculations from velocity/time graphs
  We can calculate:
  – The acceleration.
  – The distance travelled.

Calculating acceleration

Acceleration is defined as the rate at which an object changes its velocity.

$$\text{Acceleration} = \frac{\text{Change in velocity (m/s)}}{\text{Time taken for change (s)}}$$

The units are m/s^2, this may be written as m/s per second.

It's worth learning the equation for acceleration.

Look at Fig 11 Graph of journey of a car

From part A of the graph – Velocity goes from 0m/s to 10m/s.
Time taken is 10s.

$$\text{Acceleration} = \frac{10\text{m/s}}{10\text{s}} = 1\text{m/s}^2$$

From part C of the graph – Velocity goes from 10 m/s to 0m/s.
Time taken is 5s.

$$\text{Acceleration} = \frac{-10\text{m/s}}{5\text{s}} = -2\text{m/s}^2$$

This is a deceleration of 2m/s^2.

The acceleration is given by the slope (gradient) of the velocity/time graph.

Calculating distance travelled

Part A) Velocity goes from 0 to 10m/s uniformly. The average velocity is therefore 5m/s for the first 10 seconds.
Distance travelled = 5 × 10 = 50m.

Part B) Velocity is constant at 10m/s for 10s.
Distance travelled = 10 × 10 = 100m.

Part C) Velocity goes from 10 to 0m/s uniformly. The average velocity is therefore 5m/s for the last 5 seconds.
Distance travelled = 5 × 5 = 25m.

Total distance travelled = 50 + 100 + 25 = 175 metres.

The distance travelled is given by the area under the velocity time graph.

QUESTION

The graph shows the speed of a cyclist along a route.

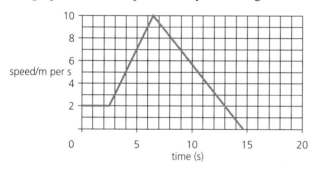

Fig 12

i Give the time when the cyclist was slowing down.
....(1 mark)

ii What was the acceleration of the cyclist at 2 seconds?
....(1 mark)

iii Give a time when the acceleration was the largest?
....(1 mark)

iv State and explain when the net force on the cyclist was largest.
....
....
....(2 marks)
[MEG]

ANSWER

i From 6.5 to 14.5 seconds.
ii 0 *(constant speed).*

iii Any time between 2.5 and 6.5 seconds is suitable.
iv The biggest net force is when the cyclist is accelerating. This is between 2.5 and 6.5 seconds. *(You need to look for when the slope is steepest – this can be either accelerating or decelerating.)*

Work, energy and power

• Work:
When a force acts on something to make it move we say that **work** is being done. Work has to be done whenever there is movement against an opposing force. The opposing force in many cases is friction or gravity.

The definition of work is given by the equation:

work done = force × distance moved

If force is measured in newtons and distance in metres, the work done will be in joules. The work done is 1 joule (J) if a force of 1 newton moves a distance of 1 metre.

• Energy
Before any work can be done **energy** must be available. When work is done this energy is transferred. The units of energy must be the same as the units of work. You need to transfer 1 joule of energy in order to do 1 joule of work.

See ch 15 for more about energy.

• Power
Power is the rate at which work is done (or the rate at which energy is transferred).

$$power = \frac{work\ done\ (joule)}{time\ taken\ (seconds)}$$

Power is measured in watts (W)
If 1 joule of work is done in 1 second the power used is 1 watt. One watt is one joule per second.

Calculating work: some examples

1 A force of 100 newtons was used to push a trolley of equipment into the laboratory. The distance moved was 5 metres and it took 4 seconds to do it.

a How much work was done?
work = force × distance moved =
100 × 5 = 500 joules.   Ans = 500J.

b What power was used?
power = work done/time taken
500/4 = 125 watts.   Ans = 125W.

2 A piece of equipment of mass 3kg was put away
onto a shelf. It had to be lifted from the floor a
height of 2 metres. It took 3 seconds to do the lift.

a How much work was done?
The force of gravity on a 1kg mass is about
10 N. A 3kg mass therefore has a weight of
3 × 10 = 30 newtons.
work = force × distance moved
30 × 2 = 60 joules.   Ans = 60J.

b What power was used?
power = work done/time taken
60/3 = 20 watts.   Ans = 20W.

QUESTION

The graph shows how the drag force on a motor boat
varies with its speed.

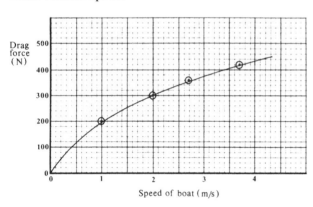

Fig 13

a i Use the graph to find the value of the drag force
acting on the boat when its speed is 1.5m/s.
....(1 mark)

ii What driving force is needed to keep the boat
moving at a constant speed of 1.5m/s? Explain
your answer.
....
....(2 marks)

iii How far does the boat travel in 20s when its
speed is constant at 1.5m/s?
....(1 mark)

iv Calculate the minimum work done by the engine
in maintaining a speed of 1.5m/s for 20s.
....
....
....(2 marks)

v Calculate the minimum power output of the
boat engine during this time.
....
....(2 marks)
[ULEAC]

ANSWER

i 250N. *(Read this value directly from the graph.)*
ii 250N. For constant speed the driving force
must exactly balance the drag force. Resultant
force is then zero.
iii 1.5 × 20 = 30m *(speed = distance/time, so
distance = speed × time).*
iv work done = force × distance moved.
250 × 30 = 7500 joules.   Ans = 7.5kJ
v power = work done/time taken.
7500/20 = 375 watts.

Circular motion

If an object (such as a cork on the end of a string) is
swung in a circle, then a force acts towards the centre
of the circle. This is called the centripetal force.
If you let go of the string then the cork will continue
to move in a **straight line**. Newton's first law of
motion tells us that an object moves in a straight line
unless a force acts on it.

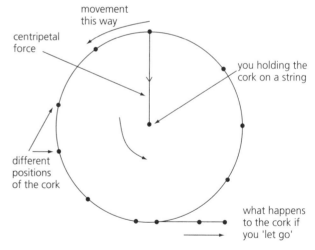

Fig 14 Circular motion and centripetal force

You can calculate this centripetal force in newtons
(N) from this formula: $F = mv^2/r$

m is the mass of the object (kg), v is the speed of the
object (m/s), r is the radius of the orbit (m).

*Gravity provides the centripetal force that keeps
satellites circulating around the Earth (see p 372 for
more details of satellites).*

Projectiles

A javelin is an example of a projectile. To achieve the maximum distance it is thrown upwards and forwards. The javelin is acted on by the force of gravity. After reaching its maximum height it begins to fall but continues to move forwards. This gives the characteristic curved path. The javelin goes furthest if it is launched at an angle of 45°.

The horizontal and vertical components of the force acting on a projectile can be thought of as independent of one another.

To project an object so that it can get away from the gravitational force provided by the Earth, it must have a large enough velocity to escape from being in orbit around the Earth. The velocity needed is called the **escape velocity**. The escape velocity for any satellite depends upon the mass of the satellite and the radius of its orbit.

Important equations that you must be able to use when thinking about forces and motion:

Speed (m/s) = distance (m)/time (s)

Acceleration (m/s²)= change in velocity (m/s)/
time taken for change (s)

Work (J) = force (N) × distance moved (m)

Power (W) = work done (J)/time taken (s)

Centripetal force (N) = mass of object (kg) ×
speed in orbit² (m/s)²/radius of orbit (m)

Momentum and collisions

Important equations used in this chapter are summarised on p 305

Why momentum is important

To be able to start something moving is important. It may be you or the car you travel in. Once something is moving it may be more important still to be able to stop it! To start or stop a moving object a force is needed. The effect of the force is to change the momentum of the object.

We calculate the momentum of an object using this equation:

momentum = mass × velocity
The units of momentum are kg m/s.

The greater the mass of an object, the more difficult it is to start it moving. It is easier to push-start a car than to push-start a bus! Exactly the same is true for stopping. The heavier the vehicle the more difficult it is to stop.

If you double the force used to start something moving, then the acceleration produced is also doubled. This leads to another useful equation:

force = mass × acceleration   F = m × a

One newton is the force which gives a mass of one kilogram an acceleration of one metre per second² or 1 metre per second per second.

When using this equation you must remember that:

• F (the force) is the **resultant** force. (If there is more than one force involved, find the resultant force first (see p 292).)
• The units are: F (newtons), m (kg), a (m/s²). This equation is sometimes referred to as Newton's second law of motion.

Newton's second law of motion
Newton realised that if an object is free to move and a force is applied to it, the momentum change is given by the force multiplied by the time.

change in momentum = force × time

but the change in momentum = (mass × speed at end) – (mass × speed at start) = mv – mu

Then force × time = m(v – u)
F × t = m(v–u)
F = m(v–u)/t

But v–u is the change in speed which when divided by the time is the acceleration.
(v–u)/t = a

Therefore F = ma. This is the equation usually associated with Newton's second law of motion.

Collisions

When two snooker balls collide the first ball exerts a force on the second for a short time. The second ball in turn exerts an opposite and equal force on the first ball. It can be shown that the momentum in a collision always stays the same.

total momentum before collision =
total momentum after collision

This is sometimes called the law of momentum or the law of conservation of momentum.

Calculations involving collisions

Examples:

1 Two girls are roller skating. The first girl has a mass of 40kg and is standing still. Her friend who has a mass of 50kg bumps into her while travelling at 5m/s and grabs hold of her. How fast are the girls going after the collision?

Answer
Use: Momentum = mass × velocity, to work out the momentum of each girl before the collision.

Momentum before collision
Girl one m × v = 40 × 0 = 0kgm/s
Girl two m × v = 50 × 5 = 250kgm/s
Total momentum before collision = (250 + 0) = 250kgm/s.

After the collision you know that the combined mass is (40 + 50) kg = 90kg.

Total momentum after collision (girl one and two together) = m × v = 90 × v.
(It is v, the final velocity, that you need to calculate.)

Using total momentum before collision = total momentum after collision,

250 = 90 × v   v = 250/90 = 2.8m/s.

2 Two railway wagons (A and B), each of mass 12,000kg, are coupled together and are moving down the line at 1m/s. They are hit by another wagon (C) of the same mass, moving in the opposite direction with a speed of 2m/s. Assuming the wagons do not derail what will happen after the collision?

Use: Momentum = mass × velocity to calculate the momentum before collision.

For A and B m × v = 24,000 × 1 = 24,000kgm/s.

For C m × v = 12,000 × (−2) = −24,000kgm/s.

(Because C is moving in the opposite direction to A and B we must make its momentum negative.)
Total momentum before collision = 0.
Therefore total momentum after collision = 0.
If there is no momentum and the wagons stick together the velocity is zero. Therefore the wagons are not moving after the collision.

QUESTION

Car X has a mass of 750kg and a velocity of 90kmph. Car X has a head-on collision with a second car Y. Car Y has a mass of 550kg and a velocity before the collision of 70kmph. After the collision the cars are interlocked.

    i Calculate the momentum of car X and of car Y before the collision.
      Car X...
      ....
      Car Y...
      ....(3 marks)
      What is the momentum of the two cars after the collision?
      ....
      ....
      ....
      ....(2 marks)
                               [SEG 1994]

ANSWER

i *At this level you would expect to be given the full three marks without the change to m/s (metres per second).*

Car X momentum =
m × v = 750 × 90 = 67,500kgkm/h
Car Y momentum =
m × v = 550 × −70 = −38,500kgkm/h

Because the velocities of X and Y are in opposite directions one MUST be given a negative sign. Velocity (and momentum) are vectors!

If you do use m/s then:

For car X:
750 × 90,000/3,600 = 18,750kgm/s.

For car Y:
550 × −70,000/3,600 = −10,694kgm/s.

ii Total momentum is 67,500 – 38,500 =
29,000kgkm/h.
OR 18,750 – 10,694 = 8,056kgm/s.
This will be in the direction in which car X was
travelling.

Gravity and falling objects

The force of gravity acts on everything on our planet.
The strength of the force of gravity is measured by
the force it exerts on a one kilogram mass. On Earth
this force is 9.8 newtons. (We often approximate this
to 10N.)

*Remember that on Earth the force of gravity on a 1kg
mass is about 10 newtons.*

There is an important equation involving gravity:

Force of gravity = mass × gravitational field strength (g)

$9.8N = 1kg \times g$ Therefore $g = 9.8N/kg$

Using the equation: $F = m \times a$

You can see that: $g = a$

g can also be called the acceleration due to gravity.

On Earth g is $9.8m/s^2$. This is also often given as
$10m/s^2$.

If an object falls freely its acceleration due to gravity
will always be the same.

For example:
If two pieces of concrete, the first of 1kg and the
second of 10kg, are dropped from a helicopter, what
is the acceleration of each?

$F = m \times a$ For the 1kg mass $10N = 1kg \times 10m/s^2$
For the 10kg mass $100N = 10kg \times 10m/s^2$

A bigger force acts on the bigger mass to produce the
same acceleration.

QUESTION

The diagram below shows the construction of the
rocket used to take the first astronauts to the Moon.
The three stages were used to project the command
and lunar modules. At the Moon, the command
module was placed in orbit as the lunar module
landed. Later, the lunar module left the Moon's
surface and rejoined the command module for the
return journey to Earth.
The table gives the thrust, and the times for which
they were produced, for each stage of the rocket.

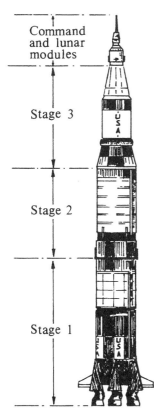

Command and lunar modules
Stage 3
Stage 2
Stage 1

STAGE	THRUST (Newtons)	TIME USED (Seconds)	MASS (kg)
Command module	–	–	0.02×10^6
Lunar module	–	–	0.14×10^6
3	1.05×10^6	480	0.12×10^6
2	4.45×10^6	390	0.45×10^6
1	34.5×10^6	150	2.3×10^6

Fig 1

a At takeoff, the rocket is accelerated by the thrust from the stage 1 motors.

i Calculate the total weight of the rocket before takeoff.

You can assume that the gravitational field strength is 10N/kg.

....

....

....(2 marks)

ii Calculate the resultant force on the rocket when the stage 1 motors are firing.

....

....

....(2 marks)

iii Calculate the initial acceleration of the rocket.

....

....

....(2 marks)

b The thrust from the stage 1 motor is maintained for 150s.

Assuming that during this time the acceleration of the rocket remains constant:

i Calculate the speed of the rocket after 150s;

....

....

....(2 marks)

ii Calculate the distance travelled in this time.

....

....

....(2 marks)

c Give TWO reasons why the assumption made about the acceleration in part (b) is NOT correct.

1 ....

2 ....(2 marks)

[ULEAC]

ANSWER

a i 3.03×10^7N.

0.02×10^6

$+ 0.14 \times 10^6$

$+ 0.12 \times 10^6$

$+ 0.45 \times 10^6$

$+ 2.30 \times 10^6$

_____

3.03×10^6kg total weight

$\times 10$ to turn into newtons $= 3.03 \times 10^7$N.

ii 4.2×10^6N.

Weight $= 3.03 \times 10^7$N or 30.3×10^6N

Upthrust $= 34.5 \times 10^6$N

Resultant $= 34.5 \times 10^6 - 30.3 \times 10^6 = 4.2 \times 10^6$N

iii 1.39m/s².

$F = ma$

$4.26 \times 10^6 = 3.03 \times 10^6 \times a$

$a = 4.2/3.03 = 1.39$m/s².

b i $v = 208.5$m/s.

acc = change in velocity/time

$1.39 = v/150$

(initial velocity, $v = 0$)

ii $15,637$m.

Given that the acceleration is constant from

$v = 0$ to $v = 208.5$

Average velocity $= 208.5/2$

Distance $= (208.5/2) \times 150 = 15,637$m.

c Mass of the rocket changes as the fuel is released. Distance from the Earth is changing so the force of gravity on the rocket decreases as it moves away. Air resistance varies with speed.

Terminal velocity

When a parachutist jumps from a plane, gravity pulls her downwards with a force depending on her mass. As her speed increases, however, the force of friction with the air rushing past (air resistance) also increases. After a while the downward force of gravity is balanced by the upward force of friction. When the forces are balanced, the parachutist does not fall more quickly. She falls at a constant speed called the terminal velocity.

The terminal velocity can be reduced by increasing the frictional force upwards. Free fall parachutists can control their speed of descent by spreading themselves out as much as possible. A parachute provides so much friction that the terminal velocity is low enough for a safe landing.

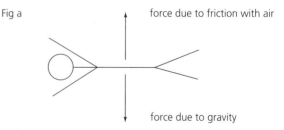

Fig a · force due to friction with air · force due to gravity

Once the upward and downward forces are the same a steady speed has been reached.

Fig b

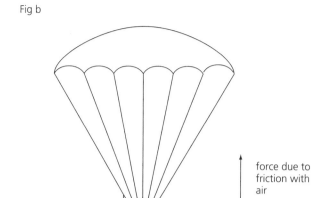

force due to friction with air

force due to gravity

The parachute increases the force due to friction with the air. The two forces balance but the parachutist falls at a much slower speed.

Fig 2 Forces on a parachutist

In both cases the upward and downward forces are balanced and the parachutist has reached terminal velocity. There is no resultant force so the parachutist falls at a constant speed in a straight line.

QUESTION

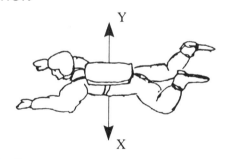

Y

X

Fig 3 Sky diver

A sky diver is falling from an aeroplane

a Name:
   i force X..(1 mark)
   ii force Y...(1 mark)
b State how each force changes as the sky diver speeds up
   i force X..(1 mark)
   ii force Y...(1 mark)
c Why does the sky diver reach a steady speed (terminal velocity)?

   ....
   ....
   ....(2 marks)

d Describe and explain what happens when the sky diver deploys (opens) the parachute.

   ....
   ....
   ....
   ....(3 marks)
   [WJEC]

ANSWER

a i Gravity.
   ii Friction or air resistance.
b i Stays the same.
   ii Increases.
c The air friction (drag) increases until it is the same as the force of gravity (weight). The resultant force is then zero so the sky diver does not fall any faster.
d The parachute increases force Y, the drag, so the sky diver slows down to a new terminal velocity. This is much less than before.

Work and energy

Potential energy

If you do work by lifing something, the force you apply upwards is equal to the gravitational force acting downwards. The force you use is therefore calculated from the mass times the accleration due to gravity.

In order to start the object moving, the upwards force must be just greater than the gravitational force.

Force (in lifing an object up) = mass × acceleration due to gravity

$F = m \times g$

By using the equation: work = force × distance, you can rewrite this equation as:

work done in lifting an object against gravity
$= m \times g \times h$

where h is the height, or the distance, that the object is lifted.

This work that is done increases the energy of the object lifted. We call this type of energy potential energy.

potential energy = mgh

Calculating potential energy

Use the equation: potential energy = $m \times g \times h$.

In the example on page 298 a 3kg mass was lifted through 2 metres. The weight of a 3kg mass on Earth is 30 newtons (remember 1kg weighs 10N). The work done was calculated to be 60 joules (30×2). The potential energy gained by the piece of equipment must also be 60 joules.

potential energy = $m \times g \times h = 3 \times 10 \times 2 = 60$ joules

Kinetic energy

If a book falls from a shelf it loses all the potential energy gained by being lifted to the shelf, by the time it reaches the floor.
We call movement energy **kinetic energy** (see page 320). When something falls freely under the action of gravity, its potential energy becomes smaller as its kinetic energy increases.
In the example above, if the object had 60 joules of potential energy when on the shelf, this would have been transformed to 60 joules of kinetic energy just before it hit the floor.

Energy cannot be lost, it can only be transferred (see page 320).

Calculating kinetic energy

The kinetic energy of a moving object can be calculated using the formula:

kinetic energy = $\frac{1}{2}mv^2$ where m is the mass and
v is its speed.

Example:
What is the speed of an object as it falls to the floor, if it has a mass of 3kg and kinetic energy calculated to be 60 joules?
Answer:
Use KE = $\frac{1}{2}mv^2$.
$60 = \frac{1}{2} \times 3 \times v^2$ therefore $v^2 = 60 \times 2/3 = 40$.

Therefore v = 6.3m/s.

The object was travelling at 6.3m/s as it hit the floor.

Stopping moving objects

The connection between momentum and stopping safely

If you travel by car, bus or train it is very important that the driver can stop the vehicle safely. This means applying a force to reduce the momentum. We use frictional forces in the brakes to do this. If you are unlucky enough to be in a collision the time taken to stop the vehicle is very short. This means that the force involved becomes very large, and damage can be done to vehicles and their occupants.
For example, imagine a bus full of pupils travelling at 30mph. It must stop safely. The momentum of the bus and pupils has to be reduced to zero, i.e. the speed must become zero mph!

Thinking about the equation: change in momentum =
force × time

… you can see that for the same change in momentum:

*   If the time for using the brakes is long (they are used slowly) then the force is small.
*   But if the time for using the brakes is short (they are used fast) then the force is large.

Stopping distances

Stopping distance is the thinking distance and the braking distance added together.

To avoid a collision between you and the car in front, you must always leave enough space to have time to stop if necessary. The table below gives the normal stopping distances for a car on a dry road with efficient brakes. Lorries need greater stopping distances because they have more mass and therefore more momentum.

Shortest stopping distances

Speed (mph)	stopping distance (m)	number of car lengths
20	12	3
30	23	6
40	36	9
50	53	13
60	73	18
70	96	24

These values for stopping distances assume several things:

*   That the driver is fit and well, and not under the influence of alcohol or any drug that might slow his or her reaction time (see Section 4, Co-ordination).
*   That the vehicle is in good order with sufficient tread on the tyres and efficient brakes.
*   That the road surface is clean and dry. Leaves, stones and water can all reduce friction and start a skid.

Energy in collisions

When a collision happens and vehicles stop suddenly, the kinetic energy must be transferred. Looking at the formula for kinetic energy (KE = $\frac{1}{2}mv^2$) you can see that the two factors governing the amount of energy are mass and speed. A car with double the mass doubles the kinetic energy that has to be lost. However, doubling the speed of a vehicle gives four times as much energy to the collision.

- **Doubling the mass** of the car – **doubles the kinetic energy** involved in the collision.
- **Doubling the speed** of the car – increases the kinetic energy of the collision by **four times**. You can work this out using the equations: KE = $\frac{1}{2}mv^2$.
  Kinetic energy = $\frac{1}{2}mv^2$. If v turns into 2v the kinetic energy becomes $\frac{1}{2}m(2v)^2 = \frac{1}{2}m4v^2 = 2mv^2$ which is four times bigger.

This is why it is particularly important that vehicles should keep within speed limits.

Making cars safer

- Seat belts stop you being thrown forward onto the dashboard or even through the front window. They give a little in an accident, so your body takes longer to stop than the car itself. A longer stopping time means a smaller force on you.
- Air bags inflate in a collision and slow down the forward movement of your body even more. They also spread the force over a larger area of your body, making the pressure on you less (see page 307).
- Crumple zones allow the front of the car to give way gradually during the collision. This makes the length of time needed to stop the car longer, and once again the force is reduced.

QUESTION

2 a
   i   What is the braking distance of a car?

   ....
   ....(1 mark)
   ii Explain the connection between the braking distance of a car and its speed.

   ....
   ....
   ....
   ....
   ....

....(4 marks)

b i   What is the equation which links mass, momentum and velocity?

   ....
   ....(1 mark)
   ii What is the connection between force and momentum?

   ....
   ....(1 mark)
   iii Use the idea of momentum to explain why wearing a seat belt is likely to reduce the chance of serious injury in a car crash.

   ....
   ....
   ....
   ....
   ....(3 marks)

Part question [SEG 1994]

ANSWER

a i   The distance the car travels after the brakes have been applied. *(Note this is not the same as the stopping distance which also includes thinking time.)*
   ii The faster the car is travelling the more kinetic energy it has. This energy must be transferred to another form for the car to stop. Kinetic energy is given by $\frac{1}{2}mv^2$. Braking distance depends on v^2. Doubling the speed gives four times the braking distance.

b i   Momentum = mass × velocity.
   ii Force × time = change in momentum.
   iii In a crash your momentum must be reduced to zero. The seat belt slows you down gradually. The time for the change in momentum is longer, so that the force on you is reduced.

Important equations that you must be able to use when thinking about momentum and collisions:

Momentum (kg m/s) = mass (kg) × velocity (m/s)

Force (N) = mass (kg) × acceleration (m/s)

Change in momentum (kg m/s) =
force (N) × time (s)

Total momentum before collision =
total momentum after collision

Potential energy (J) = mass (kg) × acceleration due to gravity (m/s²) × height (h)

Kinetic energy (J) = $\frac{1}{2}$ mass (kg) × velocity² (m/s)²

Forces and materials

> **Important equations used in this chapter are summarised on p 314**

Stretching forces

We can measure these forces by using a spring balance or newton meter. The spring becomes longer when a stretching force is applied. This increase in length is called the **extension**. Often, doubling the force doubles the extension. When this happens we say that the extension is proportional to the force being applied. Any material that does this is said to obey **Hooke's Law**.

A spring balance can therefore be calibrated in newtons and used to measure pulling forces applied to it. It is also possible to make springs with open coils so that they can be used to measure pushing forces. In this case the spring becomes shorter when a force is applied.

Checking Hooke's Law
The force of gravity on 10g is 0.1N. The extension (increase in length) of the spring is measured as 10g masses are added to the hanger.

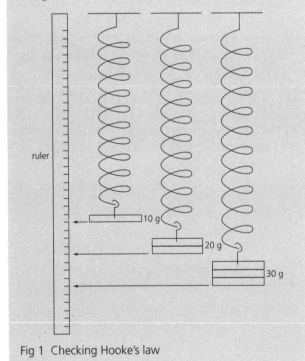

Fig 1 Checking Hooke's law

How forces affect materials:

- Elastic:
  If a material returns to its original length after being stretched it is said to be elastic. The material used to make the spring in Fig 1 is elastic.
- Plastic:
  If a material changes shape when a force is applied and does not return to its original shape when the force is removed, it is said to be plastic. Plasticine is an example of a plastic material.
- Brittle
  If a material breaks when a force is applied it is brittle.

See p 239 for a discussion of elastic, plastic and brittle in relation to the behaviour of rocks.

Going beyond the elastic limit
A similar experiment was carried out as described above (to check Hooke's Law). Weights were added to just beyond the elastic limit. By continuing to take measurements as the load was reduced the dotted line on the graph was obtained. The spring was found to have a **permanent extension** when all the masses had been removed.

Most newton meters and spring balances have a stop so that you cannot stretch the spring beyond its elastic limit. If you do, it will no longer give the correct reading when a force is applied.

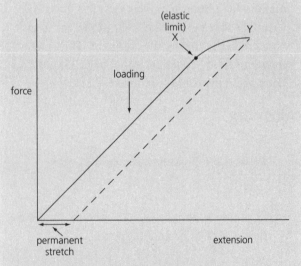

Fig 2 Going beyond the elastic limit

Up to X, the spring obeys Hooke's Law. Between X and Y, the spring has plastic behaviour.

Not all materials obey Hooke's Law. The graph in Fig 3 was drawn after an experiment was done to stretch a piece of rubber. The extension was not proportional to the force.

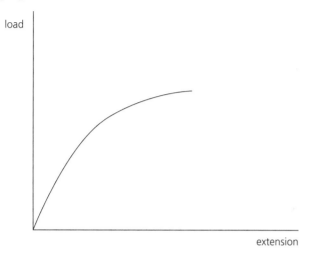

Fig 3 Stretching a material that does not obey Hooke's Law

Force and pressure

When we think about pushing forces it is very important to consider the area over which they are spread. It is easy to push a drawing pin into a piece of wood with your finger but not so easy to push in an ordinary sewing pin. The force needed may be similar but the large head on the drawing pin spreads the force over the end of your finger. The small head of the sewing pin has a very small area where all the force is concentrated. The pin may go into your finger rather than into the wood!

The equation for working this out is:

$$\text{Pressure} = \frac{\text{Force (N)}}{\text{Area (m}^2\text{)}}$$

One newton per square metre is called one pascal (Pa).

Pressure calculations

Examples

1 An elephant of mass 5,000kg (i.e. a weight of 50,000N) was standing with all four feet on the ground. Each foot had an area of 200cm². What was the pressure exerted on the floor?

Answer: 62.5N/cm².

The total area covered by the elephant's feet was 200 × 4 = 800cm².

Pressure = force/area = 50,000/800 = 62.5N/cm².

2 A girl has a mass of 50kg (i.e. a weight of 500N). She is wearing shoes with heels which each have an area of 1cm². What is the pressure on the floor if all her weight is applied through her heels?

Answer: 250N/cm².

Her two heels have an area of 2cm².

Pressure = force/area = 500/2 = 250N/cm².

The elephant may weigh 100 times more than the girl but the girl exerts four times more pressure on the floor than the elephant does (250/62.5 = 4). The girl will certainly do more damage to the floor!

Other examples of using a large area to reduce pressure:

• The use of snow shoes and skis to stop sinking into soft snow.
• Camels have evolved large feet that stop them sinking into desert sand.

Pressure in liquids

Pressure in liquids is transmitted throughout the liquid and acts in all directions. Pressure increases with depth.

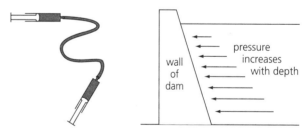

Fig 4 Pressure in liquids

Pressure is transmitted from one syringe to the other. As one is pushed in the other is pushed out.

Calculations involving pressure in liquids

Because liquids are almost impossible to compress, pressure is transmitted through the liquid in all directions. This is useful because we can:

• Use liquids to move forces to where we want them.
• Use pressure in liquids to magnify a force.

Example

What is the pressure on the right hand cylinder?

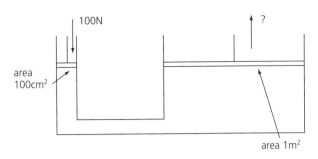

Fig 5 Pressure in liquids calculation

Force on left hand side = 100N.
Area of left hand cylinder = 100cm².

Force on right hand side = ?
Area of right hand cylinder = 1m².

Answer
Area of left hand cylinder = 100cm² = 0.01m².
(1cm² = 0.0001m² see above.)

Pressure applied to left hand cylinder
= force/area = 100/0.01
= 10,000N/m² = 10,000Pa.

Because the pressure is transmitted through the liquid this is also the pressure on the right hand cylinder. This cylinder has an area of 1m².

Pressure = force/area. Therefore 10,000 = force/1.

Therefore force on right hand cylinder = 10,000N.

The force that was applied to the left hand cylinder has been magnified 100 times. This is because the area of the cylinder has been increased by this amount.

A hydraulic braking system

Using a liquid to transmit and magnify pressure is an essential feature of hydraulic jacks, hydraulic control systems for cranes and earth-moving vehicles, and vehicle braking systems. In a braking system, pressure is applied through a pedal to liquid (brake fluid) in the so called 'master' cylinder. This is connected by a system of pipes to 'slave' cylinders at each wheel. The pressure transmitted through the liquid and the slave cylinder acts to apply the brake pads to the wheels. In this way the force applied to the foot pedal can be applied to all wheels simultaneously and magnified at the same time. This enables a vehicle to be stopped by a small force from the foot.

QUESTION

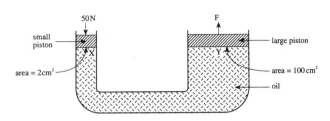

Fig 6

The diagram above shows the principle of the hydraulic car jack. A small force applied to the small piston enables a large load (the car) to be lifted by the large piston.

a i If a force of 50N is applied to the small piston, calculate the pressure measured in N/cm² produced in the oil at X.

....
....
....(2 marks)

ii What is the pressure exerted by the oil at Y?

....
....(1 mark)

iii Calculate the upward force, F, acting on the large piston.

....
....
....(1 mark)

b i If the piston moves down a distance of 5cm, how far upwards does the large piston move?

....
....(2 marks)

ii Describe one change to this basic design which would enable the jack to lift the car up high enough so that you can work under it.

....
....
....
....(1 mark)
[WJEC]

ANSWER

a i 25N/cm².
    Use pressure = force/area
    p = 50/2 = 25N/cm²

ii The same pressure is exerted at Y, 25N/cm².

iii 2,500N.

Again, use pressure = force/area
Rearrange to give: pressure × area = force
25 × 100 = 2500N.

b i 0.1cm.
The volume moved on both sides of the jack is
the same, so:
(small piston) 5 × 2 = d × 100 (large piston)
(5 × 2)/100 = d
distance moved = 0.1cm.
or you can do it this way:
$F_1 × d_1 = F_2 × d_2$
as work done on both sides is equal
50 × 5 = 2500 × d
d = 0.1cm.

ii Increase the length of the left hand side.
or: Increase the area of the left hand side
(or decrease the area of the right hand side).
or: Use a piston/valve so that more liquid can
be pumped in on the left hand side.

Pressure in gases

If air gets into a hydraulic braking system, it stops
working. This is because gases are compressible and
when pressure is applied to a gas its volume simply
gets smaller. The pressure that is applied to the
brakes is absorbed by the gas and the brakes do not
work. (See p 153 for Boyle's Law which helps you
with calculations involving gases under pressure.)

Floating and sinking
The weight of liquid that the boat displaces
determines the size of the upthrust force.
When the boat sinks, it has displaced as much
water as possible and there is too much weight
in the boat to be balanced by the upthrust.

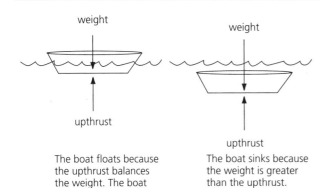

The boat floats because
the upthrust balances
the weight. The boat
is in equilibrium.

The boat sinks because
the weight is greater
than the upthrust.

Fig 7 Floating and sinking

Machines that seem to make work easier

A **machine** is the name given to a device which
makes a job easier to do.

Inclined plane

A slope or incline is a type of machine, as it makes
the force needed to move an object upwards smaller
than that needed to move it vertically against gravity.
Roads and railway lines are sloped upwards
gradually to keep the force required from the vehicle
as low as possible. Wedges, knife blades and screws
are other examples of how the principle of the
inclined plane makes a job easier to do.

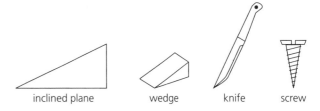

inclined plane   wedge   knife   screw

Fig 8 Inclined planes

A hydraulic system also makes a job easier to do.

Pulleys

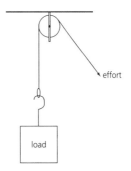

effort

load

Fig 9 One pulley system
This pulley does not make the force smaller, but it is easier to
pull downwards because you can use the force of gravity on
you to help.

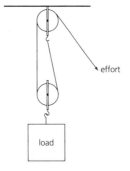

effort

load

Fig 10 Two pulley system
With two pulley wheels the effort needed will be
approximately half the force needed to lift the load directly.

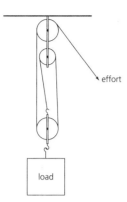

Fig 11 Three pulley system
With three pulleys the effort is reduced to about one third of the load.

Beware: Machines do not make the work less!
Although machines may reduce the force that is needed to do a job they can never reduce the amount of work we have to do.

Work = force × distance moved by force (see p 297)

It is important to realise that you do not get more work out of a machine than you put in. You may get a force that is one hundred times bigger, but it will only move one hundredth the distance. If the machine were to work perfectly (with 100% efficiency) you would get the same amount of work out of the machine as you put in.

Efficiency

The efficiency of a machine can be calculated from the equation:

$$\text{Efficiency} = \frac{\text{useful energy output}}{\text{total energy input}} = \frac{\text{work done on load}}{\text{work done by effort}}$$

Efficiency is often expressed as a percentage by multiplying this fraction by 100.

Pulleys and efficiency

The more strings you have in a pulley system the further you need to move the effort to have the same effect on the load. Any gain you make in reducing the force is at least made up for by the increased distance that you have to move the effort.

- With one pulley
  The effort must be slightly greater than the load, because it must overcome any friction in the pulley as well as doing the lifting.

- With two pulleys
  There are two strings that must be shortened to lift the load. While the effort moves two metres the load will only rise by one metre. If there were no friction and the bottom pulley – which also has to be lifted – was weightless, the effort would be half the load and the machine would be 100% efficient. All the energy put in would be converted into useful work.

Example

For a two pulley system working at 100% efficiency:
work put in = work got out
To move a load of 10 newtons a height of 1 metre, the effort will have to move 2 metres, but will only need to be 5 newtons.

$$\text{force (effort)} \times \text{distance} = \text{force (load)} \times \text{distance}$$
$$5N \times 2m = 10N \times 1m$$

In practice no machine is ever 100% efficient, as some of the work put in is used to overcome friction and therefore wasted.

QUESTION

Below is a diagram of a crane lifting a load.

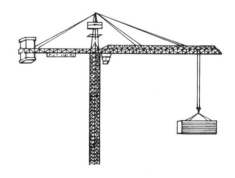

Fig 12

To lift the load requiring 250,000J it used 625,000J of energy in fuel. What is the efficiency of the crane?

A 20%

B 25%

C 30%

D 40%

[SEG 1994]

ANSWER

D

Efficiency = Useful energy output / Total energy input
        = (250,000 / 625,000) × 100%
        = 40%

QUESTION

The diagram below shows one way of lifting a bucket of bricks.

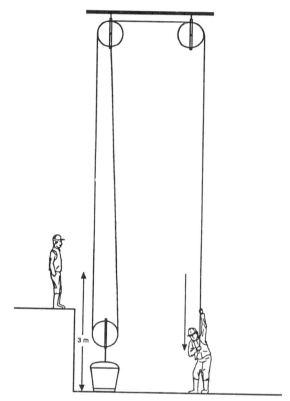

Fig 13 Pulley system

a When the free end of the rope is pulled down, the load is lifted. Complete the following sentence. The work done in pulling the rope down is used to increase the .... energy of the .... and bricks. (2 marks)

b The weight of the bricks is 100N and they are lifted 3m. Calculate the work done on the bricks.

....

....

    Answer.. (2 marks)

c To lift the bricks 360J of work has to be done at the free end of the rope. Calculate the efficiency of the system.

....

.... (2 marks)

d Suggest one reason why the efficiency of the pulley system is less than 100%.

....

....(1 mark)
[NEAB]

ANSWER

a potential, bucket *(See p 303 for a discussion of potential energy.)*

b 300J
    Work done = force × distance moved.
        = 100 × 3 = 300 joules   Ans 300J.

c 83.3%.
    Efficiency(%) = work done on load/work done by effort × 100.
        = 300/360 × 100 = 83.3%

d Some of the effort is used to overcome the friction in the three pulleys.
    Energy is transferred into heat rather than lifting the load.
    OR: The calculation used the work done on the bricks. The bucket and lowest pulley also have to be lifted by three metres.
    Question (d) asked for ONE reason. Do not give more than one. Decide which is the best reason and explain it as clearly as you can.

Levers and turning forces

Many machines have levers in their mechanism. To understand how a lever works we use the Principle of Moments. A moment is the turning effect of a force.

Moment = force × the perpendicular distance between the point where the force acts and the pivot.

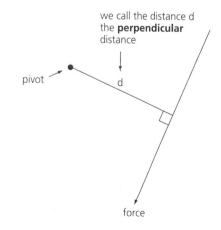

Fig 14

An object does not move when the turning forces on it balance. But the slightest extra force on one side will cause a movement and a job can be done.

The Principle of Moments says that at equilibrium:
Total clockwise moment =
                    Total anti-clockwise moment

Example

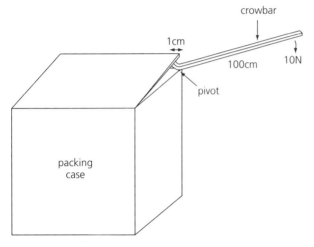

Fig 15 Using a lever

At the point where the crowbar is just about to open the packing case, the forces are balanced (ignore the weight of the crowbar).
Total clockwise moment =
                    total anti-clockwise moment

$$10 \times 100 = \text{Load} \times 1$$
Therefore Load = 1,000N

An effort of 10N has been used to provide a force of 1,000N to open the packing case.

Centre of mass (or gravity)

In some problems relating to levers and balancing forces, the weight of the object acting as a lever becomes important. In order to perform the necessary calculations we can use the idea of a **centre of gravity** or **centre of mass**. While gravity actually acts on every part of an object, there is a point through which the whole weight of an object seems to act. This is called the centre of gravity or centre of mass.

Centre of mass (gravity) and moments

In the example with the crowbar above, we assumed that the weight of the crowbar was small compared to the effort that had to be applied. In the next problem you cannot do this.

QUESTION

A boy finds that he can use a plank of wood as a see-saw if he tries to balance it one metre from the end. If he then stands on the shorter side the plank will balance his weight. The plank is four metres long and weighs 400 newtons. What is the weight of the boy?

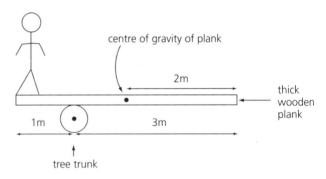

Fig 16 A boy balancing a plank of wood

ANSWER

400N.

We must assume that the plank is uniform (the same width and depth and density for all of its length) if we are to know where its centre of gravity is situated. If this is the case its centre of gravity will be half way along. This is where the plank would balance if the boy does not stand on it.
If we then use the Principle of Moments:

total clockwise moment = total anti-clockwise moment

$400 \times 1 = $ weight of boy $\times 1$

Therefore weight of boy = 400N. He was the same weight as the plank!

QUESTION

The diagram shows a wheelbarrow.

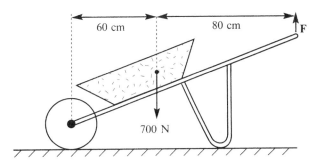

Fig 17

What force in newtons do you need to lift the wheelbarrow?

A 300
B 525
C 600
D 1633

[SEG 1994]

ANSWER

A
(The pivot is at the centre of the wheel.)
Total clockwise moment = total anti-clockwise moment
$700 \times 60 = F \times 140$
so, $(700 \times 60)/140 = F$
$F = 300N$.

What do we mean by stable equilibrium?

stable equilibrium

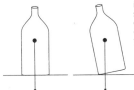

if pushed (gently!) to one side, it will return to the original position. (The centre of mass acts through the base).

unstable equilibrium

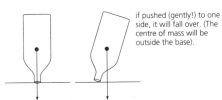

if pushed (gently!) to one side, it will fall over. (The centre of mass will be outside the base).

To make an object more stable we:
• lower the centre of mass
• widen the base to increase the chance of the centre of mass acting through the base.

Fig 18 A milk bottle in two different positions

QUESTION

A child stands a wooden brick on its end as shown in the diagram.

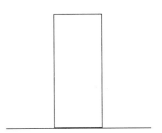

Fig 19

The child then pushes the brick to make it tilt.

Fig 20

How far must the brick be tilted to make it fall over? Explain your answer.

[You may draw a labelled diagram if you wish.]

....
....
....(2 marks)

[NEAB]

ANSWER

It must be tilted so far that the centre of mass would not be directly above the base of the brick.

You could draw this on a diagram to make it clear what you mean.

QUESTION

The diagram below shows an outline of a balance. The balance is used to weigh lorries. A fraction of the weight of the lorry is used as the load on the right side of the pivot. A standard weight W is moved along the arm until the weight is balanced.

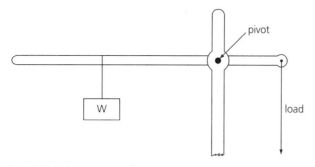

Fig 21 A balance

a As the weight W is moved away from the pivot it can support a heavier load. Why is this?

....

....

....(2 marks)

b i The weight W is 100N. When it is 0.2m from the pivot it balances the load. Calculate the moment of the weight W about the pivot.

....

....

Answer.................................Nm (2 marks)

ii The load is one hundredth of the weight of a lorry and is 0.02m from the pivot. Calculate the weight of the lorry.

....

....

Answer.................................N (2 marks)

[NEAB]

ANSWER

a The moment of W is W × distance from pivot. As it is moved further away the moment gets bigger so W can support a heavier load.

b i 20Nm.
Moment = W × distance = 100 × 0.2
= 20 newton metres.
Answer 20Nm.

ii 100,000N
Total clockwise moment =
total anti-clockwise moment
load × 0.02 = 20Nm (calculated in part (b) (i))
Therefore load = 20/0.02 = 1,000N.
This is one hundredth weight of lorry.
So the weight of the lorry = 100 × 1,000N
Answer 100,000N

Important equations that you must be able to use when thinking about forces and materials

Pressure (Pa) = Force (N)/Area (m²)

Efficiency = useful energy output (J)/total energy input (J)

Efficiency = work done on load (J)/work done by effort (J)

(Efficiency is often given as a percentage, by multiplying the answer to the two equations above by 100.)

Moment (Nm) = force (N) × perpendicular distance between the point where the force acts and the pivot (m)

Total clockwise moment = total anti-clockwise moment

Revision sheet

Forces and motion

1 a What is a push or a pull known as?
b What is the equation linking: distance, force and work?
c What are the units of force?
d In diagrams how can we show the direction and size of a force?
e Finish this:
.... = work done (joules)/time taken
(seconds)

2 Finish these sentences:
a When an object is not moving, the resultant force on it is ....
b If a force acts on a stationary object, the object.................. .
c If a force meets an object moving in the opposite direction to the force the object
....
d Friction is a force that.................. .

3 How are 'mass' and 'weight' different?

4 a What is the equation linking: distance, speed and time?
b What is the difference between 'speed' and 'velocity'?
c Finish this equation:
acceleration (m/s²) = change in velocity (m/s)/
....

5 What do you understand by 'centripetal force'?

Momentum and collisions

1 a What is the equation linking: mass, momentum and velocity?
  b Finish this equation: force = mass × ....
  c How can you calculate the 'change in momentum' of an object?
2 What is meant by terminal velocity?
3 What is meant by each of the following and give a formula for calculating it:
  a Kinetic energy?
  b Potential energy?

Forces and materials

1 a What is Hooke's Law?
  b What is meant by 'beyond the elastic limit'?
2 Explain each of these terms as they apply to forces and materials:
  a Elastic.
  b Plastic.
  c Brittle.
3 Finish this equation:
  Pressure (................) = Force (................)/
                    Area (................)
4 Complete these sentences:
  a Pressure .... with depth.
  b Pressure is transmitted through liquids in all directions as liquids are nearly impossible to................ .
  c Air must not get into a hydraulic braking system because gases are .... and would prevent the system working.
5 a Name two types of machines which make a job easier to do.
  b Explain 'No machine makes the work less.'
  c What is the equation for calculating the efficiency of a machine?
6 a Explain what is meant by a 'moment' in terms of forces?
  b What information do you need to calculate the mass of an object on a balancing beam using the 'Principle of Moments'?
7 Write a sentence explaining:
  a Stable equilibrium.
  b Centre of mass (or gravity).

Revision sheet answers

Forces and motion

1 a Force.
  b Work = force × distance.
  c Newtons (N).
  d The way the arrow is pointing shows the direction of the force, the size of the arrow can show the size of the force.
  e Power (watts) = work done (joules)/
                    time taken (seconds).
2 a When an object is not moving the resultant force on it is zero.
  b If a force acts on a stationary object, the object begins to move (accelerates).
  c If a force meets an object moving in the opposite direction to the force the object slows down (decelerates).
  d Friction is a force that tries to stop things moving.
3 Mass – the amount of matter in an object (measured in kg).
  Weight – the force of gravity on an object (measured in newtons).
4 a Speed (m/s) = distance (m)/time (s).
  b Velocity is the term used when we know the direction as well as the speed. It is a vector quantity.
  c Acceleration (m/s^2) = change in velocity (m/s)/
                    time (seconds).
5 Centripetal force – when an object moves round in a circle this is the force that acts towards the centre of the circle.

Momentum and collisions

1 a Momentum = mass × velocity.
  b Finish this equation: force = mass × acceleration.
  c Change in momentum = force × time.
2 Terminal velocity: when an object is falling and the downward force of gravity is balanced by the upward force of friction (due to air resistance), the falling object has a constant speed which is called the terminal velocity.

3 a Kinetic energy: movement energy: $KE = \frac{1}{2}mv^2$.
  b Potential energy: when an object has energy due to its position: If you lift an object: $PE = mgh$.

Forces and materials

1 a Hooke's Law: Extension of a material is proportional to the force being applied.
  b 'Beyond the elastic limit': When a material has been stretched beyond the point (elastic limit) up to which it obeys Hooke's Law.
2 a Elastic – material returns to original size after force removed.
  b Plastic – material stays in new shape after force removed.
  c Brittle – material breaks when force applied.
3 Finish this equation:
   Pressure (Pa) = Force (N)/Area (m²)
4 Complete these sentences:
  a Pressure increases with depth.
  b Pressure is transmitted through liquids in all directions as liquids are nearly impossible to compress.
  c Air must not get into a hydraulic braking system because gases are compressible and would prevent the system working.
5 a Two types of machines which make a job easier to do:
   Inclined plane, pulley, lever, hydraulic system.
  b 'No machine makes the work less': Machines make the work seem easier by reducing the force required, but the work is actually more.
  c The equation for calculating the efficiency of a machine:
   Efficiency = useful energy output/
                         total energy input
   or
   Efficiency = work done on load/
                         work done by effort
6 a A 'moment' in terms of forces: Turning effect of a force.
  b Information needed to calculate the mass of an object on a balancing beam using the 'Principle of Moments': Another mass and the distance of both of them from the pivot.
7 a Stable equilibrium: An object in stable equilibrium if gently tilted will return to its original position.
  b Centre of mass (or gravity): The point at which the whole weight of the object seems to act.

Student Answer with Comments

A faulty 600kg car leaked one drip of oil every second as it rolled down a hill.

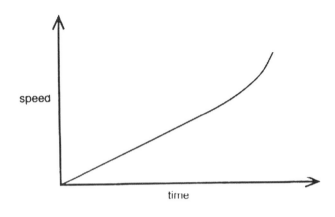

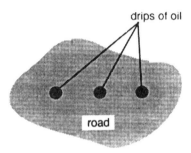

Fig 1

a Explain how the graph could be obtained from the drops of oil.
   The time could be plotted as the drops of oil fell at regular intervals (1 a second). ✔ *The speed could be plotted using speed = distance/time. This refers to the distance between the drops* ✔ *of oil and how often they fell.* ②
   As the time between drops was 1 s you can plot distance as speed
                                                     (2 marks)
b What can you say about the steepness of the hill? Explain your reasons.
   The hill was a uniform slope to begin with as the car accelerated uniformly. ✔ *The hill then got steeper as the car began to accelerate non-uniformly.* ✔ ②
                                                     (3 marks)
   Make clear that gradient of graph is acceleration.
c The car crashed into a stationary van at the bottom of the hill. The speed just before the crash was 5m/s.

Calculate the momentum of the car before the collision.

5 × 600 = 3,000

momentum = 3,000kg m/s ✓ ②

(2 marks)

before crash

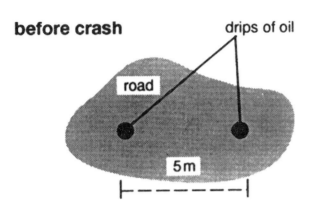

after crash

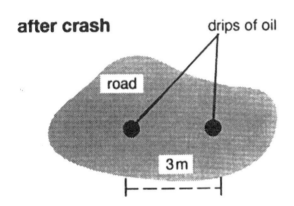

d Why was there a sudden drop in the speed of the car after it crashed?

Some of the car's kinetic energy had been absorbed by the van. ✓ ①

(1 mark)

e When they collided the van and the car stuck together. What was their momentum?

3000kg m/s. The momentum is the same after as it was before. ✓ ①

(1 mark)

f Calculate the mass of the van.

The mass was:

(2 marks)

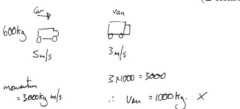

This would probably get you one mark. ①

You have forgotten that the car and van stuck together. The total mass after collision was 1000 kg but 600 kg was the mass of the car. Therefore mass of van = 400 kg.

9/11 [MEG]

An exam question for you to try

The diagrams below show the hydraulic brake system of a car.

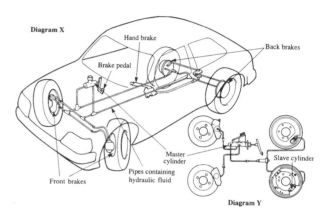

Fig 25

a Use the diagrams to help you explain how a hydraulic brake system works.

....
....
....
....
....
....
....
....
....

(4 marks)

b i The piston in the master cylinder has an area of 30cm². It is pushed with a force of 100N. Calculate the pressure that the piston exerts on the brake fluid. Show how you obtained your answer.

....
....
....

(3 marks)

ii What happens if a small amount of air gets into the brake fluid?

....
....

....

....

(2 marks)

Part question [SEG 1994]

Answer

a When the brake pedal is pushed the master cylinder causes pressure to build up in the brake fluid. Brake fluid is a liquid so it is not compressed like gases. The pressure causes the slave piston to be forced out. This applies the brakes. The hydraulic system allows an equal pressure to be applied to all wheels.

b i Pressure = Force/Area

    $= 100/30 = 3.3$ N/cm^2

    Ans $= 3.3$ N/cm^2

  ii The gas would be compressed. The brakes might fail as there would be a lower pressure in the liquid. This means that the slave cylinder might not be pushed with sufficient force to cause the brakes to be applied.

15 Using energy

Using energy	Midland (MEG)				Northern (NEAB)		London (ULEAC)				Southern (SEG)		Welsh (WJEC)
	Own	Nuffield	Salters	Suffolk	Co-ordinated	Modular	Modular GASP	Combined	Co-ordinated	Modular	Double	Modular	Co-ordinated
ENERGY RESOURCES													
Importance of energy	✓	✓	✓	✓	✓	✓	✓	✓	✓	✓	✓	✓	✓
Energy forms and energy transfer	✓	✓	✓	✓	✓	✓	✓	✓	✓	✓	✓	✓	✓
Renewable and non-renewable energy sources	✓	✓	✓	✓	✓	✓	✓	✓	✓	✓	✓	✓	✓
Generating electricity	✓	H	✓	✓	✓	✓	✓	H	✓	✓	✓	✓	✓
Efficiency of energy transfers	H	✓	✓	H	✓	✓	✓	✓	✓	✓	✓	✓	✓
ENERGY AND TEMPERATURE													
Heat and temperature	✓	✓	✓	✓	✓	✓	✓	✓	✓	✓	✓	✓	✓
Changing the temperature of solids, liquids and gases	✓	✓	✓	✓	✓	✓	✓	✓	✓	✓	✓	✓	✓
Energy transfer involving a change in temperature	✓	✓	✓	✓	✓	✓	✓	✓	✓	✓	✓	✓	✓
Keeping warm	✓	✓	✓	✓	✓	✓	✓	✓	✓	✓	✓	✓	✓
Saving energy in the home	✓	✓	✓	✓	✓	✓	✓	✓	✓	✓	✓	✓	✓

Energy resources

What is energy?

Whenever something happens you can be absolutely certain that energy is involved. Any sort of movement requires energy, although it is difficult to explain exactly what energy is. Energy can be defined as the ability to do work. It is easy to spot energy moving about if you observe carefully. When an object moves or gets hot then energy is being transferred. You could say that whenever anything happens energy changes from one sort into another!

Waves are a way of transferring energy from one place to another without any matter being transferred. See the 'using waves' section for details of this, and don't forget to look at the chapters on light and sound as well as the one on waves.

Anything that moves by itself usually contains a source of energy. Some examples of this 'source of energy' are:

- Chemical energy – in our food, in a battery, in petrol in a car.
- Potential energy – in wound up springs and stretched elastic bands.

The energy is hidden but is available to be transferred at any time.

Energy forms

We sometimes think of energy as existing in various forms. These may help us to think about how energy is transferred. It is the transfer of energy that is useful.

Chemical energy is the name given to energy that becomes available when chemical bonds are broken and remade in a different way. During the reaction between glucose and oxygen in our cells (respiration), large amounts of chemical energy are released. This energy appears as thermal energy to keep us warm and kinetic energy when we move.

Kinetic energy is the name given to the energy carried by all moving objects. A moving object has the ability to do work and because of this is likely to be associated with energy transfer.

Thermal energy – or heat – is transferred whenever there is a temperature difference between two adjacent objects.

Gravitational potential energy is given to any object when it is lifted. The object can turn the energy into kinetic energy quite easily by falling back down! This is one type of stored or potential energy.

Electrical energy is one of the most useful 'forms' of energy. It can easily be taken to wherever it is needed as an electric current (a flow of electrons) and transferred into heat, light, sound and movement.

Nuclear energy is the form of energy that is transferred when an atomic nucleus undergoes a fission reaction in a nuclear power station or atom bomb. The nuclei of the atoms split apart and energy is transferred as heat – together with light, sound and movement if there is an explosion.

While it may be useful to think of energy in various forms, it is the transfer of energy that is important. There is a basic rule for energy transfer: *energy cannot be created or destroyed*. This is called the Principle of Conservation of Energy. At the end of the energy transfer there must be the same amount of energy as there was at the beginning. It is unlikely that all the energy will be in the desired form. Some energy is *always* transferred into the surroundings, making them warmer. The total energy at the end is the same as at the beginning, but it is in a variety of different 'forms'.

Where does energy come from?

Apart from food, we obtain most of our energy from the fossil fuels coal, oil and gas. When fuels burn they react chemically with oxygen to give new products. Energy is transferred from chemical energy in the fuel to heat, which may be used to warm up the surroundings. We can also use these reactions to boil water and make steam, which can be used to drive a turbine and produce electricity.

Non-renewable energy sources

These are energy sources that will one day run out. Once used they cannot be used again.

- Coal, Oil and Gas
  Fossils fuels are the remains of animal and plant life that grew millions of years ago. Plants use energy from the sun to turn carbon dioxide and water into sugar by photosynthesis (see p 23). The plant then uses the sugars to make other products. In this way energy from the sun is 'locked into' the plant. By burning these fuels the energy

obtained millions of years ago from the sun is released.

Disadvantages of using fossil fuels:
- Reserves of oil and gas are relatively short although coal will keep us going for many years.
- All these fuels burn to produce carbon dioxide as one of the products of the reaction. Carbon dioxide is a 'greenhouse gas' (see 'Natural cycles and energy flow' chapter for more details).

It will obviously be a great advantage if we can make our fossil fuels go further. By being economical with them we save money and put less carbon dioxide into the atmosphere.

- Nuclear power
  This depends upon uranium which we obtain from minerals that are found in the Earth's crust. It too will eventually run out.

These energy sources *cannot* be replaced by the Earth in the timespan in which we will use them up. Therefore they will run out.

Renewable energy resources

These will not run out. The more we use this type of energy source the longer we can conserve our supplies of fossil fuels. If they do not put carbon dioxide into the atmosphere it is an extra advantage.

- Wind
  Wind farms (more than one windmill) can be a good source of energy.

  Disadvantages:
  - They are weather dependent.
  - A lot of windmills are needed to provide enough electricity for a town.
  - Not everyone likes to see windmills on the horizon. As they have to be placed where there is most wind, they tend to be high up on hills and moors. There have already been strong objections from local people that they are an eyesore.

- Tides
  In some places around our coast the tide rises and falls by over 10 metres twice every day. If a barrage is built across a tidal estuary where such a change in level occurs, the difference in height of the water between one side of the barrage and the other can be used to drive a turbine and produce electricity.

Disadvantages:
- Expensive to build.
- Disrupts shipping.
- Disturbs the wild life of the area by changing the pattern of the tides in the estuary.

- Wave energy
  This uses the up and down movement of waves on the sea as a source of energy. One technique involves using a large number of floats that bob up and down as a wave goes past.

  Disadvantages:
  - The technology is difficult as the up and down motion depends on the size and frequency of the waves, and has to be turned efficiently into rotation in order to drive a turbine.
  - Large numbers of floats are needed and this technique is still under investigation.

- Geothermal
  Natural processes within the Earth's crust frequently generate heat. Sometimes, as in Iceland, hot water may be naturally forced to the surface as hot springs and geysers. In some places it has proved possible to pump cold water far down underground to be heated by hot rocks surrounding the pipes. On return to the surface this hot water can be used directly for central heating or to make steam to produce electricity.

- Solar
  This is the energy that we obtain directly from the sun. Solar cells can be used even when the sun is partly obscured. They turn the rays from the sun directly into electricity. Having been developed for use in space, they are now finding more and more uses in everyday life. On a small scale they may power your calculator; on a large scale they can be used to heat a whole office block!

- Hydroelectricity
  This is an important source of energy in mountainous countries. Rain which falls in the mountains is trapped behind a dam. As it is allowed to escape through the dam it drives a turbine to make electricity.

- Wood
  Wood is used more than any other fuel on our planet. In many countries burning wood is the usual means of cooking and keeping warm. Wood produces carbon dioxide and adds to the

greenhouse effect, but it is a renewable source of energy – provided that enough trees are grown to replace the ones that are cut down.

These energy sources *can* be replaced as quickly as we use them. Therefore they will not run out.

Other energy sources

Some power stations burn waste products that otherwise might be difficult to dispose of. However, they do produce carbon dioxide.

- Waste from rearing chickens.
  Chicken litter – the waste sawdust and droppings from rearing hens inside for the poultry industry – and unwanted straw can be used as the fuel for power stations.
- Old tyres from motor vehicles
  The metal strengthening in the tyres is reclaimed. The temperature of the furnace at the power station is hot enough to make sure that the poisonous gases produced by burning rubber are made safe.

Another alternative to burning material from animals and plants, such as dung and straw (called **biomass**), is to allow it to be broken down by bacteria inside a container called a digester. Under properly controlled conditions methane gas is produced, which is then burnt to release energy. On a small scale many farms now use this type of process to get rid of unwanted animal waste and provide a cheap source of energy.

Where does our energy come from originally?

Fossil fuels, wood and biomass all originate in growing plants which obtain energy directly from the sun. Tides are a product of the sun and moon, which produce the gravitational forces that cause them. Wind, waves and rain (to give hydroelectricity) are all a product of our climate, which is driven by energy from the sun (see p 370). In other words, virtually all the energy we use comes from the sun.

Using energy resources to generate electricity
Using non-renewable energy
Energy from fuel is used to generate electricity. Most power stations in Britain use fossil fuel – coal, oil or gas.
Some power stations use nuclear fuel – mainly uranium and plutonium.
Whichever fuel is used the power stations have the same key features:
- The fuel is used to heat water.
- The water is turned into steam.
- The steam turns turbines.
- The turbines then turn generators.
- The generators produce electricity.
'Electricity in the home' (p 271) gives more detail of this.
Using renewable energy
Water may be heated by passing it underground where it is heated by hot rocks (called a geothermal process). This cuts out the first stage of the traditional power station as the steam produced can then be used to turn the turbines.
The turbine can also be turned directly; in effect the first three stages of the process above are omitted. The turbines can be turned by:
- Allowing water to escape from a dam in a hydroelectric scheme.
- Allowing water to pass through a tidal barrier.
- The up-and-down movement of the tides.
- The wind.
Using pumped storage
There are certain times of the day, such as the time that most people get up, when the demand for electricity is very high. We must have enough power stations to meet this demand even if they stand idle for much of the rest of the day.
Pumped storage uses electricity from power stations at times of little demand to pump water from a lower mountain lake to a higher one. Instead of the turbines making electricity they are used to pump the water upwards. At times of high demand the water is allowed to run back into the lower lake. The turbines act to make electricity, which is fed into the National Grid. This system means you do not need as many expensive fossil fuel power stations to meet the peaks in demand.
Electricity can be generated directly from the sun (using solar cells).

QUESTION

a Here are three examples of power stations;
Drax – coal fired
Hinkley B – nuclear
Severn barrage – a tidal barrage which may be built in the future.
Describe ONE advantage and ONE disadvantage of each power station, considering such factors as the environment, reliability and costs of building, operating and closing.

Drax ....
....
....
....

Hinkley B ....
....
....

Severn Barrage..
....
....
....(6 marks)
[ULEAC]

ANSWER

Note – Only one advantage and disadvantage of each is asked for. There are 6 marks so you will only get 1 mark for each advantage or disadvantage. Some of the alternatives that would get you credit are given below.

Drax   Adv.   Coal is cheap/easily available.
       Disad.   Coal is non-renewable/burning it gives carbon dioxide (greenhouse gas)/and sulphur dioxide (acid rain).

Hinkley B   Adv.   Little environmental damage when in operation/does not produce carbon dioxide or sulphur dioxide.
       Disad.   Expensive to build and to take out of use. Severe environmental damage if a leak.

Severn barrage   Adv   Renewable energy source/no air pollution.
       Disad.   Expensive to build/changes environment of estuary.

Energy transfer

Many things you use each day carry out energy transfers. Often you cannot see these happening but you will be aware of them! Some items that allow energy to be transferred are listed below:

Items	Energy transfer	
	from	to
electric motor	electrical	kinetic
loudspeaker	electrical	sound
microphone	sound	electrical
solar cell (as in a calculator)	light	electrical
electric fire	electrical	heat
battery	chemical	electrical
bow and arrow then	chemical elastic potential	elastic potential kinetic
lift then	electrical kinetic	kinetic gravitational potential

How efficient are energy transfers?

Whenever energy is transferred the *total amount of energy stays the same*. However, only part of it is transferred usefully. In other words, only part of the energy goes where we want it. The fraction of the energy that is usefully transferred is called the efficiency.

$$\text{Efficiency} = \frac{\text{Useful energy transferred}}{\text{Total energy supplied}}$$

We often multiply this fraction by one hundred to express efficiency as a percentage.

Because energy is the capacity to do work we can use this formula to apply to machines:

$$\text{Efficiency} = \frac{\text{Work out of machine}}{\text{Work put into machine}} \times 100\,\%$$

(see 'Forces and materials' p 310).

A modern car engine is between 30% and 35% efficient. This means that no more than 35% of the energy from the fuel can be transferred into the movement of the car (its kinetic energy). We can show this in a diagram.

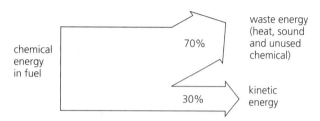

Fig 1

The width of the arrow indicates how much energy is transferred in each of the ways specified.

This type of diagram is sometimes called a 'Sankey' diagram and is a useful way of picturing energy transfers.

When we use a filament light bulb the process is very wasteful. Most of the energy that is transferred to heat the filament is given out as invisible infra-red radiation (see 'Waves and how they work'). Only a small proportion appears as visible light.

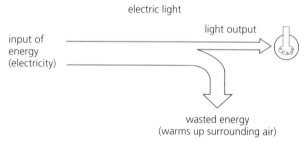

Fig 2

QUESTION

The diagram below represents the changes taking place in a torch during one second.

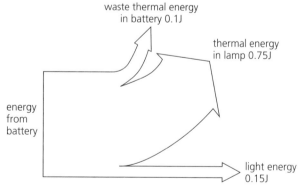

Fig 3

a Use the information shown on the diagram to calculate;

i the total energy available from the battery during one second;

....
....(1 mark)

ii the efficiency of the lamp;

....
....(2 marks)
[ULEAC]

ANSWER

i Total energy = 0.15 + 0.75 + 0.1 = 1.0J.

ii Efficiency = (0.15/0.90) × 100 = 16.67%.
The question asked for the efficiency of the lamp, not the torch. Only 0.9J of the energy reaches the lamp so the efficiency is (0.15/0.90) × 100%.

QUESTION

The diagram shows what happens to each 100 joules of energy from crude oil when it is used as petrol in a car. The widths of the arrows show exactly how much energy is transferred in each particular way.

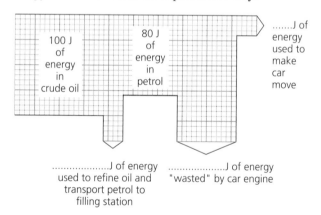

Fig 4

a Complete the diagram by adding the correct energy value alongside each arrow. (3 marks)

b Calculate how efficient the car engine is at transferring the energy from petrol into useful movement. (Show your working.)

....
....
....(2 marks)
[NEAB]

ANSWER

a Used to make the car move – 20J.
Used to refine oil – 20J.

'Wasted' by car engine – 60J.
Each small square = 5J.
b The car engine is 25% efficient.
80J is available in the petrol.
60J of this is 'wasted'.
20J is used by the car.
Efficiency = 20/80 = 25%.

Energy and temperature

If two objects in contact are at different temperatures, energy flows from the higher temperature ('hotter') object to the lower temperature ('colder') object. We usually call this type of energy 'heat'. We can think of all matter as being made of very small particles. Each particle has a certain amount of energy and the total energy of all the particles is called **internal energy** of the substance. The internal energy of an object increases with temperature. However, energy is not the same as temperature.

You will often see 'heat' called 'thermal energy'.

How do we distinguish between heat and temperature?

Imagine that you have two beakers of boiling water. One beaker holds 1,000cm³ of water at 100°C while the other holds only 100cm³ water at the same temperature. We can compare the energy contained in the water in each beaker.

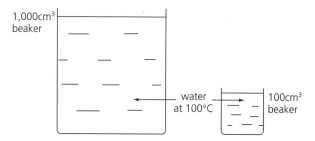

Fig 1

The amount of energy ('heat') held by the molecules in the two beakers must be different. It will have taken much more energy to boil the large beaker of water than the small beaker, assuming they both started at room temperature. In fact there will be 10 times more energy in the 1,000cm³ of water than in the 100cm³ of water. The amount of energy in the water depends on the mass as well as the temperature.

When energy is supplied to a substance its temperature usually rises. The particles then have more kinetic energy.
The energy needed to raise the temperature of 1kg of substance by 1°C is called the specific heat capacity of the substance.
The units of specific heat capacity (s.h.c.) are J/kg°C.
We can calculate how much energy is needed to produce a particular temperature rise by using the following equation:

Energy transfer (J) = Mass (kg) × s.h.c (J/kg°C) ×
Change in temperature (°C)

Water has a specific heat capacity of 4,200J/kg°C. This is the amount of energy needed to raise the temperature of 1kg of water by 1°C.

Substances with large specific heat capacities need lots of energy to produce a temperature rise. They absorb energy without getting too hot!

QUESTION

The information given in the table below shows the specific heat capacities of different substances:

Substance	s.h.c. J/kg°C
A	900
B	120
C	400

Use the information above to answer the following.

a i Calculate the energy supplied to a 2kg block of A which would raise its temperature from 15°C to 35°C.

....
....
....
....(2 marks)

ii What is happening to the particles of which this block is made during the heating process?

....
....(1 mark)

b i What temperature rise would 1,800J of energy produce when given to 1kg of substance B?

....
....
....
....(2 marks)

ii Explain why this amount of energy would produce a smaller temperature rise when given to 1 kg of substance C.

....

....(1 mark)

[WJEC]

ANSWER

a i 36,000J.

Energy = mass × s.h.c. × temperature change
Temperature change is 20°C (from 15°C to 35°C)
Energy = 2 × 900 × 20 = 36,000J.

  ii The particles are vibrating more as their kinetic energy increases.

b i 15°C

Energy = mass × s.h.c. × temperature change
1,800 = 1 × 120 × temperature change
temperature change = 1,800/120 = 15°C.

  ii C has a larger s.h.c. than B, so the same amount of energy will produce a smaller temperature rise.

Changing the temperature of solids, liquids and gases

You are probably aware that the size (or volume) of a substance (whether a solid, liquid or gas) increases as its temperature increases. This is called **expansion**.

Solids

If a solid is heated the particles in it have more energy, they vibrate more and push themselves further apart. The solid expands. Engineers designing large objects have to consider the possible problems that expansion could cause. This is particularly important when a design involves different substances which expand at different rates – otherwise cracks could appear.

- Bridges must have gaps to allow for expansion.
- Railway lines traditionally had frequent gaps to allow for the changes in length of the metal rails caused by expansion and contraction (getting smaller). Nowadays, with pre-stressed rails, concrete sleepers and bigger angled gaps, long lengths of continuous rail can be laid.

You probably have several bi-metal strips in your home! These use expansion and can be used as simple switches to control temperatures and act as safety devices.

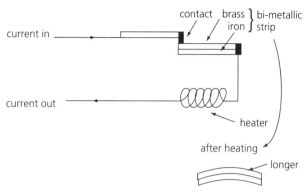

Fig 2 A bi-metal strip

A thermostatically controlled electric fan heater works on this principle. As the heater gets hot the bi-metallic strip also heats up. The brass expands more than the iron, gets longer and curves down from the contact. This breaks the circuit and switches the heater off until the bi-metallic strip cools and returns to its original position.

Two metals which expand by different amounts for the same temperature change are fastened side by side. When the strip is heated it bends, with the metal that expands most on the outside.

Liquids

As the temperature increases the particles have more energy and push themselves further apart. You use an example of this every time that you use a thermometer.

One exception to this rule is water! As you cool water down it behaves as you would expect (contracts) until you reach 4°C. Then water actually expands as it is cooled from 4°C down to its freezing point at zero. This is because of the special structure of ice in which the water molecules are held apart and is the reason why pipes burst if ice forms inside them. This expansion of water to form ice is important in the weathering of rocks (see chapter on rocks). One advantage of this behaviour of water is that ice is less dense and therefore floats on water. This is important for animal and plant life in winter. The top surface of the pond might be frozen but living organisms can survive quite happily under the ice. If the pond were to freeze from the bottom upwards very little would be able to survive!

Gases

As the temperature of a gas increases, there is more energy for the particles, they move more quickly and try to take up more space. Balloons soon burst if they become too hot! Look in Section 7 if you need remindng about Charles' Law which allows you to work out the link between temperature and volume for a gas.

Energy transfer involving a change in temperature

Conduction

When the temperature of one part of a solid is increased, the particles vibrate more as their energy is increased. As these particles vibrate they soon pass on energy to adjacent particles that are not vibrating so much. The energy is gradually spread throughout the whole solid. The transfer of energy in this way is called **conduction**. Conduction is particularly good in metals where the free electrons can move around and help to spread the energy quickly. Conduction also occurs in liquids and in gases, but other methods of energy flow are likely to be more important.

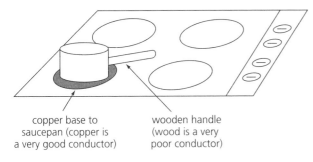

copper base to saucepan (copper is a very good conductor)

wooden handle (wood is a very poor conductor)

Fig 3 Conduction

Convection

When a liquid or a gas (fluid) is heated, it expands (see above). The particles push themselves further apart and the density of the fluid decreases. If a volume of liquid or gas has a lower density than the surrounding fluid it tries to float on top of it. In other words it tries to move upwards. We call this movement **convection**. It means that the hottest part of the liquid or gas always tries to move upwards. The currents that develop because of this movement are called convection currents.

The term 'fluid' can be used when we wish to talk about liquids and gases. For example, water and methane are both fluids.

Radiation

Energy can be transferred by **radiation**. This does not involve the transfer of any matter or contact

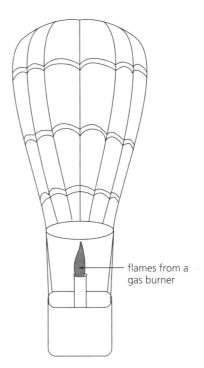

Fig 4 Convection

Hot air balloons rise because of convection.

between substances. The waves of the electro-magnetic spectrum have the ability to transfer energy in this way (see Chapter 13 'The electromagnetic spectrum'). Infra-red rays can travel through a vacuum but when they are absorbed by molecules they cause the particles in the molecules to vibrate more. In this way thermal energy from the sun is transferred to the Earth. All objects give out a certain amount of energy by radiation. The higher the temperature of the object the more energy is given out.

QUESTION

This question is about conduction, convection and radiation. Mountain walkers often wear three layers of clothing.

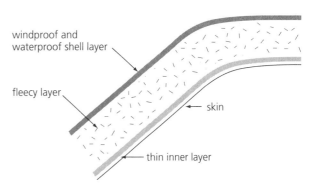

windproof and waterproof shell layer

fleecy layer

skin

thin inner layer

Fig 5

a Explain how the fleecy layer reduces energy loss from the body.

....

....(2 marks)

b Give two reasons why the fleecy layer does not work so well if the shell layer is removed.

1 ....

2 ....

(2 marks)

c Some shell layers have a reflective lining. What process of energy loss does this reduce?

....(1 mark)

[MEG]

ANSWER

a The fleecy layer traps air. Air is a poor conductor. The fleece reduces movement in the air so reduces heat loss by convection.

b 1 The air is not trapped so can move away and be replaced by cold air.

2 Water can get into the fleece and conduct heat away from the body.

c Radiation.

Keeping warm

Good radiators

You may have done an experiment to find out about ways of keeping things warm.

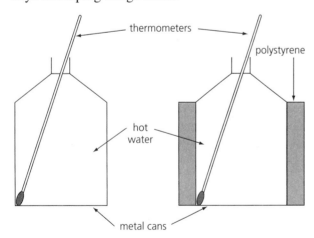

Fig 6

If you put boiling water into both containers and take the temperature every 30 seconds for about 15 minutes, you will see that the insulated can cools more slowly. The layer of air trapped in the polystyrene is a poor conductor and reduces the transfer of energy to the surroundings.

Containers used for heat experiments are sometimes called calorimeters. We used to measure heat energy in calories.

However, other factors also affect the transfer of energy from the can. If you repeat the experiment using a container painted a dull black colour and compare it with one where the metal has been highly polished, you will find that the polished, shiny container remains hotter.

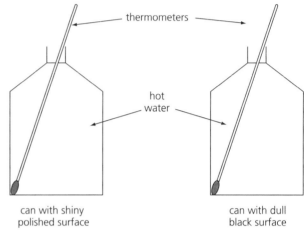

Fig 7

If you plot your results onto a graph they will look like this.

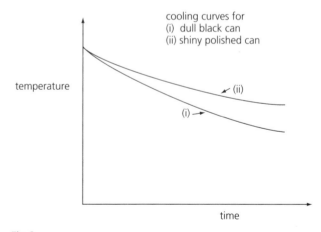

Fig 8

Conduction and convection from the two cans should be the same, so it must be radiation that is causing the difference. The black surface radiates better than the shiny surface. The cooling fins of a car radiator are usually painted black so that they are more efficient at doing their job. If you are choosing a teapot, however, a bright shiny one will keep the tea hot for longer because less energy is lost by radiation – the shiny surface is a poor radiator.

Good absorbers

The absorption of energy also depends on the surface. A dull black surface is good at absorbing energy but a bright shiny surface reflects away most of the radiation that hits it. The shiny back to an electric fire is designed to reflect as much heat radiation as possible out into the room. The shiny surface is a poor absorber.

The vacuum flask

It is relatively easy to design a container that reduces the transfer of energy to the surroundings as 'heat'. A vacuum flask is a double-walled glass container that is remarkably good at preventing energy moving either in or out. A vacuum flask can keep something very hot or very cold for many hours.

- The air is sucked out from between the glass walls to give a vacuum. This means that conduction and convection – but not radiation – are both stopped.
- The inside surfaces of the glass are 'silvered' so they are exceptionally shiny. The inner surface therefore radiates very little thermal energy and the outer surface reflects back any that has been given off.
- An insulated stopper and supports for the glass container are used.

A vacuum flask is sometimes called a 'Thermos' flask after a manufacturer and sometimes a 'Dewar' flask after its inventor.

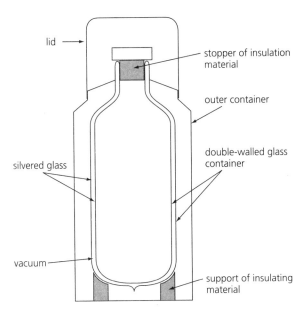

Fig 9 Vacuum flask

QUESTION

Aluminium foil is put on the wall behind the radiator.

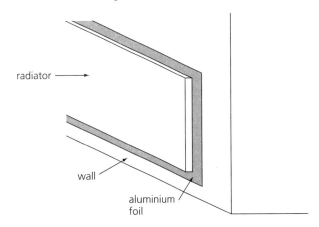

Fig 10

Explain how this will reduce the heating bills.

....
....
....(2 marks)
[MEG]

ANSWER

It reflects the heat back into the room.
It stops the heat being absorbed by the wall.

QUESTION

The diagram below shows a vacuum flask.

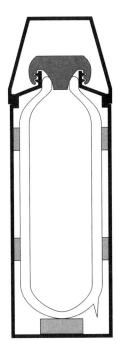

Fig 11

a Give two features of the flask which reduce heat loss by conduction.

1 ....

2 ....

(2 marks)

b Give one feature of the flask which reduces heat loss by radiation.

....(1 mark)

[NEAB]

ANSWER

a Any two from:

The vacuum; the top is made of material which acts as an insulator; the glass/plastic walls.

b Silvering on the inner glass walls.

Solar panels

Solar panels can be used to absorb energy directly from the sun and transfer the energy to a hot water system. The water passes through the panel in pipes that are painted a dull black colour. This means they absorb as much energy as possible. The pipes are inside a glass container. Shorter wavelength radiation from the sun can enter through the glass. As the pipes become warm they give off radiation of a longer wavelength. The glass reflects this back and traps it inside the container, which acts as a greenhouse, so that a lot of solar energy is trapped. As water passes through the pipes it becomes hot and is taken into the water system. This method won't provide all the hot water needed for a house but it will reduce the cost, because of the energy supplied directly from the solar panels.

The sun is at a very high temperature and therefore gives off shorter wavelength radiation than objects at a lower temperature.

Saving energy in the home

Providing energy is expensive and it will become more expensive as our non-renewable sources of energy run out. Keeping warm has always been important, but houses are now built with much better insulation than in the past. This will:

- Reduce energy costs.
- Save on the Earth's resources.
- Help reduce the greenhouse effect.

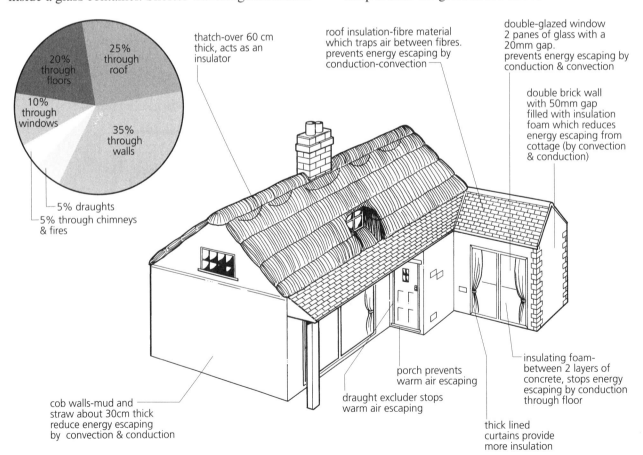

Fig 12 Ways of preventing energy escaping – a cottage built in the 16th century with a modern extension

Remember that most of our electricity is made by burning fossil fuels. This releases carbon dioxide into the atmosphere.

Revision sheet

Energy resources

1 Describe what is meant by each of these forms of energy: chemical, electrical, gravitational potential, kinetic, nuclear, thermal.
2 Give two examples of each of the following types of energy source:
   a Renewable.
   b Non-renewable.
3 Give the main stages which occur at a power station to turn the energy in fuel into electrical energy.
4 a Finish this sentence about energy transfer: At the end of the energy transfer there must be ....
   b Why is no energy transfer 100% efficient?
5 Finish these equations:
   a Efficiency = ?/ total energy supplied.
   b Efficiency = (?/ work put into a machine) × 100%.
6 In a Sankey diagram, to show energy transfer, what does the width of each arrow tell you?

Energy and temperature

1 What is meant by the total internal energy (of a substance)?
2 Finish this equation: Energy transfer = mass × ? × ?
3 a Why do solids expand when they are heated?
   b Explain how a bi-metal strip works.
   c Put these in order of how much they usually expand, beginning with the one that expands most: liquid, solid, gas.
4 Explain and give an example for each of the following:
   a Conduction.
   b Convection.
   c Radiation.
5 Complete the following:
   .... surfaces are good radiators while .... surfaces are poor radiators. .... surfaces are good absorbers of radiation while .... surfaces are good reflectors of radiation.
6 List four things you can check to make sure that your home is well insulated.

7 Explain how, in a vacuum flask, each of the following is reduced:
   a Conduction.
   b Convection.
   c Radiation.

Revision sheet answers

Energy resources

1 Chemical – energy which is available when bonds are broken and remade in a chemical reaction.
   Electrical – a flow of electrons forming an electric current.
   Gravitational potential – energy given to an object when it is lifted up.
   Kinetic – energy in moving objects.
   Nuclear – energy available when the nucleus of an atom splits up (fission).
   Thermal – energy transfer between a hot and cold object (often called 'heat').
2 Renewable: geothermal, hydroelectricity, solar, tides, waves, wind, wood. Non-renewable: coal, gas, nuclear, oil.
3 Fuel heats water → steam turns turbines → turbines turn generators → generators produce electricity.
4 a At the end of an energy transfer there must be as much energy as there was before the transfer.
   b Some energy is always transferred ('lost') into the surroundings making them warmer.
5 a useful energy transferred
   b work out of machine
6 How much energy is being transferred in each way.

Energy and temperature

1 Total energy of all the particles in a substance.
2 Energy transfer = mass × specific heat capacity × change in temperature.
3 a The particles have more energy and vibrate more and push further apart.
   b A bi-metal strip is made of two metals fastened together. One metal expands more than the other. The metal that expands more is on the outside. This means that the strip moves and becomes curved as it is heated. This type of strip can be used in a thermostat, such as in an electric iron.
   c Gas, liquid, solid.

4 a Conduction – the spread of energy through a substance as the particles vibrate more and pass on energy to adjacent particles. Solids, particularly metals, are good conductors.

b Convection – when a fluid is heated it expands as the particles push further apart. As they do this they float upwards and form convection currents, that is the hottest part moves to the top. Convection occurs in liquids and gases.

c Radiation – the transfer of energy when no particles are involved. All substances give out a certain amount of energy by radiation.

5 Dull/black, shiny/polished, dull/black, shiny/polished.

6 Any four from: insulation in the loft, draught excluders around doors, insulation under carpets, lining in curtains, double glazing, wall insulation.

7 Conduction and convection are reduced by the vacuum between the glass walls. Conduction needs a substance to travel through, convection occurs when there are particles of a liquid or gas. Radiation is reduced by the silvered inner layer (which is a poorer radiator) and the silvered outer layer (which reflects energy back).

Student Answer with Comments

Some electrical devices can become very hot when in use. A method of preventing this overheating is shown below. The electrical device is fixed to an aluminium block which takes excess thermal energy away.

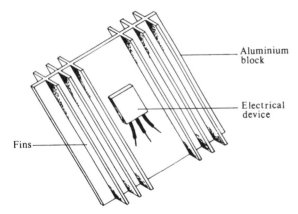

Fig 1

a i Why is it necessary to have good thermal contact between the electrical device and the aluminium block?

So as much heat is taken away from the device by conduction as possible. ✔ ①

(1 mark)

ii The aluminium block is sometimes known as a 'heat sink'. Explain why you think it is given this name.

Because it gets rid of excess heat comparable to a sink getting rid of water. ✔ ① (1 mark)

iii Explain why the aluminium block has fins.

This is to increaes surface area and lose as much heat as possible. ✔ ①

(1 mark)

iv The rate of thermal energy transfer from the block should be as high as possible. State, with a reason, whether the fins should be placed horizontally or vertically.

Vertically ✔ *so that convection currents can be set up in the surrounding air and more heat can be lost.* ✔ ②

(2 marks)

b The diagram shows two different designs for a heat sink.

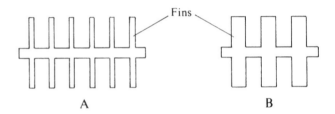

A   B

Fig 2

In each case the heat sinks are made from the same material. They have the same mass and are at the same initial temperature.

Identical electrical devices are attached to them. State and explain which heat sink is likely to show the greater temperature rise.

B because it has a lower surface area than A. ✔ *This means less heat can be taken away by the air by conduction. If less heat can be conducted to the air B will retain more heat and show the greater temperature rise.* ✔ ③

A will lose heat more quickly because of greater surface area. Heat sink A can set up more convection currents.

[ULEAC]

⁸⁄₉

(4 marks)
(Total 9 marks)

An exam question for you to try

a Explain clearly the difference between renewable and non-renewable energy.

....

....(1 mark)

b Give two examples of

  i renewable energy sources..

....(1 mark)

  ii non-renewable energy sources............................

....(1 mark)

c Give two reasons why it is necessary to cut down the use of non-renewable energy sources.

  i ....

....

....

  ii ....

....

....(2 marks)

d A coal-fired power station generates electrical power for the National Grid. Explain how the energy from the coal is used to generate electricity.

....

....

....

....

....

....(3 marks)

[WJEC]

Answer

a Renewable energy sources will not run out, they are constantly being replaced. Non-renewable energy sources are being used up.

b i Renewable – wind, tides, wave, geothermal, solar, hydroelectric, wood.

  ii Non-renewable – coal, gas, oil, nuclear.

c Any two from:

As they are being used up all the time, they will last longer if we are careful with their use.

It can be expensive to build the structures needed to harness the alternative renewable energy sources.

Renewable energy cannot supply all our energy needs at present.

(You may include pollution as a problem of using non-renewable energy sources. If you do, try to be specific and make sure that you answer the question. Do not just give 'pollution' as a bad effect of using non-renewable energy.)

d As the coal is burned it heats water (in a large boiler) and steam is formed. The steam turns large turbines which turn a generator. This produces the electricity *(see 'Electricity in the Home', Chapter 13 for more details).*

16

Using waves

Using waves	Midland (MEG)				Northern (NEAB)		London (ULEAC)				Southern (SEG)		Welsh (WJEC)
	Own	Nuffield	Salters	Suffolk	Co-ordinated	Modular	Modular GASP	Combined	Co-ordinated	Modular	Double	Modular	Co-ordinated
WAVES AND HOW THEY WORK													
Transverse and longitudinal waves	✓	✓	✓	✓	✓	✓	✓	✓	✓	✓	✓	✓	✓
Terms used with waves	✓	✓	✓	✓	✓	✓	✓	✓	✓	✓	✓	✓	✓
Properties of waves	✓	✓	✓	✓	✓	✓	✓	✓	✓	✓	✓	✓	✓
Interference	H	H	✓	H	H	H	H	H	H	H	✓	H	H
Resonance	✓	✓	H	H	✓		H	✓	✓	✓	✓	✓	✓
Seismic waves	H	H	✓	H	H	H	H	H	H	✓	✓	✓	H
THE ELECTROMAGNETIC SPECTRUM													
Waves and wavelengths	✓	✓	✓	✓	✓	✓	✓	✓	✓	✓	✓	✓	✓
Safety and the electromagnetic spectrum	✓	✓	✓	✓	✓	✓	✓	✓	✓	H	✓	H	✓
LIGHT													
Facts about light	✓	✓	✓	✓	✓	✓	✓	✓	✓	✓	✓	✓	✓
Reflection at mirrors	✓	✓	✓	✓	✓	✓	✓	✓	✓	✓	✓	✓	✓
Refraction	✓	✓	✓	✓	✓	✓	✓	✓	✓	✓	✓	✓	✓
Optical fibres	✓	✓	✓	✓	✓	✓	✓	✓	✓	✓	✓	✓	✓
The eye	✓	✓	✓		✓	✓	✓	✓	✓		✓	✓	✓
Seeing coloured objects	✓	✓	✓		✓	✓	✓		✓	✓		✓	✓
SOUND													
Facts about sound	✓	✓	✓	✓	✓	✓	✓	✓	✓	✓	✓	✓	✓
How we hear sounds	✓	✓	✓	✓	✓	✓	✓	✓	✓	✓	✓	✓	✓
Sounds from musical instruments	✓	✓	✓	✓	✓	✓	✓	✓	✓	✓	✓	✓	✓
Looking at sound waves	✓	✓	✓	H	✓	✓	✓	✓	✓	✓	✓	✓	✓
Audible and inaudible sounds	✓	✓	✓	H	✓	✓	✓	✓	✓	✓	✓	✓	✓
Ultrasound	✓	H	✓	H	H	H	✓	✓	H	H	✓	H	H

Waves and how they work

What are waves?

Waves carry energy. A wave is only formed if there is a disturbance. When a stone falls into a pond, some of the kinetic energy possessed by the stone is transferred to the water. This causes the water to move up and down, and we see waves spreading out from the point of impact. If there is a leaf floating on the pond it moves up and down as the wave passes it. The leaf receives some of the kinetic energy that came from the stone. The water which carries the wave just moves up and down, it is *not* carried along. Waves carry energy without transferring matter. Light and sound both travel as waves. The speed of the wave depends on the substance that it is travelling through.

See p 134 if you are unsure what 'matter' is.

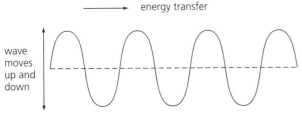

Fig 1

Different sorts of waves

There are two sorts of waves:

* Transverse waves.
* Longitudinal waves.

Transverse waves

When the vibration moves at right angles to the transfer of energy, the wave is called a transverse wave. Waves in water, like in the pond mentioned above, are transverse waves. We can use a spring to see transverse waves. We need to move the spring from side to side.

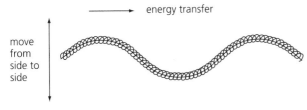

Fig 2 A transverse wave

A wave passes down the spring transferring the energy. This is a transverse wave.

Longitudinal waves

If we move the spring so we get a regular compression and expansion (called rarefaction) of the coils – instead of a sideways movement – we get a longitudinal wave. The vibration is in the same direction as the transfer of energy.

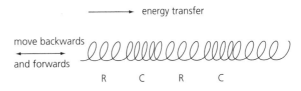

C represents compression, R represents rarefaction

Fig 3 A longitudinal wave

We can think of two sorts of waves:
* *Those that travel through a material, such as sound, water and seismic waves.*
* *Those that do not need a material to travel through, such as electromagnetic waves (which include light).*

Some important definitions

Wavefront: When a stone is thrown into a pond, the waves spread out in circles from the point where the stone landed. The wavefront is the term given to each of the circles.

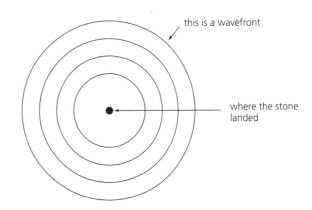

Fig 4 Wavefronts

We will use a digram of a transverse wave to help us define some more of the terms used to describe waves.

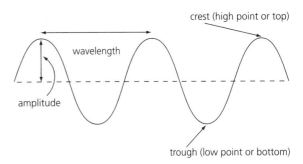

Fig 5

Wavelength(λ)   Distance between one crest (or trough) and the next.

Amplitude   Height of a crest (or depth of a trough) from the midway point between crest and trough.

Frequency (f)   The number of complete waves that pass a point in one second. The unit of frequency is the hertz (Hz). One hertz is a frequency of one wave per second.

Speed (v)   The speed of the wave is the distance travelled by the wave in one second.
Speed = Frequency × Wavelength
$$v = f \times \lambda$$

This triangle may help you to remember this equation.

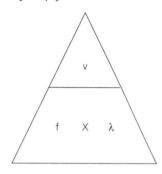

Fig 6

QUESTION

This is a diagram of a wave travelling down a rope.

Fig 7

a   What is the wavelength of the wave?
b   What is the amplitude of the wave?
c   If it takes two seconds for the waves shown in the diagram to go past, what is the frequency of the wave?
d   Use your answer to parts a and b to calculate the speed of the wave.

ANSWER

a   2cm.
b   1cm.

(These are both measured from the diagram. Don't forget to include the units.)
c   *Frequency is the number of waves per second. There are 3 complete waves in the diagram. If 3 waves go past in 2 seconds the frequency is 1.5 (i.e. 3/2) hertz. Answer 1.5Hz.*
d $v = f \times \lambda$ $v = 1.5 \times 2$ $v = 3$cm per second.

QUESTION

A stone is dropped into still water. After 10 seconds the resulting waves have spread to a distance of 5 metres from the point of impact. A photograph taken at this time shows 40 waves between the point of impact and the outer edge of the disturbance.

a   Is the wave being studied transverse or longitudinal?
b   What is the wavelength of the wave?
c   What is the frequency of the wave?
d   At what speed is the wave travelling?

ANSWER

a   Waves in water are transverse. *The water moves up and down at right angles to the transfer of energy.*
b   *If 40 complete waves are spread over 5 metres the wavelength is given by 5 divided by 40.*
   5/40 = 0.125 metres.
   or: 5 metres is 500 centimetres. 500/40 = 12.5cm.
c   Answer = 4Hz.
   In 10 seconds 40 waves have been produced. The frequency is the number of waves going past a given point in one second. If we take a point next to where the stone hit the water 40 waves have passed in 10 seconds. In one second 4 waves have passed this point (40/10). The frequency is 4 hertz.
d   Answer = 0.5m/s.
   *Speed is given by the formula $v = f \times \lambda$
   $v = 4 \times 0.125$ $v = 0.5$ metres per second.*

Properties of waves

This means: what happens when waves meet different types of barrier?

If there are no gaps in the barrier then one of three things will happen:

• Reflection.
• Refraction.
• Absorption.

If there are gaps in the barrier then there will be:

• Diffraction.

1 Reflection

We can send a wave down a spring by giving a sharp up and down movement to one end, while someone holds the other end still. If you do this you will find that the wave bounces off the other end and returns to you. This is called **reflection**.

Fig 8 Reflection in a spring

We can draw a diagram to show this reflection.

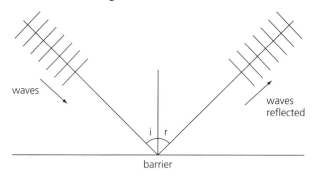

Fig 9 Reflection from a straight barrier

The angle of incidence (i) is equal to the angle of reflection (r)

Examples of reflection of waves:

• When water waves are reflected from harbour walls and breakwaters at the seaside.
• Light waves being reflected from the surface of a mirror.

2 Refraction

When a wave hits a different material it may pass into it. This causes a change in the **speed** and hence a change in the **wavelength** of the wave. If the wave meets a denser material then the speed decreases and the wavelength shortens.
If the wave does not hit the new material at 90° the wave also changes direction. This is called **refraction**. We can use water waves to demonstrate refraction. We cannot see the wave entering a

different material, but we get the same effect when we change the depth of the water.

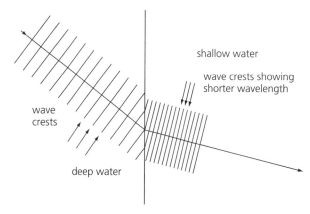

Fig 10 Refraction using water waves

Examples of refraction of waves:

• When light enters the eye it is refracted by the cornea, lens and the fluids in the eye.
• A camera lens refracts the light to form an image on the film.

3 Absorption

When a wave hits an object the energy it carries may be absorbed by the object it hits. When a water wave hits a shingle beach much of the energy is taken up by moving the stones and pebbles, and the disturbance of the water as the wave breaks. This transfers the energy carried by the wave and results in a very slight warming of the beach and water. This is far too small for us to notice!

Examples of absorption of waves:

• Soundproofing.

4 Diffraction

There must be gaps in the barrier to get diffraction.

• If the barrier has a wide gap in it
  If a water wave hits a barrier with a gap in it the wave can pass through. With a wide gap there may be some curving at the edge of the wave, but most of the wave carries straight on. The part of the wave that hits the barrier is reflected.

• If the barrier has a narrow gap in it
  If the gap in the barrier is similar (or smaller) in width than the wavelength of the wave, the gap appears to act as a new source of waves. Waves spread out from the gap as circular waves. This

effect is called **diffraction**. The wave bends around the corners of the barrier.

It is important to realise that the waves don't just pass straight through, they spread out.

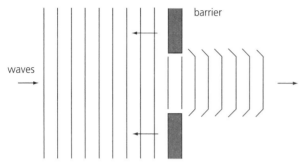

Fig 11 A barrier with a wide gap

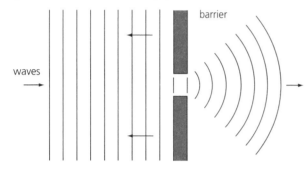

Fig 12 A barrier with a narrow gap – diffraction

Examples of diffraction of waves:

- Being able to hear around corners.

QUESTION

A ripple tank is a device for showing water waves in the laboratory. An electric motor causes a beam to vibrate and produce waves in a shallow tray of water. The following diagrams were drawn by a student after doing some experiments with a ripple tank. Explain which property of waves the student was demonstrating in each experiment.
The diagrams show the waves in the tank from above. The motor and beam producing the waves have not been drawn.

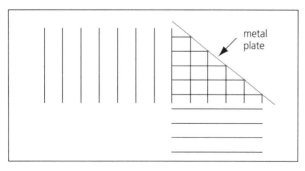

Fig 13 Experiment One

Experiment One...
....
....(2 marks)

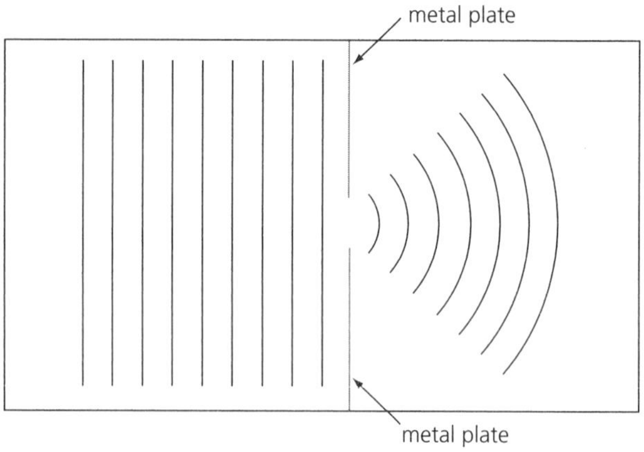

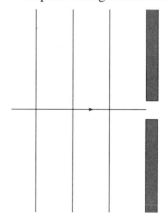

Fig 14 Experiment Two

Experiment Two ....
....
....(2 marks)

ANSWER

Exp 1 The student is showing reflection.
The metal plate is reflecting the water waves through an angle of 90°.

Exp 2 The student is showing diffraction.
The two plates have been placed so the gap is about the same as the wavelength of the wave. This means that the wave spreads out from the gap – it is diffracted.

QUESTION

Complete the following diagrams to show what happens when:
a straight waves pass through a narrow gap;

Fig 15

(2 marks)

b straight waves pass from medium 1 to medium 2 in which they travel more slowly.

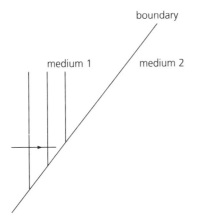

Fig 16

(2 marks)
[WJEC]

ANSWER

a Semicircles should spread out from the gap. *Make sure that you keep the wavelength constant.*

b The waves should have a shorter wavelength in medium 2. *Notice that the question tells you that the waves move more slowly in medium 2 than medium 1. Make sure also that your lines join up with those already drawn, for example:*

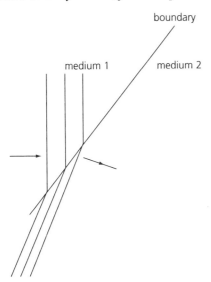

Fig 17

What is interference?

Imagine you have a rope, you hold one end and your friend holds the other. You both make a wave. Three things can happen as the waves meet:

• A crest from your wave might meet a trough of your friend's wave.

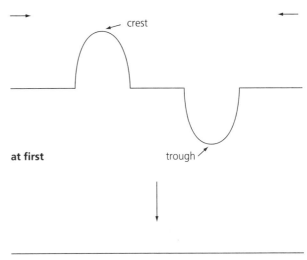

at first

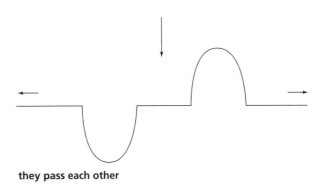

as they pass they cancel each other out

they pass each other

Fig 18 Crest meets trough

These waves are 'out of phase'.

In this case, the waves cancel each other out as they pass.

• A crest from your wave might meet a crest from your friend's wave (see next page).

In this case, the crests make a even bigger crest as they pass.

• A trough from your wave might meet a trough from your friend's wave (see next page).

In this case, the troughs make an even bigger trough as they pass.

If the amplitude of the wave is increased, i.e. when two troughs or two crests meet, this is called constructive *interference. If the amplitude is decreased, for example if a trough meets a crest, this is called* destructive *interference.*

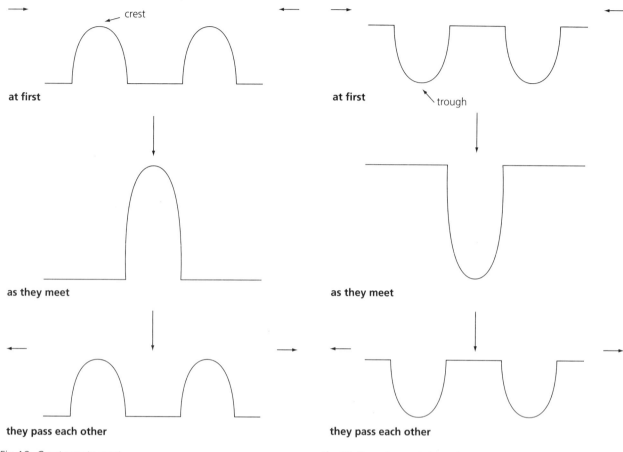

Fig 19 Crest meets crest

These waves are 'in phase'.

Fig 20 Trough meets trough

These waves are 'in phase'.

Examples of interference

* From loudspeakers at an airport.
  There are some places in the departure lounge where you can hear really well (constructive interference) and some places where you can hardly hear at all (destructive interference).

* Colours in soap bubbles and oil films
  These are caused by the reflection of light from both the inner and outer surface of the thin film of soap or oil. The way that these waves interfere gives the characteristic effects.

* Holograms
  In the production of a hologram the light from a laser is split into two beams. The reflected wave from the object is made to interfere with a reference wave to produce 3-D information about the object (this information is called the hologram). On credit cards when light is reflected from the hologram a 3-D image is seen.

* Television reception
  If you live in a hilly part of the country or near a tall building you may not be able to get a good picture on your television. This may be due to interference. Two signals are picked up by your television aerial, one from the television transmitter and another which is reflected from the tall building or surrounding hills.

QUESTION

The diagram (Fig 21) shows the compressions of sound waves from two identical loudspeakers. The compressions are spreading out and overlapping. State and explain:

a   i   why a loud sound is heard at X;

....

....

....

....(2 marks)

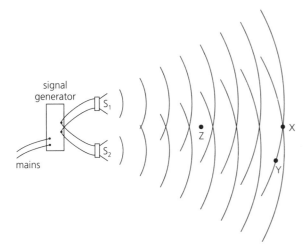

Fig 21

ii why no sound would be heard at Y;

....
....
....
....(2 marks)

iii what would be heard at Z.

....
....(2 marks)

b what is meant by a longitudinal wave?

....
....(1 mark)

[WJEC]

ANSWER

a i This is an example of constructive interference. The amplitude of the waves is increased when the waves meet (for example the crests of each wave) and this results in a louder sound at X.

   ii This is an example of destructive interference. The crest of one wave meets the trough of another and they cancel each other out. No sound would be heard.

   iii At Z two troughs meet. This would give a loud sound as in (i). The sound would be louder at Z as it is closer to the loudspeakers.

b The vibrations travel in the same direction as the transfer of energy.

What is resonance?

An object which vibrates has its own frequency. This is called the **natural frequency**. If you tap a glass so that it vibrates it sounds differently from a cup – their natural frequencies are different. Think back to when you sat on a swing as a young child. You moved your legs to get you going, but it is likely that you asked someone to push you higher. They pushed the swing each time it came near them. In other words the (forcing) frequency of the pushing was the same as the natural frequency of the swing. You went higher. This was because the amplitude of the vibrations increased. This is an example of resonance. We say the swing is **resonating**.

Resonance occurs when:

*   An object is vibrating at its natural frequency.
*   It receives additional vibrations at this natural frequency.

Examples of resonance

*   The seats rattling on a bus when it reaches a certain speed.
    The seats vibrate at their natural frequency because of vibrations produced by the engine of the bus.
*   The washing machine 'jumps about' during the spin cycle of the wash.
    The frequency of the drum reaches the natural frequency of the washing machine motor.
*   Soldiers marching across a bridge may make the bridge vibrate.
    This happens if the frequency of their marching steps is at the natural frequency of the bridge. Soldiers march out of step when crossing a bridge to prevent this.
*   The Tacoma Narrows (USA) bridge disaster in 1940.
    The frequency of vibrations produced by the wind matched the natural frequency of the bridge and the four-month-old bridge collapsed.
*   Tuning in a radio to a station.
    The frequency of the radio waves reaching the aerial coincides with the natural frequency of the receiver circuit when the station is found.
*   Musical instruments.
    If you play an instrument that needs blowing, such as a saxophone, you make use of resonance. The reed vibrates and causes the air in the saxophone to resonate. Different sounds occur as the holes are opened and closed, changing the length of the column of air in the saxophone (see page 357 for more about sound).

QUESTION

When Bill moored his yacht for the night he found it very hard to sleep because the boat was rocked by the waves, as shown in the diagram.

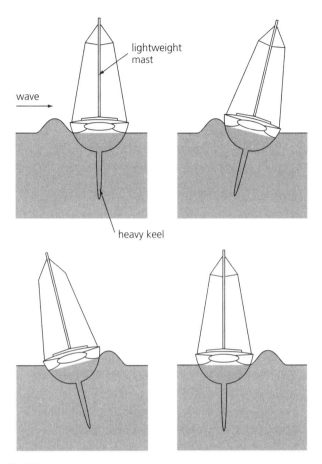

Fig 22

a Explain why Bill's yacht always returned to the upright position after the passage of a wave.

....
....(2 marks)

b Bill found that smaller, more frequent waves sometimes produced larger rocking amplitudes than larger, less frequent waves. Suggest why this was so.

....
....
....
....
....
....(3 marks)

c Suggest and explain what Bill could have done to his yacht that night to reduce the rocking amplitude.

....
....(2 marks)

d Bill sometimes finds that his yacht is hit side on by waves even when he is moored behind a headland. Name the process responsible for this change in direction of the waves and complete the diagram to show how it happens.

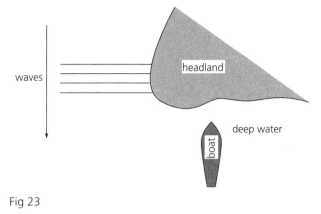

Fig 23

Name..(3 marks)

[MEG]

ANSWER

a Gravity acted on the heavy keel and pulled the boat back to the upright position.

b The boat had a natural rocking frequency. The frequency of the small waves (the forcing frequency) coincided with the natural frequency of the boat. This increased the amplitude of the natural frequency. This is an example of resonance. The larger, less frequent waves, did not correspond to the natural frequency of the boat.

c He could have changed the direction of the boat so that the waves met it head on.

There are other things he could do: He needed to alter the natural frequency of the boat. He could change the mass of the boat either by taking more water in or reducing the mass in some way.

d This is an example of diffraction. You should draw smooth curves and make sure that the wavelength stays the *same*.

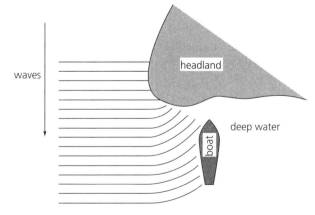

Fig 24

What are seismic waves?

Inside the Earth the rocks are moving (see p 236). If the rocks in the upper mantle or crust move with sufficient force, they break and energy is released. This break often occurs along known **fault lines**, such as the San Andreas fault which crosses California. This break causes shock waves, known as **seismic waves**. As the seismic waves reach the surface of the Earth they cause earthquakes.

Terms used when discussing seismic waves

- Focus – the point where the break in the rocks occurred deep inside the Earth.
- Epicentre – The point on the surface of the Earth directly above the focus.
- P (Primary waves) – longitudinal waves, produced by pushing and pulling forces. They travel through solids and liquids, so can travel through the liquid core.
- S (Secondary) waves – transverse waves, which cause the rock to shake at right angles to the direction of movement of the wave. They can only travel through solids, so can only travel through the crust and mantle of the Earth. They travel more slowly than P waves.
- Surface waves – have a long wavelength and cause a lot of movement. They travel more slowly than either P or S waves and only travel in the crust of the Earth.

It may help to remember: Primary push and pass through everything, Secondary shake and are stopped by liquids.

Interpreting a seismogram

A seismogram is a print out from a seismometer, an instrument for recording earthquakes.

How a seismometer works

The frame is heavy and attached to the ground. When there is an earthquake, the frame moves. The pen or light beam records the zig-zag movement.
To calculate where the earthquake is, the following information is needed:

- The speed of P waves (about 6 kilometres per second).
- The speed of S waves (about 3 kilometres per second).

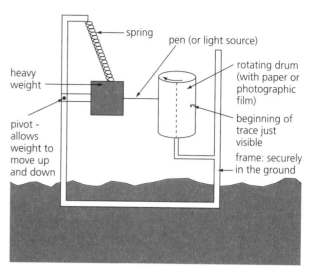

Fig 25 A seismometer

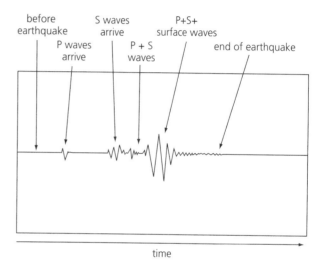

Fig 26 A seismogram

- The time interval between the arrival of the P and S waves (called the lag-time).

There is a rule of thumb which helps here: Every minute of time represents 1,000 km.

This information enables the operator to calculate the distance of the recording station from the epicentre of the earthquake. Information from at least three stations is needed to pinpoint the actual place of the epicentre.

Evidence of the layered structure of the Earth using seismic waves

Seismic waves have been used to predict the structure of the Earth. As the waves pass through the Earth they meet rocks of different densities. This means that the direction and speed of the waves change.

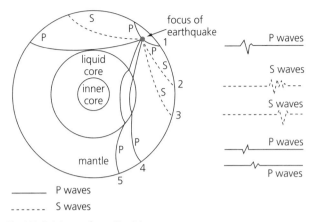

Fig 27 Evidence for a liquid core

Notice at stations 4 and 5, no S waves were recorded. S waves do not pass through liquids and so this is evidence that there is a liquid core.

By collecting data about seismic waves, scientists have deduced:

- The Earth is a layered structure.
- There are 3 main layers: a core, a mantle and a crust. There are two important boundaries, called discontinuities:
  - Mohorovicic (or Moho) between 6km and 70km separating the crust from the mantle.
  - Gutenberg discontinuity at 2,900km, separating the core from the mantle.
- The core is thought to be made up of two parts: an inner solid core and an outer liquid core.
- The crust is solid and made up of plates which move on the partly molten mantle. The crust is thicker under the continents than under the oceans.

QUESTION

Primary waves (P waves) and Secondary waves (S waves) travel out from the focus of an earthquake. Some of these are shown on Fig 29.

a Two stations record the passage of this earthquake. The seismograms from each are shown in Fig 30.

  i Which station, 1 or 2, is nearest to the epicentre of the earthquake?

  ....

  ii Give the reason for this answer.

  ....(2 marks)

b Explain the change in the P wave as it passes from the mantle to the outer core.

  ....(1 mark)

c Why do the S waves not travel through the core?

  ....(1 mark)

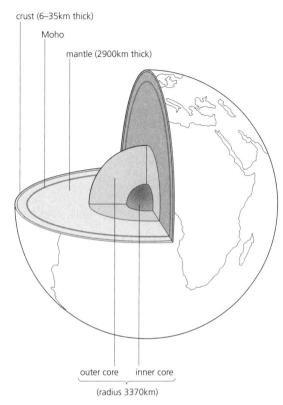

Fig 28 The layered structure of the Earth

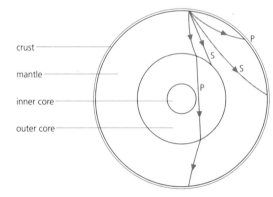

Fig 29

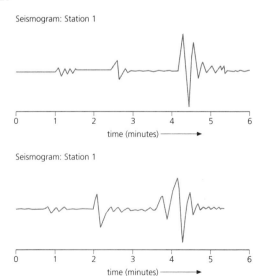

Fig 30 Seismogram: Station 1 Seisomogram: Station 2

ANSWER

a i Station 2 is closer to the epicentre.

ii It receives the waves from the earthquake before station 1.

(Do give a reason in this type of question. You might not be given the mark for part (i) if you leave part (ii) blank.)

b The material of the core is of a different density from the material of the mantle, so the speed and direction of the wave change.

c S waves can only pass through solids; they cannot travel through the (outer) core because it is liquid.

The electromagnetic spectrum

What is the electromagnetic spectrum?

Waves reach Earth all the time. These are called electromagnetic waves and are carried by vibrations in the electric and magnetic fields. These waves make up what we call the electromagnetic spectrum. We are surrounded by electromagnetic waves but they don't all come from space. For example, radio waves are transmitted from an aerial and infra-red rays from a glowing fire. Electromagnetic waves are all transverse waves. They all travel at very high speed (about 300 million metres per second or 3×10^8 m/s). The properties of each type of wave depend on its frequency.

Look at page 336 on waves if you need some reminders here.

Speed = Frequency × Wavelength
$$v \quad = \quad f \quad \times \quad \lambda$$

Two important points to remember about these waves:

- If the frequency changes the wavelength must also change (as the speed of each type is the same!). Put another way: *the higher the frequency the shorter the wavelength and vice versa.*
- The energy transferred by a wave also depends on its frequency. *The higher the frequency the bigger the energy transfer and vice versa.*

Safety and the electromagnetic spectrum
The waves in the electromagnetic spectrum are absorbed, transmitted or reflected in different ways – depending on their wavelength and the type of surface that they meet. That surface might be the surface of your body!

Gamma rays – are very penetrating (see p 165). Low doses can cause cells to reproduce 'out of control' and form a tumour, higher doses may kill normal cells.

X-rays – pass through the skin but are absorbed by denser tissues, such as bone. Low doses can cause cells to reproduce 'out of control' and form a tumour, higher doses may kill normal cells. Alternatives to X-rays are used wherever possible.

Ultra violet rays – high doses can damage the eyes and cause skin cancer. People from European countries who normally work indoors and go to hot sunny places for their holidays are particularly at risk. (Most of the sun's UV rays are absorbed by the ozone layer – see p 123).

Infra-red rays these can be absorbed by the skin and if the source is too hot the skin may scorch.

Microwaves – these are absorbed by the water in cells. The cells may be damaged by the heat involved and therefore fail to function.

QUESTION

The table below shows part of the electromagnetic spectrum.

RADIO WAVES	MICROWAVES	P	VISIBLE LIGHT	ULTRA VIOLET LIGHT	q	GAMMA RAYS

Fig 1

Name

a The missing radiation p. ....
(1 mark)

b The missing radiation q. ....
(1 mark)

c The radiation with the longest wavelength.
....(1 mark)

Type of wave and typical wavelength	Source	Detection	Uses
Gamma (γ) rays; 10^{-12}m – dangerous	nucleus of atom in radioactive decay	Geiger–Muller tube	kill dividing cells in tumours, sterilisation of medical equipment
X-rays; 10^{-10}m – dangerous	bombarding metal targets with high energy electrons	photographic film	detecting broken bones – atoms of heavier mass (in bones) absorb X-rays better than lighter atoms (in flesh); detection of digestive tract problems by a 'barium meal'
Ultra violet (UV); 10^{-8}m – dangerous	given out by high temperature gases and solids, including the sun and mercury lamps	photographic film, skin (causes sunburn), fluorescent material (which glows)	sunbeds and fluorescent lamps
Visible; 50×10^{-7}m	sun, hot objects	photographic film, the eye – colours detected range from red – long wavelength to violet – short wavelength, LDR (light dependent resistor, see p 277)	photography, optical fibres (see p 352)
Infra-red (IR); 10^{-5}m,	Sun, warm or hot objects	skin – as it gets warm, thermistor (see p 277)	toasters, radiant heaters, cameras that can be used at night, missile guidance systems (where a hot object is tracked)
Microwaves 1cm	vibrations of electrons in a magnetron	vibration of molecules	cooking – the water molecules absorb the microwaves and become hot, transfer of energy warms other parts of the food; radar and satellite communications and TV
radio waves 10^{-3}m (UHF) to 10^3m (long wave)	vibration of electrons by electric fields in aerial	cause resonance in tuned electrical circuits (see p 341)	carry signals for radio, television and telephone

Fig 2 The electromagnetic spectrum

d The radiation with the lowest frequency.
....(1 mark)

e The radiation used to send information to and from satellites.
....(1 mark)

f The measurable quantity which is the same for all of these radiations in a vacuum.
....(1 mark)
[WJEC]

ANSWER

a Infra-red.
b X-rays.
c Radio waves.
d Radio waves.
e Microwaves.
f Speed.

QUESTION

a The diagram below shows a ray of sunlight falling on the side of a prism at the point P. A screen is drawn on the other side of the prism. On leaving the prism the sunlight forms a visible spectrum on the screen between the points X and Y.

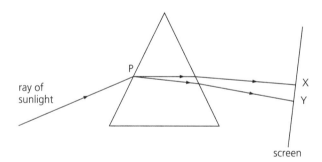

Fig 3

i Name one type of radiation to be found:
1 above X..
2 below Y ....(2 marks)
ii Give one use of:
UV radiation

....

....

microwaves

....

....(2 marks)

b i Name a part of the electromagnetic spectrum which is used to sterilise surgical instruments.
....(1 mark)

ii Explain how this radiation sterilises surgical instruments.

....

....(1 mark)
[NEAB]

ANSWER

a i 1 Above X – infra-red or microwaves or radio waves.
2 Below Y – ultra violet or X-rays or gamma rays.
ii UV radiation: to get a suntan, in fluorescent lighting.
Microwaves: heating food, radar, satellite communications.
b i Gamma rays.
ii It kills cells, for example cells of bacteria.

QUESTION

a i Use the diagram to explain why microwaves are said to have an alternating field.

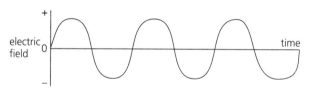

Fig 4

....

....(1 mark)

ii Microwaves travel at 3×10^8m/s. Calculate the frequency, in hertz, of a microwave of wavelength 6cm.

....

....

....

....Hz (3 marks)
[ULEAC]

ANSWER

a i The amplitude of the wave changes from positive to negative.
ii Speed = wavelength × frequency
so, freqency = speed/wavelength
= $3 \times 10^8/0.06$
= 5×10^9Hz.
(Don't forget to change 6cm into metres!)

Light

What is light?

It is the visible part of what we call the electromagnetic spectrum (see p 346). Visible light is an electromagnetic wave. Light energy is transferred through vibrations in electric and magnetic fields.

Electromagnetic waves are all transverse waves.

> Reminder:
> 1 Light travels in straight lines.
> 2 Light travels at very high speed (300 million metres per second i.e. 3×10^8 m/s).
> 3 When light is reflected at a plane flat surface, such as a mirror, there is a rule for the angle of the ray hitting the surface and then bouncing back:
>
> angle of incidence (i) is equal to the angle of reflection (r).

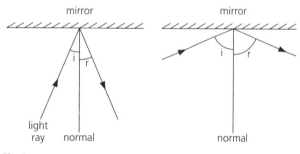

Fig 1

Reflection at mirrors

When we look in a mirror we see a reflection of ourselves. We call this an image. There are two sorts of image:

- Virtual image. The image appears to be behind the mirror, although of course the light cannot go through the mirror, it is just reflected from it.
- Real image. The image is formed in front of the mirror. This image can be projected onto a screen.

Using a plane mirror

A plane mirror produces an image which appears to be as far behind the mirror as the object is in front – a virtual image.

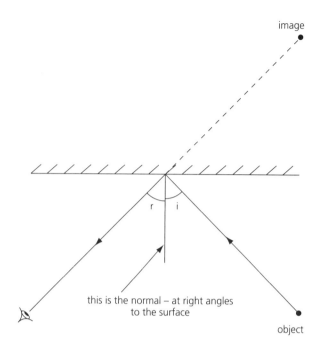

Fig 2 Reflection in a plane mirror to form a virtual image

If you look at yourself in a mirror the image of what appears to be your right ear is in fact an image of your left ear! We call this **lateral inversion**. Signs that are meant to be read by motorists through their rear view mirror must be laterally inverted for them to make sense.

For example:

ƎɔИA⅃UꓭMA

Fig 3 This will read correctly when viewed through a mirror.

Although the image is the wrong way round it is the **same size** and the **right way up**.

The normal is the name given to a line drawn at right angles to the surface.

QUESTION

The diagram shows two plane mirrors held at 90 degrees to each other. A ray of light shines onto one of the mirrors. It makes an angle of 45 degrees with the mirror.

  i Draw and label the normal line at the point where the ray hits the mirror. (1 mark)

  ii The ray of light is reflected by the mirrors and reaches the eye.
Carefully draw the path that the ray takes.
Label the sizes of the angles. (3 marks)

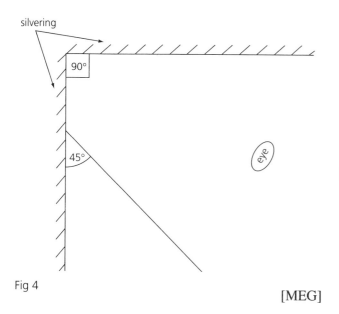

Fig 4

[MEG]

ANSWER

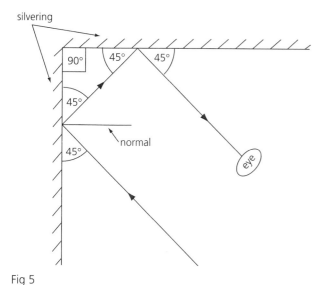

Fig 5

Using a curved mirror

The rule '**angle of incidence = angle of reflection**' is true for these mirrors too, but the resulting effect is rather different.

1 Concave mirrors
Concave mirrors reflect a parallel beam of light inwards. The rays are reflected so they come together at a point. We call this the principal focus, shown as F on diagrams.
If you put a lamp at this principle focus the light is reflected to give a parallel beam.
Concave mirrors are used as reflectors in torches. They are also used as mirrors for shaving and make-up. If you position an object, for example your face, near a concave mirror you will see a magnified image.

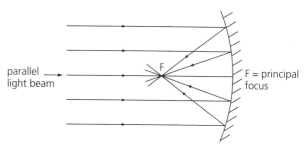

Fig 6 A concave mirror

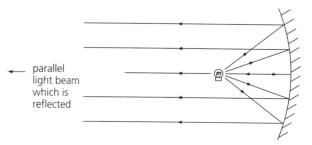

Fig 7 A concave mirror to show a reflected beam

2 Convex mirrors
Convex mirrors spread light outwards. They are used as driving mirrors to give a wide field of view of what is behind. They are used when a wide field of view is needed – but they make everything look smaller! You may also see them in shops, where they give the assistant a view behind racks of goods.

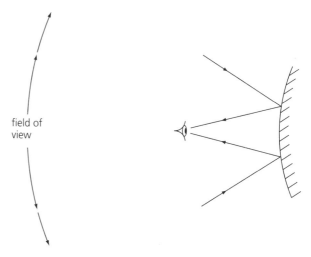

Fig 8 A convex mirror

QUESTION

The diagrams below show how curved mirrors reflect rays of light.
Give one common use of each type of mirror.

   i ....

   ii ....(2 marks)

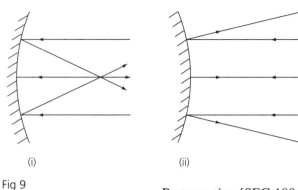

(i) (ii)

Fig 9

Part question [SEG 1994]

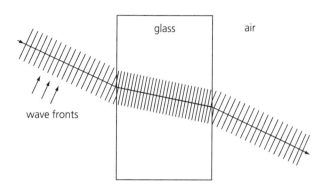

Fig 11 Wavefronts travelling through a glass block

ANSWER

i Shaving or make-up mirror, dentist's mirror, as the reflector in a radiant electric fire, in a torch, to reflect light up to the stage in a microscope, in a telescope.

ii Driving mirror, as a security mirror in a shop, by the roadside on a 'blind' corner.

There are several possible answers for each of these.

You could try and remember that in a concave mirror the side you look at caves in, so in a convex mirror it goes the other way – outwards.

Refraction

When a wave passes into a different substance its speed changes and this usually results in a change of direction. The exception is when the wave hits the new medium at 90°, it then passes straight through. If a ray of light hits a rectangular glass block at an angle other than 90° it bends towards the normal as it enters the block. As it leaves it bends away from the normal, so that it emerges parallel to the ray that went in.

The light travels more slowly in glass and its wavelength is shortened. It lengthens again as it leaves.

Refraction also occurs when light enters and leaves water. This leads to pools appearing shallower than they really are. The rays of light are refracted away from the normal as they leave the water. When the rays reach your eye they seem to come from a point that is less than the real depth. (This point is called the apparent depth).

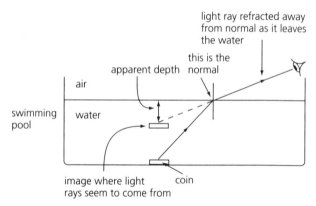

Fig 12 Refraction in a swimming pool

Light rays moving to a denser substance are bent (refracted) towards the normal. When light moves out of a denser substance the rays are bent (refracted) away from the normal.

QUESTION

The diagram shows a ray of light directed at a glass block.

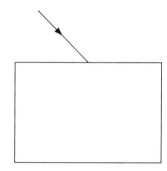

Fig 13

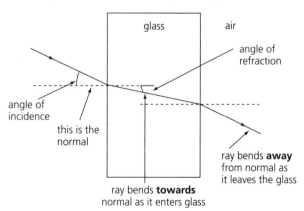

Fig 10 Refraction through a glass block

i Continue the ray to show its path as it enters
and leaves the glass block. (2 marks)

ii What happens to the velocity of light as it
leaves the glass block and re-enters the air?

....

....(1 mark)

iii What would you notice if the ray of light passed
from air to water instead of from air to glass?

....

....(1 mark)

Part question [SEG 1994]

ANSWER

i

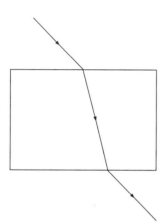

Fig 14

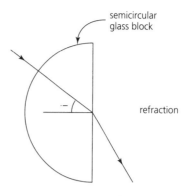

refraction

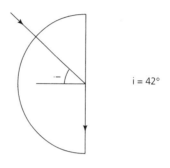

i = 42°

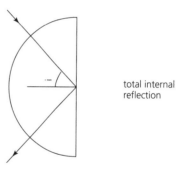

total internal
reflection

ii As it leaves the glass block the velocity of the
light increases. *(It returns to what it was before
it entered the glass block.)*

iii The ray of light would be refracted as it passed
into water. It would be refracted by a different
amount from when it entered glass.

Fig 15 Total internal reflection

QUESTION

Two 45° prisms were used to make a periscope (see
Fig 16).

Total Internal Reflection

The diagrams show rays of light being refracted
through a semicircular glass block. As the light
source is moved round, the angle of incidence for the
ray entering the block (i in the diagrams) increases.
When this angle of incidence reaches about 42°
(called the **critical angle**) the light is refracted so that
it travels along the surface of the block as it leaves. If
this angle becomes greater than 42° the light is
completely reflected back into the block. This is
called total **internal reflection**.

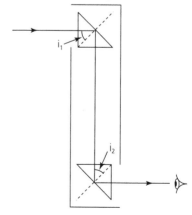

Fig Li 16 A periscope

a What is angle i_1?

....(1 mark)

b What is angle i_2?

....(1 mark)

c Explain why the light is reflected as shown.

....(1 mark)

Answer

a Angle i_1 is 45°.

b Angle i_2 is 45°.

c Both these angles are greater than 42°, this means that total internal reflection takes place.

Optical Fibres

How they work

Optical fibres are made from two types of glass, an inner core and an outer layer of cladding. Both types must be very pure so that they are exceptionally transparent. They are chosen so that if light enters the core of the fibre it is totally internally reflected each time it hits the boundary with the outer cladding. The light travels down the fibre even if the fibre turns corners or is tied into a knot!

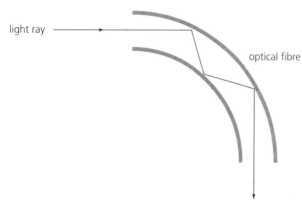

Fig 17 An optical fibre

Uses

• Hospitals
Optical fibres can be used to carry light into inaccessible places. For example, fibres can be passed through a vein to carry light into a patient's heart. Other fibres can be used to see what is happening. This device, now in common use in hospitals, is called an endoscope.

• Communications industry
We can use optical fibres to send complex messages, such as those needed to relay a telephone conversation. The signals are coded into pulses of light which travel down the fibre. Many

thousands more messages can be sent down an optical fibre than down a copper wire of the same diameter. In addition, optical fibres give better quality signals, so that complex computer data can be transmitted accurately. These fibres may also be used to carry video (TV) signals.

QUESTION

The three diagrams each show a ray of light shining onto the end of a curved glass rod.

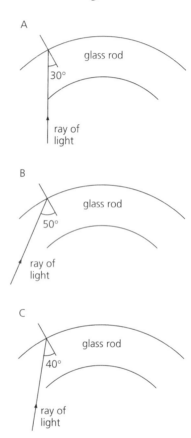

Fig 18

i The critical angle for the glass used to make the glass rod is 42°. In which one of the diagrams will the ray be reflected back into the rod? Choose from A, B or C.

....(1 mark)

ii Write down one practical use made of total internal reflection.

....(1 mark)

[MEG]

ANSWER

i B.

ii In optical fibres; for example, as an endoscope to see into a patient.

The importance of refraction

- Lenses
  Lenses are clear pieces of glass with curved surfaces. They refract light as it passes through them at both surfaces. Lenses either refract light inwards or outwards.

Refracting light inwards

Converging (or positive) lenses refract a parallel beam of light so it comes to a point at the focus of the lens.

Light is refracted towards the normal at the first surface and away from the normal at the second. The result in both cases is to bend light inwards.

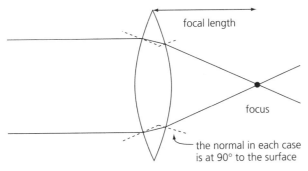

Fig 19 A converging lens

Refracting light outwards

A diverging (or negative) lens refracts light so that it spreads out. Both surfaces of the lens can be arranged to curve in the opposite direction from those in a positive lens and the light is **bent outwards** at each refraction.

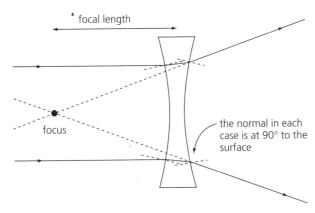

Fig 20 A diverging lens

Reminder
Positive (converging) lenses are essential in the working of the eye and the camera.

Features of the eye
- Converging lens, with refraction by cornea and fluids in the eye.
- Inverted (upside down) image formed on the retina.
- Image nearer the lens than the object, impulses in the optic nerve carry information about the image to the brain.

Remember, we see an object when light is reflected from the object into the eye. There are more details about the eye on p 67–68.

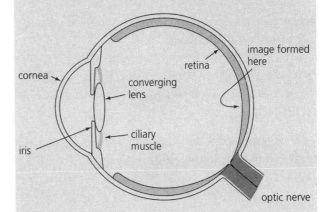

Fig 21 The eye

Features of a camera:
- Converging lens.
- Inverted (upside down) image.
- Image nearer the lens than the object.

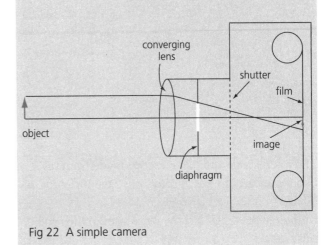

Fig 22 A simple camera

Using lenses to correct eye defects

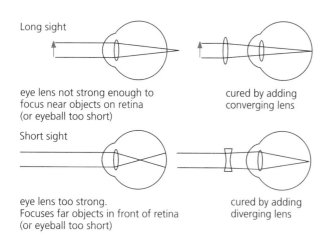

Long sight

eye lens not strong enough to
focus near objects on retina
(or eyeball too short)

cured by adding
converging lens

Short sight

eye lens too strong.
Focuses far objects in front of retina
(or eyeball too short)

cured by adding
diverging lens

Fig 23 Correcting long and short sight

*Converging lenses are also used in magnifying glasses,
microscopes and telescopes.*

QUESTION

The diagrams show how the same two lenses can be
used to make a microscope or a telescope.

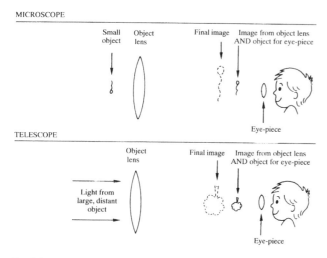

Fig 24

The microscope and the telescope made from the
two lenses are similar in some ways but different in
others.

Complete the table to show these **similarities** and
differences.   (7 marks)
                                                    [NEAB]

	similarities	differences
what the micro-scope and telescope are used for		
the job done by the eye-piece		✕
how the final image compares with the **original** object		

Fig 25

ANSWER

Use: similarities – makes the object look bigger or
nearer or clearer.
differences – microscope magnifies small
objects, telescope is used to look at
objects that are a long way away.

Eye piece: similarities – in both cases, it magnifies
the image from the object lens.

How final image compares with original:
similarities – the image is inverted.
differences – in the microscope, the image is bigger
than the object.
in the telescope, the image is smaller.

QUESTION

a What is the function of the iris of the eye?

....

....(1 mark)

b In the following diagram light from a distant
object is travelling to the eye of a person who is
short-sighted.

light from

distant object

Fig 26

On the diagram
  i place a cross (x) where this light is likely to be
     focused by the eye lens. (1 mark)
  ii draw a suitable lens to correct this condition
      and show the paths of the rays after correction.
      (2 marks)

[ULEAC]

ANSWER

a The iris controls the amount of light entering the eye (see p 65–67 if you need more help with this).

b i The × should be placed behind the lens but in front of the retina.

ii A diverging, negative lens should be placed in front of the eye. Look at Fig 23 to see how to draw the rays after correction. (*Make sure that you focus these on the retina.*)

• Prisms and their effect on light.

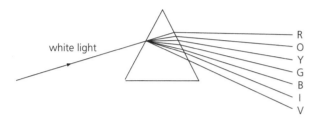

Fig 27 A prism

White light is a mixture of colours. When it is passed through a prism it is split up into the spectrum. We call this **dispersion**. It happens because the different colours of light are made up of waves of different wavelengths (see p 346). When the waves enter the glass of the prism they travel at different speeds, so they are refracted by slightly different angles. This splits the light up into the different colours. *Violet* light has the slowest speed in glass and so is refracted the *most* (see diagram). *Red* light has the fastest speed and so is refracted the *least*.

White light is the name given to 'normal' daylight.

How do light filters work?
Filters can also be used to produce coloured light from white light. They do this by only allowing certain wavelengths of light to pass through, other wavelengths being absorbed. A blue filter only allows light from the blue part of the spectrum to pass through.

Seeing coloured objects

1 Mixing colours

The primary light colours (red, green and blue) can be added together to produce white light. Mixing each pair of primary colours produces what is called a secondary colour (see Fig 28).

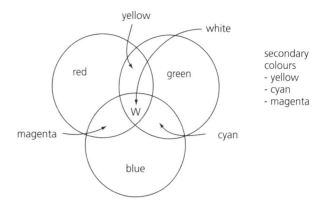

Fig 28 Mixing colours

A television screen works by using the principles of colour mixing. The screen is covered in thousands of groups of three spots. Each group of spots has one red, one green and one blue. By being stimulated to glow with different degrees of brightness the three spots give a very wide range of colour to the screen.

2 Reflecting colours

Most objects do not allow light to pass through them. They are said to be opaque. Some of the light is reflected, but as most surfaces are not very smooth the light is scattered in all directions. Some of the light is absorbed by the surface and this gives rise to objects having different colours. In white light – a mixture of all the colours of the spectrum – the wavelengths which are reflected are predominantly those that are not absorbed. If most of the reflected wavelengths are in the red part of the spectrum the object will look red. An object that equally reflects all the colours of the spectrum looks white, while an object that absorbs most of the light falling on it looks black. If blue light is shone onto a jumper that looks red in white light, it will then look black. There was no red light being shone onto it for it to reflect!

A black surface absorbs all the light falling on it and a white surface reflects all the light falling on it.

What is polarisation?

Light is a transverse wave. The vibrations move at right angles to the transfer of energy.

If you think about this in 3-D, you can imagine how the vibrations of the light waves can act in many directions – all at right angles to the direction of travel.

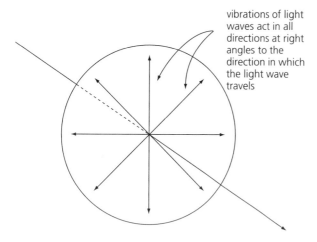

Fig 29 An unpolarised light wave

Imagine making waves in a rope. You can move the rope from side to side or up and down or at an oblique angle, but the waves still travel down the rope and energy is transferred. The rope acts as an **unpolarised wave**, because it can vibrate in all directions at right angles to the direction in which the wave travels.

When transverse waves hit a material, often only certain vibrations can pass through it. When this occurs the wave is said to be **polarised** and the material is a **polarising material**. Polarising materials can reduce the intensity of light. They are used to make polaroid sunglasses. The lenses contain a chemical substance which only allows vibrations in one plane to pass through – horizontal vibrations are cut out.

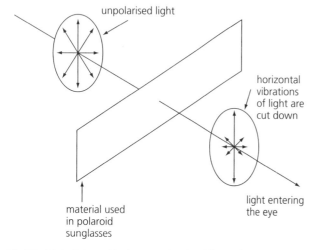

Fig 30 Material used in lenses of polaroid sunglasses cuts down horizontal vibrations.

These sunglasses are useful for driving. They can reduce the glare from the surface of a road considerably, because the reflected light is itself partially polarised by the reflection. The horizontal vibrations are reflected very strongly and cause most of the glare. It is these horizontal vibrations that the polaroid sunglasses cut out.

If two samples of polarising material are held at right angles to each other then all the vibrations are removed – no light will get through at all.

QUESTION

The following diagrams show the amount of light passing through various arrangements of polaroid sheets.

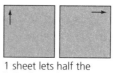

1 sheet lets half the light through

2 sheets with their axes parallel still let half the light through

2 sheets with their axes at right angles let very little light through

Fig 31

a Explain the difference between polarised and unpolarised light.

....
....
....(3 marks)

b How does a polaroid sheet produce polarised light?

....
....(1 mark)

c Why do two sheets of polaroid with their axes at right angles let no light through?

....(1 mark)
[WJEC]

ANSWER

a Unpolarised light has vibrations in all directions at right angles to the path of the wave.
Polarised light has vibrations in one direction only at right angles to the path of the wave.
This question asks you to explain the difference between two conditions, so don't just discuss one of them.

b Polaroid only lets vibrations in one direction pass through *(in sunglasses only the vertical vibrations pass through).*

c One sheet only allows the vibration in one plane to pass through and the second sheet only allows vibrations at right angles to the first to pass through. Therefore no light will pass through the combination of the two.

Sound

What is sound?

Sound is produced when an object vibrates. As it vibrates the object produces a wave by forcing molecules in the air closer together and then allowing them to move apart. The wave is made up of compression and decompression of the molecules in the air. As the movement of the particles is in the same direction as the transfer of energy the wave is said to be longitudinal (see p 335). Unlike light and other electromagnetic waves, sound is carried by vibrating particles and must therefore have a medium to travel through.

By a medium *we mean a solid, liquid or gas. The decompression is also called a* rarefaction.

You may have seen an experiment to show that sound cannot travel through a vacuum.

As the air is sucked out of the apparatus the sound of the bell becomes fainter and fainter until eventually it cannot be heard at all.

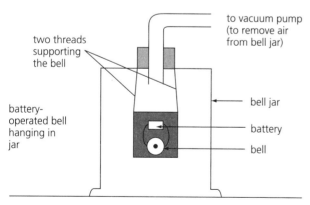

Fig 1 Sound does not travel through a vacuum

Sound is carried by a wave. If you can't remember the rules about waves, look back at p 335–336. There are two particularly important points about sound waves:

• The distance between maximum compressions is the wavelength.

• The number of compressions passing a point in one second is the frequency.

The speed of **sound** is much **slower** than the speed of light and other electromagnetic waves. It is about 330 metres per second in air.

QUESTION

During a thunderstorm a student timed the gap between seeing a lightning flash and hearing the thunder. It was 8 seconds.

How far away was the storm?

....(1 mark)

ANSWER

2,640 metres.

Light travels so quickly (300,000,000m/s) that you can assume it reached the student instantaneously. If sound travels at about 330m/s in 8 seconds it will travel 8 × 330 metres = 2,640 metres.

The sound travelled 2,640 metres to get to the student.

The storm is about 2.5 kilometres away.

(1 mile is about 1600 metres so the storm is about 1.6 miles away.

The rule of thumb is to allow 5 seconds per mile.)

If you need help with this see the speed equation on p 294.

QUESTION

The diagram shows a ship studying the depth of the sea by echosounding.

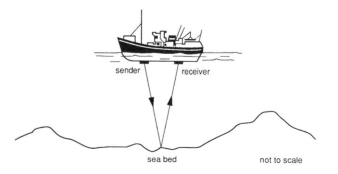

Fig 2

A short burst of sound is sent into the water and is reflected back from the sea bed.

Sound travels at 1600m/s in this water.

The echo is received after 0.6s.

Calculate the depth of the water below the ship.

....

....

....(3 marks)

[MEG]

ANSWER

480 metres.

If the sound travels at 1,600m/s and the sound is heard after 0.6s, then it has travelled 1,600 × 0.6 = 960m.

The sound has travelled down to the sea bed and up to the boat again, so the distance to the sea bed is 960/2 = 480m.

How do we hear sounds?

The vibration of an object causes **compression waves**, usually in the air, which are carried to your ear. The ear drum picks up the vibrations, which are passed to the oval window by three small bones. These amplify the vibrations. As the oval window vibrates it causes fluid in the cochlea to move. Hairs in the inner part of the cochlea detect this movement and electrical impulses about the type of sound are taken in the auditory nerve to the brain. The round window vibrates to compensate for the movement of the fluid caused by the vibration of the oval window.

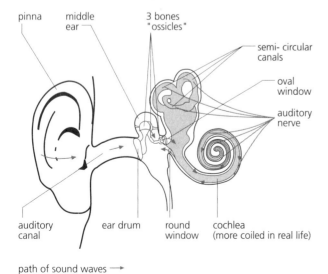

Fig 3 The ear

Hearing can be damaged by very loud sounds, such as those which come from machinery, discos or even personal stereos. If the hearing is damaged a hearing aid might be helpful. There are two sorts:

• Those that amplify the sound that goes to the eardrum.
• Those that send vibrations directly to the cochlea – this type is needed if the eardrum or the middle ear, containing the three tiny bones, is damaged.

A person will suffer from profound deafness if the cochlea or auditory nerve is damaged. It is now possible to implant electrodes into the cochlea to restore some hearing if deafness is due to malfunctioning of this part of the ear.

Sounds from musical instruments

You will probably have seen an object vibrating as it makes a sound. This can be seen in a stringed instrument such as a guitar or violin. You can see that:

• A high note is made when the string is short.
• A low note is made when the string is long.
• A loud sound is made when the string has a large vibration.
• A quiet sound is made when the string has a small vibration.

Instruments that you have to blow work in the same way. In this case you change the length of the column of vibrating air in the instrument to give different sounds.

Microphones and loudspeakers

Microphone

This is used to turn sound vibrations into electrical vibrations. The sound vibrations and electrical vibrations have the same frequency.

Loudspeaker

This is used to turn electrical vibrations into sound vibrations. The sound vibrations and electrical vibrations have the same frequency.

These two pieces of equipment are often used together. Once the sound vibrations have been turned into electrical vibrations they can be:

• Sent long distances.
• Amplified.

The electrical impulses can be turned into microwaves and sent around the world via satellites.

Looking at sound

If a microphone is connected to a cathode ray oscilloscope (CRO), the CRO turns the sound wave into a picture of a transverse wave.

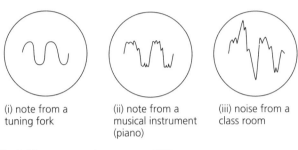

(i) note from a tuning fork

(ii) note from a musical instrument (piano)

(iii) noise from a class room

Fig 4 Three notes shown on a CRO

We can see that while a tuning fork may produce a simple wave form, most sounds, even those from musical instruments are complex. These sounds are made up of many superimposed waves.

A tuning fork gives a pure note. The note is given on each tuning fork, together with its frequency.

A signal generator is a piece of equipment that can be used to make sounds electronically. If these sounds are fed into the CRO we can see how the wave form changes as we change the loudness and pitch of the sound produced.

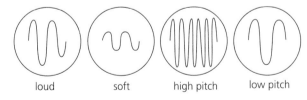

loud   soft   high pitch   low pitch

Fig 5 CRO traces of four sounds produced by a signal generator

We can see that loud sounds have a larger amplitude than soft sounds. High pitched sounds have a higher frequency than low pitched ones.

The frequency is the number of complete vibrations per second. The units for this are hertz (Hz).

QUESTION

Look at the four CRO traces shown in Fig 6.

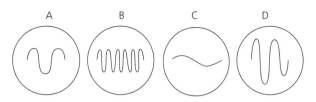

A   B   C   D

Fig 6

Identify:
a The trace with the highest frequency
....
b The trace with the smallest amplitude
....
c The trace formed by the note with the highest pitch ....
d The trace formed by the note with the loudest sound ....(4 marks)

ANSWER

a B – *most waves showing on screen – shortest wavelength.*
b C – *smallest distance from top of wave to horizontal centre line.*
c B – *must be the same as wave with the highest frequency.*
d D – *wave with biggest amplitude – biggest distance from top of wave to horizontal centre line.*

QUESTION

A xylophone is a musical instrument. When the bars are hit with a stick, they make a sound.

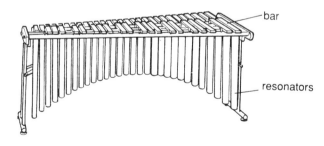

bar

resonators

Fig 7

a i Explain how hitting a bar on the xylophone makes a sound.
....
....(1 mark)
   ii Explain how this sound spreads out to the surroundings.
....
....(1 mark)

b Explain why shorter bars make notes of higher pitch.

....

....

....(2 marks)

c State one way of making louder sounds when playing the xylophone.

....(1 mark)

d The diagram shows the pattern on an oscilloscope when a bar on the xylophone is hit.

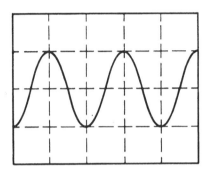

Fig 8

   i Draw on the grid the pattern that is seen if the same bar is made to produce a louder note.

(1 mark)

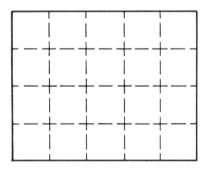

Fig 9

   ii Draw on the grid the pattern that is seen if a shorter bar is struck.

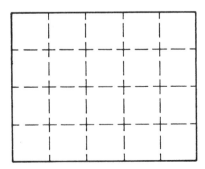

Fig 10

[MEG]

ANSWER

a i As the bar is hit it vibrates and makes the air next to it vibrate.

   ii Vibrations from the bar cause compression waves in the air. The waves spread out from the bar in all directions.

b The shorter bar vibrates with a higher frequency. This makes the air vibrate with a higher frequency and this note has a higher pitch.

c Hit the xylophone harder.

d i The waves should have a greater amplitude, they could go to the edge of the grid. *Make sure that you still draw them with the same frequency.*

   ii The waves should have a higher frequency *(that is more waves in the same space).*

Audible and inaudible sounds

Human hearing is normally in the range of frequencies from 20 to 20,000Hz. The frequency at which sound cannot be heard varies from person to person, though older people are not so good at picking up higher frequencies. Many animals detect sounds well out of the human hearing range. For example, bats use sound with a frequency of about 50,000Hz to fly accurately in the dark. They give out sound at this frequency and detect reflections of this sound from the things around them. They are so accurate that they can use this method to catch flying insects. Waves like this are called **ultrasound**. Just like sound waves they are compression waves but have too high a frequency to be detected by the human ear.

Ultrasound

Why ultrasound is so useful

Ultrasound is made up of waves – like sound – which are too high to be detected by the human ear. If higher frequencies than those used by bats are produced, a point is reached where the ultrasound travels through most materials very effectively. The range of frequencies used for this is between 1 million and 15 million hertz. Being a wave, however, means that some of the ultrasound is reflected back from boundaries between different types of material. Ultrasound can also be focused using material that is transparent to it. Curved surfaces are used in the same way that glass lenses focus light.

Uses of ultrasound

- In medicine
  Ultrasound waves can produce pictures of the inside of the body. Unlike X rays, ultrasound is not harmful and is used extensively for checking on the progress of the foetus and looking for tumours.
- At sea
  Modern fishing boats use ultrasound to detect shoals of fish. The ultrasound is reflected back to a detector on the boat. It can also be used to detect submarines and to measure the depth of the sea.

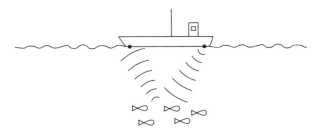

Fig 11 Ultrasound being used in fishing

- Cleaning apparatus
  Ultrasound is used for cleaning scientific apparatus that must be very clean indeed or has inaccessible areas. The apparatus can be submerged in cleaning fluid contained in an ultrasound bath. The high frequency waves help to dislodge particles of dirt and shake them off the apparatus.

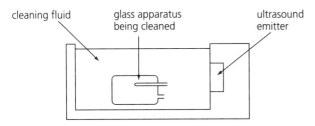

Fig 12 Ultrasound being used in cleaning apparatus

Ultrasound can also be used to help clean very old or expensive materials, such as tapestries that might be damaged by a washing machine.

QUESTION

a In hospitals, ultrasound is used to produce pictures of the inside of the human body. Some ultrasound

is reflected when it passes from one material to another. The bigger the difference in speed through the materials the greater the reflection of ultrasound.

What is ultrasound?

....

....(1 mark)

b The table below contains information about the speed of ultrasound through some different materials.

Material	Speed of sound (m/s)
air	332
bone	3,360
fat	1,476
muscle	1,540
saline gel	1,515

In the following diagram (a) shows the normal procedure for obtaining pictures of an unborn baby.

Explain why the procedure shown in (b) is not satisfactory.

....

....

....

....

(4 marks)

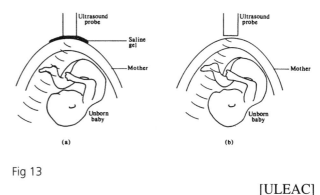

Fig 13

[ULEAC]

ANSWER

a Sound waves above the range of human hearing – i.e. 20,000 hertz.
b There is a gap of air in (b). The speed of sound is 332m/s in air and much more than this in the human tissues. This means a lot of the sound waves would be reflected from the mother's skin if the saline gel were not used.

QUESTION

a The following drawing shows a method to display sound waves as waves on an oscilloscope screen.

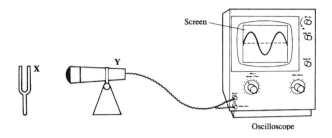

Fig 14

    i What are x and y?

      X...............................Y.............................(2 marks)

    ii The following diagram shows the screen during an investigation.

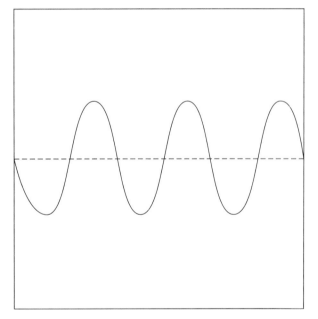

Fig 15

A How many full waves are shown in the diagram?
....(1 mark)
B What does the frequency of a wave mean?
....
....(1 mark)
C Write down either the name or the symbol for the unit of frequency. (1 mark)
D On the following diagram draw a wave with the same frequency as the one already shown but with a smaller amplitude. (2 marks)

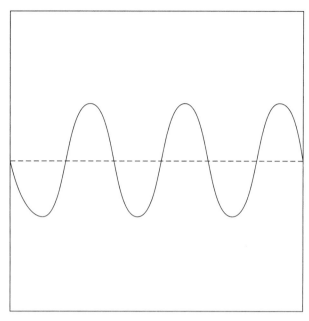

Fig 16

b If you hear two sounds which are the same in every way, except that they have different amplitudes, what will you notice about them?
....
....
....(2 marks)

c The following diagrams show the sound waves produced by two different musical instruments.

instrument A

instrument B

Fig 17

    Why will these two instruments sound different?
....
....(1 mark)

d During a thunderstorm you see the flash of lightning before you hear the clap of thunder which was produced at the same time

    i Why is this?
....
....(1 mark)

    ii Sound travels at a speed of 340 metres per second (m/s) in air. How far away does a clap of thunder occur if you hear it 5 seconds after you see its flash of lightning?

Write down the equation you are going to use. Then clearly show how you get to your answer.

....

....

....(3 marks)

Part question [SEG 1994]

ANSWERS

a i X – tuning fork Y – microphone
   ii A:3.
   B: The number of vibrations in one second.
   C: Symbol is Hz and the name of the unit is hertz.
   D: Draw your waves to be smaller (not going up and down so much) as in the diagram. You must still draw three complete waves crossing the horizontal dotted line at the same place as in the original diagram.

b One of the sounds will be much louder than the other. *(Make sure that you mention both sounds as this is a comparison question!)*

c They must sound different because the shape of the wave is different.

d i Light travels faster than sound.
   ii Distance to the thunder = speed × time
                               = 340 × 5
                               = 1,700 metres.

Revision sheet

Waves

1 Finish this sentence: Waves transfer .... but they don't transfer ....

2 Give the properties of these types of waves:
   a Transverse.
   b Longitudinal.

3 Label this diagram of a wave;

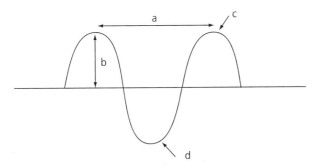

Fig 1

4 Finish this equation for a wave:
   Speed = ... × ....

5 Explain each of these terms that are used about waves:
   a Reflection.
   b Refraction.
   c Absorption.
   d Diffraction.
   e Interference.
   f Resonance.

6 Give the differences between these two types of seismic waves:
   a P waves.
   b S waves.

7 a Label this diagram of a section of the Earth.
   b i Is part (X) liquid or solid?
     ii What evidence do we have for this?

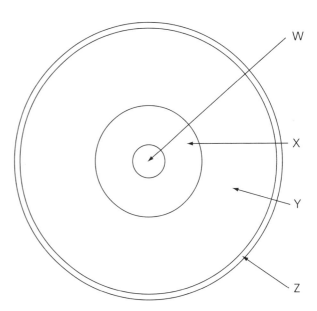

Fig 2

Electromagnetic spectrum

1 a Are electromagnetic waves – longitudinal or transverse?
   b What can you say about the speed of electromagnetic waves?
   c Which property of the waves gives the electromagnetic waves their different properties?

2 a List these electromagnetic waves in order of wavelength, shortest first:
     gamma, infra-red, microwaves, radio waves, ultra violet, visible light, X-rays.
   b Give a use for each of these waves.

Light

1 Is light a longitudinal or transverse wave?
2 What sort of image is formed in a mirror if the mirror is:
   a Plane?
   b Concave?
   c Convex?
3 Explain the following terms:
   a Reflection.
   b Total internal reflection.
   c Refraction.
   d Polarisation.
   e Dispersion.
4 Give the function of the following in the eye:
   a Lens.
   b Iris.
   c Retina.
   d Optic nerve.
5 For each of the following conditions say where the light is focused and how the condition would be corrected:
   a Long sight.
   b Short sight.
6 Give the colours formed when:
   a Red and green lights are mixed.
   b Red, green and blue lights are mixed.
7 Which part of the spectrum is being reflected by an object that looks:
   a Green?
   b White?

Sound

1 a Is sound a longitudinal or transverse wave?
   b Explain why sound does not travel through a vacuum.
   c Does light or sound travel faster?
2 In terms of compressions describe:
   a The wavelength of a sound wave.
   b The frequency of a sound wave.
3 Give the function of the following in the ear:
   a The eardrum.
   b The three tiny bones in the ear (the ossicles).
   c Cochlea.
   d Auditory nerve.
   e Round window.
4 In terms of vibrations give the difference between:
   a Loud and quiet sound.
   b High and low pitched sound.

5 a What is ultrasound?
   b Give a use of ultrasound in medicine.

Revision sheet answers

Waves

1 energy … matter
2 a Transverse: vibration moves at right angles to the energy transfer; seen as up and down movement; for example, of a rope.
   b Longitudinal: vibration is along the vibrating material, in the direction of the transfer of energy. Compression and expansion along the vibrating material.
3 a Wavelength.
   b Amplitude.
   c Crest.
   d Trough.
4 frequency × wavelength.
   a Reflection – a wave bouncing off a barrier and returning.
   b Refraction – a wave changing its speed and direction when it meets a different material.
   c Absorption – when a wave hits a material and the energy of the wave is taken in by the object.
   d Diffraction – when a wave meets a barrier with a narrow slit, the waves spread out from the gap as circular waves.
   e Interference – when waves meet: *constructive* interference if the amplitude is increased and *destructive* interference if the waves cancel out (as when a trough meets a crest).
   f Resonance – When the natural frequency of vibration of an object receives another wave of the same frequency (forcing wave) the amplitude of the vibrations is increased.
6 a P waves – primary waves, travel faster than S waves, longitudinal waves, travel through solids and liquids.
   b S waves – secondary waves, travel more slowly than P waves, transverse waves, can travel through solids but not liquids.
7 a W: inner core.
     X: outer core.
     Y: mantle.
     Z: crust.
   b i Liquid.
     ii P waves can travel through this but not S waves.

Electromagnetic spectrum

1 a Transverse.
  b All the same speed *(3 × 10⁸ metres per second)*.
  c Different frequencies.
2 a Order of wavelength – shortest first:
    gamma, X-rays, ultraviolet, visible light, infra-red, microwaves, radio waves.
  b Gamma rays: kill cells.
    X-rays: looking for broken bones.
    Ultraviolet: sunbed!
    Visible light: photography.
    Infra-red: toaster.
    Microwaves: cooking.
    Radio waves: carry radio signals.
    (other uses are listed on p 346)

Light

1 Light is a transverse wave.
2 a Plane – virtual, lateral inversion, same size, right way up.
  b Concave – magnified (provided the object is near the mirror).
  c Convex – smaller.
3 a Reflection – when light hits an object and bounces back (angle of incidence = angle of reflection).
  b Total internal reflection – when the angle of incidence in the glass block is greater than 42° to the normal, the light is completely reflected back into the block.
  c Refraction – when light enters a different substance, the speed and direction of the wave changes. The ray is bent towards the normal if the substance is denser.
  d Polarisation – when only one direction of the vibrations making up a light wave are allowed through a material.
  e Dispersion – when white light is split up by a prism to give the colours of the spectrum. Violet is refracted the most and red the least.
4 a Lens – refracts the light.
  b Iris – controls the amount of light entering the eye.
  c Retina – where the image is formed and received.
  d Optic nerve – passes information about the object, in the form of nervous impulses, to the brain.
5 a Long sight – light focused behind the retina, corrected by using a converging lens.

  b Short sight – light focused in front of the retina, corrected by using a diverging lens.
6 a Red and green lights are mixed – gives yellow light.
  b Red, green and blue lights are mixed – gives white light.
7 a Green – green light.
  b White – all colours of the spectrum.

Sound

1 a Sound is a longitudinal wave.
  b Sound is carried by vibrating particles, there are none of these in a vacuum.
  c Light travels much faster than sound.
2 a The wavelength of a sound wave – the distance between maximum compressions.
  b The frequency of a sound wave – the number of compressions passing a point in a second.
3 a The eardrum – picks up the vibrations.
  b The three tiny bones in the ear (the ossicles) – amplify and pass on the vibrations.
  c Cochlea – detects different sounds.
  d Auditory nerve – passes information about the sounds, in the form of nerve impulses, to the brain.
  e Round window – vibrates to compensate for the movement of the fluid in the cochlea.
4 a Loud and quiet sound – loud sound: large amplitude; soft sound: small amplitude.
  b High and low pitched sound – high pitched sound: high frequency; low pitched sound: low frequency
5 a Ultrasound – sounds above the range of human hearing, ie above 20,000Hz.
  b A use of ultrasound in medicine – produces pictures of the inside of the body, used in pregnancy as it does not harm the foetus.

Student Answers with Comments

a i How are sounds produced by a string instrument such as a guitar?
  The sound is made when the string is moved. ✓
  The string vibrates causing the air around it to
  vibrate. The vibrating air is a sound wave. ✓ ②
  (2 marks)

  Good – string vibrates and *mentioned air vibrating*

ii How does the sound made by a string change if the string is shortened?

The pitch will increase and the wave will have a higher frequency. ✓ ①

(1 mark)

Good

iii The following diagram represents particles of air.

Fig 20

Draw a diagram to show how the particles would appear as a sound wave passes through the air.

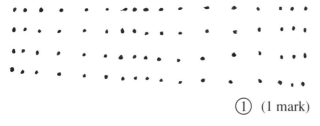

① (1 mark)

Just OK – try and use a ruler! You could label the compressions to make it clearer.

b The following diagram shows details of an ear.

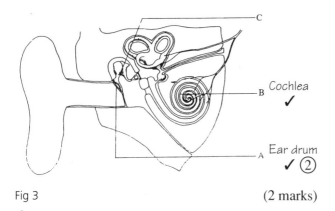

Fig 3 (2 marks)

i Label parts A and B
ii Describe TWO functions of the bones at C.

To pass on the vibrations to the cochlea and ✓ to magnify the sound. ✓ ②

(amplify sound would also be suitable)

(2 marks)

c The following diagram shows two people talking on mobile telephones.

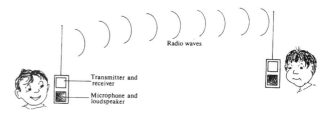

Fig 4

i What is the function of a microphone?

To convert the sound wave into an electrical signal ✓ ①

(1 mark)

Convert is a good word to use here!

ii Radio waves are part of a spectrum of radiations.
What is this spectrum called? ✓ ①

The electromagnetic spectrum. ✓ ①

(1 mark)

iii The diagram represents the energy changes which take place when the mobile telephones are used.

Fig 5

Complete a similar diagram to show the energy changes which take place in a system where the telephones are connected by optical fibres.

Would be a good idea to add 'waves' after 'light' and 'sound' (2 marks)

iv Show a likely path for a light ray travelling down the following optical fibre.

Good – the angle of reflection appears to equal the angle of incidence.

✓ ②

(2 marks)

d A radio wave has a frequency of 92MHz and travels at 3×10^8m/s. Calculate its wavelength in metres.

92MHz = 92,000,000Hz

Good – you've noticed MHz!

speed = frequency × wave length

∴ wave length = $\dfrac{\text{speed}}{\text{frequency}}$

Good – equation written and working shown

wave length = $\dfrac{300,000,000}{92,000,000}$ = $\dfrac{300}{92}$ = 3.26m ✓ ③

$^{17}/_{17}$ (3 marks)

(Total 17 marks)

[ULEAC]

An exam question for you to try

a The following boxes give the names of some of the waves which make up the electromagnetic spectrum. The waves are arranged from left to right in order of increasing wavelength.

A	X-rays	B	visible light	infra-red rays	microwaves	radio waves

Fig 23

Name the electromagnetic waves A and B.
A .... B .... (2 marks)

b The following diagram shows a regular wave.

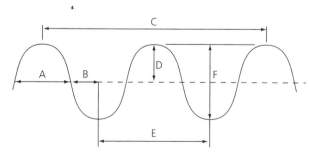

Fig 6

Which measurement on the diagram, A, B, C, D, E, or F, shows the wavelength of this regular wave?
....(1 mark)

c Some distant stars emit radio waves and these can be studied using a radio telescope.

i Complete the following diagram to show how radio waves from a distant star can be focused by the dish of a radio telescope. (4 marks)

ii Why does the radio telescope have to move in order to keep pointing at the same star?

....
....(1 mark)

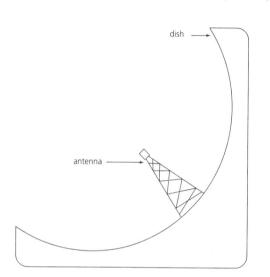

Fig 7

d The following diagram shows the direction of a light beam as it travels from air into a glass block. Explain why the light waves change their direction when entering the block. You may add to the diagram to help your answer if you wish.
(2 marks)

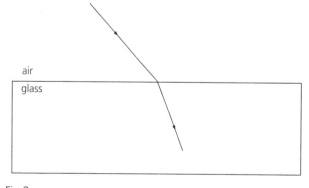

Fig 8

....
....
....

[SEG 1994]

Answer

a A – gamma B – ultraviolet.

b E.

c (i).

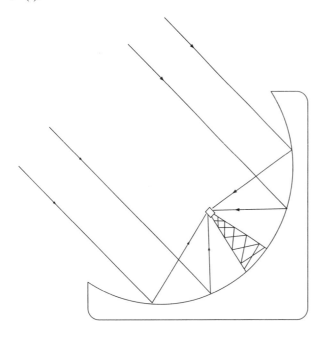

ii The Earth is spinning on its axis all the time.

d The glass is more dense than the air. The speed of light becomes less as the light enters the glass block (called refraction). This causes a change in the direction of the light waves. *(You could draw the wavefronts on the diagram – see p 350.)*

17

Earth and the solar system

Earth and the solar system	Midland (MEG)				Northern (NEAB)		London (ULEAC)				Southern (SEG)		Welsh (WJEC)
	Own	Nuffield	Salters	Suffolk	Co-ordinated	Modular	Modular GASP	Combined	Co-ordinated	Modular	Double	Modular	Co-ordinated
EARTH AND THE SOLAR SYSTEM													
What is in the solar system	✓	✓	✓	✓	✓	✓	✓	✓	✓	✓	✓	✓	✓
Length of year and day	✓	✓		✓	✓	✓	✓	✓	✓	✓	✓	✓	✓
The seasons					✓	✓	✓		✓	✓		✓	✓
Satellites – artificial	✓	H		✓	✓	✓	✓	H	✓	H	✓	H	✓
Eclipses	✓				✓	✓	✓		✓				✓
Tides	✓	✓	✓		✓	✓	✓	✓	✓		✓		✓
Life cycle of a star	✓	✓	✓	H	✓	✓	✓	H	✓	✓	✓	✓	✓
Origin of the Universe	H	H	✓	H	H	H	✓	H	H	H	✓	H	H
Future of the Universe	H		✓	H	H	H	✓	H	H	H	✓	H	H

Earth and the Solar System

What is the solar system?

The **universe** is the name given to space and everything that is in it. The **solar system** is the part containing our Sun and the bodies that orbit it. These include the nine planets and their satellites as well as asteroids and comets. The solar system is thought to have formed about 4.6 billion years ago. 99% of the mass of the solar system is made up of the Sun.

The Sun

The Sun is a star which is only 150 million kilometres from the Earth. It is made up of 70% hydrogen and 28% helium, with other elements making up the remaining 2%. We see the Sun shining because:

- It is so close.
- The surface is very hot – about 6,000°C.

Sunlight is due to nuclear fusion reactions which turn hydrogen into helium at the core of the Sun. The helium nuclei have less mass than the hydrogen nuclei that fuse to form them. The 'lost' mass is converted into energy. The amount of energy released in each reaction is quite small but as the Sun uses up 4 million tonnes of matter every second, the total energy released is considerable. It is thought the temperature in the core is 15 million °C.

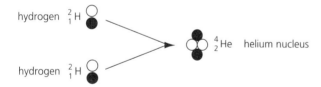

Fig 1 Nuclear fusion – Two light hydrogen nuclei join to form a heavier helium nucleus. The helium nucleus is not quite as heavy as the two hydrogen nuclei.

We use the term light year for the distance that light travels (in a vacuum) in one year. It is about 9.46 million million kilometres. The speed of light is about 300,000 kilometres per second.

The planets

There are nine planets in the solar system. We can see several of these in the sky at different times of the year. Unlike the Sun they do not produce light. We are able to see them because they reflect light from the Sun.

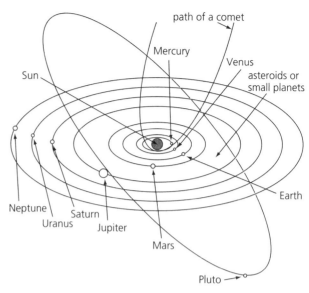

Fig 2 The planets orbiting the Sun

It may be helpful to learn this mnemonic to help you remember the order of the planets:
My Very Expensive Maroon Jaguar Speeds Uphill Never Pausing

The planets (except for Pluto and the latest discovery beyond it) can be divided into two groups:

- Rocky dwarf planets – Mercury, Venus, Earth, Mars – which are dense because they are made of iron and rock.
- Gassy giant planets – Jupiter, Saturn, Uranus, Neptune – low density (similar to water), mostly made up of gases.

Pluto doesn't really fit into either of these two groups. It is beyond Neptune and is the smallest planet, thought to be a solid mixture of rock and ice. In 1992 another body, called 1992 QBI, was found orbiting beyond Pluto. It is smaller than Pluto and thought to be made up of ice.
Between the 'rocky dwarfs' and the 'gassy giants' there is an asteroid belt.

About the planets

It is difficult to appreciate the scale involved in the solar system. If the Earth were the size of a golf ball, it would be over 450m away from a model Sun and Pluto would be about 17,000m away!

(Conversion factor 1cm = 3,189km)

Although the average surface temperature of Mercury is 350°C, it ranges from 400°C on one side to –170°C on the other.

Planet	average distance from Sun (millions of km)	diameter at equator (km)	mass (if mass of the Earth is taken as 1)	average surface temperature (°C)	'Year' (time to orbit the Sun)	'Day' (time to rotate on axis)
Mercury	58	4,880	0.05	350	88 days	59 days
Venus	108	12,112	0.81	500	226 days	243 days
Earth	150	12,742	1	20	365 days	1 day
Mars	228	6,790	0.11	−40	694 days	1 day
Jupiter	778	142,600	318	−150	11.9 years	10 hours
Saturn	1,427	120,200	95	−160	29.5 years	10 hours
Uranus	2,870	49,000	14.5	−220	84 years	17 hours
Neptune	4,500	50,000	17.5	−230	165 years	16 hours
Pluto	5,900	2,284	0.003	−230	248 years	6 days

How the planets orbit the Sun

All the planets travel around the Sun in orbits. They all move in the same direction – anti clockwise if you could look from above. All the planets orbit the Sun in the same plane except Pluto, whose orbit is at an angle to the others.

See p 298 and p 301 for more information on gravitational forces and circular motion.

Length of a year

The planets that are nearer to the Sun travel round it in a shorter time. The time that a planet takes to orbit the Sun is called a year. The 'year' of each planet is given in the table above.
The planets orbit the Sun due to the gravitational force that the Sun exerts upon them. All masses have gravitational forces between them (see p 301), but the Sun has such a large mass that it can hold the planets in orbit.

Length of a day

As each planet orbits the Sun it rotates about its axis. The time for one complete rotation is called a day. The length of a day for each of the planets is given in the table above. Different parts of the planet face the Sun during this rotation. It takes the Earth 24 hours to rotate once on its axis. It is daylight on the part of the Earth facing the Sun, while the rest of the planet is in darkness (night).

The seasons

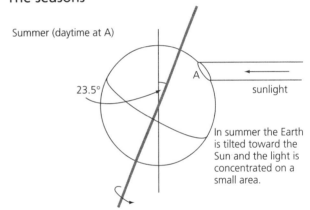

Summer (daytime at A)

23.5°

sunlight

In summer the Earth is tilted toward the Sun and the light is concentrated on a small area.

In the six months between midsummer and midwinter the Earth has travelled to the opposite side of the Sun.

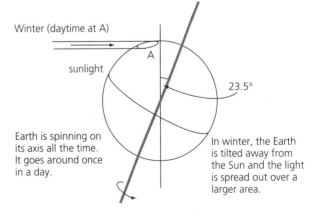

Winter (daytime at A)

sunlight

23.5°

Earth is spinning on its axis all the time. It goes around once in a day.

In winter, the Earth is tilted away from the Sun and the light is spread out over a larger area.

Fig 3 How the tilt of the Earth gives the seasons

Although the Earth orbits the Sun, the Earth's rotation is not at right angles to the plane of the orbit. It is tilted at 66.5° to this plane, which is sometimes expressed as 23.5° to the vertical. The tilt does not change during the year but it is the reason why there are temperature changes during the year which result in the seasons. During the summer in the northern hemisphere the north pole is tilted towards the Sun. The Sun is more directly overhead and so the energy from the Sun is concentrated on a smaller area, making it hotter. In winter, the north pole is tilted away from the Sun, so the energy from the Sun is spread out over a larger area and so has less heating effect. It feels colder.

Satellites

Many of the planets in the solar system have moons (only Mercury and Venus do not). These are natural satellites (bodies which orbit other larger bodies). A satellite is kept in orbit by gravitational forces between the satellite and the body it is orbiting. The Moon is the natural satellite of the Earth. We see the Moon because it reflects light from the Sun and half the Moon is always lit by the Sun. The Moon spins on its own axis so that the same side of the Moon always faces the Earth. However, the amount of the Moon we see depends on which particular stage of its 28 day orbit the Moon is in.

There are also many satellites around the Earth which have been put there by humans. There are two important types:

• Satellites in geo-stationary orbits
  These are put into orbit high above the equator (36,000km above the Earth). They move at the same speed as the Earth rotates, so in effect they stay in the same position relative to the earth. They are used for communications. Three satellites can give global coverage.
• Monitoring satellites
  These are usually in a low orbit. They are launched in an orbit travelling over the north and south poles; that is, at 90° to the equator. The Earth rotates beneath them and they are able to view the whole surface of the Earth. These satellites are able to locate objects to within 100m.

To stay in orbit at a particular distance from the Earth, monitoring satellites must move at a particular speed. The further away the satellite is from the Earth, the longer it takes to make one orbit.

What is an Eclipse?

We see an eclipse when one body moves through the shadow of another.

Solar eclipse

This occurs when the Moon moves between the Earth and the Sun. The Sun appears to be covered over. This can only happen at a new Moon.

Lunar eclipse

This occurs when the Earth prevents the light from the Sun reaching the Moon.

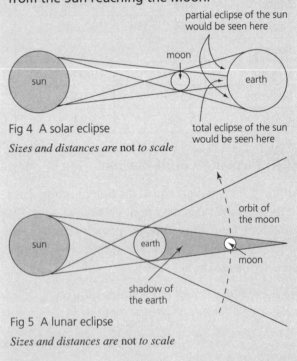

Fig 4 A solar eclipse
Sizes and distances are not *to scale*

Fig 5 A lunar eclipse
Sizes and distances are not *to scale*

How are tides formed?

Tides occur mainly due to the gravitational force of the Moon. The water is at its highest (called high tide) when the water is on a direct line connecting the centres of the Earth and Moon. As the Earth rotates once in 24 hours, the water falls and rises twice a day.

When the Earth, Moon and Sun are in line at new and full Moons there are even bigger tides. These are called spring tides. Neap tides occur when the Sun and the Moon are at right angles. These tides are smaller as the gravitational pulls of the Sun and Moon partially cancel each other out. There are usually two spring tides and two neap tides every month. Neap tides occur half way between two spring tides.

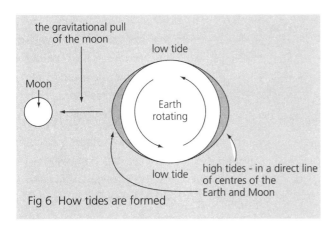

Fig 6 How tides are formed

QUESTION

a When two large lead masses are hung close together, they do not hang vertically but are slightly attracted.

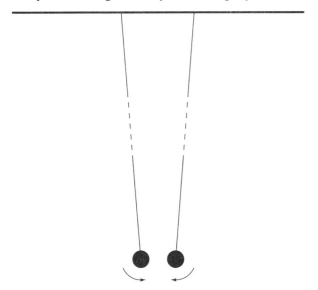

Fig 7

What would you notice if wooden balls of the same size were used in place of the lead balls?

....
....(1 mark)

b Tides are caused by the pull of the Sun and Moon. Explain the reasons for the difference between the spring and neap tides.

....
....
....
....(3 marks)

Part question [SEG 1994]

ANSWER

a They would not be attracted as much as the lead balls are. They are likely to hang nearly vertically.

(The wood balls are less dense, their mass is less and so they have less of a gravitational effect.)

b Spring tides occur when the gravitational force of the Moon and the Sun are combined. This gives rise to a big difference between high and low tide. Neap tides occur when the gravitational pull of the Moon and the Sun are at right angles to one another. These gravitational pulls partially cancel each other out.

Asteroids

Between Mars and Jupiter there are many thousands of rocky bodies. Like the planets these orbit the Sun. They are thought to be fragments that were left over when the Solar System was formed.

Comets

These are thought to have been formed at the beginning of the Solar System. Each comet is a small body of ice and dust. It is thought that there are comets on the outer edges of the solar system beyond Pluto. Gravitational effects of other stars cause some comets to travel towards the Sun. When this occurs we may see them from Earth. As a comet approaches the Sun it warms up and expands, and can be observed with a long 'tail'. Eventually the comet passes out into deep space. Some comets (called periodic comets) have orbits that bring them into view at regular intervals. Halley's Comet is the most famous. It has a fixed orbit around the Sun (in the opposite direction to the planets) which takes 76 years. It will reappear in 2061.

QUESTION

a Rewrite the following in order of size starting with the smallest.
galaxy, the Moon, planet, solar system, universe
....(1 mark)

b i Name the attractive force that exists between the earth and the Moon.

....(1 mark)

  ii What evidence is there on Earth to show the attractive force of the Moon?

....(1 mark)

  iii State two factors which affect the size of the attractive force between any two objects.

....
....(2 marks)

[WJEC]

ANSWER

a Moon, planet, solar system, galaxy, universe.
b i Gravity.
   ii Tides at the seaside are evidence of the attractive force of the Moon.
   iii How far apart they are, the mass of each object.

The life cycle of a star

The Sun is the star at the centre of our solar system. Although all stars are quite different from each other, the Sun is a fairly typical star – ie a body which produces its own heat and light by nuclear reactions. Although stars shine for many billions of years they do change in appearance during that time. It has been possible to work out the life history of a typical star.

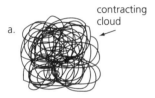

a.

contracting cloud

A star begins to form as gravity pulls together a cloud of gas (mostly hydrogen) and tiny particles. The cloud contracts.

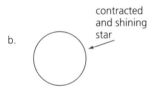

b.

contracted and shining star

The contraction of the cloud results in an increase in the temperature and pressure of the core. When the temperature reaches about 10 million °C, nuclear reactions begin and the star begins to give out light (shine). The contraction stops and the star is in a balanced state. The Sun is in this state now. It is likely to remain like this for another 5 million years.

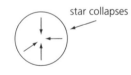

c.

star collapses

Eventually all the hydrogen in the star is converted into helium and the energy released reduces. The star starts to collapse.

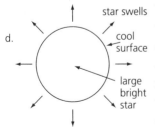

d.

star swells
cool surface
large bright star

The collapse of the star causes the inside core to get very hot, causing the star to swell to about 100 times its previous size. The outer layer furthest from the hot core is much cooler. A star in this state is called a red giant. When this happens to the Sun, it will engulf the Earth!

e.

small dense white dwarf

When no more nuclear reactions can occur in the star the outer layers are blown into space. The core collapses to form a very small dense body called a white dwarf.

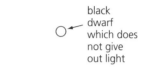

f.

black dwarf which does not give out light

Eventually this fades away leaving a dark body which does not give out light, called a 'black dwarf'.

Fig 8 The life cycle of a star approximately the same size as the Sun.

Giant and supergiant stars
These are much bigger than our Sun. If Aldebaran (one of these giants) replaced our sun it would reach halfway to Mercury, and a supergiant such as Betelgeuse would reach beyond Mars into the asteroid belt. These stars have a short life cycle and are quite rare.

The stars follow the same pattern as our Sun, but once the hydrogen at the core is used up other elements begin to fuse and iron is formed. At this stage the star explodes as a supernova. The remains may collapse into a small, dense neutron star or a black hole may be formed.

QUESTION

Light from the Sun can be analysed to show what elements the Sun is made of.
a Which element is the most common in the Sun?
....(1 mark)
b Describe the process which results in the release of energy from the Sun.
....
....
....
....
....
....(3 marks)
c Describe some of the events which take place when a star runs out of fuel.
....
....
....

....
....
....(3 marks)
[MEG]

ANSWER

a Hydrogen.

b Energy is released from the Sun by nuclear fusion reactions. Hydrogen is turned into helium, when two 'light' hydrogen *nuclei* fuse to form a heavier helium nucleus.

c When a star (such as one the size of our Sun) runs out of fuel it collapses. As it collapses it grows very hot and gets much bigger than it was originally. When all the nuclear reactions stop, the outer layers are blown into space and the core collapses to form a small dense 'white dwarf' which eventually forms a dark 'black dwarf'. *If the star is much bigger than our Sun, as the hydrogen is used up the star explodes and forms a 'supernova'. This may collapse into a 'neutron star' or 'black hole'. There are only three marks here but the question just asks about 'a star'. If you can, write about both these types.*

The origin of the universe

The '**big bang**' is the event thought by astronomers to have started the universe. This is thought to have happened 15 billion years ago. During this explosion, matter, energy, space and time – in fact everything – came into being. Since then the universe has been expanding and cooling.

The atoms that were formed clumped together due to gravity, to form billions of galaxies. (A galaxy is a collection of billions of stars held together by gravity.) The Milky Way which contains our Solar System is one of these galaxies. Evidence that scientists have used to develop the 'big bang' theory includes:

• The universe is expanding (discovered in 1929 by Edwin Hubble). This implies that it was smaller in the past and there must have been a point when it was born.

• The existence of cosmic background radiation, formed as a result of the 'big bang'.

• 25% of the universe is helium. The only way to explain this is that at sometime in the past there was a hot dense phase.

Red shift
Evidence for an expanding Universe has come from what is known as the 'red shift'. As any object (such as a star or galaxy) moves away from us the wavelength of light reaching us from it is increased. This is a *shift* to the *red* end of the spectrum. By measuring the amount of red shift in the light from stars and galaxies, the speed at which they are moving away from us can be calculated.

The future of the universe

This depends on how much matter it contains. It is predicted that one of two things could occur:

• If the universe contains sufficient matter then it will stop expanding. There will in effect be a reverse of the 'big bang' – called a 'big crunch'.

• If the universe contains insufficient matter it will carry on expanding and grow in size for ever. The galaxies will then be separated by large distances in space.

What actually happens will be determined by gravity. All the bodies in the universe are held together by gravitational forces and the combined mass of all the matter will determine which of the predictions occurs.

QUESTION

Our nearest star is just one of millions of stars which make up our galaxy. Beyond our galaxy are millions of other galaxies. The nearest of these is the Andromeda Nebula. This galaxy is about 2.5 million light years away from us.

a Apart from differences in size and material, give two ways in which a star is different from a planet.
Difference 1 ....
....
Difference 2 ....
....(2 marks)

b What is the name of our galaxy?
....(1 mark)

c i What is a light year?
....
....(1 mark)

ii Show how you could calculate the approximate distance from us to the Andromeda Nebula.

(Do not carry out the calculation.)

....
....
....
....(3 marks)

d The American astronomer, Edwin Hubble, studied the Andromeda Nebula and found that it is moving away from us. When he studied other galaxies he found that every galaxy is moving away from every other galaxy. He also found that the further apart they are the faster they are travelling.

  i What evidence is there to show that galaxies are moving apart from each other?

....
....
....
....
....(3 marks)

  ii What conclusion did Hubble and other astronomers come to about what is happening to the Universe now and to how it all started? What popular name was given to this first event in the life of the Universe?

....
....
....
....
....(3 marks)

[SEG 1994]

ANSWER

a *You must make clear the differences in your answer, so you need to compare a star and a planet. There are many points that you could describe such as:*
A star gives out light (shines), a planet does not.
A star is much hotter than a planet.
A planet reflects light, a star 'produces' light.
Planets orbit stars.

b The Milky Way.

c i The distance that light travels in a year *(It is 9.46 million million kilometres).*

  ii 2.5 million × speed of light (in km/s) × number of seconds in one year (answer in km).

d The evidence that the Universe is expanding comes from 'red shift'. As a star or galaxy moves away the light from it moves towards the red end of the spectrum (the wavelength increases). *Not*

strictly needed in this answer: By measuring the rate at which this happens the speed of movement of galaxies can be calculated.)

  ii Astronomers believe that the Universe is expanding and that the Universe started with a large explosion.
We call this the Big Bang.
(There is likely to be a mark for the name, even if you can't remember the details.)

Revision sheet

1 Explain these terms:
  a Universe.
  b Solar system.
  c Planet.
  d Satellite.
  e Asteroid.
  f Comet.
  g Galaxy.
  h Star.
2 List the planets in the solar system, in order, from the Sun outwards.
3 How is sunlight 'made'?
4 For Earth what determines:
  a The length of a year.
  b The length of a day?
  c The seasons?
5 How is a geo-stationary satellite different from a monitoring satellite?
6 Explain the difference between:
  a Solar eclipse and lunar eclipse.
  b High tide, spring tide and neap tide.
6 Put these in order to describe the life cycle of a star, such as our Sun: black dwarf, gravity pulling together a cloud of mostly hydrogen gas, star begins to collapse, Sun shining, white dwarf.
7 Give two differences between 'Giants and Supergiants' and our Sun.
8 What is meant by:
  a Big Bang?
  b Red shift?

Revision sheet answers

  a Universe – space and all that is in it.
  b Solar system – the part of the universe containing our sun and the bodies that orbit it.

c Planet – Nine of these in our solar system that orbit the Sun, only reflect light.

d Satellite – a body which orbits another body, such as the moon orbiting Earth.

e Asteroid – Rocky bodies, many found in a belt between Mars and Jupiter.

f Comet – A small body of ice, thought to have been formed at the beginning of the Solar System.

g Galaxy – Collection of billions of stars held together by gravity.

h Star – a body which 'produces' light.

2 Planets in the solar system, in order, from the Sun outwards: Mercury, Venus, Earth, Jupiter, Saturn, Uranus, Neptune, Pluto

3 Sunlight is 'made' by nuclear reactions. Hydrogen is turned into helium. As the helium nuclei have less mass than the hydrogen nuclei which fuse, the 'lost' mass is turned into energy.

4 a The length of a year – the time that the Earth takes to orbit the Sun.

b The length of a day – the time for one complete rotation of the Earth on its axis.

c The seasons – the Earth is tilted towards the Sun during the summer. Rays from the Sun are concentrated on a smaller area of the Earth than when the Earth is tilted away from the Sun and the rays are spread over a larger area.

5 Geo-stationary satellite – above the equator, orbits at the same speed as the Earth rotates.
Monitoring satellite – in a lower orbit, the Earth rotates below them so they are able to view the whole of the Earth's surface.

6 a Solar eclipse – when the Moon moves between the Earth and the Sun so the Sun appears to be covered.
Lunar eclipse – when Earth prevents light from the Sun reaching the Moon (Earth is between Moon and Sun).

b High tide – when the attraction of the Moon causes the water level in the sea to be high – it occurs twice a day.
Spring tide – particularly high tide when Earth, Moon and Sun are in line.
Neap tide – particularly low tide when the Sun and Moon are at right angles.

6 In order to describe the life cycle of a star, such as our Sun:
gravity pulling together a cloud of mostly hydrogen gas, Sun shining, star begins to collapse, red giant, white dwarf, black dwarf.

7 Two differences between Giants and Supergiants and our Sun:
– Giants and Supergiants are bigger.
– They have a shorter life cycle.

8 a Big Bang – the explosion that is thought to have started the universe.

b Red shift – evidence for an expanding universe. As stars and galaxies move away from us the wavelength of their light moves towards the red end of the spectrum.

Student Answer with Comments

a The following diagram shows a likely path for a comet orbiting the Sun. Explain why a comet does not travel at constant speed as it orbits the Sun.

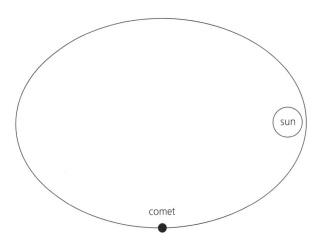

The sun is at an extremity of the comets trajectory. Therefore the comet will speed up as it nears ✓ the Sun due to the Sun's gravitational pull ✓ and slows as it goes away from the Sun. ✓

(3 marks)

b The diagram on the next page shows how stars may be placed into groups on the basis of their brightness and temperature.
The Sun is now in the main sequence.

i What major forces may be considered to be in equilibrium in the Sun at present?
The force of gravity pulling the Sun in and the force of the reactions pushing the Sun outwards. ✓ ①

energy from the reactions would get you the second mark

(2 marks)

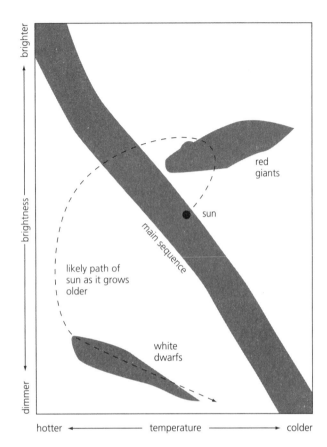

ii Explain what will happen to the Sun as it passes into the red giant stage.

It will become slightly colder and brighter than it is at present. It will also expand and become bigger. ✓ ①

You need to explain that the forces caused by the high temperature are bigger than the gravity pulling it in.

(2 marks)

iii How does this differ from the white dwarf stage which follows?

In the white dwarf stage the Sun would be much dimmer but would be hotter than at present. ✓ ①

(2 marks)

You've correctly noted it is dimmer but you have not said that it collapsed because gravity is now more important than the expansion caused by the high temperature.

c i Name the process by which energy is produced by the Sun and give a brief account of this process.

This process is called nuclear fusion. ✓ In this process 2 hydrogen atoms fuse to form an atom of helium. ②

It is the nuclei which fuse. Some mass is converted into energy.

(4 marks)

ii The Sun loses approximately 4×10^6 tonnes of mass each second (1 tonne = 1000kg). Use the equation:

Energy given out (J) = Change in mass (kg) × [Speed of light (m/s)]²

to calculate the amount of energy, in joules, released by the Sun each second.
(Speed of light = 3×8 10^8m/s).

energy released = $4 \times 10^9 \times (3 \times 10^8)^2$ ✓
= 3.6×10^{26} J ✓ ②
(4×10^6 tonnes = 4×10^9 kg)

(2 marks)

d Explain what is meant by the 'red shift' and discuss possible implications this has for the nature of the Universe.

Pity you didn't have a go at this – There are 6 marks here!

Light from distant stars has its wavelength shifted to the red end of the spectrum (ie longer wavelength). This is thought to mean that the stars are moving away from us at high speed. This is evidence for the Universe expanding and evidence towards the Big Bang theory for the origin of the Universe.

$^{10}/_{21}$ (6 marks)
(Total 21 marks)
[ULEAC]

An exam question for you to try

The diagram on the next page represents the orbits of the two planets nearest the Sun. These are Mercury (M) and Venus (V).

a Use the diagram to describe one way in which the orbits of Mercury and Venus differ.
....(1 mark)

b Mercury travels at an average speed of 48km/s around the Sun. Venus travels at an average speed of 35km/s around the Sun.

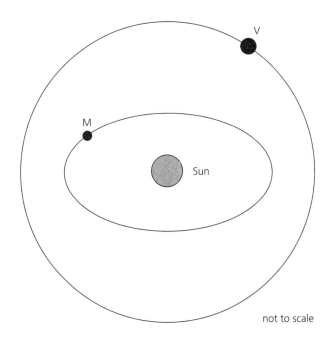

Fig 9

State two reasons why Venus takes longer to orbit the Sun than Mercury does.

1 ....

....

2 ....

....(2 marks)

c State briefly why heat from the Sun cannot travel by conduction or convection to the surface of Mercury.

....

....(1 mark)

d i The gravitational force which the Sun exerts on Mercury is not constant. Describe how this force changes as Mercury orbits the Sun once.

....

....(1 mark)

   ii The Sun exerts a bigger gravitational force on Venus than it does on Mercury. Suggest a reason for this.

....

....(1 mark)

e Pictures sent back to Earth from a space probe showed that Mercury has a Moon-like surface. It has craters ranging from 100m to 1300km in diameter. Suggest how craters of such different size were caused.

....

....

....

....(3 marks)

f Venus and Earth each have an atmosphere. The table shows the approximate composition of the atmospheres of these planets:

gas	atmosphere of Earth (%)	atmosphere of Venus (%)
nitrogen	78	3
oxygen	20	trace
carbon dioxide	0.03	97
water vapour	2	0.01

   i Use the information in the table to explain how the temperature of the surface of Venus might compare with the temperature of the surface of the Earth.

....

....

....(3 marks)

   ii The atmosphere of Venus extends to a greater height above the planet's surface than the atmosphere of Earth.
   Use this fact and the information in the table to explain how the pressure at the surface of Venus might compare with the pressure at the surface of Earth.

....

....

....

....(3 marks)

g On Earth sulphur dioxide gas is given out by active volcanoes. Astronomers are monitoring the concentration of sulphur dioxide gas in the atmosphere of Venus. What conclusions could astronomers draw from the information they receive?

....

....

....

....(2 marks)

[MEG]

Answer

a Either: Mercury has an elliptical orbit and Venus has a circular orbit or Mercury has a smaller orbit than Venus.
(You must mention both orbits as the question asks you how they differ.)

b Venus has a bigger orbit than Mercury.
Venus orbits at a slower speed.
c There is no air between the Sun and Mercury.
Space is a vacuum.
d i When Mercury is near the Sun in its orbit the
gravitational forces will be greater than when it
is further away in its elliptical orbit.
   ii Venus is a bigger planet than Mercury. *(It is
more correct to say that Venus has a bigger
mass, see p 301 for more details about
gravitational forces.)*
e The craters could have been formed by objects of
different mass, size or speed hitting the surface.
The surface of Mercury may not be of uniform
texture.

f i There is much more carbon dioxide in the
atmosphere of Venus than Earth's. This
suggests that there will be a much greater
'greenhouse effect' on Venus than on Earth.
This suggests that the surface temperature of
Venus will be much higher than that of Earth.
   ii There is a greater depth of atmosphere on
Venus and a higher proportion of heavier gas
(carbon dioxide). This means that the pressure
at the surface of Venus is likely to be higher
than the pressure at the surface of the Earth.
g By comparing the sulphur dioxide concentration
on Venus and Earth this could indicate:
   i Whether there are any volcanoes on Venus.
   ii If so, their activity level could be compared
with that on Earth.

Index